INTEGER PROGRAMMING AND NETWORK FLOWS

T. C. HU

Professor, Mathematics Research Center
and
Department of Computer Sciences
University of Wisconsin

ADDISON-WESLEY PUBLISHING COMPANY
Reading, Massachusetts
Menlo Park, California · London · Don Mills, Ontario

Second printing, November 1970

 Library of Congress Catalog Card No. 75-85384.

Dedicated to my Mother
Ya–Su Yeh Hu

PREFACE

This book consists of three parts, linear programming, network flows, and integer programming. It is a book which emphasizes the algorithm, its proof, and the theory. In selecting subjects for the various parts, I have kept in mind three criteria: (1) subjects which are considered important, (2) subjects which are familiar to me, and (3) subjects which have not been included or described in detail in other books.

The linear programming part is fairly standard; it includes all the materials needed for the remaining parts. One section which is not found in other linear programming books is Section 6.1 on the mutual primal-dual method of Balinski and Gomory [7].* Because the simplex tableau uses row elimination and the integer programming algorithm usually uses column elimination, Section 4.2 on the column tableau is also included.

The part on network flows includes many new materials which are not found in other books. In Chapter 8 we include a new proof for the unimodular matrix by Veinott and Dantzig [199] and an upper bound on the number of labelings needed to get the maximal flow established by Edmonds and Karp [58]. In Chapter 9 we give a new proof for the analysis of multi-terminal network flows. Chapters 10 and 11 are all new results, most published since 1962. These include the papers on the shortest paths by Floyed [63], Dijkstra [49], the decomposition algorithm by Hu and Torres [113], the minimal cost flow algorithms by Busacker and Gowen [22], Klein [130], the multicommodity flows by Ford and Fulkerson [66], Gomory and Hu [91], and Hu [107]. We have not included the "Out-of-kilter" method because an excellent treatment is available in Ford and Fulkerson [67]. Since the book is primarily for algorithms not for special applications, we have not included PERT, which is a special application of the minimal cost flow algorithm. In general the second part either includes material not in the book by Ford and Fulkerson or treats the same material from a different point of view. Thus I hope that this treatment may complement their book.

---

* Numbers in brackets are keyed to the references at the end of this book.

Chapter 12 is an isolated chapter derived from the preliminary study of Dr. R. E. Gomory and myself. It gives an entirely new approach to problems usually considered as analysis problems. The discussion, which is most abbreviated, simply informs the reader that such an approach exists. The interested reader can then study the paper by Gomory and Hu [92].

Chapters 13, 14, and 15 give in detail Gomory's cutting plane algorithms [79], [80], and [81], and the partitioning algorithm of Benders [18]. Chapter 16 deals with the paper by Witzgall [215] on the integer program with parabolic constraints. Chapter 17, written by R. D. Young, reports on his primal integer algorithm [225] and the work of Glover [76]. Chapters 18 to 20 deal with the new results of Gomory [86], some of which come from private communication with Dr. Gomory. I am sorry that due to my limited knowledge I must exclude the works of Edmonds [55], [56], [57] and others [6] and [216] on matching and the connection between matroid theory and networks as reported by Fulkerson [69], Minty [154], Tutte [194], and others.

A word about references is necessary here. In the beginning of each section we usually list the paper on which the section or the chapter is based. This paper is not necessarily the first original paper on the subject. If a survey paper presents the material better, we may have listed both the survey paper and the original paper. There are more than two-hundred references listed at the back of the book. Some of them are not directly related to the book. My original intention was to omit all references not directly related to the book, but the idea of suggested reading greatly enlarged the list of references. Some books on mathematical programming are also listed as general references for the reader.

With few exceptions a numerical example usualy follows an algorithm after it has been explained. Exercises are given following Chapters 1 to 10. Open questions and suggested readings which deal with subjects not treated in the book are also listed. Sections and chapters marked with * in the Table of Contents can be omitted without disturbing the continuity of the book. The relationships between the chapters are shown in the accompanying diagram. The first part can be used in a one-semester course on linear programming. The second part can be used separately as a text on network flows. The third part also can be used separately as a text on integer programming.

It is a pleasure to acknowledge the persons who have helped me in various ways. When I was a graduate student at Brown University, I was introduced to operations research by Professor William Prager, an inspiring teacher and a gentle friend to all his students. After leaving Brown, I went to IBM Research Center to work under Dr. R. E. Gomory. This rare opportunity was definitely the turning point of my career. I had the opportunity not only to learn integer programming from Dr. Gomory directly but also to

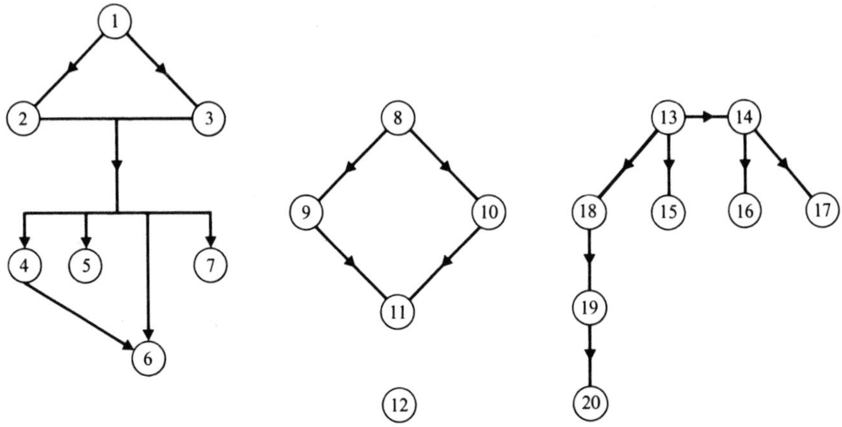

produce joint papers with him on network flows. The years at IBM provided me with excellent conditions for research, and many of the results in this book were obtained at that time. In 1964 Professor G. B. Dantzig invited me to visit the University of California at Berkeley. There I prepared a very rough draft of lecture notes which formed the first draft of this book. This draft was enlarged at Columbia University in 1965–1966. In September 1966 I joined the Mathematics Research Center and the Computer Sciences Department of the University of Wisconsin. This position enabled me to work almost full time on the book. Thus I would like to thank Professor J. B. Rosser, Director of the Mathematics Research Center, and Professor J. B. Rosen, Chairman of the Computer Sciences Department, for their support. Professor R. D. Young read the third draft and gave helpful comments, and Mrs. Dain Wetterstrand did the copy editing for the fourth draft. Many graduate students at Wisconsin read the manuscript and pointed out errors. In particular, I would like to mention Mr. K. C. Tan, Mr. W. T. Torres. Mr. D. I. Good, Mr. James Kho, and Mr. Donald Adolphson,

Financial assistance was provided by the National Science Foundation under grant GP-8557, the Air Force Office of Scientific Research under grant 68-1594, and WARF at the University of Wisconsin. The typing of the manuscript was done mainly by outside typing agencies and partially by Mrs. Pat Hanson and Mrs. Doris Whitmore, technical typists at the University.

I am indebted to my wife Pu-chu and my children Dale, Rona, and Alan for their lost evenings and weekends. Last but not least I thank Addison-Wesley for their unfailing cooperation.

Madison, Wisconsin
March 1969

Te Chiang Hu

CONTENTS

LIST OF NOTATIONS

$\mathbf{A}$	matrix, usually of size $m \times n$
a_{ij}	elements of the matrix $\mathbf{A}$
a_{rs}	the pivot
$\mathbf{a}_i$	the ith row of the matrix $\mathbf{A}$
$\mathbf{a}_j$	the jth column of the matrix $\mathbf{A}$
$\mathbf{B}$	matrix, usually of size $m \times m$ and nonsingular
$\mathbf{B}^{-1}$	the inverse of $\mathbf{B}$
$\mathbf{b}$	column vector, usually with m components $\mathbf{b} = [b_1, \ldots, b_m]$
$\mathbf{c}$	row vector, usually with n components $\mathbf{c} = (c_1, \ldots, c_n)$
$\bar{c}_j$	the relative cost coefficient, $\bar{c}_j = c_j - \boldsymbol{\pi}\mathbf{a}_j$
$\mathbf{e}$	a vector with all its components equal to unity
$\mathbf{e}_i$	a row vector with all its components zero except the ith component, which is one
$\mathbf{e}_j$	a column vector with all its components zero except the jth component, which is one
$\mathbf{I}$	identity matrix
M	a large constant
$\mathbf{N}$	the submatrix of $\mathbf{A}$ with its columns corresponding to nonbasic variablles x_N
s_i	the slack variable for the ith inequality
w	objective function of the dual program, $w = \mathbf{yb}$ or $w = \boldsymbol{\pi}\mathbf{b}$
$\mathbf{x}$	column vector, usually with n components, $\mathbf{x} = [x_1, \ldots, x_n]$
x_i^a	the artificial variable for the ith equation
$\mathbf{x}_B$	a column vector with its components basic variables
$\mathbf{x}_N$	a column vector with its components nonbasic variabes
$\mathbf{y}$	a row vector, usually with m components $\mathbf{y} = (y_1, \ldots, y_m)$
z	a scalar, the value of the objective function
$\boldsymbol{\alpha}_i$	the ith row vector of $\mathbf{B}^{-1}\mathbf{A}$
$\boldsymbol{\alpha}_j$	the jth column vector of $\mathbf{B}^{-1}\mathbf{A}$
$\boldsymbol{\beta}_i$	the ith row vector of $\mathbf{B}^{-1}$
ϵ	an arbitrarily small scalar

ξ	the sum of artificial variables
$\boldsymbol{\pi}$	row vector, usually of m components $\boldsymbol{\pi} = (\pi_1, \ldots, \pi_m)$
A_{ij}	the arc leading from node i to node j
b_{ij}	the arc capacity of the arc A_{ij}
d_{ij}	distance of the arc A_{ij}
f_{ij}	the flow value from node i to node j
L_{sj}	the shortest distance from the source s to the node j
N_s	the source
N_t	the sink
N_i	the ith node
x_{ij}	the arc flow from N_i to N_j in the arc A_{ij}
$(X, \bar{X})$	a cut
$c(X,\bar{X})$	capacity of the cut $(X, \bar{X})$
D	absolute value of a determinant
f_j	the fractional part of a positive number
$\bar{F}_i$	the Gomory cut
$\mathbf{R}_i$	the ith row
t_j	the nonbasic variable
$\mathbf{u}$	a row vector, $\mathbf{u} = (u_1, \ldots, u_m)$ variables of the dual program
$[x]$	the largest integer less than or equal to x
$\langle x \rangle$	the least integer larger than or equal to x
$\{Z\}$	the Abelian group whose elements are integer m-vectors
$\bar{\boldsymbol{\alpha}}$	the fractional part of $\boldsymbol{\alpha}$, $\boldsymbol{\alpha} = \mathbf{B}^{-1}\mathbf{A}$
β_0	$B^{-1}b$
λ	a positive scalar
ϕ	a mapping
$\psi_k(y)$	optimum value when the weight limitation is y and only the first k items are chosen

FOUNDATIONS 1

1.1 PROBLEMS OF LINEAR PROGRAMMING

In this section, we shall give three examples in which problems of linear programming are formulated.

Example 1. Consider a housewife going to the supermarket to purchase nutrients required by her family. Assume that there are m varieties of nutrients and the family needs b_1 units of the first kind, b_2 units of the second kind, . . ., and b_m units of the mth kind. There are n different foods in the market. Each food can be represented by a vector $\mathbf{a}_j$ with m components. The ith component of the vector denotes the amount of the ith nutrient contained in one unit of the given food. Therefore, we can use an $m \times n$ matrix $\mathbf{A} = [a_{ij}]$ to indicate the relationship between the foods and the amounts of nutrients they contain. Each column of the matrix represents one kind of food. Thus a_{ij} is the amount of the ith nutrient contained in one unit of the jth food. Let $x_1, x_2, \ldots, x_n$ be the amounts of foods that the housewife will buy. In order that the nutrient requirements be satisfied, she must have

$$\mathbf{Ax} \geq \mathbf{b}, \tag{1}$$

where $\mathbf{A} = [a_{ij}]$, $\mathbf{x} = [x_1, x_2, \ldots, x_n]$, and $\mathbf{b} = [b_1, b_2, \ldots, b_m]$.

There are many ways that (1) can be satisfied, but this housewife likes to choose the one among these that will minimize the total cost of the foods. If $c_1, c_2, \ldots, c_n$ are the costs per unit of the foods, respectively, the total cost z to be minimized is expressed as:

$$z = c_1x_1 + \cdots + c_nx_n. \tag{2}$$

The fact that she can only buy from but not sell to the supermarket is expressed by the additional constraints

$$x_j \geq 0 \qquad (j = 1, \ldots, n). \tag{3}$$

The problem is then to minimize (2) subject to (1) and (3).

Example 2. Now let us consider a person who wants to get the most money from the housewife. This example is more artificial than the first.

Consider a pill salesman selling pills containing pure nutrients of all kinds. Let $y_1, y_2, \ldots, y_m$ be the prices of the pills that contain one unit of the ith nutrient. Assume that the pill salesman also knows the amount of nutrient contained in each kind of food, i.e., the $[a_{ij}]$ matrix which indicates the relationship between foods and the amounts of nutrients they contain. In order to meet the competition from the supermarket, the prices y_i are fixed such that

$$\sum_{i=1}^{m} y_i a_{ij} \leq c_j \qquad \text{(for all } j = 1, \ldots, n). \tag{4}$$

If (4) is satisfied, then no matter what the housewife buys, it is always as cheap for her to buy the pills to satisfy the nutrient requirements rather than the food. The total amount of money spent on the pills (for the family which needs b_i units of the ith nutrient) is then

$$w = y_1 b_1 + \cdots + y_m b_m. \tag{5}$$

The pill salesman wants to fix the prices y_i in such a way that (5) is maximized and (4) is satisfied. Naturally, all the prices y_i have to be nonnegative, i.e., $y_i \geq 0$ $(i = 1, \ldots, m)$. The salesman's problem is again a linear programming problem, i.e., maximizing or minimizing a linear function subject to linear constraints and nonnegativity of the variables.

Example 3. Consider a chemical plant required to produce b_1 units of material 1, b_2 units of material 2, ..., and b_m units of material m. There are different processes by which these materials are produced. Each process or activity can be represented by a vector which represents the amount of each kind of material that the activity would produce if the activity were operated at a unit level. A component of the vector may be negative if the activity consumes instead of produces a material. Let $x_1, x_2, \ldots, x_n$ be the levels of operation of the n different activities, let $\mathbf{a}_1, \mathbf{a}_2, \ldots, \mathbf{a}_n$ be the vectors representing the activities, and let $c_1, \ldots, c_n$ be the operating costs associated with these vectors. Then the problem is again

$$\min\ z = \sum_{j=1}^{n} c_j x_j$$

subject to

$$\sum_{j=1}^{n} \mathbf{a}_j x_j = \mathbf{b} \qquad x_j \geq 0.$$

Since there are many expressions in this book which are summations of many terms we need a summation convention. There are several of these, but for simplicity we shall use the double index convention. If in some expressions a certain index appears twice, it is understood that that expression is summed with respect to that index for all admissible values of the index. Thus $c_j x_j$ $(j = 1, \ldots, n)$ means $c_1 x_1 + c_2 x_2 + \cdots + c_n x_n$, and

$y_i a_{ij}$ $(i = 1, \ldots, m)$ means $y_1 a_{1j} + y_2 a_{2j} + \cdots + y_m a_{mj}$. An expression like $y a_{ij} \leq c_j$ $(i = 1, \ldots, m; j = 1, \ldots, n)$ then stands for the n inequalities with m terms on the left-hand side of each inequality. Sometimes, we do not write the admissible values of the index if these values are known.

1.2 EQUIVALENT FORMULATIONS

The problem of linear programming is to minimize a linear function subject to linear inequalities, i.e., we want to minimize

$$z = c_j x_j \qquad (j = 1, \ldots, n), \tag{1}$$

subject to

$$a_{ij} x_j \geq b_i \qquad (i = 1, \ldots, m), \tag{2}$$

and

$$x_j \geq 0, \tag{3}$$

where x_j are unknown variables and a_{ij}, b_i, and c_j are given constants. The linear function z in (1), which we want to minimize, is called the *objective function*, and inequalities (2) and (3) are called *constraints*. Some of the inequalities in (2) may also be equalities, and they are also called constraints.

We see immediately three distinct features of the problem of linear programming: 1) the constraints are of the inequality type, 2) the objective function which we want to minimize is a linear function, 3) the variables are restricted to be nonnegative. In most classical methods of optimization the fundamental tool is the differential operator. The maximum or minimum of the function is characterized by the vanishing of the derivative. Here the objective function is linear, the maximum or minimum of the function is always at a boundary point of the domain, and the one-sided derivative of the function does not vanish at that point. The nonnegativity of the variables x_j can be replaced by introducing $x_j = u_j^2$ with $u_j \gtrless 0$, but this will make constraints nonlinear and does not render the problem solvable by the classical methods of optimization. New techniques are needed to solve these linear programming problems which, from now on, will be called *linear programs*.

Several formulations which are equivalent to (1), (2), and (3) are listed below. We shall use the form which is most convenient to our immediate purpose.

First, minimizing a function is equivalent to maximizing the negative of that function. So we can replace (1) by

$$\max z' = -c_j x_j.$$

Second, for an inequality constraint in (2), say

$$a_{ij} x_j \geq b_i,$$

we can introduce a new unknown variable s_i $(s_i \geq 0)$, called a *slack variable*, and convert this inequality into an equality:

$$a_{ij}x_j - s_i = b_i.$$

For an inequality $a_{ij}x_j \leq b_i$ we can also introduce $s_i \geq 0$ and replace that inequality by

$$a_{ij}x_j + s_i = b_i.$$

Third, if an equality $a_{ij}x_j = b_i$ appears in the constraints, we can always replace it by two inequalities:

$$a_{ij}x_j \geq b_i, \qquad \text{and} \qquad a_{ij}x_j \leq b_i.$$

If we have m equalities $a_{ij}x_j = b_i$ $(i = 1, \ldots, m)$, it can be replaced by $m + 1$ inequalities $a_{ij}x_j \geq b_i$ $(i = 1, \ldots, m)$ and $\sum_i (a_{ij}x_j - b_i) \leq 0$.

Fourth, if a variable x_j is not restricted in sign, then we can replace it by two variables x_j^+ and x_j^-, which are to be nonnegative,

$$x_j = x_j^+ - x_j^-,$$

and require

$$x_j^+ \geq 0 \qquad \text{and} \qquad x_j^- \geq 0.$$

If we have n variables x_j $(j = 1, \ldots, n)$ all unrestricted in sign, then we can replace them by $n + 1$ nonnegative variables x_j^+ and x_0, where $x_j = x_j^+ - x_0$. Let the original linear program be

$$\begin{aligned} \min c_jx_j & \qquad (j = 1, \ldots, n), \\ a_{ij}x_j = b_i & \qquad (i = 1, \ldots, m), \\ x_j \gtreqless 0. & \end{aligned}$$

Then the new linear program is

$$\begin{aligned} & \min c_jx_j^+ - (\sum_j c_j)\, x_0, \\ & a_{ij}x_j^+ - (\sum_j a_{ij})\, x_0 = b_i \qquad (i = 1, \ldots, m), \\ & x_j^+ \geq 0 \qquad (j = 1, \ldots, n), \\ & x_0 \geq 0. \end{aligned}$$

With the above transformations between equivalent formulations, we can define a linear program. *A linear program* is a problem of minimizing or maximizing a linear function subject to linear constraints where these constraints may include both inequalities and equalities and the unknown variables may include nonnegative variables and variables that are unrestricted in sign (see Dantzig [37]).

Sometimes, we shall also write (1), (2), and (3) in matrix notation (see the list of notation in the front of the book), where boldface letters indicate a matrix or vector:

$$\min \ z = \mathbf{cx} \tag{1'}$$

subject to

$$\mathbf{Ax} \geq \mathbf{b}, \tag{2'}$$

$$\mathbf{x} \geq \mathbf{0}. \tag{3'}$$

We shall say that a vector $\mathbf{x}$ is nonnegative if each of its components $x_j \geq 0$ for all j; $\mathbf{x}$ is positive if $x_j > 0$ for all j; and $\mathbf{x}$ is semipositive if $x_j \geq 0$ for all j but with at least one positive component.

Before we consider the question of how to find an $\mathbf{x}$ which satisfies (2′) and (3′) and minimizes (1′), the question of the existence of an $\mathbf{x}$ which satisfies (2′) and (3′) should be answered. We shall study the solutions of linear inequalities in the next section.

1.3 INEQUALITIES

In this section we say that a vector $\bar{\mathbf{x}}$ is a solution to a set of inequalities $\mathbf{Ax} \geq \mathbf{b}$ (or equalities $\mathbf{Ax} = \mathbf{b}$) if $\bar{\mathbf{x}}$ satisfies $\mathbf{Ax} \geq \mathbf{b}$ (or $\mathbf{Ax} = \mathbf{b}$). Components of $\mathbf{x}$ may be positive, negative, or zero.

Theorem 1.1. *Solvability of linear equations.* Either the equation

$$\mathbf{Ax} = \mathbf{b} \qquad (\mathbf{b} \neq \mathbf{0}) \tag{1}$$

has a solution or the equations

$$\mathbf{yA} = \mathbf{0}, \tag{2a}$$

$$\mathbf{yb} = \lambda \neq 0. \tag{2b}$$

have a solution.

Proof. We shall first prove that (1) and (2) cannot both be true. This is easily done. Multiplying (1) by $\mathbf{y}$ on the left, we have, from (2b),

$$\mathbf{yAx} = \mathbf{yb} = \lambda. \tag{3}$$

Multiplying (2a) by $\mathbf{x}$ on the right, we have

$$\mathbf{yAx} = \mathbf{0x} = 0. \tag{4}$$

Equations (3) and (4) provide the desired contradiction.

Second, we shall prove that if (1) has no solution, then (2) has a solution. Let $\mathbf{a}_1, \mathbf{a}_2, \mathbf{a}_3, \ldots, \mathbf{a}_n$ be the column vectors of $\mathbf{A}$ and $\mathbf{a}_1, \mathbf{a}_2, \mathbf{a}_3, \ldots, \mathbf{a}_r$ be a set of basis vectors of $\mathbf{A}$ with $r < m$ (r is strictly less than m, otherwise every vector $\mathbf{b}$ can be expressed as a linear combination of $\mathbf{a}_1, \ldots, \mathbf{a}_m$). That (1) has no solution implies that $\mathbf{a}_1, \ldots, \mathbf{a}_r$ and $\mathbf{b}$ are independent or the set of $r + 1$ vectors $[\mathbf{a}_1, \mathbf{a}_2, \ldots, \mathbf{a}_r, \mathbf{b}]$ is of rank $r + 1$. Let $[\mathbf{a}_1, \ldots, \mathbf{a}_r, \mathbf{b}] = [\mathbf{A}_r, \mathbf{b}]$. Since the column rank of a matrix is equal to the row rank of a matrix, the matrix $[\mathbf{a}_1, \mathbf{a}_2, \ldots, \mathbf{a}_r, \mathbf{b}]$ is also of row rank $r + 1$. Therefore, the $r + 1$ row vector $(0, 0, \ldots, 0, \lambda)$ will be a linear combination of the row basis of $[\mathbf{A}_r, \mathbf{b}]$. Let the coefficient of the linear combination be y_i; we have

$$(y_1, y_2, \ldots, y_m)\,[\mathbf{a}_1, \ldots, \mathbf{a}_r, \mathbf{b}] = (0, 0, \ldots, 0, \lambda),$$

or

$$\mathbf{yA}_r = \mathbf{0}, \qquad \mathbf{y} = (y_1, y_2, \ldots, y_m),$$
$$\mathbf{yb} = \lambda.$$

Since every $\mathbf{a}_k$ not in the basis is a linear combination of $\mathbf{a}_1, \ldots, \mathbf{a}_r$, let $\mathbf{a}_k = \mu_i \mathbf{a}_i$ $(i = 1, \ldots, r)$. Then $\mathbf{ya}_k = \mu_i \mathbf{ya}_i = 0$ $(i = 1, \ldots, r;\ k = 1, \ldots, n)$, or we have

$$\mathbf{yA} = \mathbf{0}, \qquad \mathbf{yb} = \lambda.$$

This is exactly (2), and Theorem 1.1 is proved.

Theorem 1.2. *Nonnegative solution of linear equations.* Either the equation

$$\mathbf{Ax} = \mathbf{b} \qquad (\mathbf{b} \neq \mathbf{0}), \tag{5}$$

has a nonnegative solution or the inequalities

$$\mathbf{yA} \geq \mathbf{0}, \tag{6a}$$
$$\mathbf{yb} < 0 \tag{6b}$$

have a solution.

Proof. First, (5) and (6) cannot both be true. Multiplying (5) by $\mathbf{y}$ on the left, and using (6b), we have

$$\mathbf{yAx} = \mathbf{yb} < 0. \tag{7}$$

Multiplying (6a) by $\mathbf{x}$ on the right, we have

$$\mathbf{yAx} \geq \mathbf{0} \cdot \mathbf{x} = 0. \tag{8}$$

The contradiction is provided by (7) and (8).

We have just proved that (5) and (6) are mutually exclusive, and now we want to show that they are collectively exhaustive. If (5) has no solution at all, then let $\lambda = -1$ in Theorem 1.1. We have

$$\mathbf{yA} = \mathbf{0}, \qquad \text{and} \qquad \mathbf{yb} = -1 < 0,$$

which satisfies (6).

Assume now that (5) has a solution but *not a nonnegative solution*. We shall then show that (6) has a solution. The proof is by *induction* on the number of columns of $\mathbf{A}$. If $\mathbf{A}$ has only one column $\mathbf{a}_1$ and (5) has a solution

$$\mathbf{a}_1 x_1 = \mathbf{b} \qquad \text{or} \qquad \mathbf{a}_1 = \frac{\mathbf{b}}{x_1},$$

then $\mathbf{y} = -\mathbf{b}^T$ is a solution of (6), since

$$\mathbf{yb} = -\mathbf{b}^T \cdot \mathbf{b} = -\mathbf{b}^2 < 0,$$

and, at the same time,

$$\mathbf{y}\mathbf{a}_1 = \mathbf{y}\frac{\mathbf{b}}{x_1} = -\frac{\mathbf{b}^2}{x_1} > 0 \qquad \text{as } x_1 < 0.$$

Let (5) have no nonnegative solution and assume that Theorem 1.2 is true for $k < n$; i.e., if

$$\sum_{j=1}^{n-1} \mathbf{a}_j x_j = \mathbf{b} \tag{9}$$

has no nonnegative solution, then there exists a $\bar{\mathbf{y}}$ such that

$$\bar{\mathbf{y}}\mathbf{a}_j \geq 0 \qquad (\text{for } j = 1, \ldots, n-1),$$

and

$$\bar{\mathbf{y}}\mathbf{b} < 0.$$

If $\bar{\mathbf{y}}\mathbf{a}_n \geq 0$, then $\bar{\mathbf{y}}$ satisfies (6) for $k = n$ and, by induction, we have $\bar{\mathbf{y}}\mathbf{A} \geq \mathbf{0}$ and $\bar{\mathbf{y}}\mathbf{b} < 0$ and the theorem is proved. Therefore let us assume that $\bar{\mathbf{y}}\mathbf{a}_n < 0$, and that we can construct $\mathbf{a}'_j$ and $\mathbf{b}'$ as follows:

$$\mathbf{a}'_j = \mathbf{a}_j + \lambda_j \mathbf{a}_n \qquad \text{where} \qquad \lambda_j = -\frac{\bar{\mathbf{y}}\mathbf{a}_j}{\bar{\mathbf{y}}\mathbf{a}_n} \geq 0 \qquad (\text{for } j = 1, \ldots, n-1),$$

$$\mathbf{b}' = \mathbf{b} + \lambda_0 \mathbf{a}_n \qquad \text{where} \qquad \lambda_0 = -\frac{\bar{\mathbf{y}}\mathbf{b}}{\bar{\mathbf{y}}\mathbf{a}_n} < 0. \tag{10}$$

Consider the equation

$$\sum_{j=1}^{n-1} x'_j \mathbf{a}'_j = \mathbf{b}'. \tag{11}$$

*We assert that (11) has no nonnegative solution, since substituting (10) into (11) yields

$$\sum_{j=1}^{n-1} x'_j \mathbf{a}_j + \left[\sum_{j=1}^{n-1} \lambda_j x'_j - \lambda_0\right] \mathbf{a}_n = \mathbf{b}, \tag{12}$$

where the coefficient of $\mathbf{a}_n$ in (12) is positive if $x'_j \geq 0$. This would imply that there exists $\mathbf{x} \geq 0$ such that $\mathbf{A}\mathbf{x} = \mathbf{b}$ for $\mathbf{A}$ with n columns. This means that we cannot have $x'_j \geq 0$ for $j = 1, \ldots, n-1$ in (11). Applying the induction hypothesis to (11), we have

$$\bar{\mathbf{y}}'\mathbf{a}'_j \geq 0 \qquad (j = 1, \ldots, n-1),$$
$$\bar{\mathbf{y}}'\mathbf{b}' < 0. \tag{13}$$

Now let

$$\mathbf{y} = \bar{\mathbf{y}}' - \frac{\bar{\mathbf{y}}'\mathbf{a}_n}{\bar{\mathbf{y}}\mathbf{a}_n}\bar{\mathbf{y}}. \tag{14}$$

*Note that we are still working under the assumption that (5) has no nonnegative solution.

This $\mathbf{y}$ satisfies $\mathbf{ya}_j \geq 0$ ($j = 1, \ldots, n-1, n$ and $\mathbf{yb} < 0$). This can be easily checked by using (13) and (14):

$$\begin{aligned}
\mathbf{ya}_j &= \left(\bar{\mathbf{y}}' - \frac{\bar{\mathbf{y}}'\mathbf{a}_n}{\bar{\mathbf{y}}\mathbf{a}_n}\bar{\mathbf{y}}\right)\mathbf{a}_j = \bar{\mathbf{y}}'\mathbf{a}_j - \frac{\bar{\mathbf{y}}'\mathbf{a}_n}{\bar{\mathbf{y}}\mathbf{a}_n}\bar{\mathbf{y}}\mathbf{a}_j \\
&= \bar{\mathbf{y}}'\mathbf{a}_j + \lambda_j\bar{\mathbf{y}}'\mathbf{a}_n = \bar{\mathbf{y}}'(\mathbf{a}_j + \lambda_j\mathbf{a}_n) = \bar{\mathbf{y}}'\mathbf{a}_j' \geq 0 \qquad (\text{for } j = 1, \ldots, \text{n} - 1), \\
\mathbf{ya}_n &= \left(\bar{\mathbf{y}}' - \frac{\bar{\mathbf{y}}'\mathbf{a}_n}{\bar{\mathbf{y}}\mathbf{a}_n}\bar{\mathbf{y}}\right)\mathbf{a}_n = \bar{\mathbf{y}}'\mathbf{a}_n - \frac{\bar{\mathbf{y}}'\mathbf{a}_n}{\bar{\mathbf{y}}\mathbf{a}_n}\bar{\mathbf{y}}\mathbf{a}_n = 0. \\
\mathbf{yb} &= \left(\bar{\mathbf{y}}' - \frac{\bar{\mathbf{y}}'\mathbf{a}_n}{\bar{\mathbf{y}}\mathbf{a}_n}\bar{\mathbf{y}}\right)\mathbf{b} = \bar{\mathbf{y}}'\mathbf{b} - \frac{\bar{\mathbf{y}}'\mathbf{a}_n}{\bar{\mathbf{y}}\mathbf{a}_n}\bar{\mathbf{y}}\mathbf{b} \\
&= \bar{\mathbf{y}}'\mathbf{b} + \lambda_0\bar{\mathbf{y}}'\mathbf{a}_n = \bar{\mathbf{y}}'(\mathbf{b} + \lambda_0\mathbf{a}_n) = \bar{\mathbf{y}}'\mathbf{b}' < 0.
\end{aligned}$$

Theorem 1.3. *Nonnegative solution of linear inequalities, Minkowski-Farkas' lemma.* Either the inequality

$$\mathbf{Ax} \leq \mathbf{b} \tag{15}$$

has a nonnegative solution or the inequalities

$$\mathbf{yA} \geq \mathbf{0}, \qquad \mathbf{yb} < 0 \tag{16}$$

have a nonnegative solution.

Proof. In Theorem 1.2, we have either $\mathbf{A}^*\mathbf{x}^* = \mathbf{b}$ has a nonnegative solution or the inequalities

$$\mathbf{yA}^* \geq \mathbf{0}, \qquad \mathbf{yb} < 0$$

have a solution. Let

$$\mathbf{A}^* = [\mathbf{A}, \mathbf{I}], \qquad \mathbf{x}^* = [\mathbf{x}, \mathbf{s}].$$

Theorem 1.2 becomes: either the equation

$$\mathbf{Ax} + \mathbf{Is} = \mathbf{b} \tag{17}$$

has a solution $\mathbf{x} \geq \mathbf{0}$, $\mathbf{s} \geq \mathbf{0}$, or the inequalities

$$\mathbf{yA} \geq \mathbf{0}, \qquad \mathbf{yI} \geq \mathbf{0}, \qquad \mathbf{yb} < 0 \tag{18}$$

have a solution.

But (17) is equivalent to $\mathbf{Ax} \leq \mathbf{b}$ has a nonnegative solution, and (18) is equivalent to $\mathbf{yA} \geq \mathbf{0}$ and $\mathbf{yb} < 0$ have a nonnegative solution.

Since Theorem 1.3 is true for any $\mathbf{A}$ and $\mathbf{b}$, we can let $-\mathbf{A}^*$ and $-\mathbf{b}^*$ replace $\mathbf{A}$ and $\mathbf{b}$ and then multiply both sides of the inequalities by -1 and reverse the sense of inequality. We shall state this result as a corollary, and omit the "*" of $\mathbf{A}$ and $\mathbf{b}$.

Corollary 1.1. Either the inequality

$$\mathbf{Ax} \geq \mathbf{b} \tag{19}$$

has a nonnegative solution or the inequalities

$$\mathbf{yA} \leq \mathbf{0}, \qquad \mathbf{yb} > 0 \tag{20}$$

have a nonnegative solution.

Theorem 1.4. The inequalities

$$\mathbf{Kx} \geq \mathbf{0}, \qquad \mathbf{x} \geq \mathbf{0}, \tag{21}$$

where $\mathbf{K}^T = -\mathbf{K}$, have at least one solution $\bar{\mathbf{x}}$ such that

$$\mathbf{K}\bar{\mathbf{x}} + \bar{\mathbf{x}} > \mathbf{0}.$$

Proof. Let $\mathbf{K}^i$ be the ith row of $\mathbf{K}$. We shall first show that there exists a vector $\bar{\mathbf{x}}_i = [\bar{x}_{i1}, \bar{x}_{i2}, \ldots, \bar{x}_{ii}, \ldots, \bar{x}_{in}]$ such that

$$\mathbf{K}^i\bar{\mathbf{x}}_i + \bar{x}_{ii} > 0, \qquad \mathbf{K}^j\bar{\mathbf{x}}_i + \bar{x}_{ij} \geq 0.$$

(No summation on the index i.)

In Corollary 1.1, let $\mathbf{b} = \mathbf{e}_i$ and $\mathbf{A} = \mathbf{K}$. If (19) is true, then there exists $\bar{\mathbf{x}}_i \geq \mathbf{0}$ such that

$$\mathbf{K}\bar{\mathbf{x}}_i \geq \mathbf{e}_i$$

or

$$\mathbf{K}^i\bar{\mathbf{x}}_i \geq 1, \qquad \mathbf{K}^j\bar{\mathbf{x}}_i \geq 0 \qquad (j \neq i).$$

Thus

$$\mathbf{K}^i\bar{\mathbf{x}}_i + \bar{x}_{ii} > 0.$$

If (20) is true, then there exists $\mathbf{x}_i^T \geq \mathbf{0}$ such that

$$\bar{\mathbf{x}}_i^T\mathbf{K} \leq \mathbf{0} \quad \text{or} \quad \mathbf{K}^T\bar{\mathbf{x}}_i \leq \mathbf{0} \quad \text{or} \quad -\mathbf{K}\bar{\mathbf{x}}_i \leq \mathbf{0} \quad \text{or} \quad \mathbf{K}\bar{\mathbf{x}}_i \geq \mathbf{0}$$

$$\bar{\mathbf{x}}_i^T\mathbf{e}_i > 0 \quad \text{or} \quad \bar{x}_{ii} > 0 \quad \text{and} \quad \bar{x}_{ij} \geq 0.$$

In both cases, we have $\mathbf{K}^i\bar{\mathbf{x}}_i + \bar{x}_{ii} > 0$, $\mathbf{K}^j\bar{\mathbf{x}}_i + \bar{x}_{ij} \geq 0$ $(j \neq i)$. If we let $\mathbf{b}$ in Corollary 1.1 be $\mathbf{e}_1, \mathbf{e}_2, \ldots, \mathbf{e}_n$ successively and denote the corresponding solutions by $\bar{\mathbf{x}}_i$, then

$$\bar{\mathbf{x}} = \sum_{i=1}^{n} \bar{\mathbf{x}}_i$$

is the desired solution of (21) with $\mathbf{K}\bar{\mathbf{x}} + \bar{\mathbf{x}} > \mathbf{0}$.

1.4 CONES, CONVEX SETS, AND CONVEX FUNCTIONS

In n-dimensional Euclidean space every vector of n components corresponds to a point in the space, where the components of the vector correspond to the coordinates of the point. Given a vector $\mathbf{a}$, the set of points in the straight line containing the origin and $\mathbf{a}$ is denoted by $\{\mathbf{x} \mid \mathbf{x} = \lambda\mathbf{a}, \lambda \gtreqless 0\}$. We shall call a half-line with one end at the origin and one end extended to infinity a *ray*. We can denote the ray from the origin to infinity containing the vector **a** by

$$\{\mathbf{x} \mid \mathbf{x} = \lambda\mathbf{a},\ \lambda \geq 0\}.$$

A straight line with both ends at finite distances is called a *segment*. Thus the segment from the point **a** to the point **b** is denoted by

$$\{\mathbf{x} \mid \mathbf{x} = \lambda\mathbf{a} + (1 - \lambda)\mathbf{b},\ 1 \geq \lambda \geq 0\}.$$

Analogous to a plane in three-dimensional space, a hyperplane in E^n is denoted by

$$\{\mathbf{x} \mid \mathbf{ax} = \alpha\}.$$

Then the closed half-space consisting of the hyperplane and all points on one side of the hyperplane is denoted by

$$\{\mathbf{x} \mid \mathbf{ax} \geq \alpha\}.$$

A *cone* C is a set of points such that if

$$\left.\begin{matrix}\mathbf{x} \in C \\ \lambda \geq 0\end{matrix}\right\} \quad \text{then} \quad \lambda\mathbf{x} \in C.$$

Example 1. Any straight line through the origin is a cone, with **x** being any vector in the straight line.

Example 2. Any half-line through the origin is also a cone. (How about a half-line with the origin deleted?)

Example 3. Any hyperplane passing through the origin in E^n is a cone.

Example 4. The closed half-space with the hyperplane passing through the origin is a cone.

Example 5. The shaded area shown in Fig. 1.1 is a cone.

Example 6. The shaded area shown in Fig. 1.2 is a cone.

Example 7. The solution of $\mathbf{Ax} \geq \mathbf{0}$ forms a cone.

Example 8. How about a segment and a straight line through two given points?

$$\{\mathbf{x} \mid \mathbf{x} = \lambda\mathbf{a} + (1 - \lambda)\mathbf{b},\ 1 \geq \lambda \geq 0\},$$
$$\{\mathbf{x} \mid \mathbf{x} = \lambda\mathbf{a} + (1 - \lambda)\mathbf{b},\ -\infty < \lambda < \infty\}.$$

A set of points C in E^n is called a *convex cone* if

$$\mathbf{x}, \mathbf{y} \in C \quad \text{then} \quad \mathbf{x} + \mathbf{y} \in C,$$

and if

$$\mathbf{x} \in C \quad \text{and} \quad \lambda \geq 0, \quad \text{then} \quad \lambda\mathbf{x} \in C.$$

The cones in Examples 1, 2, 3, 4, and 6 are convex cones, but the cone in Example 5 is not convex, because it is possible to find the sum of two vectors

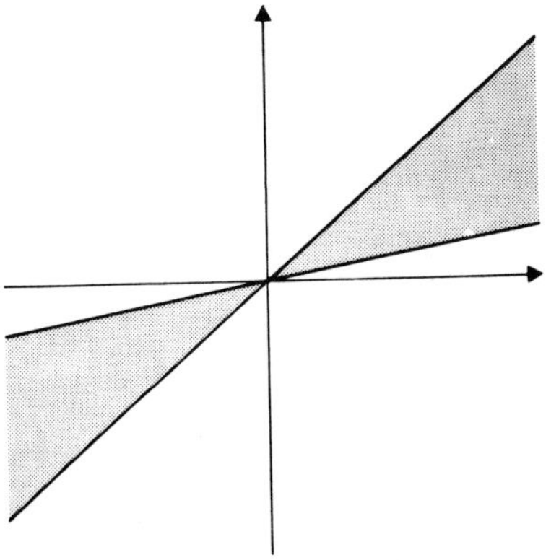

Fig. 1.1

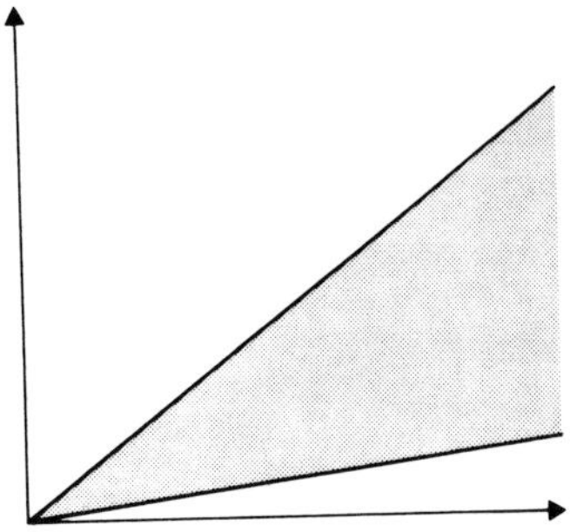

Fig. 1.2

not belonging to C. We shall define the following operations and properties of convex cones.

If C_1 and C_2 are convex cones, their *sum* $C_1 + C_2$ is defined by

$$C_1 + C_2 = \{\mathbf{x} | \mathbf{x} = \mathbf{x}_1 + \mathbf{x}_2, \mathbf{x}_1 \in C_1 \text{ and } \mathbf{x}_2 \in C_2\}.$$

It is clear that the sum of two convex cones is also a convex cone. For example, the sum of two straight lines through the origin (two convex cones) is the plane containing the two straight lines. The sum of two half-lines is a convex cone in Example 6.

If C_1 and C_2 are convex cones, their *intersection* $C_1 \cap C_2$ is defined by

$$\{\mathbf{x} | \mathbf{x} \in C_1 \text{ and } \mathbf{x} \in C_2\}.$$

It is clear that the intersection is also a convex cone. For example, the intersection of two half spaces in E^2 will be a convex cone shown in Example 6.

If C is a convex cone, the *dual cone* C^* is defined by

$$C^* = \{\mathbf{y} | \mathbf{yx} \leq 0 \text{ for all } \mathbf{x} \in C\}.$$

The dual cone consists of vectors which make nonacute angles with all vectors in C (Fig. 1.3). The dual cone C^* to Example 1 is the plane orthogonal to the straight line. The dual cone C^* to Example 2 is the half-space $\{\mathbf{y} | \mathbf{yx} \leq 0\}$ where $\mathbf{x}$ is a nonzero vector in the half-line.

A convex cone C is called a *finite cone* if it is the sum of a finite number of half-lines. We write

$$C = (\mathbf{a}_1) + (\mathbf{a}_2) + \cdots + (\mathbf{a}_n).$$

The vectors contained in these half-lines are called the *generators* of the convex cone C. From the definition of sum of convex cones, it is seen that

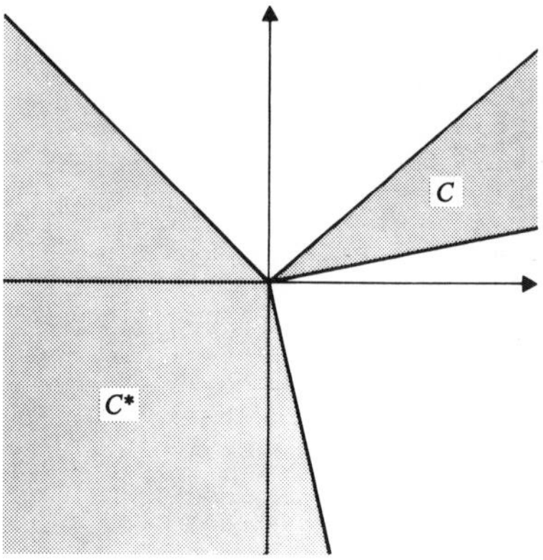

Fig. 1.3

any vector in a finite cone can be written as $\mathbf{x} = \lambda_1\mathbf{a}_1 + \cdots + \lambda_n\mathbf{a}_n$, where $\lambda_j \geq 0$ and $\sum_{j=1}^{n} \lambda_j = 1$, and where $\mathbf{a}_i$ are arbitrary vectors contained in these half-lines, i.e. they are not fixed vectors. We shall say that $\mathbf{x}$ is a linear convex combination of the generators $\mathbf{a}_j$ ($j = 1, \ldots, n$).

If we consider those vectors $\mathbf{a}_j$ ($j = 1, \ldots, n$) as column vectors of a matrix $\mathbf{A}$, then the set of points in the finite cone can be written as

$$C = \{\mathbf{y} | \mathbf{y} = \mathbf{Ax} \quad \text{for} \quad \mathbf{x} \geq \mathbf{0}\},$$

i.e., every vector $\mathbf{y}$ in the cone is a nonnegative linear combination of the column vectors of $\mathbf{A}$.

A set X is a *convex set* if for any two points $\mathbf{x}_1, \mathbf{x}_2$ in the set, all the points of the form $\lambda\mathbf{x}_1 + (1 - \lambda)\mathbf{x}_2$ also belong to X for $0 \leq \lambda \leq 1$. This definition of a convex set can be put into more general form as follows. If X is convex and if $\mathbf{x}_1, \ldots, \mathbf{x}_k$ are points of X, then every point $\mathbf{x}$ of the form

$$\mathbf{x} = \sum_{i=1}^{k} \lambda_i \mathbf{x}_i \qquad (\lambda_i \geq 0; \sum_{i=1}^{k} \lambda_i = 1)$$

also belongs to X. Then $\mathbf{x}$ is said to be a *linear convex combination* of the points $\mathbf{x}_i$.

For $k = 2$, this definition is the same as the one above. Assume inductively that it is true for $k = m$. Let $\mathbf{x}$ be a point of the form

$$\mathbf{x} = \lambda_1\mathbf{x}_1 + \cdots + \lambda_m\mathbf{x}_m + \lambda_{m+1}\mathbf{x}_{m+1} \qquad (\lambda_i \geq 0; \lambda_1 + \cdots + \lambda_{m+1} = 1).$$

If $\lambda_{m+1} = 1$, then $\mathbf{x} = \mathbf{x}_{m+1}$, which is assumed to be a point of X. If $\lambda_{m+1} < 1$, then we can put $\mathbf{x}$ as (note $1 \geq \lambda_1 + \cdots + \lambda_m = 1 - \lambda_{m+1} > 0$)

$$\mathbf{x} = (\lambda_1 + \cdots + \lambda_m)\left(\frac{\lambda_1}{\lambda_1 + \cdots + \lambda_m}\mathbf{x}_1 + \cdots + \frac{\lambda_m}{\lambda_1 + \cdots + \lambda_m}\mathbf{x}_m\right) + \lambda_{m+1}\mathbf{x}_{m+1}$$

$$= (\lambda_1 + \cdots + \lambda_m)\mathbf{z} + \lambda_{m+1}\mathbf{x}_{m+1},$$

where $\mathbf{z}$ belongs to X by the induction hypothesis, and this shows that $\mathbf{x}$ also belongs to X.

Example 9. A hyperplane $\mathbf{cx} = z$ is a convex set where $\mathbf{c}$ is a given vector, z is a scalar, and $\mathbf{x}$ denotes any point on the hyperplane.

Proof. Let $\mathbf{x}_1, \mathbf{x}_2$ be any two points on the hyperplane, i.e., $\mathbf{cx}_1 = z$, and $\mathbf{cx}_2 = z$. But this implies that $\mathbf{x} = \lambda\mathbf{x}_1 + (1 - \lambda)\mathbf{x}_2$ is also on the hyperplane:

$$\mathbf{cx} = \mathbf{c}[\lambda\mathbf{x}_1 + (1 - \lambda)\mathbf{x}_2] = \lambda z + (1 - \lambda)z = z.$$

Example 10. A half-space $\mathbf{cx} \leq z$ (or $\mathbf{cx} < z$) is a convex set, because

$$\mathbf{cx} = \lambda\, \mathbf{cx}_1 + (1 - \lambda)\, \mathbf{cx}_2 \leq z.$$

Lemma. The intersection of convex sets is convex.

A point $\mathbf{x}$ of a convex set X is an *extreme point* if and only if

$$\mathbf{x} = \lambda\mathbf{x}_1 + (1 - \lambda)\mathbf{x}_2 \qquad (1 > \lambda > 0) \quad \text{implies} \quad \mathbf{x} = \mathbf{x}_1 = \mathbf{x}_2,$$
$$\text{or} \quad \mathbf{x}_1 \notin X \quad \text{or} \quad \mathbf{x}_2 \notin X.$$

Note that extreme points of a convex set are always boundary points of the set but not vice versa.

Consider the set of equations

$$\mathbf{Ax} = \mathbf{b} \qquad (\mathbf{A} \text{ is } m \times n)$$

which can be written as

$$\mathbf{a}_i\mathbf{x} = b_i \qquad (i = 1, \ldots, m)$$

where $\mathbf{a}_i$ is the ith row vector of $\mathbf{A}$. The set of points satisfying the ith equation comprises the hyperplane

$$\mathbf{a}_i\mathbf{x} = b_i.$$

The dimension of the convex set $\{\mathbf{x} | \mathbf{Ax} = \mathbf{b}\}$ is $n - m$. (The equations are independent.)

Given a set P convex or not, it is possible to find a convex set X containing P, i.e., $\mathbf{x} \in P$ implies $\mathbf{x} \in X$.

The *convex hull* of a set P is the intersection of all convex sets X_i which contain P.

The convex hull of a finite number of points is called the *convex polyhedron* spanned by these points. It is clear that a convex polyhedron is spanned by its extreme points. (A convex polyhedron in higher dimension is called a *convex polytope*.)

We shall review the definition of the minimum of a function $f(\mathbf{x})$. The minimum of a function as frequently defined in calculus textbooks is a local minimum or relative minimum, since we compare the values of a function only in a small neighborhood. More precisely, a function $f(\mathbf{x})$ has a strict local minimum at $\mathbf{x}_0$ if there exists an $\epsilon > 0$ such that $f(\mathbf{x}_0) < f(\mathbf{x})$ for all $\mathbf{x}$ with $|\mathbf{x} - \mathbf{x}_0| < \epsilon$. A function $f(\mathbf{x})$ has a local minimum at $\mathbf{x}_0$ if there exists an $\epsilon > 0$ such that $f(\mathbf{x}_0) \leq f(\mathbf{x})$ for all $\mathbf{x}$ with $|\mathbf{x} - \mathbf{x}_0| < \epsilon$.

In mathematical programming we are interested in a *global minimum* of a function defined on X, i.e., we want to find $f(\mathbf{x}_0) \leq f(\mathbf{x})$ for all $\mathbf{x} \in X$. Since a local minimum does not imply a global minimum in general, a possible way to get a global minimum of a function is to compare all local minima of the function. For a certain class of functions called *convex functions* it will be shown that a local minimum of the function implies a global minimum of the function.

A function $f(\mathbf{x})$ *defined on a convex set* X is called a *convex function* if

$$f[\lambda \mathbf{x}_1 + (1 - \lambda)\mathbf{x}_2] \leq \lambda f(\mathbf{x}_1) + (1 - \lambda) f(\mathbf{x}_2) \qquad (\text{for } 1 \geq \lambda \geq 0)$$

for any $\mathbf{x}_1, \mathbf{x}_2 \in X$.

A function $f(\mathbf{x})$ defined on a convex set X is called a *strictly convex function* if

$$f[\lambda \mathbf{x}_1 + (1 - \lambda)\mathbf{x}_2 < \lambda f(\mathbf{x}_1) + (1 - \lambda) f(\mathbf{x}_2) \qquad (\text{for } 1 > \lambda > 0)$$

for any two distinct points $\mathbf{x}_1, \mathbf{x}_2 \in X$.

Note that a convex function is always defined on a convex set X; otherwise the point $\lambda \mathbf{x}_1 + (1 - \lambda)\mathbf{x}_2$ may not be in X. Geometrically, if we consider X as a plane and $f(\mathbf{x})$ as a surface plotted above the plane, then the surface of the convex function has the property that a line segment connecting any two points on the surface lies entirely above or on the surface. For a strictly convex function the line segment lies entirely above the surface except at the two endpoints.

Theorem 1.5. If $f(\mathbf{x})$ is a convex function defined on a closed and bounded convex set X, then a local minimum (strict or not strict) of $f(\mathbf{x})$ is a global minimum of $f(\mathbf{x})$.

Proof. Although the proof is for X of n dimensions, we shall draw a diagram for which X is an interval to make the argument plausible (Fig. 1.4). Let $f(\mathbf{x})$ have a local minimum at $\mathbf{x}_0$, i.e., there exists a neighborhood of $\mathbf{x}_0$ such that $f(\mathbf{x}) \geq f(\mathbf{x}_0)$ for $|\mathbf{x} - \mathbf{x}_0| < \epsilon$. Let $\mathbf{x}^*$ be any other point in X with $f(\mathbf{x}^*) < f(\mathbf{x}_0)$. All the points of the form $\lambda \mathbf{x}^* + (1 - \lambda)\mathbf{x}_0$ $(1 \geq \lambda \geq 0)$ belong to X since X is convex. We can take λ sufficiently small, say ϵ^2, such that $\bar{\mathbf{x}} = \lambda \mathbf{x}^* + (1 - \lambda)\mathbf{x}_0$ is in the ϵ neighborhood of $\mathbf{x}_0$. By the assumption that $\mathbf{x}_0$ is a local minimum of $f(\mathbf{x}_0)$, we have $f(\bar{\mathbf{x}}) \geq f(\mathbf{x}_0)$ or

$$f(\bar{\mathbf{x}}) \geq f(\mathbf{x}_0) = (1 - \lambda) f(\mathbf{x}_0) + \lambda f(\mathbf{x}_0) > (1 - \lambda) f(\mathbf{x}_0) + \lambda f(\mathbf{x}^*)$$
$$(\text{for } 0 < \lambda \leq \epsilon^2). \qquad (1)$$

From the definition of convex functions

$$f(\bar{\mathbf{x}}) \leq (1 - \lambda) f(\mathbf{x}_0) + \lambda f(\mathbf{x}^*) \qquad (\text{for } 0 \leq \lambda \leq 1). \qquad (2)$$

Since $0 < \lambda \leq \epsilon^2$ is a subinterval of $0 \leq \lambda \leq 1$, (1) and (2) provide the desired contradiction. Note that we did not assume that there is a global minimum at $\mathbf{x}^*$. This existence of a global minimum at $\mathbf{x}^*$ in a closed and

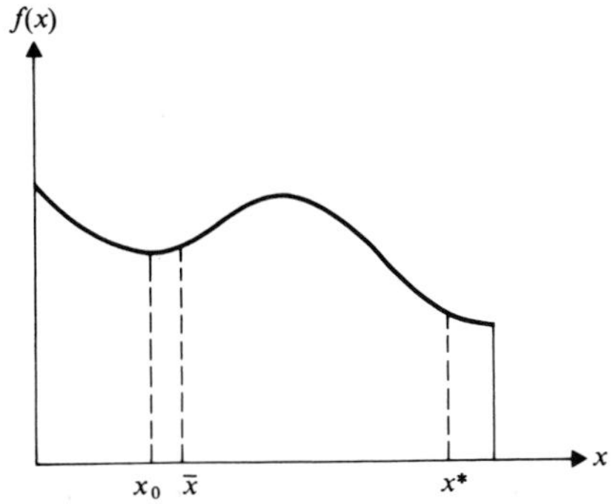

Fig. 1.4

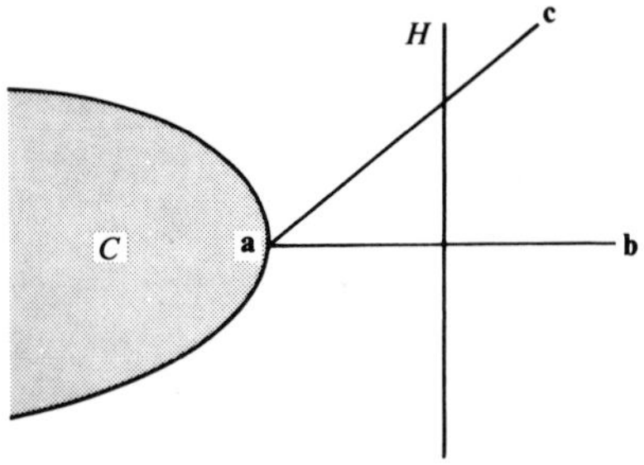

Fig. 1.5

bounded set requires the theorem of Weierstrass. We just take $\mathbf{x}^*$ to be any point with $f(\mathbf{x}^*) < f(\mathbf{x}_0)$. Q. E. D.

The negative or opposite of a convex function is called a *concave function*; thus a function $f(\mathbf{x})$ defined on a convex set is a concave function if

$$f[\lambda\mathbf{x}_1 + (1-\lambda)\mathbf{x}_2] \geq \lambda f(\mathbf{x}_1) + (1-\lambda)f(\mathbf{x}_2) \qquad (\text{for } 1 \geq \lambda \geq 0) \quad (3)$$

for any $\mathbf{x}_1, \mathbf{x}_2 \in X$.

If in the above definition the inequality is replaced by a strict inequality, then the function is called a *strictly concave function*.

Theorem 1.6. If $f(\mathbf{x})$ is a concave function defined on a closed and bounded convex set X, then there exists a global minimum at an extreme point of X.

Proof. Let $\mathbf{v}_i$ be the extreme points of X and $\mathbf{x} = \sum\lambda_i\mathbf{v}_i$ $(\sum\lambda_i = 1, \lambda_i \geq 0)$. Then $f(\mathbf{x}) = f(\sum\lambda_i\mathbf{v}_i) \geq \sum\lambda_i f(\mathbf{v}_i) \geq \min_i f(\mathbf{v}_i)$.

Theorem 1.7. *Separating hyperplanes.* Given a closed convex set C and a point $\mathbf{b}$, then either $\mathbf{b}$ belongs to C or there exists a hyperplane H which contains $\mathbf{b}$ in one of its half-spaces and contains all points of C in its other half-space. (This theorem is essentially the same as Corollary 1.1, but the proof is different.)

Proof. If C is bounded, for every point $\mathbf{x} \in C$ we define the distance function $f(\mathbf{x}) = |\mathbf{x} - \mathbf{b}|$. This function is continuous in the closed and bounded set C and must take its minimum at some point in the set C (theorem of Weierstrass).

If the convex set C is not bounded, then we consider a closed ball B centered at $\mathbf{b}$ such that $B \cap C = C' \neq \phi$ (Fig. 1.5). Since the ball B is convex, closed, and bounded, the intersection $B \cap C = C'$ is also convex, closed, and bounded. Clearly the function $f(\mathbf{x})$ will take its minimum in C′.

Let

$$\min_{x \in C'} |\mathbf{x} - \mathbf{b}| = |\mathbf{a} - \mathbf{b}|, \qquad (3)$$

i.e. **a** is the nearest point to **b**. Consider the hyperplane H which is perpendicular to $\mathbf{b} - \mathbf{a}$ and let $\mathbf{y}$ be a generic point on H. The equation of the hyperplane is

$$(\mathbf{b} - \mathbf{a})^T\mathbf{y} = k, \tag{4}$$

where k is a constant. If we let H pass through the middle point of **a** and **b**, i.e., $\frac{1}{2}(\mathbf{b} + \mathbf{a})$, we have from (4)

$$(\mathbf{b} - \mathbf{a})^T \tfrac{1}{2}(\mathbf{b} + \mathbf{a}) = k. \tag{5}$$

Or substituting (5) into (4) we have the equation of the hyperplane

$$(\mathbf{b} - \mathbf{a})^T\mathbf{y} = \tfrac{1}{2}(\mathbf{b} - \mathbf{a})^T(\mathbf{b} + \mathbf{a}). \tag{6}$$

Let **b** be on one side of H, i.e.,

$$(\mathbf{b} - \mathbf{a})^T\mathbf{b} > \tfrac{1}{2}(\mathbf{b} - \mathbf{a})^T(\mathbf{b} + \mathbf{a}). \tag{7}$$

We shall then show that there is no point of C which is also on this side of H. Assume that there is a point $\mathbf{c} \in C$ which is on the same side as **b.** Then from (7) we have

$$(\mathbf{b} - \mathbf{a})^T\mathbf{c} > \tfrac{1}{2}(\mathbf{b} - \mathbf{a})^T(\mathbf{b} + \mathbf{a}). \tag{8}$$

Since both **c** and **a** belong to C and C is convex, any point of the form $\lambda\mathbf{a} + (1 - \lambda)\mathbf{c}$ for $1 \geq \lambda \geq 0$ also belongs to C. By our previous assumption, the minimum distance between **b** and any point on the segment $\lambda\mathbf{a} + (1 - \lambda)\mathbf{c}$ should occur at **a**, i.e., $\lambda = 1$. If we can find a minimum distance function for which $\lambda \neq 1$, then it means that the assumption that there is a point **c** on the same side of H as **b** is incorrect. The square of the distance function between any point on the line segment and **b** is

$$\begin{aligned} f^2(\lambda) &= [\lambda\mathbf{a} + (1 - \lambda)\mathbf{c} - \mathbf{b}]^2 \\ &= (\mathbf{a}^2 + \mathbf{c}^2 - 2\mathbf{a}^T\mathbf{c})\lambda^2 + (2\mathbf{a}^T\mathbf{c} - 2\mathbf{c}^2 + 2\mathbf{b}^T\mathbf{c} - 2\mathbf{a}^T\mathbf{b})\lambda + (\mathbf{b} - \mathbf{c})^2 \\ &= (\mathbf{a} - \mathbf{c})^2\lambda^2 - 2(\mathbf{a} - \mathbf{c})^T(\mathbf{b} - \mathbf{c})\lambda + (\mathbf{b} - \mathbf{c})^2, \end{aligned} \tag{9}$$

$$\frac{df^2(\lambda)}{d\lambda} = 0 \Rightarrow \lambda = (\mathbf{a} - \mathbf{c})^T(\mathbf{b} - \mathbf{c})/(\mathbf{a} - \mathbf{c})^2, \tag{10}$$

$$\frac{d^2f^2(\lambda)}{d\lambda^2} = 2(\mathbf{a} - \mathbf{c})^2 > 0$$

so the point with

$$\lambda = \frac{(\mathbf{a} - \mathbf{c})^T(\mathbf{b} - \mathbf{c})}{(\mathbf{a} - \mathbf{c})^2}$$

is a minimum distance.

Assume that there exists a point for which $\lambda \neq 1$, and let $\lambda < 1$, i.e.,

$$(\mathbf{a} - \mathbf{c})^T(\mathbf{b} - \mathbf{c}) < (\mathbf{a} - \mathbf{c})^2 \qquad \text{or} \qquad \mathbf{a}^T\mathbf{b} - \mathbf{a}^2 < (\mathbf{b} - \mathbf{a})^T\mathbf{c}. \tag{11}$$

From (8)

$$(\mathbf{b} - \mathbf{a})_T\mathbf{c} > \tfrac{1}{2}(\mathbf{b} - \mathbf{a})^T(\mathbf{b} + \mathbf{a}), \tag{12}$$

since

$$\tfrac{1}{2}(\mathbf{b} - \mathbf{a})^T(\mathbf{b} + \mathbf{a}) - (\mathbf{a}^T\mathbf{b} - \mathbf{a}^2) = \tfrac{1}{2}(\mathbf{b}^2 - \mathbf{a}^2 - 2\mathbf{a}^T\mathbf{b} + 2\mathbf{a}^2) = \tfrac{1}{2}(\mathbf{b} - \mathbf{a})^2 > 0,$$

that is,

$$\tfrac{1}{2}(\mathbf{b} - \mathbf{a})^T(\mathbf{b} + \mathbf{a}) > \mathbf{a}^T\mathbf{b} - \mathbf{a}^2. \tag{13}$$

From (12) and (13) we see that (11) is true, i.e., there is a $\lambda < 1$ from which the minimum distance is obtained. This means that the assumption that there is a point **c** on the same side as **b** of the hyperplane is incorrect.

We have shown that there exists a point with $\lambda < 1$ for which the minimum distance is achieved. If $0 \leq \lambda < 1$, then the point belongs to the convex set, and this contradicts the assumption that **a** is the point in the convex set with its distance a global minimum. If $\lambda < 0$, this means that the point is on the extension of the line segment $\overline{\mathbf{ac}}$ and the point may not belong to the convex set C. However, the distance function is a convex function. If the minimum is achieved for $\lambda < 0$, then it would imply that $f(\mathbf{x}) < f(\mathbf{a})$ which is again a contradiction. [Note from Theorem 1.5 that a local minimum implies a global minimum; thus the point obtained by setting the derivative of $f^2(\lambda)$ equal to zero is a global minimum.]

A hyperplane containing at least one point of a convex set and having all points of the convex set in one of its closed half-spaces is called a *supporting hyperplane* of the convex set.

1.5 BASIC, FEASIBLE, AND OPTIMUM SOLUTIONS

We are interested in finding nonnegative solutions to linear inequalities (or equivalently to linear equations, by the transformation in Section 1.2). As we are interesed only in a linear program where a finite optimum solution exists, we shall assume that the convex set defined by the constraints of the linear program is compact. Since any point of a compact convex set can be considered as a linear convex combination of its extreme points, we shall show that these extreme points correspond to so-called *basic solutions*.

Let

$$\mathbf{Ax} = \mathbf{b} \qquad (\mathbf{A} \text{ is } m \times n) \tag{1}$$

be a system of linear equations. This system of linear equations is said to be *consistent* if it has at least one solution. This system is said to be *redundant* if one of the equations can be expressed as a linear combination of the other equations; otherwise it is *nonredundant*. A system is *inconsistent* if the rank of **A** is r and the rank of $[\mathbf{A}, \mathbf{b}]$ is greater than r. Non-redundancy and consistency imply that the rank of **A** equals m ($m \leq n$). If $m > n$, then the system will have no solution unless it is redundant. In the following we shall assume that the system is consistent and nonredundant. In other words we can assume that a nonredundant subsystem of equations is selected.

Let $\mathbf{A} = [\mathbf{B}, \mathbf{N}]$, where **B** is a nonsingular square matrix, and $\mathbf{x} = [\mathbf{x}_B, \mathbf{x}_N]$, where $\mathbf{x}_B$ is a vector with m components and $\mathbf{x}_N$ is a vector with $n - m$ components. Then the solution of $\mathbf{Ax} = \mathbf{b}$ obtained by setting $\mathbf{x}_B = \mathbf{B}^{-1}\mathbf{b}$ and $\mathbf{x}_N = \mathbf{0}$ is called a *basic solution*. The components of $\mathbf{x}_B$ are called the *basic variables*, and the components of $\mathbf{x}_N$ are called *nonbasic variables*. A basic solution is called *degenerate* if one or more components of $\mathbf{x}_B$ are zero. The column vectors of **B** are called the basic vectors. Sometimes we say that the m independent column vectors of **B** form the basis.

A definition of a basic solution for the general case that **A** in (1) is $m \times n$ ($m \gtreqless n$) can be stated as follows: A solution **x** of (1) is a basic solution if the column vectors corresponding to nonzero components of **x** are independent.

The idea of basic solutions is also useful in a system of linear inequalities. We can certainly introduce slack variables to convert the inequalities into equations and then apply the above definition. However, we can also treat inequalities directly.

A system of linear inequalities is consistent if it has at least one solution. The system is redundant if one of the inequalities is implied by the other inequalities. Let $\mathbf{Ax} \geq \mathbf{b}$, ($\mathbf{x} \geq \mathbf{0}$) be the system of inequalities where **A** is $m \times n$. Thus there are $m + n$ inequalities in the system. These $m + n$ inequalities define a nonempty convex set if they are consistent. A basic feasible solution is an extreme point of the convex set where n inequalities among the $m + n$ inequalities are satisfied as equalities. Furthermore, the point satisfies the other m inequalities. Each inequality defines a closed half-space on one side of a hyperplane. If there are more than n of these hyperplanes intersecting at an extreme point of the convex set, then we have a degenerate basic feasible solution. This is one way of explaining how a degenerate basic solution occurs geometrically. If the solution of n inequalities as equalities does not satisfy the rest of the m inequalities, then it represents an intersection of n hyperplanes which does not belong to the convex set.

Consider the system of inequalities

$$\begin{aligned} -x_1 + 2x_2 &\leq 8, \\ x_1 + x_2 &\leq 10, \\ 2x_1 + x_2 &\leq 16, \\ x_1 \qquad &\leq 6, \\ x_1 \qquad &\geq 0, \\ x_2 &\geq 0. \end{aligned}$$

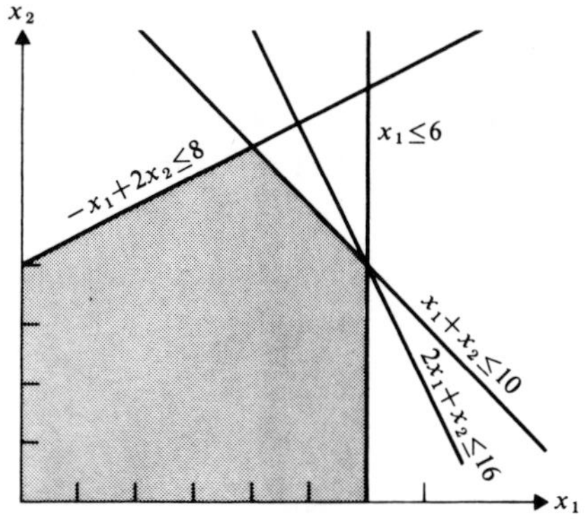

Fig. 1.6

The convex set defined by this system of inequalities is shown in Fig. 1.6. Note that there are three hyperplanes intersecting at $x_1 = 6$, $x_2 = 4$, i.e., $2x_1 + x_2 \le 16$ is implied by $x_1 \le 6$ and $x_1 + x_2 \le 10$.

The solution obtained by solving $-x_1 + 2x_2 = 8$ and $x_1 + x_2 = 10$ is not a degenerate solution. The solution obtained by solving $x_1 = 6$ and $x_2 = 0$ is also not a degenerate solution. But if we choose any two equations of the three equations $x_1 + x_2 = 10$, $2x_1 + x_2 = 16$, and $x_1 = 6$ and solve for x_1 and x_2, we would get a degenerate solution.

Let us convert the above inequalities into equations with nonnegative variables. Then we have:

$$\begin{aligned}
-x_1 + 2x_2 + s_1 \qquad\qquad\qquad &= 8,\\
x_1 + x_2 \qquad + s_2 \qquad\qquad &= 10,\\
2x_1 + x_2 \qquad\qquad + s_3 \qquad &= 16,\\
x_1 \qquad\qquad\qquad\qquad + s_4 &= 6,\\
x_1, x_2 \ge 0, \qquad s_1, s_2, s_3, s_4 &\ge 0.
\end{aligned}$$

Note the solution associated with the intersection of $-x_1 + 2x_2 = 8$ and $x_1 + x_2 = 10$ is $x_1 = 4$, $x_2 = 6$, $s_1 = 0$, $s_2 = 0$, $s_3 = 2$, $s_4 = 2$. The solution associated with the intersection of $x_1 = 6$ and $x_2 = 0$ is $x_1 = 6$, $x_2 = 0$, $s_1 = 14$, $s_2 = 4$, $s_3 = 4$, $s_4 = 0$. In both cases we have four nonzero components from four equations, and they are not degenerate. The solution associated with the intersection of $x_1 + x_2 = 10$ and $2x_1 + x_2 = 16$ is $x_1 = 6$, $x_2 = 4$, $s_1 = 6$, $s_2 = 0$, $s_3 = 0$, $s_4 = 0$. There are only three nonzero components; hence the solution is degenerate.

It is clear that if there is a solution of (1) with vectors not independent, then taking any vector in the set, we can express it as a linear combination of other vectors and reduce the number of vectors which are dependent to constitute a basic solution. This result can be summed up as follows.

Theorem 1.8. If there exists a solution to a system of linear equations, there exists a basic solution to the linear equations.

A solution to linear equations is called a *feasible solution* if all of its components are nonnegative. We shall now prove an important extension to Theorem 1.8.

Theorem 1.9. If there exists a feasible solution to a system of linear equations, there exists a basic feasible solution.

Proof. Consider the equations

$$\sum_{j=1}^{n} x_j \mathbf{a}_j = \mathbf{b}, \tag{2}$$

$$x_j \geq 0 \qquad (j = 1, \ldots, n).$$

This is proved by induction on the number of columns $\mathbf{a}_j$. The theorem is certainly true for $j = 1$. Assume now for $j < n$ that the theorem is true. (The variables x_j are strictly positive; otherwise, it reduces to the case of $n - 1$.) By assumption, there is a feasible solution of (2). If these $\mathbf{a}_j$ corresponding to positive x_j are independent, then the solution is basic by definition and the theorem is proved. If these $\mathbf{a}_j$ are not independent, then there exists a linear relation among the $\mathbf{a}_j$ such that

$$\sum_{j=1}^{n} \lambda_j \mathbf{a}_j = \mathbf{0}. \tag{3}$$

We can assume that some λ_j are positive; if not, we can multiply (3) by -1. Among those positive λ_j one of them must give maximal value to the ratio λ_j/x_j. Let that ratio be λ_n/x_n, say, and denote its value by θ. The value θ is nonnegative because λ_n and x_n are positive. That is,

$$\theta = \max_j \frac{\lambda_j}{x_j} = \frac{\lambda_n}{x_n} > 0. \tag{4}$$

Multiplying (3) by $1/\theta$ and subtracting it from (2), we have

$$\frac{1}{\theta} \sum_{j=1}^{n} \left(\theta - \frac{\lambda_j}{x_j}\right) x_j \mathbf{a}_j = \mathbf{b}. \tag{5}$$

Therefore (5) gives a linear nonnegative combination of $\mathbf{a}_j$ that equals $\mathbf{b}$. But the coefficient of $\mathbf{a}_n$ is zero since $\theta = \lambda_n/x_n$. So this reduces to the case of fewer than n vectors.

Theorem 1.10. The set of all feasible solutions to a linear program is a convex set.

Proof. Let $\mathbf{x}_1$ and $\mathbf{x}_2$ be two feasible solutions, i.e.,

$$\mathbf{A}\mathbf{x}_1 = \mathbf{b} \qquad (\mathbf{x}_1 \geq \mathbf{0}),$$

$$\mathbf{A}\mathbf{x}_2 = \mathbf{b} \qquad (\mathbf{x}_2 \geq \mathbf{0}).$$

Then for $1 \geq \lambda \geq 0$, $\lambda \mathbf{x}_1 + (1 - \lambda)\mathbf{x}_2 \geq \mathbf{0}$, since each of the two terms is a product of nonnegative numbers. Furthermore

$$\mathbf{A}[\lambda \mathbf{x}_1 + (1 - \lambda)\mathbf{x}_2] = \lambda\, \mathbf{A}\mathbf{x}_1 + (1 - \lambda)\mathbf{A}\mathbf{x}_2 = \lambda \mathbf{b} + (1 - \lambda)\mathbf{b} = \mathbf{b}.$$

Therefore $\lambda \mathbf{x}_1 + (1 - \lambda)\mathbf{x}_2$ is also a feasible solution.

We shall next show that basic feasible solutions correspond to extreme points of a convex polytope.

Let us consider n-dimensional space and consider the convex polytope

$$T = \{\mathbf{x} \,|\, \mathbf{a}_i\mathbf{x} \leq b_i,\ i = 1, \ldots, m\} \qquad (m \geq n).$$

A face of T of dimension p is defined by

$$F_p = \left\{\mathbf{x} \left| \begin{array}{l} \mathbf{a}_i\mathbf{x} = b_i,\ i \in Q;\ Q = \{1, \ldots, q\} \\ \mathbf{a}_i\mathbf{x} \leq b_i,\ i \notin Q \end{array} \right.\right\}.$$

where $p = n - q$. For a vertex, $p = 0$ or $q = n$. A face of T of dimension zero is called a vertex. Therefore the necessary and sufficient condition for the existence of a vertex is that there exists a submatrix $\bar{\mathbf{A}}$ whose rank

$$r(\bar{\mathbf{A}}) = r(\bar{\mathbf{A}}, \bar{\mathbf{b}}) = n \qquad \text{and} \qquad \bar{\mathbf{A}}\mathbf{x} = \bar{\mathbf{b}},$$

where $\bar{\mathbf{b}}$ is the corresponding n-dimensional vector.

Theorem 1.11. Given a convex polytope T of R^n defined by the system of inequalities $\mathbf{a}_i\mathbf{x} \leq b_i$ $(i = 1, \ldots, m)$, the necessary and sufficient condition for a point $\mathbf{x}$ of T to be an extreme point of T is that $\mathbf{x}$ be the solution of

$$\begin{array}{lll} \mathbf{a}_i\mathbf{x} = b_i, & i \in N, & N = \{1, \ldots, n\},\ (n \leq m), \\ \mathbf{a}_i\mathbf{x} \leq b_i, & i \notin N. & \end{array}$$

Proof.

Proof of sufficiency. Let $\bar{\mathbf{x}}$ be the solution of $\bar{\mathbf{A}}\mathbf{x} = \bar{\mathbf{b}}$, where $\bar{\mathbf{A}}$ is nonsingular, and let $\bar{\mathbf{x}} = \lambda \mathbf{x}_1 + (1 - \lambda)\mathbf{x}_2$ $(0 < \lambda < 1)$. By assumption $\mathbf{x}_1, \mathbf{x}_2 \in T$. Therefore $\bar{\mathbf{A}}\mathbf{x}_1 \leq \bar{\mathbf{b}}$ and $\bar{\mathbf{A}}\mathbf{x}_2 \leq \bar{\mathbf{b}}$, and

$$\bar{\mathbf{A}}\bar{\mathbf{x}} = \bar{\mathbf{A}}[\lambda \mathbf{x}_1 + (1 - \lambda)\mathbf{x}_2] = \lambda\, \bar{\mathbf{A}}\mathbf{x}_1 + (1 - \lambda)\bar{\mathbf{A}}\mathbf{x}_2 \leq \bar{\mathbf{b}} \quad (\text{for } 0 < \lambda < 1).$$

The last inequality will not be an equality unless

$$\bar{\mathbf{A}}\mathbf{x}_1 = \bar{\mathbf{b}}, \qquad \bar{\mathbf{A}}\mathbf{x}_2 = \bar{\mathbf{b}}.$$

So we have

$$\bar{\mathbf{A}}\bar{\mathbf{x}} = \bar{\mathbf{b}} = \bar{\mathbf{A}}\mathbf{x}_1 = \bar{\mathbf{A}}\mathbf{x}_2.$$

But $\bar{\mathbf{A}}$ is nonsingular, $\bar{\mathbf{x}} = \bar{\mathbf{A}}^{-1}\bar{\mathbf{A}}\mathbf{x}_1 = \mathbf{x}_1$, and $\bar{\mathbf{x}} = \bar{\mathbf{A}}^{-1}\bar{\mathbf{A}}\mathbf{x}_2 = \mathbf{x}_2$ contradicts the fact that $\mathbf{x}_1, \mathbf{x}_2$ are distinct points, i.e., if $\bar{\mathbf{x}}$ is a basic solution, then $\bar{\mathbf{x}}$ is an extreme point.

Proof of necessity. If $\bar{\mathbf{x}}$ is an extreme point of T, then $\bar{\mathbf{x}}$ satisfies the system

$$\mathbf{a}_i\bar{\mathbf{x}} \leq b_i \qquad (i = 1, \ldots, m).$$

This implies that there exists a set I such that

$$\begin{aligned} \mathbf{a}_i\bar{\mathbf{x}} &= b_i, \qquad i \in I, \\ \mathbf{a}_i\bar{\mathbf{x}} &< b_i, \qquad i \notin I. \end{aligned} \tag{6}$$

Let $\bar{\mathbf{x}}$ be a point such that

$$\mathbf{a}_i\bar{\mathbf{x}} < b_i \qquad (i = 1, \ldots, m).$$

Then we can get

$$\mathbf{a}_i(\bar{\mathbf{x}} \pm \Delta\bar{\mathbf{x}}) \leq b_i \qquad (i = 1, \ldots, m).$$

This shows that

$$\bar{\mathbf{x}} = \tfrac{1}{2}(\bar{\mathbf{x}} + \Delta\bar{\mathbf{x}}) + \tfrac{1}{2}(\bar{\mathbf{x}} - \Delta\bar{\mathbf{x}}),$$

which contradicts the assumption that $\bar{\mathbf{x}}$ is an extreme point. Let us show that the columns $\mathbf{a}_i$ of

$$\mathbf{a}_i\bar{\mathbf{x}} = b_i, \qquad i \in I,$$

are independent.

We shall illustrate the proof by a short example. The reader should have no trouble in writing out a formal proof. Let $\mathbf{a}_1 = (a_{11}, a_{12})$, $\mathbf{a}_2 = (a_{21}, a_{22})$, $\mathbf{a}_3 = (a_{31}, a_{32})$, and $\bar{\mathbf{x}} = [x_1, x_2]$, where $\mathbf{a}_1\bar{\mathbf{x}} = b_1$, $\mathbf{a}_2\bar{\mathbf{x}} = b_2$, and $\mathbf{a}_3\bar{\mathbf{x}} < b_3$.

Assume that $\mathbf{a}_1$ and $\mathbf{a}_2$ are not independent, i.e., the row rank of the matrix

$$\begin{bmatrix} a_{11} & a_{12} \\ a_{21} & a_{22} \end{bmatrix}$$

is not of rank 2. This implies that the column rank is not of rank 2, so that there exists $\boldsymbol{\lambda} = (\lambda_1, \lambda_2)$ with components not all equal to zero such that

$$\lambda_1 \begin{bmatrix} a_{11} \\ a_{21} \end{bmatrix} + \lambda_2 \begin{bmatrix} a_{12} \\ a_{22} \end{bmatrix} = \begin{bmatrix} 0 \\ 0 \end{bmatrix}. \tag{7}$$

Let ϵ be a small scalar. We have from (7)

$$\begin{aligned} \mathbf{a}_1(\bar{\mathbf{x}} \pm \epsilon\boldsymbol{\lambda}^T) &= \mathbf{a}_1\bar{\mathbf{x}} \pm \epsilon(\lambda_1 a_{11} + \lambda_2 a_{12}) = b_1 \pm \epsilon \cdot 0 = b_1, \\ \mathbf{a}_2(\bar{\mathbf{x}} \pm \epsilon\boldsymbol{\lambda}^T) &= \mathbf{a}_2\bar{\mathbf{x}} \pm \epsilon(\lambda_1 a_{21} + \lambda_2 a_{22}) = b_2 \pm \epsilon \cdot 0 = b_2. \end{aligned}$$

Since $\mathbf{a}_3\bar{\mathbf{x}} < b_3$, if ϵ is sufficiently small, we have

$$\mathbf{a}_3(\bar{\mathbf{x}} \pm \epsilon\boldsymbol{\lambda}^T) = \mathbf{a}_3\mathbf{x} \pm \epsilon\mathbf{a}_3\boldsymbol{\lambda}^T \leq b_3.$$

Therefore, the two vectors $\bar{\mathbf{x}} + \epsilon\boldsymbol{\lambda}^T$ and $\bar{\mathbf{x}} - \epsilon\boldsymbol{\lambda}^T$ both are in the convex set and

$$\bar{\mathbf{x}} = \tfrac{1}{2}(\bar{\mathbf{x}} + \epsilon\boldsymbol{\lambda}^T) + \tfrac{1}{2}(\bar{\mathbf{x}} - \epsilon\boldsymbol{\lambda}^T),$$

which contradicts the assumption that $\bar{\mathbf{x}}$ is an extreme point.

Theorem 1.12. If all feasible solutions of a linear program are bounded, any feasible solution is a linear convex combination of basic feasible solutions.

Proof. Feasible solutions form a compact convex set, where basic feasible solutions correspond to extreme points of the convex set. Since any point of a convex set is a linear convex combination of its extreme points*, any feasible solution is a linear convex combination of basic feasible solutions.

A feasible solution $\mathbf{x}^*$ is called an optimum solution if $\mathbf{cx}^* \leq \mathbf{c\bar{x}}$ for all feasible solutions $\bar{\mathbf{x}}$, and $-\infty < \mathbf{cx}^*$.

Theorem 1.13. If there exists an optimum solution, then there exists a basic optimum solution.

Proof. By assumption, the optimum solution is finite. From Theorem 1.7, a linear function which is a concave function will attain its global minimum at an extreme point of the convex set. Theorem 1.11 states that an *extreme point corresponds to a basic solution.*

1.6 GEOMETRIC INTERPRETATION OF LINEAR PROGRAM

Let the linear program be min $z = \mathbf{cx}$ subject to $\mathbf{Ax} \geq \mathbf{b}$, $\mathbf{x} \geq \mathbf{0}$, where $\mathbf{A}$ is $m \times n$. This can be represented geometrically in two ways. One way is to represent the linear program in the space of $\mathbf{x}$, called the *activity space;* the other way is to represent the linear program in the space of $\mathbf{b}$, called the *requirement space* (see Example 3 of Section 1.1). The activity space is of n dimensions, and the solution space† in the activity space is then the intersection of m half-spaces $\mathbf{a}_i\mathbf{x} \geq b_i$ and n half-spaces $x_j \geq 0$. If we consider z as a parameter in $z = \mathbf{cx}$, then this would define a series of parallel hyperplanes in the activity space with the normal vector $\mathbf{c}$. The optimum solution is the vertex on the supporting hyperplane with normal vector $\mathbf{c}$. The optimum solution is not unique if the hyperplane $z = \mathbf{cx}$ is parallel to one of the hyperplanes intersecting at the optimum vertex.

In the representation of the linear program in a requirement space, we are in a space of m dimensions, where $\mathbf{b}$ is represented by a vector (or a point). Any column vector in the matrix $\mathbf{A}$ of $\mathbf{Ax} = \mathbf{b}$ is also a vector with $\mathbf{m}$ components. There exists a feasible solution of $\mathbf{Ax} = \mathbf{b}$ if $\mathbf{b}$ is in the finite cone spanned by the $\mathbf{a}_j$. Since the space is of m dimensions, m column vectors are needed to span the vector $\mathbf{b}$, in general. If $\mathbf{b}$ is in a cone spanned by less than m vectors, then it becomes a case of degeneracy. Every $\mathbf{a}_j$ has associated with it a cost c_j; the optimum solution is the minimum cost combination of the vectors $\mathbf{a}_j$ to produce $\mathbf{b}$.

*This fact, although intuitively obvious, requires a nontrivial proof. See for example Berge and Ghouila-Houri [19], pp. 57-58.

†Solution space is also called solution set.

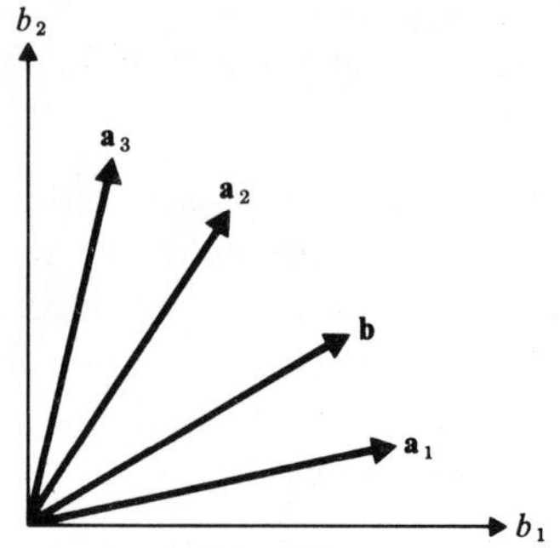

Fig. 1.7

Consider the linear program of

$$\min \; x_1 + 4x_2 + 5x_3$$

subject to

$$\begin{bmatrix}4\\1\end{bmatrix} x_1 + \begin{bmatrix}2\\3\end{bmatrix} x_2 + \begin{bmatrix}1\\4\end{bmatrix} x_3 = \begin{bmatrix}3\\2\end{bmatrix},$$

$$x_j \geq 0 \qquad (j = 1, 2, 3).$$

The representation of this program is shown in Fig. 1.7. Note that the optimum solution is $x_1 = 2/3$, $x_2 = 0$, $x_3 = 1/3$. If the constraints are inequalities, say $\mathbf{a}_j x_j \geq \mathbf{b}$, then we want to combine the vectors $\mathbf{a}_j$ to get to a point to the upper right of the point $\mathbf{b}$.

EXERCISES

1. Given an $m \times n$ matrix $\mathbf{A} = [a_{ij}]$ ($m \leq$ n) and an m-component vector $\mathbf{b} = [b_i]$. Let $a_{ij} > 0$ and $b_i > 0$ for all i and j ($i = 1, \ldots, m$; $j = 1, \ldots, n$). Is it always possible to find a vector $\mathbf{x}$ such that $\mathbf{Ax} \geq \mathbf{b}$? Is it always possible to find a vector $\mathbf{x}$ such that $\mathbf{Ax} = \mathbf{b}$? Is it always possible to find a vector $\mathbf{x} \geq \mathbf{0}$ such that $\mathbf{Ax} = \mathbf{b}$? Why?
2. Given the matrix

$$\mathbf{A} = \begin{bmatrix}2 & 1 & 2 & 3\\1 & 2 & 4 & 3\\3 & 3 & 6 & 6\end{bmatrix}, \qquad \mathbf{b} = \begin{bmatrix}3\\1\\2\end{bmatrix}.$$

   Show that there exists no $\mathbf{x}$ such that $\mathbf{Ax} = \mathbf{b}$.
3. Does the solution of $\mathbf{Ax} \geq \mathbf{0}$ form a cone? A convex cone?
4. Consider the four theorems in Section 1.3. Draw four circles representing the theorems and draw arrows between two circles if one theorem is needed in proving the other. Do the same thing for all 13 theorems in this chapter.
5. Prove the alternative useful form of Minkowski-Farkas' lemma: $\mathbf{Ax} \leq \mathbf{b}$ has a nonnegative solution if and only if for all $\boldsymbol{\pi} \geq \mathbf{0}$, $\boldsymbol{\pi}\mathbf{A} \geq \mathbf{0}$ implies $\boldsymbol{\pi}\mathbf{b} \geq 0$.

6. Given a finite number of points in the plane, consider its convex hull. Are all the given points, the extreme points of the convex hull? If the points are (5, 0), (2, 1), (0, 6), and (0, 0), what is the convex hull?
7. Determine whether the following functions defined on the real line are convex

$$f(\mathbf{x}) = |\mathbf{x}|, \qquad f(\mathbf{x}) = \mathbf{x}^2 \qquad \begin{cases} f(\mathbf{x}) = \;\; c & \text{for } \mathbf{x} \geq \mathbf{0}, \\ f(\mathbf{x}) = -c & \text{for } \mathbf{x} < \mathbf{0}. \end{cases}$$

   Which of the above functions is strictly convex? Construct a continuous function which is neither convex or concave.
8. Construct (a) a cone which is not a convex set; (b) a convex set which is not a convex cone.
9. A function $f(\mathbf{x})$ is called a quasi-convex function if and only if the set $\{\mathbf{x} \mid f(\mathbf{x}) \leq d\}$ is convex for all real values of d. Prove that a strict local minimum of a quasi-convex function is also a global minimum.
10. Define a convex function on the convex set $-3 \leq x \leq 4$ such that $f(-3) = 3$ and $f(4) = 2$. What is the maximum value of this convex function? Why?

OPEN QUESTION

Consider a linear program min $z = \mathbf{cx}$ subject to $\mathbf{Ax} = \mathbf{b}$, $\mathbf{x} \geq \mathbf{0}$, where $\mathbf{A}$ is of rank m. The theory of linear programming tells us that we can always find an optimum solution with at most m nonzero components. (Assume that the linear program has at least one optimum solution.) What if we insist that there are at most q nonzero components ($q < m$)?

SIMPLEX METHOD 2

2.1 INTRODUCTION

We have studied in Chapter 1 the fundamental theorems of linear programming. In this chapter and in Chapters 4, 5, 6, and 7, we shall develop computational methods. A linear program is in *standard form* if the constraints (not including $x_j \geq 0$) are all equations and in *canonical form* if the constraints are all inequalities. Consider a linear program in standard form:

$$\min\ z = c_j x_j \qquad (j = 1, \ldots, n)$$

subject to

$$a_{ij} x_j = b_i \qquad (i = 1, \ldots, m) \qquad (m \leq n),$$
$$x_j \geq 0.$$

Theorem 1.9 states that if there is a feasible solution, there is a basic feasible solution. Theorem 1.13 states that if there is an optimum solution, there is a basic optimum solution. So, in order to get an optimum solution, we can choose m columns at a time from the matrix **A** and solve the m simultaneous equations for the m variables. But this approach requires that $\binom{n}{m}$ sets of simultaneous equations be solved. This is not practical except for very small n. The most practical method is called the simplex method (due to G. B. Dantzig [29]), which involves a very small number of steps to solve a linear program. The high efficiency of the simplex method helps to popularize the subject of linear programming and makes industrial and military applications practical.

We shall introduce the simplex method by a short numerical example. Consider the linear program

$$\min\ z = x_1 + x_2 + x_3 \tag{1}$$

subject to

$$x_1 - x_2 + 2x_3 = 2, \tag{2}$$
$$-x_1 + 2x_2 - x_3 = 1, \tag{3}$$
$$x_j \geq 0 \qquad (j = 1, 2, 3).$$

Rewrite (1), (2), and (3) as

$$z - x_1 - x_2 - x_3 = 0, \tag{1'}$$

$$x_1 - x_2 + 2x_3 = 2, \tag{2'}$$

$$-x_1 + 2x_2 - x_3 = 1. \tag{3'}$$

In (1′), (2′), and (3′), we have four unknowns, z, x_1, x_2, and x_3, and three equations. If we use Gauss' elimination method to solve for z, x_1, and x_2, say, we will have the following system of equations:

$$z \quad + 3x_3 = 8, \tag{1''}$$

$$x_1 \quad + 3x_3 = 5, \tag{2''}$$

$$x_2 + x_3 = 3. \tag{3''}$$

This system is called the *diagonal form* with respect to z, x_1, and x_2. One solution which is immediate in the diagonal form is $z = 8$, $x_1 = 5$, and $x_2 = 3$. Let any other variable such as x_3 be equal to zero. Note that x_1 and x_2 are called basic variables of the system and x_3 is called the nonbasic variable of the system (see Section 1.5).

It so happens in this problem that x_1 and x_2 are both nonnegative in this solution, so they provide a feasible solution with $z = 8$. From (1″), we see that if x_3 is not zero but any positive number, the value of z will be decreased; in effect, the value of z is related to x_3 by the expression $z = 8 - 3x_3$. Since we want to minimize z, we shall make x_3 as large as possible. But from (2″) and (3″) we see that we cannot make x_3 arbitrarily large without making either x_1 or x_2 negative.

In the present case, $x_1 = 5 - 3x_3$ and $x_2 = 3 - x_3$. So the maximum amount that x_3 can be increased without making either x_1 or x_2 negative is determined by

$$x_3 = \min(5/3, 3/1) = 5/3.$$

If $x_3 = \frac{5}{3}$, then $x_1 = 5 - 3(\frac{5}{3}) = 0$. Let us put the system into diagonal form with respect to z, x_2, and x_3. This gives

$$z - x_1 \qquad = 3,$$

$$(1/3)\,x_1 \qquad + x_3 = 5/3,$$

$$-(1/3)\,x_1 + x_2 \qquad = 4/3,$$

and the immediate solution $z = 3$, $x_2 = 4/3$, $x_3 = 5/3$, $x_1 = 0$. Now if x_1 is increased from zero, the value of z will be increased, and thus we claim that $z = 3$ is the minimum value of z.

The simplex method is just what we have gone through, but does it more systematically. Before we can accept it as a valid method, many questions have to be answered.

First, given a system of simultaneous equations, there is a solution space associated with it. The solution is the set of points which satisfies the simultaneous equations. When the number of variables is equal to the number of equations and the determinant of the coefficient matrix is nonsingular, the solution is a point, and we have a unique solution. When the number of variables is greater than the number of equations, the solution space is generally a line, a plane, or a higher dimensional space. Two systems of simultaneous equations are said to be equivalent if they have the same solution space.

Theorem 2.1. Gauss elimination does not change the solution space of a system of simultaneous equations.

Proof. The Gauss elimination procedure involves two elementary operations:

1. Multiply an equation E_1 by a nonzero constant k_1 and replace the equation E_1 by the new equation k_1E_1.
2. Add an equation E_1 to another equation E_2 and replace the equation E_2 by $E_1 + E_2$.

Clearly, if $E_1(\mathbf{x}) = 0$, then $k_1E_1(\mathbf{x}) = 0$ and vice versa. Also $E_1(\mathbf{x}) = 0$ and $E_2(\mathbf{x}) = 0$ implies that $E_1(\mathbf{x}) + E_2(\mathbf{x}) = 0$. So the elimination procedure does not change the solution space. For example, the two sets of equations below are equivalent:

$$\left.\begin{aligned} E_1(\mathbf{x}) + E_2(\mathbf{x}) &= 0 \\ k_1E_1(\mathbf{x}) \qquad\qquad &= 0 \end{aligned}\right\} \Leftrightarrow \left\{\begin{aligned} E_1(\mathbf{x}) &= 0, \\ E_2(\mathbf{x}) &= 0. \end{aligned}\right.$$

Second, in the example we started with a feasible solution $x_1 = 5$, $x_2 = 3$ and the feasibility is maintained throughout the process. Had we chosen to put the system into diagonal form with respect to z, x_1 and x_3 first, we would get

$$\begin{aligned} z \quad - 3x_2 \qquad &= -1, \\ x_1 - 3x_2 \qquad &= -4, \\ x_2 + x_3 &= 3, \end{aligned}$$

with $z = -1$, $x_1 = -4$, and $x_3 = 3$. The discussion of the procedure of starting with a feasible solution will be delayed until Section 2.3.

Third, when the z-equation becomes

$$z - a_{0,m+1}x_{m+1} - a_{0,m+2}x_{m+2} - \cdots - a_{0n}x_n = a_{00}, \tag{4}$$

where $a_{0j} \geq 0$ for $j = m + 1, \ldots, n$, how do we know that a_{00} is the minimal value of z?

Suppose we had put the system into diagonal form with respect to another set of x's. Could we get a z-equation

$$z - \bar{a}_{0,m+1}x'_{m+1} - \bar{a}_{0,m+2}x'_{m+2} - \cdots - \bar{a}_{0n}x'_n = \bar{a}_{00}, \tag{4'}$$

where $\bar{a}_{0j} \geq 0$ and $\bar{a}_{00} < a_{00}$? Or, why should we always put the system into diagonal form?

There are at least two ways to answer this question. We shall first give one answer which does not require any of the material developed in Chapter 1. Note that the solution of a system of linear equations is not changed by Gauss elimination. Thus a solution satisfying (4) is also a solution of original system. In (4), since all variables are nonnegative, we conclude that a_{00} is a lower bound of z without considering the other equations of the diagonal form with respect to $z, x_1, \ldots, x_m$. (Constraints cannot decrease the lower bound when we want to minimize a function.) If the other equations of the diagonal form give $x_j \geq 0$ $(j = 1, \ldots, m)$, then a_{00} is indeed the minimal value of z.

Another way to answer the same question uses the materials developed in Chapter 1 and is actually longer, but it has the advantage of having geometric meaning associated with it. The function z is called the objective function in Chapter 1 and for a linear function represents a hyperplane. The other equations are also hyperplanes, and their intersection together with $x_j \geq 0$ defines the solution space. Since hyperplanes are convex, the intersection of convex sets is convex, and it follows that the solution space is convex. For a linear function, being convex and defined on a convex set, a relative minimum implies a global minimum. Equation (4) gives a relative minimum to z. Furthermore, a basic solution represents a vertex or an extreme point of the convex set, and we know the linear function, being also concave, will attain its minimum at an extreme point, which is Theorem 1.13. (If there is an optimum solution, there is a basic optimum solution.) Hence we put the system into a diagonal form (with respect to certain variables), which gives a basic solution.

Fourth, how do we know that the method is a finite one? Since we change from one basis to another, and there are a finite number of bases, in fact at most $\binom{n}{m}$, this would guarantee finiteness unless a basis can be repeated. If the value of z is always decreasing strictly, then a different value of z implies a different basis, and this will guarantee finiteness. However in a problem at some stage we may have $\bar{b}_i = 0$. Since the value of the objective function is changed by $\bar{c}_j$ min $(\bar{b}_i/\bar{a}_{ij})$, the change may be zero. This means that the value of the objective function may not change after the pivot. If several bases all correspond to the same value of z, it is possible to cycle among these bases. (See Hoffman [102] or Beale [9].) We shall discuss a procedure which will guarantee finiteness in Section 2.4.

Fifth, suppose that we have chosen a variable with positive coefficients in the z-equation and there is no positive constant in the column corresponding to that variable. Then we can make that variable arbitrarily large without making any other variables negative. This will make z as negative as one wants. Therefore, the program has no finite optimum solution.

2.2 TABLEAU OF THE SIMPLEX METHOD

Consider a linear program in standard form

$$\min z = c_j x_j \qquad (j = 1, \ldots, n)$$

subject to

$$a_{ij} x_j = b_i \qquad (i = 1, \ldots, m) \qquad (m \leq n),$$
$$x_j \geq 0.$$

Assume that we have put this into diagonal form with respect to $-z$, $x_1, \ldots, x_m$. This gives (we use $\bar{c}_j$ and $\bar{a}_{ij}$ to indicate the coefficients in the diagonal form as compared with c_j and a_{ij} in the standard form)

$$\begin{array}{llll} -z & + \bar{c}_{m+1} x_{m+1} + \cdots + \bar{c}_n x_n & = -\bar{z}_0, \\ \quad x_1 & + \bar{a}_{1,m+1} x_{m+1} + \cdots + \bar{a}_{1n} x_n & = \bar{b}_1, \\ \quad\quad x_2 & + \bar{a}_{2,m+1} x_{m+1} + \cdots + \bar{a}_{2n} x_n & = \bar{b}_2, \\ \quad\quad\quad \ddots & & \vdots \\ \quad\quad\quad\quad x_m & + \bar{a}_{m,m+1} x_{m+1} + \cdots + \bar{a}_{mn} x_n & = \bar{b}_m. \end{array}$$

The basic solution is $z = \bar{z}_0$, $x_i = \bar{b}_i$ $(i = 1, \ldots, m)$, $x_{m+1} = x_{m+2} = \ldots = x_n = 0$. We shall assume that all $\bar{b}_i$ are nonnegative so that we have a starting feasible basis.

Let us rewrite the diagonal form as (omitting the – over coefficients)

$$\begin{array}{llll} x_0 & + a_{0,m+1} x_{m+1} + \cdots + a_{0n} x_n & = a_{00}, \\ \quad x_1 & + a_{1,m+1} x_{m+1} + \cdots + a_{1n} x_n & = a_{10}, \\ \quad\quad x_2 & + a_{2,m+1} x_{m+1} + \cdots + a_{2n} x_n & = a_{20}, \\ \quad\quad\quad \ddots & & \vdots \\ \quad\quad\quad\quad x_m & + a_{m,m+1} x_{m+1} + \cdots + a_{mn} x_n & = a_{m0}, \end{array}$$

where $x_0 = -z$, $a_{00} = -\bar{z}_0$, $a_{0j} = \bar{c}_j$, $a_{i0} = \bar{b}_i$. This is usually put into the following tableau:

	1	x_1,	x_2	. . .	x_m,	x_{m+1},	. . .	, x_n
x_0	a_{00}	0	0	. . .	0,	$a_{0,m+1}$,	. . .	, a_{0n}
x_1	a_{10}	1				$a_{1,m+1}$	. . .	a_{1n}
x_2	a_{20}		1			$\vdots$		$\vdots$
$\vdots$	$\vdots$			$\ddots$				
x_m	a_{m0}				1	$a_{m,m+1}$	. . .	a_{mn}

The top row of the tableau expresses x_0 in terms of all variables. Every row in the tableau is an equation, the constant term of which appears in the left-most column. To the left of the tableau are the *current* basic variables.

We started with a tableau in which $a_{i0} \geq 0$ $(i=1, \ldots, m)$. This condition is usually called *primal feasible* as it implies that we have a feasible solution for the program which we want to solve (i.e., the basis variables $= a_{i0}$). The condition $a_{0j} \geq 0$ $(j = 1, \ldots, n)$ is called *dual feasible* as it implies that we have a feasible solution for the dual program.* If both $a_{i0} \geq 0$ $(i = 1, \ldots, m)$ and $a_{0j} \geq 0$ $(j = 1, \ldots, n)$, then the solution is optimum.

The simplex algorithm can be described in the following steps:

0. Start with a tableau where $a_{i0} \geq 0$ $(i = 1, \ldots, m)$.
1. If all $a_{0j} \geq 0$, stop. The current solution is the optimum solution. Otherwise, among $a_{0j} < 0$, let $a_{0s} = \min_j a_{0j} < 0$, i.e., a_{0s} is the most negative coefficient. This column s is called the pivot column.
2. Among $a_{is} > 0$, let $a_{r0}/a_{rs} = \min_i a_{i0}/a_{is}$ $(i = 1, \ldots, m)$, i.e., among the positive coefficients in the column s, we take all the ratios. a_{rs} is called the pivot. The row r is called the *pivot row*.
3. We use Gauss elimination on rows so that all coefficients in the sth column become zero except a_{rs}, which becomes one. Change the basic variable x_r into x_s on the left of the tableau. Return to step 1.

In step 1, we could choose any $a_{0j} = \bar{c}_j < 0$ and the algorithm will still work. The criterion $\min_j \bar{c}_j < 0$ is used analogous to the steepest descent. In step 2, the test $\min_i a_{i0}/a_{is}$ for selecting the pivot row is called the *ratio test*. It is used to maintain $a_{i0} \geq 0$.

The three steps are repeated until in step 1 there are no negative coefficients in the 0th row. Then the optimum solution is obtained by setting the basic variables x_i on the left of the tableau equal to a_{i0} in that current tableau.

Let us do a numerical example using the simplex tableau.

Example 1. Consider

$$\min\ z = 11 - x_3 - x_4 - x_5$$

subject to

$$\begin{aligned} x_1 \quad + x_3 - x_4 + 2x_5 &= 2, \\ x_2 - x_3 + 2x_4 - x_5 &= 1, \\ x_j \geq 0 \qquad (j = 1, \ldots, 5)&. \end{aligned}$$

This can be written as

$$\begin{aligned} -z \qquad - x_3 - x_4 - x_5 &= -11, \\ x_1 \quad + x_3 - x_4 + 2x_5 &= 2, \\ x_2 - x_3 + 2x_4 - x_5 &= 1. \end{aligned}$$

* The terms "dual feasible" and "dual program" will be explained in Chapter 3. For the moment, $a_{0j} \geq 0$ indicates that z cannot be further decreased by increasing any current nonbasic variable from zero.

This is already in diagonal form with respect to $-z$, x_1, and x_2. We write x_1 and x_2 to the left of Tableau 2.1 to indicate that they are the basic variables of this tableau. A feasible solution is always ready at hand by setting the basic variables equal to the constants in the 0th column.

Tableau 2.1

	1	x_1	x_2	x_3	x_4	x_5
$-z$	-11	0	0	-1	-1	-1
x_1	2	1	0	1	-1	2
x_2	1	0	1	-1	2*	-1

Now in the 0th row, we have three negative coefficients of the same magnitude (in Section 2.3 we shall give a rule in case of a tie). Let us arbitrarily choose the column under x_4.

In the column under x_4 there is only one positive coefficient, namely $a_{24}=2$;so we choose a_{24} to be the pivot. This is indicated by an * on the upper right corner of a_{24}. Then we make a_{24} equal to 1 by dividing all elements in the row containing the pivot by the pivot and performing Gauss elimination on rows to make $a_{i4} = 0$ $(i = 0,1)$. The result is shown in Tableau 2.2.

Tableau 2.2

	1	x_1	x_2	x_3	x_4	x_5
$-z$	$-21/2$	0	1/2	$-3/2$	0	$-3/2$
x_1	5/2	1	1/2	1/2*	0	3/2
x_4	1/2	0	1/2	$-1/2$	1	$-1/2$

Note in this tabulation that x_4 has replaced x_2 as a basic variable.

Among the negative coefficients in the 0th row, we can either choose the column under x_3 or the column under x_5. Let us arbitrarily choose the third column. In the third column only $a_{13} = \frac{1}{2}$ is positive, so it is chosen as the pivot. The result of the pivot operation is shown in Tableau 2.3.

Tableau 2.3

	1	x_1	x_2	x_3	x_4	x_5
$-z$	-3	3	2	0	0	3
x_3	5	2	1	1	0	3
x_4	3	1	1	0	1	1

Note that x_3 has replaced x_1 as a basic variable. In Tableau 2.3 there are no negative constants $a_{0j} \geq 0$ $(j = 1, \ldots, n)$, so it is optimum. The optimum solution is $x_3 = 5$, $x_4 = 3$, $x_1 = x_2 = x_5 = 0$, $z = 3$.

Example 2. Consider

$$\min z = x_1 + x_2 + 2x_3 + 8x_4$$

subject to

$$2x_1 - x_2 + 3x_3 - 2x_4 = 3, \tag{1}$$

$$-x_1 + 3x_2 - 4x_3 + 4x_4 = 1, \tag{2}$$

$$x_j \geq 0 \qquad (j = 1, \ldots, 4).$$

This is not in a diagonal form with respect to any set of variables. Let us use x_3 and x_4 as the starting basic variables. Multiplying (1) by 4 and adding it to (2) multiplied by 3, we have

$$5x_1 + 5x_2 + 4x_4 = 15$$

or

$$(5/4)x_1 + (5/4)x_2 + x_4 = 15/4. \tag{3}$$

Multiplying (1) by 2 and adding it to (2), we have

$$3x_1 + x_2 + 2x_3 = 7$$

or

$$(3/2)x_1 + (1/2)x_2 + x_3 = 7/2. \tag{4}$$

Using (3) and (4), we can put the linear program in Tableau 2.4.

Tableau 2.4

	1	x_1	x_2	x_3	x_4
$-z$	0	1	1	2	8
x_4	15/4	5/4	5/4	0	1
x_3	7/2	3/2	1/2	1	0

Since the costs associated with the basic variables x_3 and x_4 in the 0th row are not zero, we multiply the first row by 8 and the second row by 2 and subtract them from the 0th row. The result is shown in Tableau 2.5.

Tableau 2.5

	1	x_1	x_2	x_3	x_4
$-z$	−37	−12	−10	0	0
x_4	15/4	5/4	5/4	0	1
x_3	7/2	3/2*	1/2	1	0

Now since the cost under x_1 is the most negative entry in the 0th row, we shall make x_1 into a basic variable. The ratio test gives $\min((15/4)\,/\,(5/4), (7/2)\,/\,(3/2)) = 7/3$; thus 3/2 should be the pivot. The result of the pivot is shown in Tableau 2.6.

Tableau 2.6

	1	x_1	x_2	x_3	x_4
$-z$	-9	0	-6	8	0
x_4	5/6	0	5/6*	$-5/6$	1
x_1	7/3	1	1/3	2/3	0

Now -6 is the only negative entry in the 0th row, and x_2 should be brought into the basis. From the ratio test $\min\{(5/6)/(5/6), (7/3)/(1/3)\} = 1$, and 5/6 should be the pivot. The result of the pivot is shown in Tableau 2.7.

Tableau 2.7

	1	x_1	x_2	x_3	x_4
$-z$	-3	0	0	2	36/5
x_2	1	0	1	-1	6/5
x_1	2	1	0	1	$-2/5$

Since every entry a_{0j} $(j = 1, 2, 3, 4)$ is nonnegative, Tableau 2.7 is optimum with $z = 3$, $x_1 = 2$, $x_2 = 1$, $x_3 = x_4 = 0$.

2.3 STARTING FEASIBLE BASIS AND DEGENERACY

In this section we shall study the technique of getting a starting feasible basis. Let the linear program be written in standard form as

$$\min\ z = c_j x_j \qquad (j = 1, \ldots, n)$$

subject to

$$a_{ij} x_j = b_i \qquad (i = 1, \ldots, m),$$
$$x_j \geq 0.$$

We can always multiply equations by -1 if necessary to make all b_i nonnegative. Then we can add to each equation an *artificial variable* x_i^a * so that the artificial variables will form a starting basis:

$$\begin{aligned} x_1^a \qquad\qquad & + a_{11}x_1 + a_{12}x_2 + \cdots = b_1, \\ x_2^a \qquad & + a_{21}x_1 + a_{22}x_2 + \cdots = b_2, \\ x_3^a & + a_{31}x_1 + a_{32}x_2 + \cdots = b_3. \end{aligned}$$

These artificial variables are to be distinguished from the slack variables which are used to convert inequalities into equations. Actually, if the original constants of the linear program are in the form of

$$a_{ij} x_j \leq b_i,$$

* An artificial variable is required to be nonnegative.

adding a slack variable to every inequality, we have

$$a_{ij}x_j + s_i = b_i.$$

If $b_i \geq 0$, s_i can be used as starting basic variables.

The difference between artificial variables x_i^a and slack variables s_i is this: In the optimum solution of the program the value of artificial variables should be all zero, since there is no such variable to start with. On the other hand, it is possible for a slack variable to be positive in an optimum solution. In order to make artificial variables zero, we can arbitrarily change the objective function to be

$$\min z = c_j x_j + M_i x_i^a,$$

where M_i are arbitrarily large positive constants. (In a maximizing problem, the M_i would be large negative constants.) This device, called the method of penalty, is due to Charnes, Cooper, and Henderson [26]. It is equivalent to giving arbitrarily high costs to the artificial variables. This will force the artificial variables to be zero in the optimum solution.

There is another way of getting a starting feasible basis; it also uses artificial variables as the starting basic variables. A new objective function ξ is introduced. We want to minimize ξ, which is the sum of all artificial variables, and treat the original z-equation as one of the constraints. If the original system of equations has a feasible solution, all artificial variables should be zero. Hence the minimal value of $\xi = \sum x_i^a$ should be zero; if it is greater than zero, then the original system of equations has no feasible solution. If the minimal value of ξ is zero, then we would drop the objective function $\xi = \sum_i x_i^a$ and use the optimal basis for the ξ-form as a starting feasible basis to minimize z. In the literature, this is called the two-phase simplex method because phase I gets a feasible basis by minimizing ξ and phase II gets an optimal basis by minimizing z. (See Dantzig [37].)

Take the following linear program, for example:

$$\min z = c_1 x_1 + c_2 x_2 + \cdots + c_n x_n$$

subject to

$$\begin{aligned} a_{11} x_1 + a_{12} x_2 + \cdots + a_{1n} x_n &= b_1, \\ a_{21} x_1 + a_{22} x_2 + \cdots + a_{2n} x_n &= b_2, \\ \vdots \qquad\qquad\qquad\qquad & \quad \vdots \\ a_{m1} x_1 + a_{m2} x_2 + \cdots + a_{mn} x_n &= b_m, \end{aligned} \tag{1}$$

where all b_i are nonnegative.

If we introduce the artificial variable x_i^a and the new objective function

$$\xi = \sum_{i=1}^{m} x_i^a,$$

then we have

$$\min \xi = x_1^a + x_2^a + \cdots + x_m^a$$

subject to

$$\begin{array}{llll} (-z) & & + c_1x_1 + c_2x_2 + \cdots + c_nx_n = 0, & \\ & x_1^a & + a_{11}x_1 + a_{12}x_2 + \cdots + a_{1n}x_n = b_1, & \\ & \quad x_2^a & + a_{21}x_1 + a_{22}x_2 + \cdots + a_{2n}x_n = b_2, & (2) \\ & \quad\quad \ddots & \vdots & \\ & \quad\quad\quad x_m^a & + a_{m1}x_1 + a_{m2}x_2 + \cdots + a_{mn}x_n = b_m. & \end{array}$$

If we subtract all the equations containing b_i from the ξ-form, we have

$$\begin{array}{llll} (-\xi) & & + d_1x_1 + d_2x_2 + \cdots + d_nx_n = -\xi_0, & \\ \quad (-z) & & + c_1x_1 + c_2x_2 + \cdots + c_nx_n = 0, & \\ & x_1^a & + a_{11}x_1 + \quad \cdot \quad \cdot \quad \cdot \quad + a_{1n}x_n = b_1, & (3) \\ & \quad x_2^a & + a_{21}x_1 + \quad \cdot \quad \cdot \quad \cdot \quad + a_{2n}x_n = b_2, & \\ & \quad\quad \ddots & \vdots & \\ & \quad\quad\quad x_m^a & + a_{m1}x_1 + a_{m2}x_2 + \cdots + a_{mn}x_n = b_m, & \end{array}$$

where

$$d_j = -(a_{1j} + a_{2j} + \cdots + a_{mj}), \qquad \xi_0 = (b_1 + b_2 + \cdots + b_m).$$

System (3) is in diagonal form with respect to $(-\xi)$, $(-z)$, $x_1^a, \ldots, x_m^a$. Phase I of the simplex method is to minimize ξ subject to the constraints in (3) with no sign restriction on z. During the course of computation of minimizing ξ, once an artificial variable becomes nonbasic and its coefficient is strictly positive in the ξ-form, then that artificial variable and its column vector are dropped from future computation. Let us see why this is permissible.

Note that all tableaux are equivalent to one another. During the computation of phase I, we have

$$\xi = \xi_0 + \sum \bar{d}_j x_j + \sum \bar{d}_i x_i^a,$$

where $\bar{d}_j \gtrless 0$ and $\bar{d}_i > 0$ and the solution is obtained by putting the nonbasic variables x_j and x_i^a equal to zero and setting $\xi = \xi_0$. If the program has a feasible solution, then $\xi = \xi_0 = 0$. Hence no artificial variable x_i^a with $\bar{d}_i > 0$ can stay in the basis at any positive level.

We have shown that artificial variables can be used to find out if a system is feasible and we shall show that they can also be used to find out if the system is redundant. Let us examine degeneracy and its relation to redundancy in more detail. Recall that a basic solution is obtained by solving $\mathbf{B}\mathbf{x}_B = \mathbf{b}$, where $\mathbf{B}$ is a square submatrix of $\mathbf{A}$ and $\mathbf{A}\mathbf{x} = \mathbf{b}$. If one or more components of $\mathbf{x}_B$ are zero, this means that $\mathbf{b}$ can be expressed in terms of

$m - 1$ vectors or less. There are two cases where this can happen: 1) The column rank of **A** is less than m, or every set of m columns of **A** are linearly dependent. Using the same reasoning as in Theorem 1.9, we can show that if a basic solution exists, a degenerate basic solution exists. 2) The rank of **B** is m but **b** lies in a convex cone spanned by a subset of vectors of **B**.

Now let us consider a system of equations

$$\mathbf{Ax} = \mathbf{b} \qquad (\mathbf{A} \text{ is } m \times n,\ m < n),$$

where *all variables are not artificial variables.* If the system of equations is redundant and consistent, this means that the row rank of **A** is the same as the row rank of [**A**, **b**] and is less than m. In particular the row rank of any submatrix **B** is less than m. Since the row rank of **B** equals the column rank of **B**, every set of m columns is linearly dependent. It follows from 1) above that every basic solution is degenerate. Thus redundancy implies that every basic solution is degenerate. But the converse is not true. Take the following system of equations:

$$\begin{aligned} 2x_1 \qquad\qquad\quad &+ \ \ x_4 = 3,\\ 4x_1 + x_2 \qquad\quad &+ 2x_4 = 6,\\ 6x_1 \qquad + x_3 &+ 3x_4 = 9. \end{aligned}$$

Every basic solution is degenerate, but this system is not redundant as it contains a nonsingular matrix which consists of the first three columns. The reason for the degeneracy here is due to 2) mentioned above.

When we have a nondegenerate basic solution, it implies the existence of a nonsingular submatrix **B** of **A**. This means that $\mathbf{Ax}=\mathbf{b}$ is not redundant. Thus, the existence of a nondegenerate basic solution implies that the system is not redundant. On the other hand, if the system is not redundant, it does not imply that there exists a nondegenerate basic solution. Take the following system of equations for example:

$$\begin{aligned} -x_1 \qquad\qquad\quad &+ \ \ x_4 = 2,\\ -x_2 \qquad &+ 2x_4 = 4,\\ -x_3 &+ 3x_4 = 6. \end{aligned}$$

The system is not redundant as its coefficient matrix contains $-\mathbf{I}$. The first three columns do not form a feasible basis and any feasible basis containing the fourth column is degenerate.

Therefore, although the existence of a nondegenerate basic solution shows that the system is not redundant, the existence of one degenerate basic solution or the fact that all feasible basic solutions are degenerate does not show whether the system of equations is redundant or not. To find out we can rely on artificial variables.

The introduction of artificial variables not only gives us a basis to start the simplex algorithm but also can be used to find out if the original system of equations is inconsistent or redundant. At the end of phase I, if $\xi > 0$, this shows that there is no feasible solution to the original system; in other words, the original system is inconsistent. If $\xi = 0$ and all basic variables are variables of the original system, then we can start phase II. If $\xi = 0$ and some artificial variables remain in the basis at zero level, then we can replace artificial variables by original variables by pivoting. If we can remove all artificial variables by pivoting, we have a degenerate basis to start phase II. If we cannot remove an artificial variable x_r^a by pivoting because $a_{rj} = 0$ for all j, then this means that the original system is redundant.

Take the following two equations for example:

$$x_1 + x_2 + x_3 = 10,$$
$$2x_1 + 2x_2 + 2x_3 = 20.$$

These two equations are clearly redundant. Suppose we use artificial variables to find out if the above system is redundant or not. We have

$$x_1^a \qquad + x_1 + x_2 + x_3 = 10,$$
$$x_2^a + 2x_1 + 2x_2 + 2x_3 = 20.$$

Then at the end of phase I, $\xi = 0$ and one of the artificial variables x_r^a ($r =$ 1 or 2) will remain in the basis at zero level. We cannot remove x_r^a by pivoting due to $a_{rj} = 0$ for $j = 3, 4, 5$, which shows that the original system of equations is redundant.

We shall now discuss some standard techniques for getting a starting basic feasible solution. Without loss of generality, we can consider the constraints of the linear program to be

$$a_{ij}x_j \lesseqqgtr b_i,$$

where $b_i \geq 0$.

If the constraint is of the type

$$a_{ij}x_j = b_i,$$

then we can easily add an artificial variable

$$x_i^a + a_{ij}x_j = b_i.$$

If the constraint is of the type

$$a_{ij}x_j \leq b_i,$$

then the slack variable added to convert the constraint into equality can be used as a starting basic variable with

$$a_{ij}x_j + s_i = b_i.$$

Consider now the m constraints

$$\begin{aligned} a_{11}x_1 + a_{12}x_2 + \cdots + a_{1n}x_n &\geq b_1, \\ a_{21}x_1 + a_{22}x_2 + \cdots + a_{2n}x_n &\geq b_2, \\ &\vdots \\ a_{m1}x_1 + a_{m2}x_2 + \cdots + a_{mn}x_n &\geq b_m. \end{aligned}$$

Let us assume that $b_m = \max_i b_i \ (i = 1, \ldots, m)$. Then we can add the m slack variables and only one artificial variable:

$$\begin{aligned} a_{11}x_1 + a_{12}x_2 + \cdots + a_{1n}x_n - s_1 \qquad\qquad &+ x^a = b_1, \\ a_{21}x_1 + a_{22}x_2 + \cdots + a_{2n}x_n \quad - s_2 \qquad &+ x^a = b_2, \\ a_{31}x_1 + a_{32}x_2 + \cdots + a_{3n}x_n \qquad - s_3 &+ x^a = b_3, \\ \vdots \qquad\qquad\qquad &\quad \vdots \\ a_{m1}x_1 + a_{m2}x_2 + \cdots + a_{mn}x_n \qquad - s_m &+ x^a = b_m. \end{aligned} \tag{4}$$

Let $E_1, E_2, \ldots, E_m$ represent the equations in (4). Then $E_m - E_1$, $E_m - E_2, \ldots, E_m - E_{m-1}, E_m$ are equivalent equations with the right-hand sides $b_m - b_1, b_m - b_2, \ldots, b_m - b_{m-1}, b_m$ which are all nonnegative, and $s_1, s_2, \ldots, s_{m-1}, x^a$ can be used as starting basic variables.

Let us consider the finiteness proof of the simplex method, the problem of degeneracy, and a procedure to follow if the ratio tests end in a tie. To do these, we need the notion of the lexicographical ordering of a vector. A vector is *lexicographically positive (or negative)* if its first nonzero component is positive (or negative). Thus the vector $(0, 0, 2, -7, 4)$ is lexicographically positive and the vector $(0, -3, 7, 4, 8)$ is lexicographically negative. A vector $\mathbf{x}$ which is lexicographically positive is written as $\mathbf{x} \succ \mathbf{0}$. A vector $\mathbf{x}_1$ is lexicographically greater than $\mathbf{x}_2$ if $(\mathbf{x}_1 - \mathbf{x}_2) \succ \mathbf{0}$. That is, $(0, 0, 2, -7, 4)$ is lexicographically greater than $(0, -3, 7, 4, 8)$ as the difference $(0, 3, -5, -11, -4)$ is lexicographically positive.

Recall that the simplex method is a systematic way of choosing different bases to improve the objective function until the optimum basis is obtained. If in the simplex method no basis will ever be chosen twice, then this would imply that the simplex method is a finite algorithm. Note that every entry in the 0th row of the simplex tableau is uniquely determined by the basis. Now if the value of $-z$ which appears in the upper left corner of the simplex tableau keeps increasing, then different values of $-z$ imply different bases. Since there are finite number of bases, in fact at most $\binom{n}{m}$, the simplex method is then a finite algorithm. Thus the values of $-z$ associated with bases serve to linearly order the bases.

Let z and z' be the values of objective functions of two successive tableaux. The value of $-z$ may not change from one tableau to the next if the basic solution is degenerate, because the ratio test gives $\min\,(a_{i0}/a_{is}) = 0$

and $-z' = -z - 0 \cdot a_{0s} = -z$. When this happens, some other devices must be used to keep bases from repeating themselves and to guarantee finiteness.

Assume that in the starting tableau, all the rows except possibly the 0th row are lexicographically positive. (If not, we can add artificial variables or permute the columns which correspond to renaming the variables.) Then if we adopt the following slightly complicated ratio test, it will guarantee finiteness. In choosing the pivot column, we take any $\bar{c}_j < 0$, although the usual simplex algorithm uses $\min_j \bar{c}_j = \bar{c}_s < 0$. Assume that the sth column is chosen as the pivot column. Then among those rows for which $a_{is} > 0$ $(i = 1, \ldots, m)$, the lexicographically smallest row formed by dividing every entry of row i by $a_{is} > 0$ is chosen as the pivot row. That is, the lexicographically smallest $(a_{i0}/a_{is}, a_{i1}/a_{is}, \ldots, a_{in}/a_{is})$ is chosen as the pivot row. Note that the first component of such a vector is given by the usual ratio test. In other words, if the ratio test ends in a tie, the contest is moved to the next entry until the tie is resolved. There are two things to be proved once this slightly complicated ratio test is adopted. 1) All rows except possibly the 0th row in successive tableaux are lexicographically positive. 2) The 0th row will increase lexicographically in each iteration.

To prove 1), we subtract $a_{is}(a_{r0}/a_{rs}, a_{r1}/a_{rs}, \ldots, a_{rn}/a_{rs})$ from each row i for which $a_{is} > 0$. Since $(a_{i0}/a_{is}, a_{i1}/a_{is}, \ldots, a_{in}/a_{is})$ is lexicographically greater than $(a_{r0}/a_{rs}, a_{r1}/a_{rs}, \ldots, a_{rn}/a_{rs})$ by the rule of choice, the difference which is the new row i in the next tableau is lexicographically positive. For a row i with $a_{is} < 0$, the addition of two lexicographically positive rows will also give a lexicographically positive row. To prove 2), note that we add $|a_{0s}/a_{rs}|$ amount of the rth row to the 0th row. Since the rth row is lexicographically positive, the 0th row increases lexicographically in each iteration. Now the 0th row in each simplex tableau serves to linearly order all the bases. When degeneracy occurs, although the value of $-z$ remains the same, all the bases corresponding to the same value of $-z$ are ordered.

Thus no basis can repeat itself, and the simplex method is finite. Take the following tableau for example.

Zeroth column
↓

0	0	0	0	−3	−3	←Zeroth row
0	1	0	0	3*	3	
0	0	1	0	−1	2*	
3	0	0	1	2	1	

Either the fourth column or the fifth column can be chosen as the pivot column, since both have negative relative cost coefficients, -3.

If the fourth column is chosen, then the first row must be chosen as the pivot row. If the fifth column is chosen as the pivot column, then the second row must be chosen as the pivot row.

Examples have been constructed so that if we always drop the first variable in case of tie in the ratio test, it is possible to continue indefinitely. (See Hoffman [102] and Beale [9].)

2.4 SIMPLEX METHOD IN MATRIX NOTATION

Consider the linear program of

$$\min z = \mathbf{cx} - a_{00} \tag{1}$$

subject to

$$\mathbf{Ax} = \mathbf{b}, \qquad \mathbf{x} \geq \mathbf{0}.$$

The linear program (1) can be written as

$$\begin{bmatrix} a_{00} & \mathbf{c} \\ \mathbf{b} & \mathbf{A} \end{bmatrix} \begin{bmatrix} -1 \\ \mathbf{x} \end{bmatrix} = \begin{bmatrix} z \\ \mathbf{0} \end{bmatrix}. \tag{2}$$

Let

$$\mathbf{A}^* = \begin{bmatrix} a_{00} & \mathbf{c} \\ \mathbf{b} & \mathbf{A} \end{bmatrix} = \begin{bmatrix} a_{00} & a_{0j} \\ a_{i0} & a_{ij} \end{bmatrix}. \tag{3}$$

The matrix $\mathbf{A}^*$ is a matrix of $m + 1$ rows and $n + 1$ columns. The pivot operation of the simplex method described in this chapter is equivalent to multiplying (2) on the left by the following square matrix:

$$\begin{bmatrix} 1 & & & -(a_{0s}/a_{rs}) & & & \\ & 1 & & \vdots & & & \\ & & 1 & \vdots & & & \\ & & & (1/a_{sr}) & & & \\ & & & \vdots & 1 & & \\ & & & \vdots & & 1 & \\ & & & -(a_{ms}/a_{rs}) & & & 1 \end{bmatrix},$$

where $r \neq 0$ and $s \neq 0$.

If the columns of $\mathbf{A}$ are partitioned into basic columns $\mathbf{B}$ and non-basic columns $\mathbf{N}$, (2) can be written as

$$\begin{bmatrix} a_{00} & \mathbf{c}_B & \mathbf{c}_N \\ & & \\ \mathbf{b} & \mathbf{B} & \mathbf{N} \end{bmatrix} \begin{bmatrix} -1 \\ \mathbf{x}_B \\ \mathbf{x}_N \end{bmatrix} = \begin{bmatrix} z \\ \\ \mathbf{0} \end{bmatrix}, \tag{4}$$

where $\mathbf{c}_B$ and $\mathbf{c}_N$ are the corresponding costs, and $\mathbf{x}_B$ and $\mathbf{x}_N$ are the basic and nonbasic variables. Letting $\mathbf{x}_B$ be the starting basic variables is equivalent to multiplying (4) on the left by (denote $\mathbf{c}_B\mathbf{B}^{-1} = \boldsymbol{\pi}$)

$$\begin{bmatrix} 1 & -\mathbf{c}_B\mathbf{B}^{-1} \\ \mathbf{0} & \mathbf{B}^{-1} \end{bmatrix} = \begin{bmatrix} 1 & -\boldsymbol{\pi} \\ \mathbf{0} & \mathbf{B}^{-1} \end{bmatrix}. \tag{5}$$

The result of multiplying (4) by (5) on the left is

$$\begin{bmatrix} a_{00} - \mathbf{c}_B \mathbf{B}^{-1}\mathbf{b} & \mathbf{0} & \mathbf{c}_N - \mathbf{c}_B \mathbf{B}^{-1}\mathbf{N} \\ \mathbf{B}^{-1}\mathbf{b} & \mathbf{I} & \mathbf{B}^{-1}\mathbf{N} \end{bmatrix} \begin{bmatrix} -1 \\ \mathbf{x}_B \\ \mathbf{x}_N \end{bmatrix} = \begin{bmatrix} z \\ \mathbf{0} \end{bmatrix},$$

where the relative cost $\bar{c}_j$ is given by

$$\bar{c}_j = c_j - \boldsymbol{\pi}\mathbf{a}_j = c_j - z_j, \qquad \text{where} \quad z_j = \boldsymbol{\pi}\mathbf{a}_j,$$

and the current $\bar{c}_j$ all appear in the 0th row of the current tableau. The basis $\mathbf{B}$ is feasible if $\mathbf{B}^{-1}\mathbf{b} \geq \mathbf{0}$, and it is optimum if $\bar{c}_j \geq 0$ for all j.

The row vector $\boldsymbol{\pi} = (\pi_1, \ldots, \pi_m)$ is the weight to be multiplied by each row and subrtacted from the cost row to eliminate the cost coefficients of the basic variables.

Assume that we have a primal program

$$\min \ z = \mathbf{cx}$$

subject to

$$\mathbf{Ax} \leq \mathbf{b}, \qquad \mathbf{x} \geq \mathbf{0}.$$

A set of slack variables is added with

$$[\mathbf{I}, \mathbf{A}] \begin{bmatrix} \mathbf{s} \\ \mathbf{x} \end{bmatrix} = \mathbf{b}.$$

If we perform row elimination on $\mathbf{A}^* = [\mathbf{I}, \mathbf{A}]$ or equivalently multiply $\mathbf{A}^*$ on the left by $\mathbf{B}^{-1}$, where $\mathbf{B}$ is the basis ($\mathbf{B}$ is a submatrix of $\mathbf{A}$), then

$$\mathbf{B}^{-1}\mathbf{A}^* = [\mathbf{B}^{-1}, \mathbf{B}^{-1}\mathbf{A}].$$

Therefore the matrix which occupies the position of $\mathbf{I}$ is the inverse of the current basis.

Furthermore, $\bar{c}_j = c_j - \mathbf{c}_B\mathbf{B}^{-1}\mathbf{a}_j$, since the cost coefficients of slack variables are zero, i.e., $c_j = 0$ and a column in $\mathbf{I}$ is $\mathbf{e}_i$, so that the relative cost coefficients in the position above the identity matrix $\mathbf{I}$ are $-\mathbf{c}_B\mathbf{B}^{-1}$ or $-\boldsymbol{\pi}$. Note that $z = \mathbf{c}_B\mathbf{x}_B = \mathbf{c}_B\mathbf{B}^{-1}\mathbf{b} = \boldsymbol{\pi}\mathbf{b}$. That is, at every stage of computation the value of the objective functions is equal to the absolute value of the current cost coefficient of $\mathbf{I}$ times the original $\mathbf{b}$. This provides an independent check on the calculation. For example, in Tableau 2.2, $\frac{21}{2} = 11 + (-0)2 + (-\frac{1}{2})1$. In Tableau 2.3, $3 = 11 + (-3)2 + (-2)1$. In Tableau 2.6, $9 = 37 + (-8)\frac{7}{2} + (-0)\frac{15}{4}$. In Tableau 2.7, $3 = 37 + (-2)\frac{7}{2} + (-\frac{36}{5})\frac{15}{4}$.

2.5 GEOMETRIC INTERPRETATION OF THE SIMPLEX METHOD (Gomory [83])

Consider an inequality such as $x_1 + x_2 \leq b_1$ with $x_1 \geq 0$ and $x_2 \geq 0$. The feasible region of this inequality is shown in Fig. 2.1. This inequality can be converted into an equation by introducing a slack variable s_1. Then we

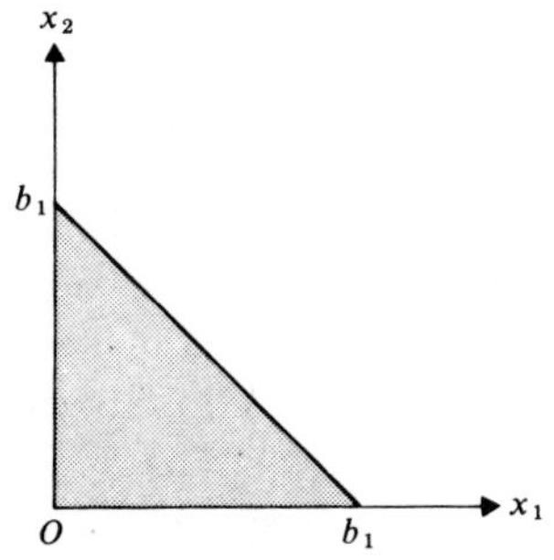

Fig. 2.1

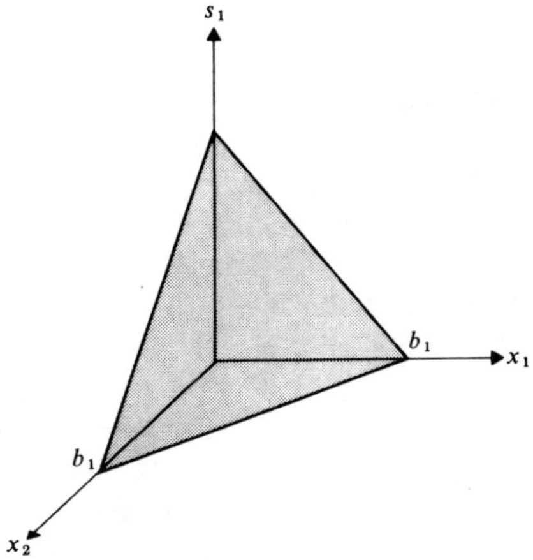

Fig. 2.2

have $x_1 + x_2 + s_1 = b_1$, $x_1 \geq 0$, $x_2 \geq 0$, $s_1 \geq 0$. The feasible region of this system is a triangular plane as shown in Fig. 2.2.

For each point of the triangular plane there is a corresponding point in the feasible region of Fig. 2.1. The correspondence is obtained by projecting the triangular plane into the x_1, x_2 plane. If the value of the slack variable is fixed at a constant c, then x_1 and x_2 have to satisfy $x_1 + x_2 = b_1 - c$, which is a line parallel to $x_1 + x_2 = b_1$. If the slack variable is zero, then we have $x_1 + x_2 = b$. Therefore, the value of the slack variable serves to measure how far away we are from the boundary of the half-space defined by the inequality.

Consider a linear program

$$\min\ z = c_1x_1 + \cdots + c_nx_n$$

subject to
$$\mathbf{Ax} \geq \mathbf{b} \qquad (\mathbf{A} \text{ is } m \times n), \tag{1}$$
$$\mathbf{x} \geq \mathbf{0}.$$

The **x**-space is of n dimensions. Introducing slack variables s_1, s_2, $\ldots$, s_m, and letting $\mathbf{x}^* = [x_1, \ldots, x_n, s_1, \ldots, s_m]$, we have

$$\min\ z = \mathbf{c}^*\mathbf{x}^*$$

subject to (2)

$$\mathbf{A}^*\mathbf{x}^* = \mathbf{b},$$
$$\mathbf{x}^* \geq \mathbf{0}.$$

where $\mathbf{A}^* = (\mathbf{A}, -\mathbf{I})$ and $\mathbf{c}^* = (c_1, \ldots, c_n, 0, \ldots, 0)$. Since there are now $n + m$ variables and m equations in (2), the $\mathbf{x}^*$-space* is of $n + m - m = n$

* The space of solutions to $\mathbf{A}^*\ \mathbf{x}^* = \mathbf{b}$.

dimensions. A vertex is then a point where n inequalities among the $m + n$ inequalities of (1) are satisfied as equalities, i.e., n components of $\mathbf{x}^*$ are zero. These components are the nonbasic variables.

The process of giving some variables the value zero is equivalent to striking out the columns in $\mathbf{A}$ which correspond to these zero-value variables. The other components of $\mathbf{x}^*$ are obtained by solving the m equations for m unknowns. Let $\bar{\mathbf{x}}$ be the m-vector of basic variables and $\mathbf{B}$ the basis; then $\bar{\mathbf{x}} = \mathbf{B}^{-1}\mathbf{b}$. If $\bar{\mathbf{x}} \geq \mathbf{0}$, then it represents a vertex of the solution space. If $\bar{\mathbf{x}} \ngeq \mathbf{0}$, then it is merely an intersection of n hyperplanes outside the solution space.

To solve (2) using the simplex method, we use Gauss elimination to get an equivalent system to (2), which is $\mathbf{I}\mathbf{x}_B + \mathbf{B}^{-1}\mathbf{N}\mathbf{x}_N = \mathbf{B}^{-1}\mathbf{b}$, where $\mathbf{B}$ is the basis and the objective function is expressed in terms of nonbasic variables. For a feasible basis, $\mathbf{x}_B \geq \mathbf{0}$, so that we can consider $\mathbf{x}_B$ as slack variables. In the space of nonbasic variables, there are m inequalities $\mathbf{B}^{-1}\mathbf{N}\mathbf{x}_N \leq \mathbf{B}^{-1}\mathbf{b}$, and the point $\mathbf{x}_N = \mathbf{0}$ corresponds to the origin of the space. The simplex method starts with a feasible vertex and then moves to a neighboring vertex that would bring an improvement to the objective function. Thus we have to make sure that 1) the neighboring vertex is a feasible vertex, and 2) the neighboring vertex would bring an improvement. In the $\mathbf{x}_N$ space, if one nonbasic variable is increased from its present value of zero and all other nonbasic variables remain zero, this corresponds to moving along one of the coordinate axes. Since $n - 1$ nonbasic variables remain zero, that means $n - 1$ inequalities of (1) are still satisfied as equalities. In other words, all neighboring vertices of the origin (which represents the present solution) have $n - 1$ faces of the convex polytope in common with the origin. Increasing one nonbasic variable from zero would make it a basic variable. We have to switch one basic variable into a nonbasic one if we want the solution to be a vertex. Let x_k be the nonbasic variable and $\mathbf{a}_k$ the corresponding column vector. If we give x_k the value θ, then the current basic variables $\bar{\mathbf{x}}$ become $\bar{\mathbf{x}}(\theta) = \mathbf{B}^{-1}(\mathbf{b} - \theta\mathbf{a}_k)$. As θ increases from zero, the value of $\bar{\mathbf{x}}(\theta)$ also varies and there must be an upper bound $\theta_{\max}$ such that for $0 \leq \theta \leq \theta_{\max}$, $\bar{\mathbf{x}}(\theta) \geq \mathbf{0}$. When $\theta = \theta_{\max}$, one component of $\bar{\mathbf{x}}(\theta_{\max})$ will become zero.

Geometrically, as θ increases, the solution point of (2) moves along one of the coordinate axes until it reaches another vertex. Going beyond this point would violate the inequality represented by $\bar{x}_i \geq 0$. (Note that $\bar{x}_i \geq 0$ corresponds to one inequality of $\mathbf{B}^{-1}\mathbf{N}\mathbf{x}_N \leq \mathbf{B}^{-1}\mathbf{b}$.)

Since the objective function z is now expressed in terms of $\mathbf{c}_N\,\mathbf{x}_N$, $\mathbf{c}_N \geq \mathbf{0}$ would imply an optimum tableau. If $\bar{c}_j < 0$ for a nonbasic variable, increasing that nonbasic variable from zero would bring an improvement.

Thus, in the simplex method we always set up a *local coordinate system*, with the current solution as the origin, and we move towards another neighboring vertex along an edge which would bring an improvement to the objective function. When the new vertex is reached, we set up another coordinate system with the new vertex as the origin. The movement of the solution point, if under the criterion of $\min_j \bar{c}_j < 0$, corresponds to steepest descent along the edges intersecting at the origin. The amount of change in the objective function in one iteration is determined by the length of the edge as well as the slope of the edge. More precisely, the amount is $\min_i |\bar{c}_j \cdot \bar{a}_{i0}/\bar{a}_{ij}|$ for a given j.

2.6 ECONOMIC INTERPRETATION OF THE SIMPLEX METHOD

Consider Example 3 in Section 1.1 where

$$\min\ z = \mathbf{cx}$$

subject to (1)

$$\mathbf{Ax} = \mathbf{b}, \qquad \mathbf{x} \geq \mathbf{0}.$$

Assume that $\mathbf{A} = [\mathbf{B}, \mathbf{N}]$, where $\mathbf{B}$ is a feasible basis. Then the program (1) can be written as

$$\min\ z = \mathbf{c}_B\mathbf{x}_B + \mathbf{c}_N\mathbf{x}_N$$

subject to (2)

$$\mathbf{Bx}_B + \mathbf{Nx}_N = \mathbf{b}, \qquad \mathbf{x}_B, \mathbf{x}_N \geq \mathbf{0}.$$

The solution of (2) is obtained by letting $\mathbf{x}_N = \mathbf{0}$ and $\mathbf{x}_B = \mathbf{B}^{-1}\mathbf{b}$. The total cost is $z = \mathbf{c}_B\mathbf{x}_B = \mathbf{c}_B\mathbf{B}^{-1}\mathbf{b}$, and $\mathbf{x}_B = [x_1, \ldots, x_m]$ are the activity levels of the vectors $\mathbf{a}_1, \ldots, \mathbf{a}_m$.

Consider another chemical plant, where the requirement vector is $\mathbf{b}^*$, and that we have m activities, each of which can be represented by a unit vector $\mathbf{e}_i$ $(i = 1, \ldots, m)$. Then we have no choice but to operate the ith activity at the level b_i^*, since it is the only activity that will produce that material. The total cost of operating the m activities is then

$$c_i^* x_i^* = c_i^* b_i^*.$$

Now, if $\mathbf{c}^* = \mathbf{c}_B\mathbf{B}^{-1}$ and $\mathbf{b}^* = \mathbf{b}$, then so far as producing the requirement $\mathbf{b}$ is concerned, the operating cost of this plant is the same as the previous one. Define $\mathbf{c}_B\mathbf{B}^{-1} = \boldsymbol{\pi} = (\pi_1, \pi_2, \ldots, \pi_m) = \mathbf{c}^*$. We can think of π_i as the price that we pay for producing one unit of the ith material in the first plant. In the first chemical plant let $\mathbf{a}_j$ denote any activity vector that is not in the basis. If the vector $\mathbf{a}_j$ is operated at the unit level, it will produce a_{ij} units of the ith material. Since each unit of the ith material costs π_i dollars in our present system, the saving that could be achieved by using $\mathbf{a}_j$ is $\boldsymbol{\pi}\mathbf{a}_j$. (This is denoted as z_j.) The actual cost of operating $\mathbf{a}_j$ at unit level is c_j. Therefore if $c_j - z_j = c_j - \boldsymbol{\pi}\mathbf{a}_j \geq 0$, then that activity should not be used.

If $c_j - z_j < 0$, that means $\mathbf{a}_j$ would bring us some saving in the present system. After $\mathbf{a}_j$ is introduced into the basis at the highest level possible and some other vector leaves the basis, then the new prices $\boldsymbol{\pi}'$ will be different from the old $\boldsymbol{\pi}$. Therefore, π_i is called the *shadow price of each row under the present basis*. The operation of checking if a given vector $\mathbf{a}_j$ should be brought into the basis by calculating $c_j - \boldsymbol{\pi}\mathbf{a}_j$ is called, in the literature, *pricing operation*.

Note that a basis $\mathbf{B}$ is an optimum basis if $\mathbf{B}^{-1}\mathbf{b} \geq \mathbf{0}$ and $c_j - \mathbf{c}_B\mathbf{B}^{-1}\mathbf{a}_j \geq 0$ for all j. Let $\mathbf{b}$ be subject to a small change, say $\Delta\mathbf{b}$ such that $\mathbf{B}^{-1}(\mathbf{b} + \Delta\mathbf{b}) \geq \mathbf{0}$. Then $\bar{c}_j = c_j - \mathbf{c}_B\mathbf{B}^{-1}\mathbf{a}_j$ is unchanged. This implies that the original basis $\mathbf{B}$ is still the optimum basis for the new righthand side $\mathbf{b} + \Delta\mathbf{b}$. Since $\boldsymbol{\pi} = \mathbf{c}_B\mathbf{B}^{-1}$, $\boldsymbol{\pi}$ is also unchanged. But we have shown in Section 2.4 that $z = \pi_i b_i$, so that the new optimum value is

$$z' = \pi_i(b_i + \Delta b_i) = z + \pi_i \Delta b_i.$$

Thus $\partial z/\partial b_i = \pi_i$.

Thus π_i gives the rate of change of z as b_i varies. In example 1 of Section 1.1, if the nutrient requirement b_k is increased by one unit and all other nutrient requirements are the same, then the minimum cost of fulfilling the diet will be increased by π_k dollars. Similarly if the nutrient requirement b_k is decreased by one unit and all other nutrient requirements are the same, then the minimum cost of fulfilling the diet will be decreased by π_k dollars.

EXERCISES

1. Given the linear program

$$\min z = 6x_1 + 3x_2 + x_3 + 7x_4 + 8x_5$$

subject to

$$\begin{aligned} x_1 + 2x_2 + 7x_3 \qquad\qquad &= 9, \\ 6x_2 + 3x_3 + x_4 - x_5 &= 9, \\ x_j \geq 0 \qquad (j = 1, \ldots, 5)&. \end{aligned}$$

Show four distinct vectors which are (a) a feasible solution, (b) a basic infeasible solution, (c) a basic feasible solution, and (d) a basic optimum solution, respectively. Use the simplex method to solve the above program.

2. What forms of the relative costs of the nonbasic variables will ensure that the optimum solution is unique? What forms will ensure that the optimum solution is not unique?

3. Consider the program

$$\min z = 10 - 2x_4 - 3x_5$$

subject to

$$x_1 - x_3 + \qquad x_4 + 3x_5 = 3,$$

$$x_2 + x_3 + (1/2)x_4 + 2x_5 = 2.$$

Use x_1 and x_2 as the starting basic variables and always select the lexicographically smallest column to enter the basis. Check your computation at each step by $z = \boldsymbol{\pi}\mathbf{b}$ [*Hint*: The constant 10 should not be included in checking $z = \boldsymbol{\pi}\mathbf{b}$.]

4. Construct a linear program for which the slack variables will be nonzero in the optimum solution.
5. Write the mathematical statements corresponding to the following two statements:
   (a) If an activity is strictly unprofitable in terms of the shadow prices, the level of that activity must be zero.
   (b) If a resource is not fully utilized, then the shadow price corresponding to that resource must be zero.
6. Consider

$$\min z = 11 - x_3 - x_4 - x_5$$

subject to

$$x_1 \quad + x_3 - \quad x_4 + 2x_5 = 2,$$

$$x_2 - x_3 + 2x_4 + \quad x_5 = 1.$$

Let x_1 and x_2 be the starting basic variables. Choose a vector to enter the basis such that the objective function will decrease most among all possible vectors entering the basis. Describe a rule of choosing such vectors in terms of $\bar{c}_j$, $\bar{a}_{ij}$, and $\bar{b}_i$.

SUGGESTED READING

The criteron of bringing the most negative column into the basis is analogous to the method of steepest descent and usually converges faster than many other criteria that can be used. However, it is possible to construct an example such that using the most negative $\bar{c}_j$ would make us go through all vertices of the polytope before reaching the optimum vertex. See Goldman and Kleinman [77].

DUALITY

3

3.1 THEOREM OF DUALITY (Gale, Kuhn, and Tucker [71])

We have studied the existence of nonnegative solutions to linear equations and inequalities and the geometric meaning of basic solutions. Now we shall study another aspect of a linear program. It turns out that for each linear program, there is another linear program associated with it such that the two linear programs have many interesting relations. We call the first linear program the *primal* linear program, and the second the *dual* linear program. To present the relations between the two programs clearly, we need to introduce some index sets.

We define

$$M = \{1, \ldots, m_1, \ldots, m\}, \quad M_1 = \{1, \ldots, m_1\}, \ \bar{M}_1 = \{m_1 + 1, \ldots, m\};$$
$$N = \{1, \ldots, n_1, \ldots, n\}, \quad N_1 = \{1, \ldots, n_1\}, \ \bar{N}_1 = \{n_1 + 1, \ldots, n\}.$$

For example, all x_j, $j \in N_1$, means all the x_j ($j = 1, \ldots, n_1$).

We shall write the primal program and dual program side by side with the index set that applies to both of them in the middle:

Primal Program		Dual Program
min $z = c_j x_j, \quad j \in N$		max $w = y_i b_i, \quad i \in M$
$a_{ij} x_j \geq b_i$	$i \in M_1$	$y_i \geq 0$
$a_{ij} x_j = b_i$	$i \in \bar{M}_1$	$y_i \gtrless 0$
$x_j \geq 0$	$j \in N_1$	$y_i a_{ij} \leq c_j$
$x_j \gtrless 0$	$j \in \bar{N}_1$	$y_i a_{ij} = c_j$

The symmetry between the two programs is apparent. To an inequality of one program corresponds a nonnegative variable of the other program. To an equality of one program corresponds an unrestricted variable of the other program. Furthermore, the dual program of the dual program is the primal program itself. Therefore, we can take any one of the pair as the primal program and the other as the dual program.

If we write a linear program in canonical form, the symmetry is more apparent. The following are the canonical form and the standard form of duality.

Canonical form of duality.

Primal Program	Dual Program	
$\min\ z = \mathbf{cx}$	$\max\ w = \mathbf{yb}$	
$\mathbf{Ax} \geq \mathbf{b}$	$\mathbf{yA} \leq \mathbf{c}$	(c)
$\mathbf{x} \geq \mathbf{0}$	$\mathbf{y} \geq \mathbf{0}$	

Standard form of duality.

Primal Program	Dual Program	
$\min\ z = \mathbf{cx}$	$\max\ w = \boldsymbol{\pi}\mathbf{b}$	
$\mathbf{Ax} = \mathbf{b}$	$\boldsymbol{\pi}\mathbf{A} \leq \mathbf{c}$	(s)
$\mathbf{x} \geq \mathbf{0}$	$\boldsymbol{\pi} \gtreqless \mathbf{0}$	

Here we use $\mathbf{y}$ to be the nonnegative variables of the dual program and $\boldsymbol{\pi}$ to be the unrestricted variables of the dual program. The canonical form of duality can also be put into a compact tableau (see Tableau 3.1).

Tableau 3.1

	1	x_1	x_2		x_n	
1	0	$-c_1$	$-c_2$	$\ldots$	$-c_n$	$= -z$
y_{n+1}	$-b_1$	a_{11}	a_{12}	$\ldots$	a_{1n}	$= x_{n+1}$
y_{n+2}	$-b_2$	a_{21}			$\vdots$	$= x_{n+2}$
$\vdots$	$\vdots$	$\vdots$				$\vdots$
y_{n+m}	$-b_m$	a_{m1}		$\ldots$	a_{mn}	$= x_{n+m}$
	$-w$	$-y_1$			$-y_n$	

In reading Tableau 3.1 multiply every row in the tableau by the column vector $[1, x_1, x_2, \ldots, x_n]$ and set it equal to the variable on the right of that row. Thus $(-b_1, a_{11}, a_{12}, \ldots, a_{1n})\,[1, x_1, x_2, \ldots, x_n] = x_{n+1}$. We multiply the row vector $(1, y_{n+1}, \ldots, y_{n+m})$ by every column in the tableau and set it equal to the entry at the bottom of that column. In this way, we determine that $(1, y_{n+1}, \ldots, y_{n+m})\,[-c_j, a_{1j}, a_{2j}, \ldots, a_{mj}] = -y_j$. All x's and y's are restricted to be nonnegative, i.e.,

$$x_j \geq 0 \qquad (j = 1, \ldots, n, \ldots, n+m),$$
$$y_i \geq 0 \qquad (i = 1, \ldots, m, \ldots, m+n).$$

For ease of exposition we shall restrict our attention to the canonical form of duality.

Lemma 3.1. If $\bar{\mathbf{x}}$ and $\bar{\mathbf{y}}$ are feasible solutions to a pair of primal and dual programs, then $\mathbf{c}\bar{\mathbf{x}} \geq \bar{\mathbf{y}}\mathbf{b}$.

Proof. Since $\bar{\mathbf{x}}$ is feasible, $\mathbf{A}\bar{\mathbf{x}} \geq \mathbf{b}$. Multiplying both sides by $\bar{\mathbf{y}} \geq \mathbf{0}$, we have $\bar{\mathbf{y}}\mathbf{A}\bar{\mathbf{x}} \geq \bar{\mathbf{y}}\mathbf{b}$. Since $\bar{\mathbf{y}}$ is feasible, $\bar{\mathbf{y}}\mathbf{A} \leq \mathbf{c}$. Multiplying both sides by $\bar{\mathbf{x}} \geq \mathbf{0}$, we have $\bar{\mathbf{y}}\mathbf{A}\bar{\mathbf{x}} \leq \mathbf{c}\bar{\mathbf{x}}$. Therefore $\mathbf{c}\bar{\mathbf{x}} \geq \bar{\mathbf{y}}\mathbf{A}\bar{\mathbf{x}} \geq \bar{\mathbf{y}}\mathbf{b}$.

Lemma 3.2. The system of linear homogeneous inequalities

$$\mathbf{A}\mathbf{x} - t\mathbf{b} \geq \mathbf{0}, \qquad \mathbf{y} \geq \mathbf{0}, \tag{1}$$

$$-\mathbf{y}\mathbf{A} + t\mathbf{c} \geq \mathbf{0}, \qquad \mathbf{x} \geq \mathbf{0}, \tag{2}$$

$$\mathbf{y}\mathbf{b} - \mathbf{c}\mathbf{x} \geq 0, \qquad t \geq 0 \tag{3}$$

has at least one solution $\mathbf{y}_0, \mathbf{x}_0, t_0$ such that

$$\begin{aligned} \mathbf{A}\mathbf{x}_0 - t_0\mathbf{b} + \mathbf{y}_0^T &> \mathbf{0}, && (4)\\ -\mathbf{y}_0\mathbf{A} + t_0\mathbf{c} + \mathbf{x}_0^T &> \mathbf{0}, \qquad \text{and} \qquad \begin{bmatrix} \mathbf{y}_0^T \\ \mathbf{x}_0 \\ t_0 \end{bmatrix} \geq \mathbf{0}. && (5)\\ \mathbf{y}_0\mathbf{b} - \mathbf{c}\mathbf{x}_0 + t_0 &> 0, && (6) \end{aligned}$$

Proof. The systems (1), (2), (3) can be rewritten in matrix form as

$$\begin{bmatrix} \mathbf{0} & \mathbf{A} & -\mathbf{b} \\ -\mathbf{A}^T & \mathbf{0} & \mathbf{c}^T \\ \mathbf{b}^T & -\mathbf{c} & 0 \end{bmatrix} \begin{bmatrix} \mathbf{y}^T \\ \mathbf{x} \\ t \end{bmatrix} \geq \mathbf{0}, \qquad \begin{bmatrix} \mathbf{y}^T \\ \mathbf{x} \\ t \end{bmatrix} \geq \mathbf{0},$$

where the matrix

$$\begin{bmatrix} \mathbf{0} & \mathbf{A} & -\mathbf{b} \\ -\mathbf{A}^T & \mathbf{0} & \mathbf{c}^T \\ \mathbf{b}^T & -\mathbf{c} & 0 \end{bmatrix}$$

is antisymmetric.

From Theorem 1.4, the system has at least one nonnegative solution $[\mathbf{y}^T, \mathbf{x}, t]$ such that

$$\begin{bmatrix} \mathbf{0} & \mathbf{A} & -\mathbf{b} \\ -\mathbf{A}^T & \mathbf{0} & \mathbf{c}^T \\ \mathbf{b}^T & -\mathbf{c} & \mathbf{0} \end{bmatrix} \begin{bmatrix} \mathbf{y}_0^T \\ \mathbf{x}_0 \\ t_0 \end{bmatrix} + \begin{bmatrix} \mathbf{y}_0^T \\ \mathbf{x}_0 \\ t_0 \end{bmatrix} > \mathbf{0}$$

which is (4), (5), and (6), the desired result.

We shall now state the theorem of duality (see Gale, Kuhn, and Tucker [71] and Von Neumann [201]).

Theorem of Duality. Given a pair of primal and dual programs as shown in (c), one and only one of the following three cases is true:

1. Both programs have optimum solutions and their values are the same, i.e., min $\mathbf{c}\mathbf{x}$ = max $\mathbf{y}\mathbf{b}$.
2. One program has no feasible solution, and the other has at least one feasible solution but no (finite) optimum solution.
3. Neither of the two programs has a feasible solution.

Proof. From Lemma 3.2, we know that there exists at least one solution $\mathbf{y}_0$, $\mathbf{x}_0$, t_0 for which (4), (5), and (6) are true and $t_0 \geq 0$.

CASE 1. $t_0 > 0$. Let $\mathbf{x}^* = \mathbf{x}_0/t_0 \geq \mathbf{0}$, $\mathbf{y}^* = \mathbf{y}_0/t_0 \geq \mathbf{0}$, $1 = t_0/t_0 > 0$. Then $\mathbf{x}^*$, $\mathbf{y}^*$, and 1 are also solutions to the linear homogeneous inequalities (1), (2), and (3) in Lemma 3.2. Rewriting the three inequalities, we have

$$\begin{aligned} \mathbf{Ax}^* - \mathbf{b} \geq \mathbf{0} \quad &\text{or} \quad \mathbf{Ax}^* \geq \mathbf{b}, \\ -\mathbf{y}^*\mathbf{A} + \mathbf{c} \geq \mathbf{0} \quad &\text{or} \quad \mathbf{y}^*\mathbf{A} \leq \mathbf{c}, \\ \mathbf{y}^*\mathbf{b} - \mathbf{cx}^* \geq 0 \quad &\text{or} \quad \mathbf{cx}^* \leq \mathbf{y}^*\mathbf{b}. \end{aligned}$$

From Lemma 3.1, any feasible solutions satisfy $\mathbf{cx} \geq \mathbf{yb}$. Therefore $\mathbf{x}^*$ and $\mathbf{y}^*$ are the optimum solutions, i.e., min $\mathbf{cx}^* =$ max $\mathbf{y}^*\mathbf{b}$, which is the first case of the duality theorem.

CASE 2A. $t_0 = 0$. Let $\mathbf{x}_0$ and $\mathbf{y}_0$ be the solution to Lemma 3.2. From (1), $t = t_0 = 0$, we have

$$\mathbf{Ax}_0 \geq \mathbf{0}, \qquad \mathbf{y}_0 \geq \mathbf{0}. \tag{1'}$$

From (2), $t = t_0 = 0$, we have

$$\mathbf{y}_0\mathbf{A} \leq \mathbf{0}, \qquad \mathbf{x}_0 \geq \mathbf{0}. \tag{2'}$$

Assume that there exist $\bar{\mathbf{x}}$ and $\bar{\mathbf{y}}$ satisfying (c), i.e.,

$$\mathbf{A}\bar{\mathbf{x}} \geq \mathbf{b}, \qquad \bar{\mathbf{x}} \geq \mathbf{0}, \tag{7}$$

$$\bar{\mathbf{y}}\mathbf{A} \leq \mathbf{c}, \qquad \bar{\mathbf{y}} \geq \mathbf{0}. \tag{8}$$

From (1′) $\mathbf{Ax}_0 \geq \mathbf{0}$. From (8) $\mathbf{y} \geq \mathbf{0}$. We have $\mathbf{yAx}_0 \geq 0$. Multiplying (8) by $\mathbf{x}_0 \geq \mathbf{0}$, we have $\mathbf{cx}_0 \geq \bar{\mathbf{y}}\mathbf{Ax}_0$. Therefore

$$\mathbf{cx}_0 \geq \bar{\mathbf{y}}\mathbf{Ax}_0 \geq 0. \tag{9}$$

Since $\mathbf{A}\bar{\mathbf{x}} \geq \mathbf{b}$ and $\mathbf{y}_0 \geq \mathbf{0}$, we have $\mathbf{y}_0\mathbf{A}\bar{\mathbf{x}} \geq \mathbf{y}_0\mathbf{b}$. Multiplying (2′) by $\bar{\mathbf{x}} \geq \mathbf{0}$, we have $0 \geq \mathbf{y}_0\mathbf{A}\bar{\mathbf{x}}$. Therefore

$$0 \geq \mathbf{y}_0\mathbf{A}\bar{\mathbf{x}} \geq \mathbf{y}_0\mathbf{b}. \tag{10}$$

From (9) and (10)

$$\mathbf{cx}_0 \geq \mathbf{y}_0\mathbf{b}. \tag{11}$$

But (11) contradicts (6) for $t_0 = 0$, $\mathbf{y}_0\mathbf{b} - \mathbf{cx}_0 > 0$. Therefore, if $t_0 = 0$, we cannot have feasible solutions $\bar{\mathbf{x}}$ and $\bar{\mathbf{y}}$ to both programs in (c).

CASE 2B. $t_0 = 0$. Assume that there are feasible solutions to only one program and that the other program has no feasible solution. Let $\bar{\mathbf{x}}$ be a feasible solution satisfying (c), i.e.,

$$\mathbf{A}\bar{\mathbf{x}} \geq \mathbf{b}, \qquad \bar{\mathbf{x}} \geq \mathbf{0}. \tag{12}$$

Then for $\lambda \geq 0$, $\bar{\mathbf{x}} + \lambda\mathbf{x}_0$ is also a feasible solution since it follows from (1′) and (12):

$$\mathbf{A}(\bar{\mathbf{x}} + \lambda\mathbf{x}_0) = \mathbf{A}\bar{\mathbf{x}} + \lambda\mathbf{Ax}_0 \geq \mathbf{b}.$$

Multiplying (2′) by $\bar{\mathbf{x}}$, we have (since $\mathbf{A}\bar{\mathbf{x}} \geq \mathbf{b}$)

$$0 \geq \mathbf{y}_0\mathbf{A}\bar{\mathbf{x}} \geq \mathbf{y}_0\mathbf{b}. \tag{13}$$

Then (13) and (6) imply $0 \geq \mathbf{y}_0\mathbf{A}\bar{\mathbf{x}} \geq \mathbf{y}_0\mathbf{b} > \mathbf{c}\mathbf{x}_0$, or $\mathbf{c}\mathbf{x}_0$ is negative.

This means that the value of $\mathbf{c}(\bar{\mathbf{x}} + \lambda\mathbf{x}_0) = \mathbf{c}\bar{\mathbf{x}} + \lambda\,\mathbf{c}\mathbf{x}_0$ can be made as negative as desired simply by taking arbitrarily large λ. Since $\bar{\mathbf{x}} + \lambda\mathbf{x}_0$ is a feasible solution, this means that the objective function z has no lower bound. Similarly if we only assume that there exists $\bar{\mathbf{y}}$ satisfying $\bar{\mathbf{y}}\mathbf{A} \leq \mathbf{c}$, then w will have no upper bounds. This is the second case of the duality theorem. For the third case, it is very easy to generate an example in which both programs have no feasible solutions. These cover the three distinct cases of duality.

We have proved the duality theorem for the canonical form. But by using many of the transformations mentioned in Chapter 1, we can easily convert the canonical form to the standard form or vice versa. For example, consider the problem of

$$\min\ c_j x_j \quad (j = 1, \ldots, n)$$

subject to

$$a_{ij}x_j \geq b_i \qquad (i = 1, \ldots, m),$$
$$x_j \geq 0 \qquad (j = 1, \ldots, n-1)$$

and x_n is unrestricted in sign.

Then we would introduce $x_n = x_n^+ - x_n^-$, where $x_n^+ \geq 0$ and $x_n^- \geq 0$. The problem becomes

$$\min\ c_1x_1 + c_2x_2 + \cdots + c_nx_n^+ - c_nx_n^-$$

subject to

$$\mathbf{a}_1x_1 + \mathbf{a}_2x_2 + \cdots + \mathbf{a}_nx_n^+ - \mathbf{a}_nx_n^- \geq \mathbf{b}.$$

In the dual problem, we have

$$\mathbf{y}\mathbf{a}_n \leq c_n, \qquad -\mathbf{y}\mathbf{a}_n \leq -c_n,$$

and this is equivalent to $\mathbf{y}\mathbf{a}_n = c_n$.

When a constraint of the primal problem $\mathbf{A}\mathbf{x} \geq \mathbf{b}$, say $\mathbf{a}_i\mathbf{x} \geq b_i$, is replaced by

$$\mathbf{a}_i\mathbf{x} - s_i = b_i, \qquad s_i \geq 0,$$

the dual variable y_i associated with this equality constraint is not restricted to be nonnegative, but the dual constraint associated with s_i is

$$-\mathbf{y}\mathbf{e}_i \leq 0, \qquad \text{or} \qquad y_i \geq 0.$$

3.2 COMPLEMENTARY SLACKNESS (Dantzig and Orden [44])

We shall study more relations between solutions of a pair of primal and dual programs. The following two theorems, usually called theorems of *complementary slackness,* like the duality theorem, show the following relations between the primal and dual programs:

Primal Program	Dual Program
$\min \mathbf{cx}$	$\max \mathbf{yb}$

subject to

$$\mathbf{Ax} \geq \mathbf{b}, \qquad \mathbf{yA} \leq \mathbf{c},$$
$$\mathbf{x} \geq \mathbf{0}. \qquad \mathbf{y} \geq \mathbf{0}.$$

Theorem of Weak Complementary Slackness. Given a pair of primal and dual problems in canonical form, the necessary and sufficient conditions for feasible solutions $\bar{\mathbf{x}}$ and $\bar{\mathbf{y}}$ to be optimum are that they satisfy the relations

$$\bar{\mathbf{y}}(\mathbf{A}\bar{\mathbf{x}} - \mathbf{b}) = 0, \qquad (\mathbf{c} - \bar{\mathbf{y}}\mathbf{A})\bar{\mathbf{x}} = 0.$$

Proof. Since $\bar{\mathbf{x}}$ and $\bar{\mathbf{y}}$ are both feasible, we have

$$\alpha = \bar{\mathbf{y}}(\mathbf{A}\bar{\mathbf{x}} - \mathbf{b}) \geq 0, \qquad \beta = (\mathbf{c} - \bar{\mathbf{y}}\mathbf{A})\bar{\mathbf{x}} \geq 0,$$

as both α and β are sums of products of nonnegative terms. Furthermore, $\alpha + \beta = -\bar{\mathbf{y}}\mathbf{b} + \mathbf{c}\bar{\mathbf{x}} \geq 0$.

From duality, in order for $\bar{\mathbf{x}}$ and $\bar{\mathbf{y}}$ to be optimum, we must have

$$-\bar{\mathbf{y}}\mathbf{b} + \mathbf{c}\bar{\mathbf{x}} = 0.$$

This implies that $\alpha + \beta = 0$, and since $\alpha \geq 0$ and $\beta \geq 0$, this in turn implies that $\alpha = 0$ and $\beta = 0$. This provides the required results.

Corollary of Complementary Slackness. Given a pair of primal and dual programs in canonical form, the necessary and sufficient conditions for feasible solutions $\bar{\mathbf{x}}$ and $\bar{\mathbf{y}}$ to be optimum are that they satisfy the relations (1), (2), (3), and (4).

We rewrite the matrix form $\bar{\mathbf{y}}(\mathbf{A}\bar{\mathbf{x}} - \mathbf{b}) = 0$ as

$$\bar{y}_i(\mathbf{a}_i\bar{\mathbf{x}} - b_i) = 0 \qquad (i = 1, \ldots, m),$$

or

$$\bar{y}_i > 0 \quad \text{implies} \quad \mathbf{a}_i\bar{\mathbf{x}} = b_i, \tag{1}$$

and

$$\mathbf{a}_i\bar{\mathbf{x}} > b_i \quad \text{implies} \quad \bar{y}_i = 0. \tag{2}$$

Similarly for

$$c_j > \bar{\mathbf{y}}\mathbf{a}_j \quad \text{implies} \quad \bar{x}_j = 0, \tag{3}$$

and

$$\bar{x}_j > 0 \quad \text{implies} \quad c_j = \bar{\mathbf{y}}\mathbf{a}_j. \tag{4}$$

The relations (1), (2), (3), and (4) must hold true for every pair of optimum solutions. It may happen that both $\bar{y}_i = 0$ and $\mathbf{a}_i\bar{\mathbf{x}} = b_i$ are true. The following theorem stresses that there will exist at least one pair of optimum salutions for which $\bar{y}_i = 0$ and $a_i\bar{x} = b_i$ cannot happen at the same time.

Theorem of Strong Complementary Slackness. Given a pair of primal and dual programs both with feasible solutions, then there exists at least one pair of optimum solutions $\bar{\mathbf{x}}$ and $\bar{\mathbf{y}}$ satisfying

$$(\mathbf{A}\bar{\mathbf{x}} - \mathbf{b}) + \bar{\mathbf{y}}^T > \mathbf{0}, \tag{5}$$

$$(\mathbf{c} - \bar{\mathbf{y}}\mathbf{A}) + \bar{\mathbf{x}}^T > \mathbf{0}. \tag{6}$$

Proof. If both programs have feasible solutions, we have the case of $t_0 > 0$ in Lemma 3.2. Dividing (4), (5), and (6) of Section 3.1 by t_0 and letting $\bar{\mathbf{x}} = \mathbf{x}_0/t_0$ and $\bar{\mathbf{y}} = \mathbf{y}_0/t_0$, we have

$$(\mathbf{A}\bar{\mathbf{x}} - \mathbf{b}) + \bar{\mathbf{y}}^T > \mathbf{0}, \qquad \text{and} \qquad (\mathbf{c} - \bar{\mathbf{y}}\mathbf{A}) + \bar{\mathbf{x}}^T > \mathbf{0}.$$

In more detail, we have

$$\mathbf{a}_i\bar{\mathbf{x}} - b_i = 0 \quad \text{implies} \quad \bar{y}_i > 0,$$
$$\bar{y}_i = 0 \quad \text{implies} \quad \mathbf{a}_i\bar{\mathbf{x}} - b_i > 0,$$

and also

$$c_j = \bar{\mathbf{y}}\mathbf{a}_j \quad \text{implies} \quad \bar{x}_j > 0,$$
$$\bar{x}_j = 0 \quad \text{implies} \quad c_j > \bar{\mathbf{y}}\mathbf{a}_j.$$

These must be true for *at least one pair* of optimum solutions.

3.3 ORTHOGONALITY OF SOLUTIONS (Tucker [193])

Let us write the canonical primal and dual programs in somewhat different notations. Let the primal program be

$$\begin{aligned}
\max\ x_0 &= \quad a_{01}x_1 + a_{02}x_2 + \cdots + a_{0n}x_n \qquad (x_0 = -z),\\
x_{n+1} &= a_{10} + a_{11}x_1 + \cdots + a_{1n}x_n \geq 0,\\
&\ \ \vdots\\
x_{n+m} &= a_{m0} + a_{m1}x_1 + \cdots + a_{mn}x_n \geq 0,\\
& \qquad x_1 \geq 0,\\
& \qquad \ddots\\
& \qquad\qquad x_n \geq 0.
\end{aligned}$$

Then the dual program is

$$\begin{aligned}
\max\ y_0 &= \quad a_{10}y_{n+1} - a_{20}y_{n+2} - \cdots - a_{m0}y_{n+m} \qquad (y_0 = w),\\
& \qquad y_{n+1} \geq 0,\\
& \qquad \ddots\\
& \qquad\qquad y_{n+m} \geq 0,\\
-y_1 &= a_{01} + a_{11}y_{n+1} + a_{21}y_{n+2} + \cdots + a_{m1}y_{n+m} \leq 0,\\
&\ \ \vdots\\
-y_n &= a_{0n} + a_{1n}y_{n+1} + a_{2n}y_{n+2} + \cdots + a_{mn}y_{n+m} \leq 0.
\end{aligned}$$

This can be put into compact tableau form just like Tableau 3.1, where $a_{0j} = -c_j$, $a_{i0} = -b_i$ (see Tableau 3.2).

Tableau 3.2

	1	x_1	x_2		x_n	
1	0	a_{01}	a_{02}	$\cdots$	a_{0n}	$= x_0$
y_{n+1}	a_{10}	a_{11}	a_{12}	$\cdots$	a_{1n}	$= x_{n+1}$
y_{n+2}	a_{20}	a_{21}			$\cdot$	$= x_{n+2}$
$\vdots$	$\vdots$	$\vdots$			$\vdots$	$\vdots$
y_{n+m}	a_{m0}	a_{m1}		$\cdots$	a_{mn}	$= x_{n+m}$
	$-y_0$	$-y_1$			$-y_n$	

In Tableau 3.2 all x's and y's are restricted to be nonnegative except x_0 and y_0.

Let

$$\begin{aligned}
\hat{\mathbf{A}} &= [a_{ij}]\,(i = 0, 1, \ldots, m;\ j = 0, 1, \ldots, n),\\
\mathbf{y}^{(m+1)} &= (1, y_{n+1}, y_{n+2}, \ldots, y_{n+m}),\\
\mathbf{y}^{(n+1)} &= (y_0, y_1, \ldots, y_n),\\
\mathbf{x}^{(m+1)} &= [x_0, x_{n+1}, \ldots, x_{n+m}],\\
\mathbf{x}^{(n+1)} &= [1, x_1, \ldots, x_n],\\
\mathbf{y}^{(m+n+2)} &= (1, y_{n+1}, \ldots, y_{n+m}, y_0, y_1, \ldots, y_n),\\
\mathbf{x}^{(m+n+2)} &= [x_0, x_{n+1}, \ldots, x_{n+m}, 1, x_1, \ldots, x_n].
\end{aligned}$$

It follows that

$$\hat{\mathbf{A}}\mathbf{x}^{(n+1)} = \mathbf{x}^{(m+1)}, \tag{1}$$

$$\mathbf{y}^{(m+1)}\hat{\mathbf{A}} = -\mathbf{y}^{(n+1)}, \tag{2}$$

and

$$\begin{aligned}
\mathbf{y}^{(m+n+2)}\mathbf{x}^{(m+n+2)} &= \mathbf{y}^{(m+1)}\mathbf{x}^{(m+1)} + \mathbf{y}^{(n+1)}\mathbf{x}^{(n+1)}\\
&= \mathbf{y}^{(m+1)}\hat{\mathbf{A}}\mathbf{x}^{(n+1)} - \mathbf{y}^{(m+1)}\hat{\mathbf{A}}\mathbf{x}^{(n+1)}\\
&= 0.
\end{aligned} \tag{3}$$

Any vector $\mathbf{x}^{(m+n+2)}$ represents a solution to the primal program provided that its components satisfy (1); if, in addition, all its components except x_0 are nonnegative, then it represents a feasible solution. Similarly, $\mathbf{y}^{(m+n+2)}$ represents a solution to the dual program if its components satisfy (2); it represents a feasible solution if all its components except y_0 are nonnegative. The result of (3) says that every vector $\mathbf{x}^{(m+n+2)}$ which represents a solution (feasible or infeasible) to the primal program is orthogonal to every vector $\mathbf{y}^{(m+n+2)}$ which represents a solution (feasible or infeasible) to the dual program. Rewriting (3) in more detail, we have

$$\mathbf{y}^{(m+n+2)}\mathbf{x}^{(m+n+2)} = x_0 + x_{n+1}y_{n+1} + \cdots + x_{n+m}y_{n+m} + y_0 + x_1y_1 + \cdots + x_ny_n$$

$$= x_0 + y_0 + \sum_{k=1}^{m+n} x_k y_k$$

$$= -z + w + \sum_{k=1}^{m+n} x_k y_k$$

$$= 0. \tag{4}$$

If $\mathbf{y}^{(m+n+2)}$ and $\mathbf{x}^{(m+n+2)}$ both represent feasible solutions, then $y_k \geq 0$ ($k = 1, \ldots, m + n$) and $x_k \geq 0$ ($k = 1, \ldots, m + n$). So the sum of products of nonnegative terms $\sum y_k x_k \geq 0$. It follows from (4) that

$$z - w = \sum y_k x_k \geq 0 \qquad \text{or} \qquad z \geq w, \tag{5}$$

which is Lemma 3.1.

If in (5) $y_k > 0$ implies that its corresponding $x_k = 0$, and $x_k > 0$ implies that its corresponding $y_k = 0$, then $\sum y_k x_k = 0$. It follows from (5) that

$$z - w = \sum y_k x_k = 0 \qquad \text{or} \qquad z = w,$$

which is the weak complementary slackness theorem.

Consider the following numerical example:

$$\begin{aligned} \max x_0 &= \quad\ \ - x_1 - x_2 - x_3 \qquad (\min z = x_1 + x_2 + x_3),\\ x_4 &= -1 - x_1 + x_2 + x_3 \geq 0,\\ x_5 &= -7 + x_1 + x_2 + 3x_3 \geq 0. \end{aligned}$$

$$\begin{aligned} \max y_0 &= \quad\ \ + y_4 + 7y_5 \qquad (\max w = y_4 + 7y_5),\\ -y_1 &= -1 - y_4 + y_5 \leq 0,\\ -y_2 &= -1 + y_4 + y_5 \leq 0,\\ -y_3 &= -1 + y_4 + 3y_5 \leq 0. \end{aligned}$$

The following table shows five vectors representing solutions to the two programs:

	$\mathbf{x}^{(1)}$	$\mathbf{x}^{(2)}$	$\mathbf{x}^{(3)}$
x_0	−7	−3	−7/3
x_4	0	0	4/3
x_5	0	0	0
1	1	1	1
x_1	3	1	0
x_2	4	0	0
x_3	0	2	7/3

	$\mathbf{y}^{(1)}$	$\mathbf{y}^{(2)}$
1	1	1
y_4	0	−1/2
y_5	1/3	1/2
y_0	7/3	3
y_1	2/3	0
y_2	2/3	1
y_3	0	0

It can be easily checked that every $\mathbf{x}^{(j)}$ $(j = 1, 2, 3)$ is orthogonal to every $\mathbf{y}^{(i)}$ $(i = 1, 2)$; $\mathbf{x}^{(1)}$, $\mathbf{x}^{(2)}$, and $\mathbf{x}^{(3)}$ are all feasible, while $\mathbf{y}^{(1)}$ is feasible and $\mathbf{y}^{(2)}$ is not feasible; $\mathbf{x}^{(3)}$ and $\mathbf{y}^{(1)}$ constitute a pair of optimum solutions since $z = -x_0 = +7/3 = y_0 = w$.

3.4 GEOMETRIC INTERPRETATION OF DUALITY AND COMPLEMENTARY SLACKNESS (Gomory [83])

Consider the problem of

$$\min z = c_j x_j \qquad (j = 1, \ldots, n)$$

subject to

$$a_{ij} x_j \geq b_i \qquad (i = 1, \ldots, m),$$
$$x_j \geq 0,$$

or

$$\min \mathbf{cx} \tag{1}$$

subject to

$$\mathbf{a}_i^* \mathbf{x} \geq b_i^* \qquad (i = 1, \ldots, m, \ldots, m + n), \tag{2}$$

where the last n row vectors $\mathbf{a}_i^*$ are unit row vectors and the last n components of $\mathbf{b}^*$ are zero.

The usual condition for the minimum or maximum of a function without constraints at an interior point is that the gradient of the function should vanish. If there are also equality conditions to be satisfied, then the condition is that the gradient should point in a direction that is normal to the equality surfaces. More precisely, the gradient should be a linear combination of the normals to these constraint surfaces. In a linear program, each inequality restricts the feasible region into a half-space. For a feasible point $\bar{\mathbf{x}}$ to be an extreme point, the gradient at $\bar{\mathbf{x}}$ should be a nonnegative combina-

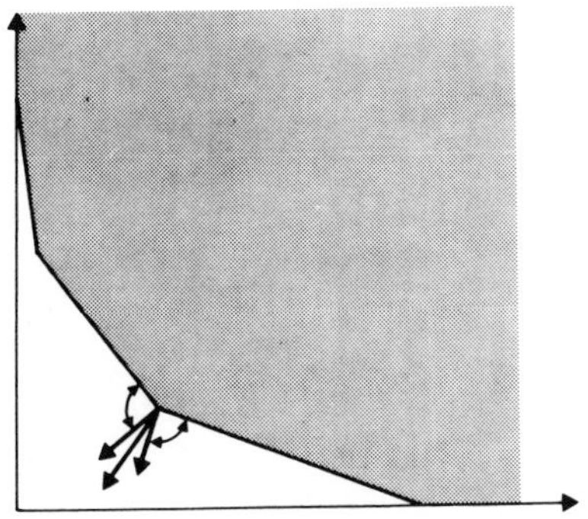

Fig. 3.1

tion of the normals of those (and only those) inequality constraints that are satisfied as equalities at $\bar{\mathbf{x}}$. (See Fig. 3.1.)

Therefore, if $\bar{\mathbf{x}}$ is a feasible point for which the minimum is obtained, then there should be nonnegative combinations $\bar{y}_i$ of the normals $\mathbf{a}_i^*$ which gives $\mathbf{c}$, the gradient of the function $\mathbf{cx}$:

$$\mathbf{c} = \sum_{i=1}^{m+n} \bar{y}_i \mathbf{a}_i^*, \tag{3a}$$

$$\bar{y}_i > 0 \Rightarrow \mathbf{a}_i^* \bar{\mathbf{x}} = b_i^*. \tag{3b}$$

To see that $\bar{\mathbf{x}}$ is indeed the minimum point, take (3a) multiplied by $\bar{\mathbf{x}}$

$$\mathbf{c}\bar{\mathbf{x}} = \sum_{i=1}^{m+n} \bar{y}_i \mathbf{a}_i^* \bar{\mathbf{x}} = \sum_{i=1}^{m+n} \bar{y}_i b_i^*. \tag{4a}$$

For any other y_i satisfying (3a)

$$\mathbf{c}\bar{\mathbf{x}} = \sum_{i=1}^{m+n} y_i \mathbf{a}_i^* \bar{\mathbf{x}} \geq \sum_{i=1}^{m+n} y_i b_i^*. \tag{4b}$$

From (4a) and (4b), $\bar{\mathbf{y}}$ solves the maximum problem

$$\max \mathbf{yb} \tag{5}$$

subject to

$$\mathbf{c} = \sum_{i=1}^{m+n} y_i \mathbf{a}_i^*. \tag{6}$$

Since the last n row vectors $\mathbf{a}_i^*$ are unit vectors, (6) is equivalent to

$$\max w = \mathbf{yb} \tag{7}$$

subject to

$$\sum_{i=1}^{m} y_i \mathbf{a}_i^* \leq \mathbf{c}, \tag{8}$$

$$y_i \geq 0, \tag{9}$$

or

$$\sum_{i=1}^{m} y_i a_{ij} \leq c_j, \tag{8'}$$

$$y_i \geq 0. \tag{9'}$$

In the theorems of complementary slackness we have

$$\bar{y}_i(\mathbf{a}_i \bar{\mathbf{x}} - b_i) = 0.$$

In the weak theorem of complementary slackness we have

$$\bar{y}_i \wedge 0 \quad \text{implies} \quad \mathbf{a}_i \bar{\mathbf{x}} - b_i = 0,$$

and

$$\mathbf{a}_i \bar{\mathbf{x}} - b_i > 0 \quad \text{implies} \quad \bar{y}_i = 0.$$

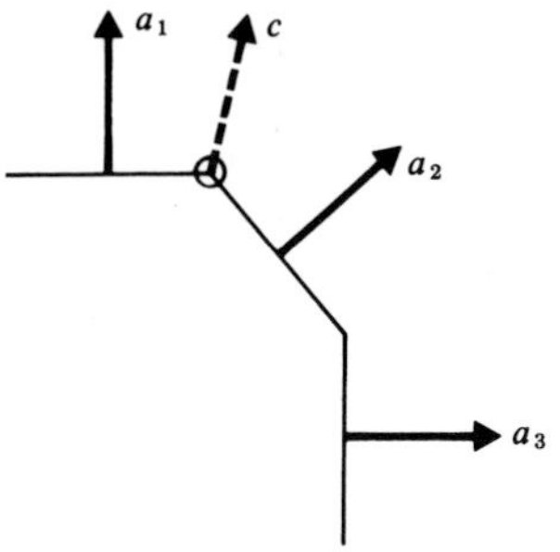

Fig. 3.2

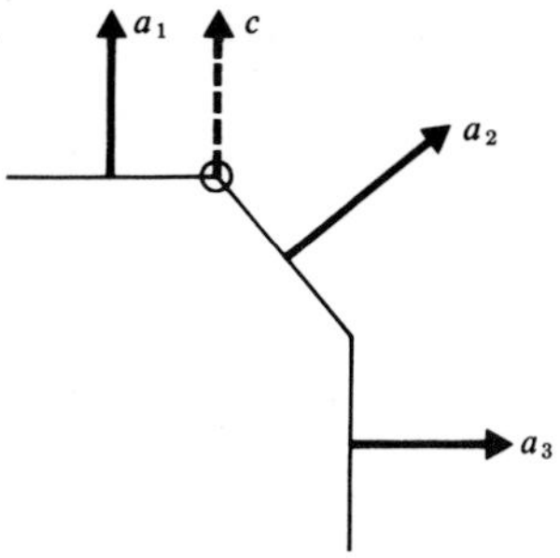

Fig. 3.3

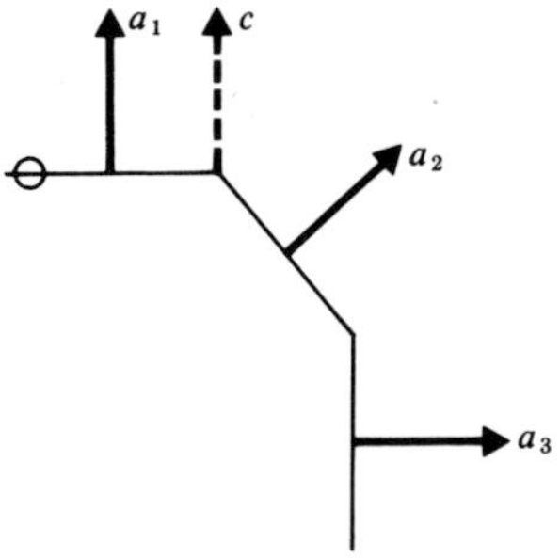

Fig. 3.4

In the strong theorem of complementary slackness we have

$$\bar{y}_i = 0 \qquad \text{implies} \qquad \mathbf{a}_i\bar{\mathbf{x}} - b_i > 0,$$

and

$$\mathbf{a}_i\bar{\mathbf{x}} - b_i = 0 \qquad \text{implies} \qquad \bar{y}_i > 0.$$

Let us interpret these results geometrically. In Fig. 3.2, we have drawn three hyperplanes $\mathbf{a}_i\mathbf{x} - b_i = 0$ $(i = 1, 2, 3)$ together with their normals $\mathbf{a}_1$, $\mathbf{a}_2$, and $\mathbf{a}_3$. If the gradient vector $\mathbf{c}$ is as shown in Fig. 3.2, then it can be expressed as the linear convex combinations of $\mathbf{a}_1$ and $\mathbf{a}_2$, and the circled vertex is the optimum vertex.

Let the coefficients of combination be $\bar{y}_1$, $\bar{y}_2$, and $\bar{y}_3$, respectively. Note that

$$\bar{y}_1 > 0 \Longleftrightarrow \mathbf{a}_1\bar{\mathbf{x}} - b_1 = 0,$$
$$\bar{y}_2 > 0 \Longleftrightarrow \mathbf{a}_2\bar{\mathbf{x}} - b_2 = 0,$$
$$\bar{y}_3 = 0 \Longleftrightarrow \mathbf{a}_3\bar{\mathbf{x}} - b_3 > 0.$$

That is to say, this optimum vertex satisfies both the weak and the strong complementary slackness conditions.

On the other hand, if the gradient vector $\mathbf{c}$ is as shown in Fig. 3.3 (i.e., $\mathbf{c}$ is normal to one of the hyperplanes $\mathbf{a}_1\mathbf{x} - b_1 = 0$), then the circled optimum vertex does not satisfy the strong complementary slackness relation, since both $\bar{y}_2 = 0$ and $\mathbf{a}_2\bar{\mathbf{x}} - b_2 = 0$. However, if the gradient vector $\mathbf{c}$ is as shown in Fig. 3.3, then the circled point in Fig. 3.4 is also an optimum solution which does satisfy both the weak and the strong complementary slackness relations:

$$\begin{aligned} \bar{y}_1 > 0 &\Longleftrightarrow \mathbf{a}_1\bar{\mathbf{x}} - b_1 = 0, \\ \bar{y}_2 = 0 &\Longleftrightarrow \mathbf{a}_2\bar{\mathbf{x}} - b_2 > 0, \\ \bar{y}_3 = 0 &\Longleftrightarrow \mathbf{a}_3\bar{\mathbf{x}} - b_3 > 0. \end{aligned}$$

EXERCISES

1. Consider the linear program

$$\min z = x_1 + x_2 + x_3$$

subject to

$$\begin{array}{rrrl} x_1 & + x_2 & & \geq 5, \\ & & + x_3 & \leq 4, \\ x_1 & & + x_3 & = 3. \end{array}$$

Write its dual program with its dual variables (a) all unrestricted in sign, and (b) all restricted to be nonnegative.

2. Give an example in which both primal and dual programs are infeasible.
3. Show that if the primal program has a degenerate optimum solution, then the optimum solution of the dual program is not unique.
4. If an inequality of a linear program is satisfied as a strict inequality in the optimum solution, then the y_i corresponding to that inequality is zero. If an inequality of a linear program is satisfied as an equality in the optimum solution, then the y_i corresponding to that inequality is positive. Interpret these results in economic terms.

SUGGESTED READING

The proof of duality developed here is based on Theorem 1.4, which in turn s based on the *theorem of separating hyperplane* or its equivalent form. It is possible to use the simplex method as a tool to prove the duality theorem. (See Dantzig [37], p.129.) An alternative proof of the duality theorem using calculus is given in Appendix B.

DUAL SIMPLEX METHOD 4

4.1 DUAL SIMPLEX METHOD (Lemke [141])

From Chapter 3, on duality, we see that for every linear program there is a dual program and that the two are closely related. We have also described, in Chapter 2, a method called the simplex method to solve a linear program. Now we shall describe a method called the *dual simplex method* for solving a linear program. The two methods are tied together by duality theory.

Recall that the simplex method consists of the following steps:

STEP 1. m of the n column vectors of $\mathbf{A}$ are selected to be the basis.

STEP 2. Row eliminations are used to make the cost coefficients associated with the basic vectors zero, and to convert the $m \times m$ matrix of basic columns to an identity matrix. The resulting right-hand side $\bar{\mathbf{b}}$ should have all components nonnegative. (If such a basis is not readily available, artificial vectors are added to form a starting basis. See Section 2.3.)

STEP 3. Select a column $\mathbf{a}_s$ with a cost coefficient $\bar{c}_s < 0$ to enter the basis and determine the column $\mathbf{a}_r$ to leave the basis by a ratio test so that $\bar{b}_i \geq 0$ is maintained.

STEP 4. The element a_{rs} is the pivot element. A row elimination is carried out to perform the change of basis. Return to step 3.

If in step 3 all $\bar{c}_j \geq 0$, then the current solution is the optimum solution. Note that at every step of the simplex method we keep a primal feasible solution, i.e., $\bar{b}_i \geq 0$, and at the end, $\bar{c}_j \geq 0$. The current solution is both primal and dual feasible, hence optimum.

To see that $\bar{c}_j \geq 0$ implies dual feasibility. Recall that if

$$\bar{c}_j = c_j - \boldsymbol{\pi}\mathbf{a}_j \geq 0 \qquad \text{(for all } j\text{)},$$

or

$$\bar{\mathbf{c}} = \mathbf{c} - \boldsymbol{\pi}\mathbf{A} \geq \mathbf{0} \qquad \text{or} \qquad \mathbf{c} \geq \boldsymbol{\pi}\mathbf{A}.$$

Hence $\boldsymbol{\pi}$ is a feasible solution to the dual program.

The dual simplex method starts with a dual feasible solution and maintains its dual feasibility. The dual simplex method is carried out in the same tableau as the primal simplex method. It first decides what variable is to leave the basis and then decides which variable is to enter the basis. The dual simplex method can be described in the following steps:

STEP 0. Start with a tableau in which $a_{0j} \geq 0$ for $j = 1, \ldots, n$.

STEP 1. If $\bar{b}_i = a_{i0} \geq 0$ for all $i = 1, \ldots, m$, then the program is solved. If not, select a $\bar{b}_r < 0$ and the variable x_r becomes a nonbasic variable. Let

$$\max_j \frac{\bar{c}_j}{a_{rj}} = \frac{\bar{c}_s}{a_{rs}} \quad (a_{rj} < 0) \qquad \text{or} \qquad \min_j \left|\frac{\bar{c}_j}{a_{rj}}\right| = \left|\frac{\bar{c}_s}{a_{rs}}\right| \quad (a_{rj} < 0).$$

(We want $\bar{c}_j = c_j - \boldsymbol{\pi}\mathbf{a}_j \geq 0$ to maintain the dual feasibility.)

STEP 2. The element a_{rs} is the pivot element, which is made $+1$ by row elimination. (Every element except a_{rs} in the sth column becomes zero.) *Note that only negative elements are possible pivot elements.*

Steps 1 and 2 are repeated until there is no $b_i < 0$.

We shall do the following example by the dual simplex method:

$$\min z = -1 + 3x_2 \qquad + 5x_4$$

subject to

$$\begin{aligned} x_1 - 3x_2 \qquad\quad - x_4 &= -4, \\ x_2 + x_3 + x_4 &= 3, \end{aligned} \tag{1}$$

$$x_j \geq 0 \qquad (j = 1, 2, 3, 4).$$

Tableau 4.1

↓

	1	x_1	x_2	x_3	x_4
$-z$	1	0	3	0	5
x_1	-4	1	-3*	0	-1
x_3	3	0	1	1	1

The system is already in diagonal form with respect to x_1 and x_3. Putting this in the usual simplex tableau, we have Tableau 4.1. Note that $a_{0j} \geq 0$ $(j = 1, \ldots, 4)$ and hence it is dual feasible. In the left-most column, $a_{10} = -4 < 0$, so it is not primal feasible. Thus we select x_1 to leave the basis. Among coefficients in the first row $a_{12} = -3$ and $a_{14} = -1$ are the potential pivots. Since

$$\left|\frac{a_{02}}{a_{12}}\right| = \left|\frac{3}{-3}\right| < \left|\frac{a_{04}}{a_{14}}\right| = \left|\frac{5}{-1}\right|,$$

Tableau 4.2

	1	x_1	x_2	x_3	x_4
$-z$	-3	1	0	0	4
x_2	4/3	$-1/3$	1	0	1/3
x_3	5/3	1/3	0	1	2/3

we select x_2 to enter the basis. a_{12} is made equal to $+1$ by multiplying the first row by $-(1/3)$. Then row elimination is used to obtain Tableau 4.2.

In Tableau 4.2, $a_{0j} \geq 0$ $(j = 1, 2, 3, 4)$ and $a_{i0} \geq 0$ $(i = 1, 2)$, so that the optimum solution is $x_2 = 4/3$, $x_3 = 5/3$, $x_1 = x_4 = 0$, $z = 3$. The dual of the linear program above is

$$\max w = -1 - 4\pi_1 + 3\pi_2$$

subject to

$$\begin{aligned} \pi_1 \qquad\quad &\leq 0, \\ -3\pi_1 + \pi_2 &\leq 3, \\ \pi_2 &\leq 0, \\ -\pi_1 + \pi_2 &\leq 5, \\ \pi_i &\gtrless 0. \end{aligned} \tag{2}$$

The optimum solution of the dual is $\pi_1 = -1$, $\pi_2 = 0$. (This can be solved by first converting it into equations and introducing $\boldsymbol{\pi} = \mathbf{y} - \mathbf{e}y_0$. Then we can use the simplex method.) From Section 3.3, the top row of the simplex tableau is $\bar{c}_j = c_j - \boldsymbol{\pi}\mathbf{a}_j$, and if $\bar{c}_j \geq 0$, then $\boldsymbol{\pi}$ is a solution to the dual program. Here in the starting Tableau 4.1, $c_1 = 0$, $c_3 = 0$, $\mathbf{a}_1 = [1, 0]$, and $\mathbf{a}_3 = [0, 1]$. Therefore what appears in the top row under x_1 and x_3 is $0 - \boldsymbol{\pi}\mathbf{e}_j = -\pi_j$. In Tableau 4.2, for example, we have $1 = -\pi_1$ and $0 = -\pi_2$; thus the optimum tableau contains *optimum solutions of both primal and dual programs*. This being the case, we have the choice of either solving the original program or its dual and using either the primal or the dual method. In the above example, it is unwise to solve the dual program, since we would need to add four slack variables and it would become a program with seven nonnegative variables and four equations.

4.2 COLUMN TABLEAU (Beale [8])

The simplex method always keeps a primal feasible solution, and the dual simplex method always keeps a dual feasible solution. In the simplex method we decide which vector is to enter the basis first, and in the dual method we decide which vector is to leave the basis first. Both methods use row elimination in the computation, since we have assumed $m < n$, and, from experience, the number of iterations required is usually $2m$ to $3m$.

If $m > n$, i.e., there are more inequalities than there are variables, we should use column elimination. Consider the following problem:

$$\min z = a_{00} + \mathbf{cx}$$

subject to

$$\mathbf{Ax} \geq \mathbf{b}, \qquad \mathbf{x} \geq \mathbf{0}.$$

If we introduce a set of slack variables, $\mathbf{s} = \mathbf{Ax} - \mathbf{b} \geq \mathbf{0}$, the problem, in matrix notation, becomes

$$\begin{bmatrix} z \\ \mathbf{x} \\ \mathbf{s} \end{bmatrix} = \begin{bmatrix} a_{00} & \mathbf{c} \\ \mathbf{0} & \mathbf{I} \\ -\mathbf{b} & \mathbf{A} \end{bmatrix} \begin{bmatrix} 1 \\ \mathbf{x} \end{bmatrix}.$$

If $-\mathbf{b} \geq \mathbf{0}$, then a primal feasible solution is obtained by letting $\mathbf{s} = -\mathbf{b}$ and all the nonbasic variables $\mathbf{x} = \mathbf{0}$. Similarly if $\mathbf{c} \geq \mathbf{0}$, then a dual feasible solution is obtained by letting $\mathbf{s} = -\mathbf{b}$ and $\mathbf{x} = \mathbf{0}$. Note that every variable (basic or nonbasic) is expressed in terms of nonbasic variables. In the starting tableau, $\mathbf{s} = [s_1, \ldots, s_m]$ are the basic variables.

Let us rewrite the program as

$$\begin{aligned}
\min z &= a_{00} + a_{01}x_1 + a_{02}x_2 + \cdots + a_{0n}x_n, \\
x_1 &= x_1 \geq 0, \\
x_2 &= x_2 \geq 0, \\
&\vdots \\
x_n &= x_n \geq 0, \\
x_{n+1} &= a_{n+1,0} + a_{n+1,1}x_1 + \cdots + a_{n+1,n}x_n \geq 0, \\
&\vdots \\
x_{n+m} &= a_{n+m,0} + a_{n+m,1}x_1 + \cdots + a_{n+m,n}x_n \geq 0.
\end{aligned}$$

Tableau 4.3

	1	$x_1,$	$x_2,$	$\ldots,$	x_n
z	a_{00}	$a_{01},$	$a_{02},$	$\ldots,$	a_{0n}
x_1	0	1			
x_2	0		1		
$\vdots$	$\vdots$			$\ddots$	
x_n	0				1
x_{n+1}	$a_{n+1,0}$	$a_{n+1,1}$	$\cdot$	$\cdot$	$a_{n+1,n}$
$\vdots$	$\vdots$				$\vdots$
x_{n+m}	$a_{n+m,0}$	$a_{n+m,1}$	$\cdot$	$\cdot$	$a_{n+m,n}$

In tableau form, we have Tableau 4.3. Assume that we have $a_{0j} \geq 0$ ($j = 1, \ldots, n$) to start with. Then let

$$a_{r0} = \min_i a_{i0} \qquad (i = 1, \ldots, n + m).$$

Let

$$\frac{a_{0s}}{a_{rs}} = \min_j \frac{a_{0j}}{a_{rj}} \qquad (\text{for all } a_{rj} > 0).$$

Then a_{rs} is the pivot element. An appropriate amount of column s is added to the other columns to make $a_{rj} = 0$ ($j = 0, \ldots, n, j \neq s$) and $a_{rs} = 1$.

So far we have the choice of a primal or a dual method and also the choice of row or column elimination. This makes four kinds of procedures. To unify all the tableaux is not easy and is unnecessary. In practice, we want all constraints to be equalities, all variables to be nonnegative, and the conditions $a_{0j} \geq 0$ and $a_{i0} \geq 0$ to imply an optimum tableau. We always start with $a_{i0} \geq 0$ (or $a_{0j} \geq 0$) and maintain this condition throughout the tableaux. The ratio test always selects the a_{rs} as the pivot, subject to the condition that

$$\left|\frac{a_{0s}}{a_{rs}}\right| \qquad \text{or} \qquad \left|\frac{a_{r0}}{a_{rs}}\right|$$

be minimum. We select the pivot column first if the tableau is not dual feasible and do the ratio test among entries of this column with entries of the 0th column. Similarly, we select the pivot row first if the tableau is not primal feasible and do the ratio test among entries of this row with entries of the 0th row. If the ratio test gives a tie, then the lexicographical ordering is used to maintain the primal feasibility or the dual feasibility of the tableau.

Consider the problem of

$$\max w = 2y_1 + 4y_2 + y_3 + y_4$$

subject to

$$\begin{aligned} y_1 + 3y_2 \qquad\quad + y_4 &\leq 4, \\ 2y_1 + y_2 \qquad\qquad\quad &\leq 3, \\ y_2 + 4y_3 + y_4 &\leq 3, \\ y_j \geq 0 \qquad (j = 1, 2, 3, 4)&. \end{aligned} \tag{1}$$

The program (1) in the column tableau is shown in Tableau 4.4. Note that we use $-w$ so that $a_{0j} \leq 0$. This is in accord with the fact that putting all nonbasic variables $y_j = 0$ in $w = 2y_1 + 4y_2 + y_3 + y_4$ does not give the maximum value of w. Here the basic variables are s_1, s_2, and s_3, and the tableau is primal feasible. Note that $a_{i0} \geq 0$ is in accord with the fact that putting all nonbasic variables equal to zero satisfies all the constraints.

Tableau 4.4

	1	y_1	y_2	y_3	y_4
$-w$	0	−2	−4	−1	−1
y_1	0	1	0	0	0
y_2	0	0	1	0	0
y_3	0	0	0	1	0
y_4	0	0	0	0	1
s_1	4	−1	−3*	0	−1
s_2	3	−2	−1	0	0
s_3	3	0	−1	−4	−1

Tableau 4.5

	1	y_1	s_1	y_3	y_4
$-w$	−16/3	−2/3	4/3	−1	1/3
y_1	0	1	0	0	0
y_2	4/3	−1/3	−1/3	0	−1/3
y_3	0	0	0	1	0
y_4	0	0	0	0	1
s_1	0	0	1	0	0
s_2	5/3	−5/3	1/3	0	1/3
s_3	5/3	1/3	1/3	−4*	−2/3

Successive tableaux are shown in Tableaux 4.5, 4.6, and 4.7, where the pivot in each tableau is indicated by an "*". Note that the labels to the left of the tableau do not change. The current nonbasic variables are written at the top of each tableau.

As a check of $w = \boldsymbol{\pi}\mathbf{b}$, we have $13/2 = 1(2) + 1(4) + \frac{1}{2}(1) + 0(1)$. In matrix notation,

$$\begin{bmatrix} z \\ \mathbf{x} \\ \mathbf{s} \end{bmatrix} = \begin{bmatrix} a_{00} & \mathbf{c} \\ \mathbf{0} & \mathbf{I} \\ -\mathbf{b} & \mathbf{A} \end{bmatrix} \begin{bmatrix} 1 \\ \\ \mathbf{x} \end{bmatrix} = [\mathbf{A}^*] \begin{bmatrix} 1 \\ \\ \mathbf{x} \end{bmatrix},$$

where $\mathbf{s}$ are the current basic variables and $\mathbf{x}$ are the nonbasic variables. Column elimination is equivalent to choosing a new set of nonbasic variables.

We have

$$\begin{bmatrix} 1 \\ \\ \mathbf{x}' \end{bmatrix} = \mathbf{P} \begin{bmatrix} 1 \\ \\ \mathbf{x} \end{bmatrix}$$

Tableau 4.6

	1	y_1	s_1	s_3	y_4
$-w$	$-23/4$	$-3/4$	$5/4$	$1/4$	$1/2$
y_1	0	1	0	0	0
y_2	$4/3$	$-1/3$	$-1/3$	0	$-1/3$
y_3	$5/12$	$1/12$	$1/12$	$-1/4$	$-1/6$
y_4	0	0	0	0	1
s_1	0	0	1	0	0
s_2	$5/3$	$-5/3$*	$1/3$	0	$1/3$
s_3	0	0	0	1	0

Tableau 4.7

	1	s_2	s_1	s_3	y_4
$-w$	$-13/2$	$9/20$	$11/10$	$1/4$	$7/20$
y_1	1	$-3/5$	$1/5$	0	$1/5$
y_2	1	$1/5$	$-2/5$	0	$-2/5$
y_3	$1/2$	$-1/20$	$1/10$	$-1/4$	$-3/20$
y_4	0	0	0	0	1
s_1	0	0	1	0	0
s_2	0	1	0	0	0
s_3	0	0	0	1	0

where $\mathbf{x}'$ are the new nonbasic variables and

$$\mathbf{P} = \begin{bmatrix} 1 \\ & 1 \\ & & 1 \\ & & & 1 \\ -(a_{r0}/a_{rs}) & \cdots & & & +(1/a_{rs}) & \cdots & & & & -(a_{rn}/a_{rs}) \\ & & & & & 1 \\ & & & & & & 1 \\ & & & & & & & 1 \\ & & & & & & & & 1 \\ & & & & & & & & & 1 \end{bmatrix}.$$

In other words $\mathbf{A}^*$ is multiplied on the right by $\mathbf{P}$.

When we have a linear program with equality constraints and nonnegative variables, it is natural to use the row tableau if the number of constraints is less than the number of variables and to use the column tableau otherwise. Although it is possible to replace a variable unrestricted in sign by two nonnegative variables, it increases the total number of variables.* Thus if the original linear program has variables unrestricted in sign, it is generally advantageous to solve the dual program instead. Before we form the dual program, we want to get rid of the equality constraints of the original program since they will give unrestricted variables in the dual. The following techniques are sometimes used to transform a linear program with equality constraints to an equivalent program with inequality constraints before forming its dual program. The transformed primal program and the original program are equivalent in the sense that the optimum values of their objective functions are equal and it is possible to retrieve from the transformed program the values of variables of the original program.

The following are four standard transformations:

1. Replace an equation containing a nonnegative variable x_i by an inequality. Suppose we have an equation $-2x_1 + 4x_2 - 2x_3 = 2$ and $x_1 \geq 0$. Then we can replace the equation by $4x_2 - 2x_3 \geq 2$.
2. Multiply an equation r by a nonzero constant λ. This does not change the primal program, but the dual variable π_r' associated with the new equation is related to the dual variable π_r associated with the old equation by $\pi_r' = \pi_r/\lambda$.
3. Add one equation to another constraint (inequality or equality). For example, we may add the first equation to the second equation to get a new second equation. Then the associated dual variables are related by $\pi_1' = \pi_1 - \pi_2, \pi_2' = \pi_2$.
4. Add one equation $a_{rj}x_j - b_r = 0$ to the objective function. This does not change the value of the objective function, but the dual variable π_r' is related to the old dual variable by $\pi_r' = \pi_r + 1$.

With the four transformations mentioned above, we can let a nonnegative variable x_r appear only in the rth equation and not in the objective function or any other constraints. Then we can convert the rth equation into an inequality. Take the following linear program for example:

$$\min z = x_1 + x_2 + x_3 + x_4$$

subject to

$$\begin{aligned} x_1 - x_2 + 2x_3 - x_4 &= 2, \\ -x_1 + 2x_2 - x_3 &= 1, \\ x_j \geq 0 \quad (j = 1, \ldots, 4).& \end{aligned}$$

* See Section 1.2.

This is already in a form suitable for the simplex algorithm. However we shall use it to illustrate the technique of reducing the number of equalities of the primal program. We shall write the successive primal programs together with their associated changes in the dual variables.

1. Adding the first equation to the objective function, we have

$$\min z = 2x_1 \qquad + 3x_3 - 2$$

subject to

$$\begin{aligned} x_1 - x_2 + 2x_3 - x_4 &= 2, & \pi_1' &= \pi_1 + 1, \\ -x_1 + 2x_2 - x_3 \qquad &= 1, & \pi_2' &= \pi_2, \\ x_j \geq 0 \quad (j = 1, \ldots, 4). \end{aligned}$$

2. Adding the second equation to the first equation, we have

$$\min z = 2x_1 \qquad + 3x_3 - 2$$

subject to

$$\begin{aligned} x_2 + x_3 - x_4 &= 3, & \pi_1'' &= \pi_1', \\ -x_1 + 2x_2 - x_3 \qquad &= 1 & \pi_2'' &= \pi_2' - \pi_1'. \end{aligned}$$

3. Multiplying the second equation by 2, we have

$$\min z = 2x_1 \qquad + 3x_3 - 2$$

subject to

$$\begin{aligned} x_2 + x_3 - x_4 &= 3, & \pi_1''' &= \pi_1'', \\ -2x_1 + 4x_2 - 2x_3 \qquad &= 2, & \pi_2''' &= \pi_2''/2. \end{aligned}$$

4. Adding the second equation to the objective function, we have

$$\min z = 4x_2 + x_3 - 4$$

subject to

$$\begin{aligned} x_2 + x_3 - x_4 &= 3, & \pi_1'''' &= \pi_1''', \\ -2x_1 + 4x_2 - 2x_3 \qquad &= 2, & \pi_2'''' &= \pi_2''' + 1. \end{aligned}$$

5. Considering x_4 as the slack variable in the first equation and x_1 as the slack variable of the second equation, we have

$$\min z = 4x_2 + x_3 - 4$$

subject to

$$\begin{aligned} x_2 + x_3 &\geq 3, \\ 4x_2 - 2x_3 &\geq 2, \\ x_2, x_3 &\geq 0. \end{aligned}$$

The dual program is then

$$\max\ 3\pi_1'''' + 2\pi_2'''' - 4$$

subject to

$$\pi_1'''' + 4\pi_2'''' \leq 4,$$
$$\pi_1'''' - 2\pi_2'''' \leq 1,$$
$$\pi_1'''', \pi_2'''' \leq 0.$$

The optimum solution of the dual program is $\pi_1'''' = 2$ and $\pi_2'''' = 1/2$, which gives the optimum solution to the primal $x_2 = 4/3$ and $x_3 = 5/3$. Then this in turn gives $x_1 = 0$ and $x_4 = 0$ for the original program. If the reader has solved the original dual program of

$$\max\ 2\pi_1 + \pi_2$$

subject to

$$\pi_1 - \pi_2 \leq 1,$$
$$-\pi_1 + 2\pi_2 \leq 1,$$
$$2\pi_1 - \pi_2 \leq 1,$$
$$-\pi_1 \leq 1,$$
$$\pi_1, \pi_2 \text{ unrestricted},$$

then $\pi_1 = 1$ and $\pi_2 = 1$. This checks with the transformal dual program of $\pi_1'''' = \pi_1 + 1$ and $\pi_2'''' = (\pi_2 - \pi_1)/2 + 1/2$.

4.3 GEOMETRIC INTERPRETATION (Lemke [141])

In this section we shall give geometric interpretations of both the primal and dual simplex methods.

Assume that we use the primal simplex method to solve the linear program

$$\min z = \mathbf{cx}$$

subject to

$$\sum_{j=1}^{n} \mathbf{a}_j x_j = \mathbf{b} \qquad (\mathbf{b} = [b_1, b_2, \ldots, b_m],\ n \geq m), \tag{1}$$
$$x_j \geq 0 \qquad (j = 1, \ldots, n),$$

and the dual simplex method to solve the dual of (1), namely

$$\max w = \boldsymbol{\pi}\mathbf{b}$$

subject to

$$\boldsymbol{\pi}\mathbf{a}_j \leq c_j \qquad (j = 1, \ldots, n), \tag{2}$$
$$\boldsymbol{\pi} \gtreqless \mathbf{0}.$$

Consider the $\boldsymbol{\pi}$-space which is m-dimensional. There are n hyperplanes defined by $\boldsymbol{\pi}\mathbf{a}_j = c_j$ $(j = 1, \ldots, n)$. The intersection of the n half-spaces

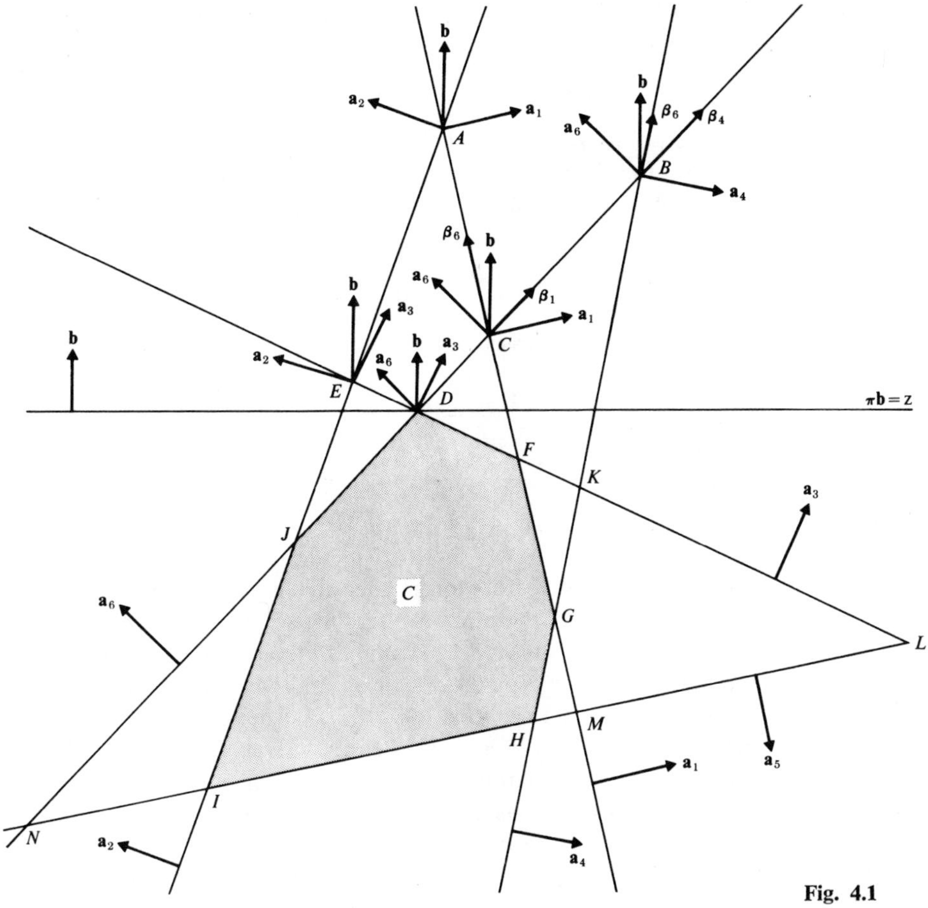

Fig. 4.1

defined by $\boldsymbol{\pi}\mathbf{a}_j \leq c_j$ is a convex set which gives the feasible solution $\boldsymbol{\pi}$ to (2). In Fig. 4.1, we draw the special case where $m = 2$ and $n = 6$.

A hyperplane in Fig. 4.1 is then represented by a line. The normal to the hyperplane $\boldsymbol{\pi}\mathbf{a}_j = c_j$ is the vector $\mathbf{a}_j$. The convex set of feasible $\boldsymbol{\pi}$ is indicated by the shaded area.

Assume that $\mathbf{B} = [\mathbf{a}_1^B, \mathbf{a}_2^B, \ldots, \mathbf{a}_m^B]$ are a set of linearly independent vectors. Then there exists a solution $\boldsymbol{\pi}^0$ satisfying

$$\boldsymbol{\pi}^0\mathbf{a}_j^B = c_j^B \qquad (j = 1, \ldots, m),$$

or

$$\boldsymbol{\pi}^0 = \mathbf{c}^B\mathbf{B}^{-1}.$$

Such a point $\boldsymbol{\pi}^0$ is called a critical point which represents the intersection of m hyperplanes. Among the n vectors $\mathbf{a}_1, \ldots, \mathbf{a}_n$, we may get $n!/(n-m)!m!$

critical points. In Fig. 4.1, we show 14 such critical points $A, B, \ldots, N$. A critical point is an extreme point of the convex set if

$$\boldsymbol{\pi}^0 \mathbf{a}_j \leq c_j \qquad (j = 1, \ldots, n).$$

We have extreme points D, F, G, H, I, and J in Fig. 4.1.

For each set of m linearly independent vectors $\mathbf{B} = [\mathbf{a}_1, \ldots, \mathbf{a}_m]$ we can find another set of m vectors $\boldsymbol{\beta}_i$ ($\boldsymbol{\beta}_i$ are the row vectors of $\mathbf{B}^{-1}$) such that

$$\boldsymbol{\beta}_i \mathbf{a}_j = \delta_{ij}, \qquad \delta_{ij} = \begin{cases} 1 & \text{if } i = j, \\ 0 & \text{if } i \neq j. \end{cases} \tag{3}$$

Since the vector $\mathbf{b}$ can be expressed as

$$\mathbf{b} = \sum_{j=1}^{m} \lambda_j \mathbf{a}_j,$$

using (3), we have

$$\mathbf{b} = \sum_{j=1}^{m} (\boldsymbol{\beta}_j \mathbf{b}) \mathbf{a}_j. \tag{4}$$

Thus a set of m independent vectors forms a feasible basis for (1) if $\boldsymbol{\beta}_j \mathbf{b} \geq 0$ for $j = 1, \ldots, m$. In Fig. 4.1 there are five feasible solutions corresponding to (1) represented by the points A, B, C, D, and E. A vector $\boldsymbol{\beta}_i$ is orthogonal to all column vectors of $\mathbf{B}$ except the vector $\mathbf{a}_i$, and $\boldsymbol{\beta}_i \mathbf{b}$ is the scalar product of $\boldsymbol{\beta}_i$ and $\mathbf{b}$, which is nonnegative for a feasible point of (1).

The objective function of (2), $w = \boldsymbol{\pi}\mathbf{b}$, defines a series of parallel hyperplanes $\boldsymbol{\pi}\mathbf{b} = k$, where k is a parameter. The normal of such hyperplanes is the vector $\mathbf{b}$, which is drawn as a vertical vector in Fig. 4.1. This means that the larger the value of the objective function associated with a point, the higher is the position of the point in Fig. 4.1. According to the theory of duality, min $z = \bar{z} =$ max $w = \bar{w}$. Therefore the hyperplane with $\boldsymbol{\pi}\mathbf{b} = \bar{w} = \bar{z}$ divides the whole space into two parts, where all feasible solutions of (1) are in one part and all feasible solutions of (2) are in the other part. The critical point on the hyperplane which is a feasible solution to both (1) and (2) is then the optimum solution to both programs. This is the point D in Fig. 4.1.

Two critical points are adjacent if they have $m - 1$ hyperplanes in common. Thus if the starting feasible solution of (2) is the point I in Fig. 4.1, we would move to J and then to D. If the starting feasible solution is H, we would move to G, then to F, and then to D.

In the primal simplex method a pivot operation indicates an exchange of a basic vector and a nonbasic vector. If the point A is the starting feasible point of (1), then the primal simplex method would move to either the point E or the point C, depending on which of the two lines AE and AC is more vertical. If the point E is reached, then the next point would be

D. If the point C is reached, then the next point would be D also. If the point B is the starting feasible point of (1), then the next point reached may be D (may be C), since C and D share the same hyperplane with the normal vector $\mathbf{a}_6$.

EXERCISES

1. Consider the problem

$$\min z = -2x_4 - 3x_5$$

subject to

$$\begin{aligned} x_1 \quad\quad - x_3 + \; x_4 + 3x_5 &= 3, \\ x_2 + x_3 + \tfrac{1}{2}x_4 + 2x_5 &= 2. \end{aligned}$$

Use x_1 and x_2 as the starting basic variables and always select the lexicographically smallest column to enter the basis. Check your computation at each step by $z = \boldsymbol{\pi}\mathbf{b}$.

2. Consider the problem

$$\min \left\{\mathbf{c}\,\mathbf{x} \,\middle|\, \begin{matrix}\mathbf{A}\mathbf{x} = \mathbf{b} \\ \mathbf{x} \geq \mathbf{0}\end{matrix}\right\} \qquad (\mathbf{A} \text{ is } m \times n)$$

and its dual. Suppose $\mathbf{B}$ is an optimal basis matrix. Show that $\boldsymbol{\pi} = \mathbf{c}_B\mathbf{B}^{-1}$ is an optimal solution to the dual problem, where the vector $\mathbf{c}_B$ consists of the components of $\mathbf{c}$ which correspond to the optimal basic variables. You may use the fact that $\mathbf{c}\mathbf{x} \geq \boldsymbol{\pi}\mathbf{b}$ holds for any $\mathbf{x}$ and $\boldsymbol{\pi}$ which are feasible solutions to the primal and dual problem, respectively.

REVISED SIMPLEX METHOD 5

5.1 INTRODUCTION (See Dantzig and Orchard-Hayes [43])

In the simplex method all entries of the simplex tableau are changed from one iteration to the next iteration. Assume that we have a constraint matrix $\mathbf{A}$ of $m \times n$ and the optimum tableau is obtained, say, in the tth iteration. Then, effectively, we have calculated $t(m + 1)(n + 1)$ numbers. During the calculation, once a tableau is obtained, we have all the information necessary to carry on the next iteration; all the preceding tableaux including the starting tableau can be ignored. Suppose that we keep the starting tableau and we wish to generate all the entries in a particular tableau. What is the information needed? Let us say that we are interested in all the entries in the 29th tableau. Then all we need is $\mathbf{B}^{-1}$ associated with the 29th tableau and the names of the current basic variables. All other entries of the 29th tableau can be generated from the entries of the starting tableau and the current inverse $\mathbf{B}^{-1}$ of the 29th tableau. Note that $\boldsymbol{\pi} = \mathbf{c}_B\mathbf{B}^{-1}$, which means that the current $\boldsymbol{\pi}$ is obtained by multiplying $\mathbf{c}_B$ of the starting tableau by the current inverse $\mathbf{B}^{-1}$. (Note that the current basic variables tell us which are the $\mathbf{c}_B$.) The $\bar{\mathbf{b}}$ is given by $\mathbf{B}^{-1}\mathbf{b}$, where $\mathbf{b}$ is from the starting tableau and $\mathbf{B}^{-1}$ is the current inverse; any column $\bar{\mathbf{a}}_j$ is given by $\bar{\mathbf{a}}_j = \mathbf{B}^{-1}\mathbf{a}_j$, where $\mathbf{a}_j$ is from the starting tableau. Also the relative cost is given by $\bar{c}_j = c_j - \boldsymbol{\pi}\mathbf{a}_j$, where c_j and $\mathbf{a}_j$ are from the starting tableau and $\boldsymbol{\pi}$ is the current shadow price. Therefore, if we have $\mathbf{B}^{-1}$ and the labels to the left of every tableau, then we can generate all the remaining entries in the tableau.

Suppose that we have the starting tableau and the $\mathbf{B}^{-1}$ of the 29th tableau. What are the additional entries in the 29th tableau that have to be generated in order to get the $\mathbf{B}^{-1}$ of the 30th tableau? The additional entries are those entries of the nonbasic column in the 29th tableau which is to enter the basis and $\bar{\mathbf{b}}$ of the 29th tableau. Now, a vector $\bar{\mathbf{a}}_j$ is a candidate to enter the basis if $\bar{c}_j < 0$. Thus, we need only to calculate some $\bar{c}_j$ of a given tableau, choose one with $\bar{c}_s < 0$, and then calculate $\bar{\mathbf{a}}_s = \mathbf{B}^{-1}\mathbf{a}_s$ and $\bar{\mathbf{b}} = \mathbf{B}^{-1}\mathbf{b}$. These will determine $\mathbf{B}^{-1}$ of the next tableau. These facts led to the discovery of the *revised simplex method*. The revised simplex method keeps the starting tableau and in each iteration generates only those data which are needed for making decisions, namely, the relative cost row $\bar{\mathbf{c}}$, the vector entering the basis, and the current $\bar{\mathbf{b}}$. These data together with the current inverse $\mathbf{B}^{-1}$ will determine the $\mathbf{B}^{-1}$ of the next tableau. When we have $\mathbf{B}^{-1}$, $\bar{\mathbf{a}}_j$, and $\bar{\mathbf{b}}$ [these form a tableau of size $(m + 1) \times (m + 2)$], we can use the ratio test to determine the pivot and then do a pivot step to get the $\mathbf{B}^{-1}$ of the next tableau. Thus, in each iteration, we calculate at most $n - m$ relative costs $\bar{c}_j$, the column $\bar{\mathbf{b}}$, and the vector $\bar{\mathbf{a}}_s$. Since the starting tableau contains an $m \times m$ identity matrix with all the m relative costs zero, the entries that later appear in these positions in any given tableau will be the $\mathbf{B}^{-1}$ and $-\boldsymbol{\pi}$ of that tableau (see Section 2.4). Knowing $\boldsymbol{\pi}$ and $\mathbf{B}^{-1}$ of a given tableau, we can generate $\bar{c}_j$ of that tableau by $\bar{c}_j = c_j - \boldsymbol{\pi}\mathbf{a}_j$. If a relative cost $\bar{c}_j$ is non-negative, we are not interested in the components of that $\bar{\mathbf{a}}_j$. Choosing any $\bar{c}_j < 0$, we can generate the vector associated with the $\bar{c}_j$ to enter the basis. Note that

$$\begin{bmatrix} 1 & -\boldsymbol{\pi} \\ \mathbf{0} & \mathbf{B}^{-1} \end{bmatrix} \begin{bmatrix} c_j \\ \mathbf{a}_j \end{bmatrix} = \begin{bmatrix} c_j - \boldsymbol{\pi}\mathbf{a}_j \\ \mathbf{B}^{-1}\mathbf{a}_j \end{bmatrix} = \begin{bmatrix} \bar{c}_j \\ \bar{\mathbf{a}}_j \end{bmatrix},$$

and

$$\begin{bmatrix} 1 & -\boldsymbol{\pi} \\ \mathbf{0} & \mathbf{B}^{-1} \end{bmatrix} \begin{bmatrix} 0 \\ \mathbf{b} \end{bmatrix} = \begin{bmatrix} -\boldsymbol{\pi}\mathbf{b} \\ \mathbf{B}^{-1}\mathbf{b} \end{bmatrix} = \begin{bmatrix} -\bar{z} \\ \bar{\mathbf{b}} \end{bmatrix}.$$

In the starting tableau the identity is its own inverse and $\boldsymbol{\pi}$ of the starting tableau is zero, since $\boldsymbol{\pi} = \mathbf{c}_B\mathbf{B}^{-1}$ and $\mathbf{c}_B = \mathbf{0}$ in the starting tableau. Thus, we can adjoin a column of $[1, 0, \ldots, 0]$ to the identity matrix in the starting tableau, so that we have

$$\begin{bmatrix} 1 & \mathbf{0} \\ \mathbf{0} & \mathbf{I} \end{bmatrix} = \begin{bmatrix} 1 & -\boldsymbol{\pi} \\ \mathbf{0} & \mathbf{B}^{-1} \end{bmatrix}.$$

That is to say, the starting tableau can be treated just as any other tableau. We shall first do a numerical example using the usual simplex method and then do the *same* example by the revised simplex method.

Consider the following numerical example:

$$\max x_0$$

subject to

$$\begin{aligned} x_0 \qquad\qquad + 2x_3 - 2x_4 - x_5 &= 0, \\ x_1 \qquad - 2x_3 + x_4 + x_5 &= 4, \\ x_2 + 3x_3 - x_4 + 2x_5 &= 2. \end{aligned}$$

As the starting tableau we have Tableau 5.1. Note that if we consider the identity matrix as $\mathbf{B}^*$, then its inverse is also the identity matrix. We shall first do the numerical example by the original simplex method, as shown in Tableaux 5.2, 5.3, and 5.4. (Note the slight changes in the form of the tableaux.)

Tableau 5.1

	x_0	x_1	x_2	x_3	x_4	x_5	Constant
Cost row x_0	1			2	−2	−1	0
Basic x_1		1		−2	1	1	4
Variables x_2			1	3	−1	2	2

Tableau 5.2

	x_0	x_1	x_2	x_3	x_4	x_5	Constant
Cost row x_0	1			2	−2	−1	0
x_1		1		−2	1*	1	4
x_2			1	3	−1	2	2

Tableau 5.3

	x_0	x_1	x_2	x_3	x_4	x_5	Constant
Cost row x_0	1	2	0	−2	0	1	8
x_4	0	1	0	−2	1	1	4
x_2	0	1	1	1*	0	3	6

Tableau 5.4

	x_0	x_1	x_2	x_3	x_4	x_5	Constant	
Cost row x_0	1	4	2	0	0	7	20	$x_0 = 20$
x_4	0	3	2	0	1	7	16	$x_4 = 16$
x_3	0	1	1	1	0	3	6	$x_3 = 6$

As a check we have $\mathbf{B}^* \cdot \mathbf{B}^{*-1} = \mathbf{I}$:

$$\begin{bmatrix} 1 & -2 & 2 \\ 0 & 1 & -2 \\ 0 & -1 & 3 \end{bmatrix} \begin{bmatrix} 1 & 4 & 2 \\ 0 & 3 & 2 \\ 0 & 1 & 1 \end{bmatrix} = \begin{bmatrix} 1 & 0 & 0 \\ 0 & 1 & 0 \\ 0 & 0 & 1 \end{bmatrix}.$$

To show the general structure of the revised simplex algorithm, we shall rewrite only part of the starting tableau as if it were in the kth iteration and show how the rest of the tableaux can be generated from the present data (Tableau 5.5). and the starting tableau (The starting tableau 5.1 must be preserved at all times.)

Tableau 5.5

	x_0	x_1	x_2	x_3	x_4	x_5	Constant
Cost row x_0	1						
x_1		1					
x_2			1				

we have

$$\mathbf{B}^* = \begin{bmatrix} 1 & 0 & 0 \\ 0 & 1 & 0 \\ 0 & 0 & 1 \end{bmatrix}$$

$$\begin{aligned} \bar{c}_3 &= c_3 - \boldsymbol{\pi}\mathbf{a}_3 = \boldsymbol{\beta}_0\,[c_3, \mathbf{a}_3] = (1, 0, 0)\,[2, -2, 3] = 2, \\ \bar{c}_4 &= c_4 - \boldsymbol{\pi}\mathbf{a}_4 = (1, 0, 0)\,[-2, 1, -1] = -2, \\ \bar{c}_5 &= c_5 - \boldsymbol{\pi}\mathbf{a}_5 = (1, 0, 0)\,[-1, 1, 2] = -1. \end{aligned}$$

Therefore, we want to bring in $\bar{\mathbf{a}}_4^*$, where

$$\bar{\mathbf{a}}_4^* = \mathbf{B}^{*-1}\,\mathbf{a}_4^* = \begin{bmatrix} 1 & 0 & 0 \\ 0 & 1 & 0 \\ 0 & 0 & 1 \end{bmatrix} \begin{bmatrix} -2 \\ 1 \\ -1 \end{bmatrix} = \begin{bmatrix} -2 \\ 1 \\ -1 \end{bmatrix},$$

$$\bar{\mathbf{b}}^* = \mathbf{B}^{*-1}\,\mathbf{b}^* = \begin{bmatrix} 1 & 0 & 0 \\ 0 & 1 & 0 \\ 0 & 0 & 1 \end{bmatrix} \begin{bmatrix} 0 \\ 4 \\ 2 \end{bmatrix} = \begin{bmatrix} 0 \\ 4 \\ 2 \end{bmatrix}.$$

Since in $\bar{\mathbf{a}}_4^*$, $\bar{a}_{14} = 1$ is the only positive coefficient, we shall drop $\mathbf{a}_1$ from the basis. Using row elimination with $\bar{a}_{14}$ as the pivot is equivalent to multiplying on the left by

$$\begin{bmatrix} 1 & -(-2/1) & 0 \\ 0 & +(\ 1/1) & 0 \\ 0 & -(-1/1) & 1 \end{bmatrix} = \begin{bmatrix} 1 & 2 & 0 \\ 0 & 1 & 0 \\ 0 & 1 & 1 \end{bmatrix},$$

$$\begin{bmatrix} 1 & 2 & 0 \\ 0 & 1 & 0 \\ 0 & 1 & 1 \end{bmatrix} \left[\begin{array}{ccc|c} 1 & 0 & 0 & 0 \\ 0 & 1 & 0 & 4 \\ 0 & 0 & 1 & 2 \end{array}\right] = \left[\begin{array}{ccc|c} 1 & 2 & 0 & 8 \\ 0 & 1 & 0 & 4 \\ 0 & 1 & 1 & 6 \end{array}\right] = [\mathbf{B}^{*-1} \mid \mathbf{b}^*].$$

Therefore, the new tableau is Tableau 5.6. Now the inverse of the new basis is

$$\begin{bmatrix} 1 & 2 & 0 \\ 0 & 1 & 0 \\ 0 & 1 & 1 \end{bmatrix},$$

$$\begin{aligned} \bar{c}_1 &= (1, 2, 0)\,[0, 1, 0] = 2, \\ \bar{c}_3 &= (1, 2, 0)\,[2, -2, 3] = -2, \\ \bar{c}_5 &= (1, 2, 0)\,[-1, 1, 2] = 1. \end{aligned}$$

As a check

$$\bar{c}_2 = (1, 2, 0)\,[0, 0, 1] = 0,$$
$$\bar{c}_4 = (1, 2, 0)\,[-2, 1, -1] = 0.$$

Tableau 5.6

	x_0	x_1	x_2	x_3	x_4	x_5	Constant
Cost row	1	2	0				8
x_4	0	1	0				4
x_2	0	1	1				6

Therefore, we should bring $\mathbf{a}_3$ into the basis:

$$\bar{\mathbf{a}}_3^* = \begin{bmatrix} 1 & 2 & 0 \\ 0 & 1 & 0 \\ 0 & 1 & 1 \end{bmatrix} \begin{bmatrix} 2 \\ -2 \\ 3 \end{bmatrix} = \begin{bmatrix} -2 \\ -2 \\ 1 \end{bmatrix}.$$

Since $\bar{a}_{23} = 1$ is the only positive element, $\mathbf{a}_2$ should be dropped. Using row elimination with $\bar{a}_{23}$ as pivot is equivalent to multiplying the matrix on the left by

$$\begin{bmatrix} 1 & 0 & -(-2/1) \\ 0 & 1 & -(-2/1) \\ 0 & 0 & (\;\;1/1) \end{bmatrix} = \begin{bmatrix} 1 & 0 & 2 \\ 0 & 1 & 2 \\ 0 & 0 & 1 \end{bmatrix},$$

$$\begin{bmatrix} 1 & 0 & 2 \\ 0 & 1 & 2 \\ 0 & 0 & 1 \end{bmatrix} \left[\begin{array}{ccc|c} 1 & 2 & 0 & 8 \\ 0 & 1 & 0 & 4 \\ 0 & 1 & 1 & 6 \end{array}\right] = \left[\begin{array}{ccc|c} 1 & 4 & 2 & 20 \\ 0 & 3 & 2 & 16 \\ 0 & 1 & 1 & 6 \end{array}\right],$$

$$\bar{c}_1 = (1, 4, 2)\,[0, 1, 0] = 4,$$
$$\bar{c}_2 = (1, 4, 2)\,[0, 0, 1] = 2,$$
$$\bar{c}_5 = (1, 4, 2)\,[-1, 1, 2] = 7.$$

As a check

$$\bar{c}_3 = (1, 4, 2)\,[2, -2, 3] = 0,$$
$$\bar{c}_4 = (1, 4, 2)\,[-2, 1, -1] = 0.$$

We have as an optimum solution $x_0 = 20$, $x_4 = 16$, $x_3 = 6$. Note that in the revised simplex method we need not calculate all $\bar{c}_j$. Once a $\bar{c}_j < 0$ is found, we can immediately bring the column into the basis.

5.2 VARIATION OF THE DATA

Since the data in a linear program may not always be accurate, it is important to know how the data will affect the solution. Let the original linear program be

$$\min z = \mathbf{c}\mathbf{x} = \mathbf{c}_B\mathbf{x}_B + \mathbf{c}_N\mathbf{x}_N$$

subject to

$$\mathbf{B}\mathbf{x}_B + \mathbf{N}\mathbf{x}_N = \mathbf{b}, \qquad \mathbf{x}_B, \mathbf{x}_N \geq \mathbf{0}. \tag{1}$$

Consider $\mathbf{x}_B$ as the basic variables; we can transform (1) into the equivalent linear program (2)

$$\min z = \mathbf{c}_B\mathbf{B}^{-1}\mathbf{b} + (\mathbf{c}_N - \mathbf{c}_B\mathbf{B}^{-1}\mathbf{N})\,\mathbf{x}_N$$

subject to

$$\mathbf{x}_B + \mathbf{B}^{-1}\mathbf{N}\mathbf{x}_N = \mathbf{B}^{-1}\mathbf{b}, \qquad \mathbf{x}_B, \mathbf{x}_N \geq \mathbf{0}. \tag{2}$$

If $\mathbf{x}_B$ is an optimum solution, it implies that

1. $\mathbf{x}_B = \mathbf{B}^{-1}\,\mathbf{b} \geq \mathbf{0}$, i.e., it is primal feasible,
2. $\mathbf{c}_N - \mathbf{c}_B\,\mathbf{B}^{-1}\,\mathbf{N} \geq \mathbf{0}$, i.e., it is dual feasible.

It should be noted that the primal feasibility does not depend on the cost vector $\mathbf{c}$, and the dual feasibility does not depend on the requirement vector $\mathbf{b}$.

Let us now consider the following types of the variations in the data:

1) The requirement vector $\mathbf{b}$ is changed into $\mathbf{b} + \Delta\mathbf{b}$. Since the dual feasibility condition does not depend on $\mathbf{b}$, the original solution $\mathbf{x}_B$ remains dual feasible. The original solution $\mathbf{x}_B$ will also be primal feasible if

$$\mathbf{B}^{-1}\mathbf{b} + \mathbf{B}^{-1}\Delta\mathbf{b} \geq \mathbf{0}. \tag{3}$$

Thus, in computation, we would keep the original basis $\mathbf{B}$ which is dual feasible and use the dual simplex method to continue the computation.

2) The cost vector $\mathbf{c}$ is changed into $\mathbf{c} + \Delta(\mathbf{c}_B, \mathbf{c}_N)$. The original solution $\mathbf{x}_B$ remains primal feasible. It is also dual feasible if

$$(\mathbf{c}_N - \mathbf{c}_B\mathbf{B}^{-1}\mathbf{N}) + (\Delta\mathbf{c}_N - \Delta\mathbf{c}_B\mathbf{B}^{-1}\mathbf{N}) \geq \mathbf{0}. \tag{4}$$

If $\Delta\mathbf{c}_B = \mathbf{0}$, condition (4) reduces to

$$c_j - \boldsymbol{\pi}\mathbf{a}_j \geq -\Delta c_j \tag{5}$$

3) If a new column vector $\mathbf{a}_{n+1}$ with cost c_{n+1} is added, then the original $\mathbf{x}_B$ will still be an optimum solution if

$$c_{n+1} - \boldsymbol{\pi}\mathbf{a}_{n+1} \geq 0.$$

In the revised simplex method, this is exactly the pricing operation of determining whether a nonbasic column vector should be brought into the basis.

EXERCISES

Do the following by the revised simplex method.

1. $\min z = x_1 + 6x_2 - 7x_3 + x_4 + 5x_5$

   subject to

$$x_1 - (3/4)\,x_2 + 2x_3 - (1/4)\,x_4 = 5,$$
$$-(1/4)\,x_2 + 3x_3 - (3/4)\,x_4 + x_5 = 5,$$
$$x_j \geq 0 \quad (j = 1, \ldots, 5).$$

2. $\max w = 78x_2 + 21x_3 - 124x_5 + 6x_7 + 17x_8 + 10x_9$

   subject to

$$x_3 + x_4 - 8x_5 + 2x_7 - x_8 - 3x_9 = 33,$$
$$6x_2 - x_3 + x_5 + x_6 - 2x_7 + 4x_8 = 27,$$
$$x_1 + 4x_2 + x_3 - 5x_5 + x_8 + x_9 = 86.$$

   (*ans.* $w = 1786$, $x_7 = 92.5$, $x_8 = 53$, $x_9 = 33$; $x_j = 0$ otherwise)

3. Consider the linear programming problem

$$\max_{\mathbf{x}} \left\{ \mathbf{cx} \,\middle|\, \begin{matrix} \mathbf{Ax} = \mathbf{b} \\ \mathbf{x} \geq \mathbf{0} \end{matrix} \right\}, \ (\mathbf{A} \text{ is } m \times n).$$

   Suppose that a basic optimal solution $\mathbf{x}_B$ is associated with a basis matrix **B**.

   (a) Suppose that **b** is replaced by $\mathbf{b} + \lambda\mathbf{d}$, where λ is a scalar and **d** is a nonzero vector in E^m. Give a condition such that the basis **B** will be optimal for all $\lambda \geq 0$.

   (b) Suppose that **c** is replaced by $\mathbf{c} + \lambda\mathbf{g}$, where **g** is a nonzero vector in E^n which has a zero component corresponding to every basic activity. Give a condition such that the basis **B** will be optimal for all $\lambda \geq 0$.

   Justify your answers.

PRIMAL-DUAL METHOD 6

6.1 MUTUAL PRIMAL-DUAL METHOD (Balinski and Gomory [7] and Thrall [184])

In both the row and column tableaux discussed earlier, we are calculating on a tableau of the size $(m + 1) \times (m + n + 1)$ or $(m + n + 1) \times (n + 1)$. The tableau discussed in this section is of size $(m + 1) \times (n + 1)$, which is a condensed one.

Consider a pair of primal and dual programs. The primal program (or row program) is

$$\min x_0 = a_{00} + a_{01} x_1 + a_{02} x_2 + \cdots + a_{0n} x_n$$

subject to

$$\begin{aligned} -x_{n+1} &= a_{10} + a_{11} x_1 + a_{12} x_2 + \cdots + a_{1n} x_n \leq 0, \\ &\vdots \\ -x_{n+m} &= a_{m0} + a_{m1} x_1 + a_{m2} x_2 + \cdots + a_{mn} x_n \leq 0, \\ x_1 &\geq 0, \\ x_2 &\geq 0, \\ &\vdots \\ x_n &\geq 0. \end{aligned} \tag{1}$$

The dual program (or column program) is

$$\max y_0 = a_{00} + a_{10} y_{n+1} + a_{20} y_{n+2} + \cdots + a_{m0} y_{n+m}$$

subject to

$$\begin{aligned} y_{n+1} &\geq 0, \\ y_{n+2} &\geq 0, \\ &\vdots \\ y_{n+m} &\geq 0, \\ y_1 = a_{01} + a_{11} y_{n+1} + \cdots + a_{m1} y_{n+m} &\geq 0, \\ &\vdots \\ y_n = a_{0n} + a_{1n} y_{n+1} + \cdots + a_{mn} y_{n+m} &\geq 0. \end{aligned} \tag{2}$$

Tableau 6.1

	1	x_1	$\cdots$	x_n	
1	a_{00}	a_{01}	$\cdots$	a_{0n}	$= x_0$
y_{n+1}	a_{10}	a_{11}	$\cdots$	a_{1n}	$= - x_{n+1}$
$\vdots$	$\vdots$	$\vdots$		$\vdots$	
y_{n+m}	a_{m0}	a_{m1}	$\cdots$	a_{mn}	$= - x_{n+m}$
	$= y_0$	$= y_1$	$\cdots$	$= y_n$	

Both programs can be conveniently put into a compact tableau as in Tableau 6.1.

Tableau 6.1 is self-explanatory; $x_1, x_2, \ldots, x_n$ are nonbasic variables of the primal program and $y_{n+1}, y_{n+2}, \ldots, y_{n+m}$ are nonbasic variables of the dual program. The basic variables of the primal program $x_{n+1}, \ldots, x_{n+m}$ are expressed in terms of its nonbasic variables; similarly the basic variables of the dual program $y_1, \ldots, y_n$ are also expressed in terms of its nonbasic variables.

A pivot operation in either (1) or (2) leads to a new partitioning of basic and nonbasic variables. Consider two typical equations in the tableau:

$$\begin{aligned} a_{i0} + a_{i1}x_1 + \cdots + a_{ij}x_j + \cdots + a_{in}x_n &= -x_{n+i}, \\ a_{0j} + a_{1j}y_{n+1} + \cdots + a_{ij}y_{n+i} + \cdots + a_{mj}y_{n+m} &= y_j. \end{aligned} \tag{3}$$

If a_{ij} is not zero ($i \neq 0$, $j \neq 0$), then it can be used as the pivot. This means that x_j will become basic and x_{n+i} nonbasic, or y_{n+i} basic and y_j nonbasic.

Dividing (3) by a_{ij} and transferring terms, we have

$$\begin{aligned} +\frac{a_{i0}}{a_{ij}} + \frac{a_{i1}}{a_{ij}}x_1 + \cdots + \frac{1}{a_{ij}}x_{n+i} + \cdots + \frac{a_{in}}{a_{ij}}x_n &= -x_j, \\ -\frac{a_{0j}}{a_{ij}} - \frac{a_{1j}}{a_{ij}}y_{n+1} - \cdots + \frac{1}{a_{ij}}y_j - \cdots - \frac{a_{mj}}{a_{ij}}y_{n+m} &= y_{n+i}. \end{aligned} \tag{4}$$

The x_j and y_{n+i} in (4) can be used in any equations implied by Tableau 6.1 to eliminate x_j or y_{n+i} as nonbasic variables. The results of the pivot can also be summarized in Tableaux 6.2 and 6.3, where α is the pivot, β denotes a generic element in the pivot row, γ denotes a generic element in the pivot column, and δ represents the element in the same column as β and the same row as γ. All other variables and labels remain in the same positions after pivoting.

In any tableau basic solutions to both programs are obtained by setting the current nonbasic variables to zero, where the current nonbasic variables are in the upper part or on the left of the tableau. For example, in a succeeding tableau of Tableau 6.1, we have Tableau 6.4. The basic solutions are $-x'_{n+1} = a'_{10}, \ldots, -x'_{n+m} = a'_{m0}$ and $y'_1 = a'_{01}, \ldots, y'_n = a'_{0n}$. A basic

Tableau 6.2. BEFORE PIVOTING

$$
\begin{array}{c|ccccc|l}
 & & x_j & & & & \\
\hline
 & & \vdots & & \vdots & & \\
y_{n+i} & \cdot\cdot & \alpha & \cdot\cdot & \beta & \cdot\cdot & = -x_{n+i}, \\
 & & \vdots & & \vdots & & \\
 & \cdot\cdot & \gamma & \cdot\cdot & \delta & \cdot\cdot & \\
 & & \vdots & & \vdots & & \vdots \\
\hline
 & & = y_j & & & &
\end{array}
$$

Tableau 6.3. AFTER PIVOTING

$$
\begin{array}{c|ccccc|l}
 & & x_{n+i} & & & & \\
\hline
\vdots & & \vdots & & \vdots & & \\
y_j & \cdot\cdot & \alpha^{-1} & \cdot\cdot & \alpha^{-1}\beta & \cdot\cdot & = -x_j. \\
\vdots & & \vdots & & \vdots & & \\
 & \cdot\cdot & -\gamma\alpha^{-1} & \cdot\cdot & \delta-\gamma\alpha^{-1}\beta & \cdot\cdot & \\
\vdots & & \vdots & & \vdots & & \\
\hline
 & & = y_{n+i} & & & &
\end{array}
$$

Tableau 6.4

	1	x'_1	$\dots$	x'_n	
1	a'_{00}	a'_{01}	$\dots$	a'_{0n}	$= x_0$
y'_{n+1}	a'_{10}	a'_{11}	$\dots$	a'_{1n}	$= -x'_{n+1}$
$\vdots$	$\vdots$			$\vdots$	$\vdots$
y'_{n+m}	a'_{m0}	a'_{m1}	$\dots$	a'_{mn}	$= -x'_{n+m}$
	$= y_0$	$= y'_1$	$\dots$	$= y'_n$	

Tableau 6.5

	1	x_1	x_2	x_3	
1	$-21/2$	$1/2$	$-3/2$	$-3/2$	x_0
y_4	$-5/2$	$1/2$	$1/2^*$	$3/2$	$-x_4$
y_5	$-1/2$	$1/2$	$-1/2$	$-1/2$	$-x_5$
	y_0	y_1	y_2	y_3	

solution is primal feasible if $a'_{i0} \leq 0$ ($i = 1, \dots, m$) and dual feasible if $a'_{0j} \geq 0$ ($j = 1, \dots, n$). If both $a'_{i0} \leq 0$ ($i = 1, \dots, m$) and $a'_{0j} \geq 0$ ($j = 1, \dots, n$), then it is the optimum solution to both programs.

Consider, for example, Tableau 6.5, where a pivot step on the starred element gives the optimum tableau (Tableau 6.6). Note that Tableau 6.5 is a primal feasible tableau, since $a_{i0} \leq 0$ ($i = 1, 2$) but not dual feasible since $a_{0j} < 0$ for some j.

Tableau 6.6

	1	x_1	x_4	x_3	
1	-18	2	3	3	x_0
y_2	-5	1	2	3	$-x_2$
y_5	-3	1	1	1	$-x_5$
	y_0	y_1	y_4	y_3	

The simplex method for solving a pair of primal and dual linear programs can be considered as a finite sequence of tableaux exhibiting equivalent pairs of linear programs. Each tableau is obtained from the preceding one by pivot steps with a prescribed rule of choosing the pivot, until the optimum tableau is obtained, or the inconsistency of constraints is revealed.

Let $\oplus$ denote nonnegative entries and $\ominus$ nonpositive entries. Then the terminating tableau of the sequence of tableaux can only be one of the three types represented by Tableau 6.7, 6.8, or 6.9.

In the primal simplex method we start with a primal feasible tableau, i. e., $a_{i0} \leq 0$ $(i \geq 1)$. We select from the 0th row some $a_{0j} < 0$. (If $a_{0j} \geq 0$ for all $j \geq 1$, then it is the optimum tableau.) If $a_{ij} \leq 0$ for all i, then it means that the dual constraints are inconsistent and the primal optimum solution is not finite. If $a_{ij} > 0$ for some i, we choose

$$\frac{a_{r0}}{a_{rj}} = \max_i \frac{a_{i0}}{a_{ij}} \qquad (a_{ij} > 0) \tag{5}$$

and let a_{rj} be the pivot.

This ratio test (5) keeps the succeeding tableau primal feasible and usually decreases the value of a_{00}. If $a_{r0} = 0$, then a_{00} will remain the same after pivoting. This is degeneracy.

The proof for finiteness of the simplex method follows from the fact that there are only $\binom{n+m}{m}$ possible sets of basic variables. If degeneracy occurs, then some forms of lexicographic order must be introduced to avoid the cycling.

For the dual simplex method, we start with a dual feasible tableau, i.e., $a_{0j} \geq 0$ $(j \geq 1)$, and select some $a_{i0} > 0$. If $a_{ij} \geq 0$ for all j, then the primal constraint is inconsistent and shows that the dual optimum solution is not finite. If $a_{ij} < 0$ for some j, then we choose

$$\frac{a_{0s}}{a_{is}} = \min_j \left| \frac{a_{0j}}{a_{ij}} \right| \qquad (a_{ij} < 0) \tag{6}$$

and let a_{is} be the pivot. The ratio test keeps the succeeding tableau still dual feasible and usually increases the value in the upper left corner.

Tableau 6.7. OPTIMUM TABLEAU

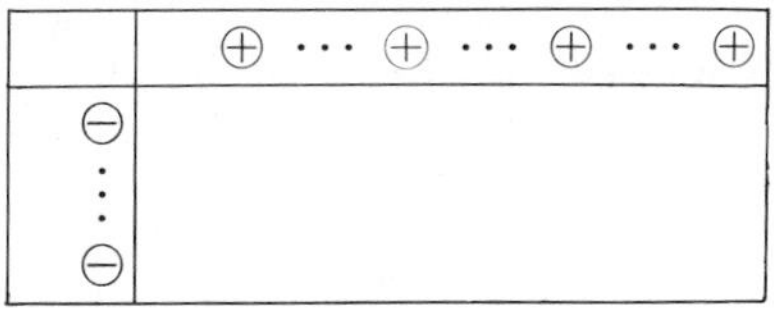

Tableau 6.8. PRIMAL CONSTRAINTS INCONSISTENT

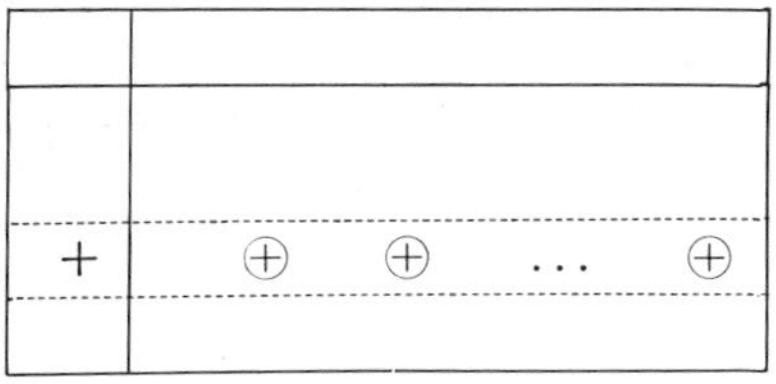

Tableau 6.9. DUAL CONSTRAINTS INCONSISTENT

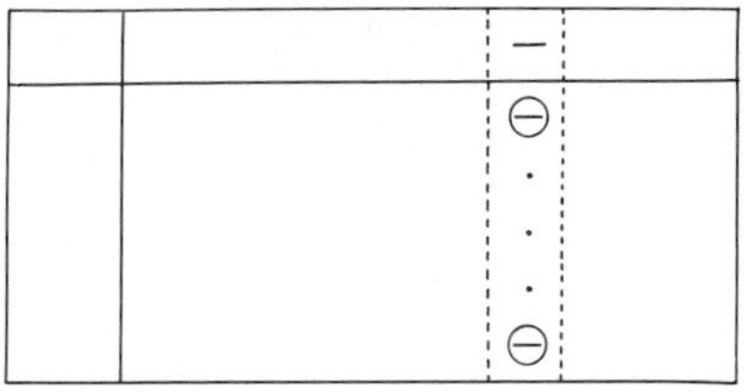

Starting with any tableau, we can use the mutual primal-dual method to perform a sequence of pivoting operations which will lead to any of the three terminal forms of Tableaux 6.7, 6.8, or 6.9. To prove this, we need some definitions and notations.

Given any tableau T, the top row of T is called its distinguished row $R(T)$ and its left-most column is called the distinguished column $C(T)$. The entry in the upper left corner is called the distinguished entry $d(T)$. The distinguished row without $d(T)$ is denoted by $R'(T)$, and the distinguished column without $d(T)$ is denoted by $C'(T)$. Thus a tableau T is primal feasible if $C'(T) \leq 0$ and is dual feasible if $R'(T) \geq 0$. If the starting tableau is primal feasible, we can use the primal simplex method to lead it to any one of the three terminal forms represented by Tableaux 6.7, 6.8 and 6.9. If the starting tableau is dual feasible, we can use the dual simplex method to lead it to one of the three terminal forms.

If the starting tableau T_0 is neither primal nor dual feasible, we can define a nested sequence of tableaux $T_1, \ldots, T_n$ such that each T_k is a sub-tableau of its preceding one, all T_i (i odd) are primal feasible, and all T_j (j even) are dual feasible. For example, if T_0 is not primal feasible, then we can take all rows of T_0 for which $a_{i0} \leq 0$ and take one row with $a_{i0} > 0$ to be the distinguished row of T_1; T_1 is then primal feasible. If T_1 has $C'(T_1) < 0$ or is of the form of Tableau 6.7 or 6.9, then the nested sequence stops at T_1. If $C'(T_1) \leq 0$, then we can take the rows of T_1 for which $a_{i0} = 0$ to be the rows of T_2, take all columns of T_1 for which $a_{0j} \geq 0$ to be the columns of T_2, and take any column of T_1 with $a_{0j} < 0$ to be the distinguished column of T_2. This is shown schematically in Fig. 6.1. The permutation of columns and rows is used to show the structure more clearly.

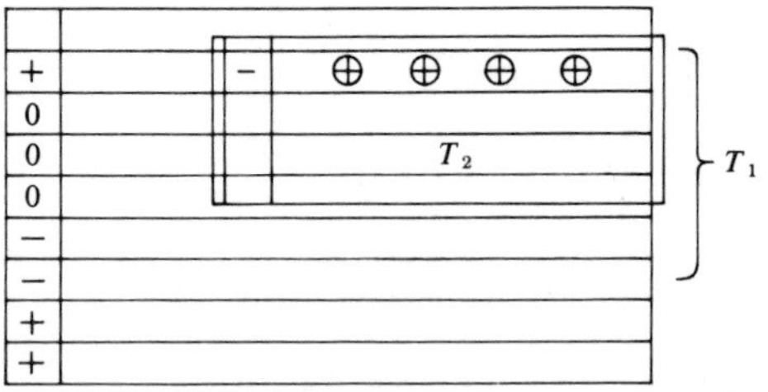

Fig. 6.1

Tableau 6.10

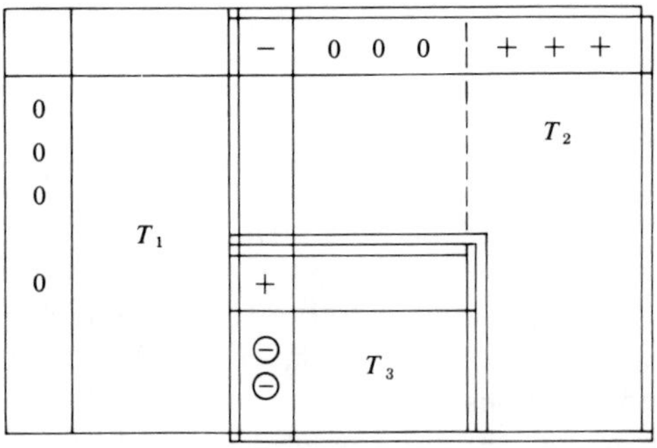

If the dual feasible subtableau T_2 still contains zeros in its distinguished row, then we can consider only the columns of T_2 that have zeros as their top entries together with the distinguished column of T_2. Among these columns we shall consider those rows which have nonpositive left entries. The rows together with a row with a positive left entry is considered to be the sub-subtableau T_3. This is shown in Tableau 6.10. The sequence of tableaux stops at T_2 if T_2 is of the form of Tableau 6.7 or 6.8 or $R'(T_2) > 0$.

Several comments are in order.

1. If we consider each subtableau as a primal or dual feasible tableau, then according to the primal simplex or the dual simplex method there is a unique pivot. Thus for any sequence of tableaux there is a sequence of positions for pivots.

2. Since we can take any row with a positive left entry as the distinguished row of a primal feasible subtableau, the definition of a nested sequence of tableaux from a given tableau is by no means unique.
3. Since each T_k has either fewer columns or fewer rows than T_{k-1}, the number of possible sequences of tableaux is finite.
4. The permutation of columns and rows as shown in Fig. 6.1 and Tableau 6.10 is purely for clarity. It is necessary to prescribe only the distinguished entry of each subtableau; then the sequence of tableaux is implicitly and uniquely defined.
5. For each tableau T_k which is primal feasible and with the distinguished entry positive we use the primal simplex method. The ratio test (5) will keep $C'(T_k^*)$ nonpositive. (Here we use the $*$ to indicate the tableau after the pivoting). On the other hand $d(T_k) \geq d(T_k^*)$. [If $C'(T_k)$ contains no zero, then $d(T_k) > d(T_k^*)$.] If $d(T_k^*) \leq 0$, then the tableau T_{k-1}^* has one more nonpositive entry in its distinguished column than T_{k-1}. The effect of the pivoting is to make T_{k-1} progress towards primal feasibility.
6. Similarly, for a dual feasible tableau T_k with a negative distinguished entry, we use the dual simplex method. The ratio test (6) will keep $R'(T_k^*)$ nonnegative. On the other hand, $d(T_k) \leq d(T_k^*)$. [If $R'(T_k)$ contains no zero, then $d(T_k) < d(T_k^*)$.] If $d(T_k^*) \geq 0$, then the tableau T_{k-1}^* has one more nonnegative entry in its distinguished row than T_{k-1}. The effect of the pivoting is to make T_{k-1} progress towards dual feasibility.

In summary, associated with any tableau and its sequence of subtableaux, there is a hierarchy of goals with goal k being to improve the subtab-

Tableau 6.11. $\alpha(T_{k-1}^*) > \alpha(T_{k-1})$ or $\alpha(T_{k-1}^*) = \alpha(T_{k-1})$; $d(T_{k-1}^*) > d(T_{k-1})$

T_k (k odd)

	0, ..., 0	+ ··· +
+ ⋮ +	T_{k-1}	
+	⊕, ..., ⊕	−*
⊖ ⋮ ⊖	T_k	

*indicates the pivot.

Tableau 6.12. $\alpha(T_k^*) > \alpha(T_k)$

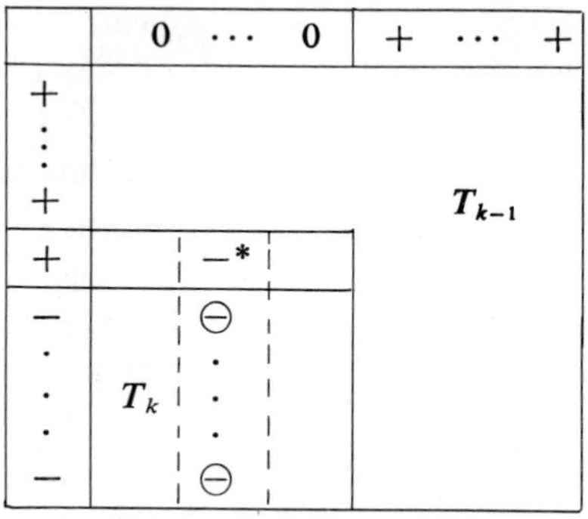

Tableau 6.13. $d(T_k^*) < d(T_k)$ and $\alpha(T_k^*) \geq \alpha(T_k)$

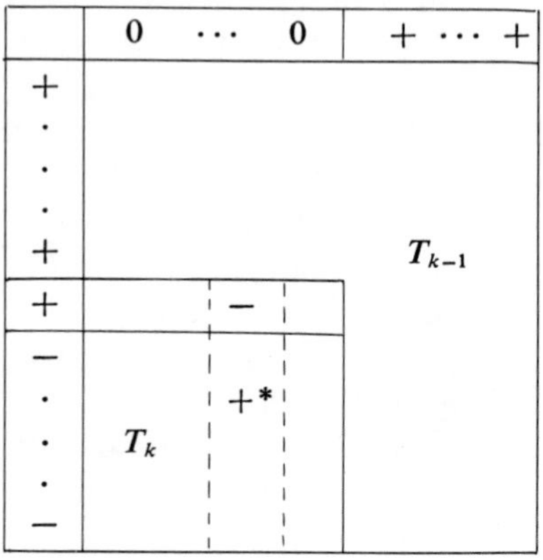

Tableau 6.14. $\alpha(T_{k-1}^*) > \alpha(T_{k-1})$ or $\alpha(T_{k-1}^*) = \alpha(T_{k-1})$; $d(T_{k-1}^*) < d(T_{k-1})$

T_k(k even)

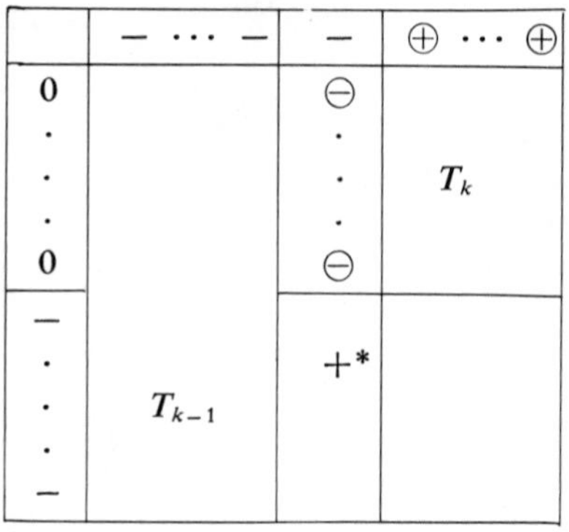

Tableau 6.15. $\alpha(T_k^*) > \alpha(T_k)$

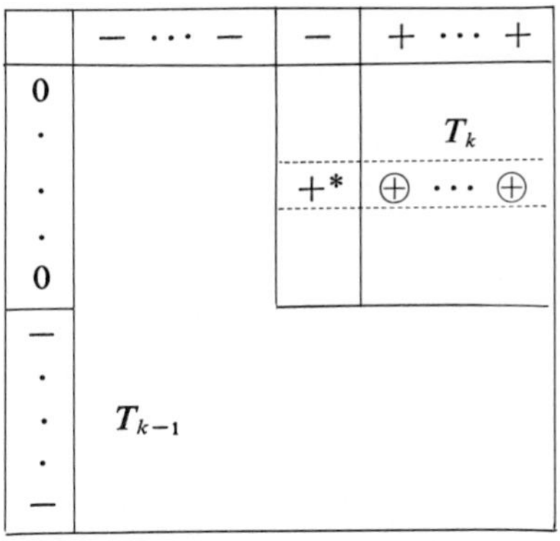

Tableau 6.16. $d(T_k^*) > d(T_k)$ and $\alpha(T_k^*) \geq \alpha(T_k)$

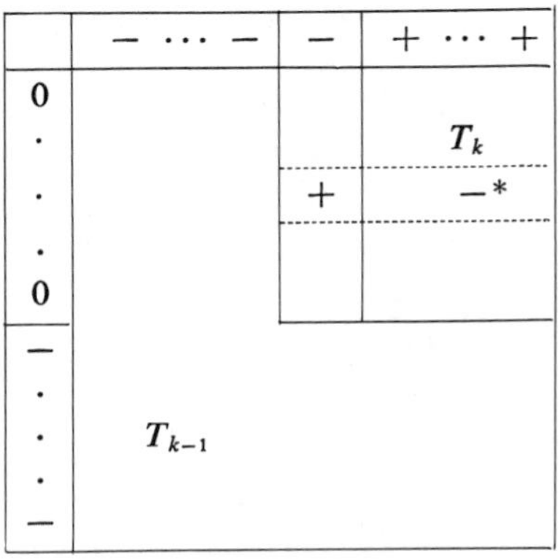

leau T_k. Because of the way $T_1, T_2, \ldots, T_k, \ldots, T_n$ are defined, improving T_k will not disturb any goals of its preceding tableaux $T_1, \ldots, T_{k-1}$. We shall use $\alpha(T_k)$ to denote the number of rows in T_k if k is odd, and $\alpha(T_k)$ to denote the number of columns in T_k if k is even. Tableaux 6.11 through 6.16 are six possible cases of selecting the pivoting and their effects. These possible outcomes show that the algorithm is a finite algorithm.

6.2 PRIMAL-DUAL METHOD (Dantzig, Ford, and Fulkerson [40])

Since there are the primal simplex method and the dual simplex method, it is no surprise that there exist methods which use both the primal and dual approaches. The method described here is formally a dual method since it has a dual feasible solution at all times. The primal simplex algorithm is used as a subalgorithm to reduce the primal infeasibility. When the solution becomes both dual and primal feasible, it is also optimum. Let the primal program be

$$\min z = \mathbf{cx}$$

subject to (1)

$$\mathbf{Ax} = \mathbf{b} \geq \mathbf{0}, \qquad \mathbf{x} \geq \mathbf{0}.$$

Then the dual program of (1) is

$$\max w = \boldsymbol{\pi}\mathbf{b}$$

subject to (2)

$$\boldsymbol{\pi}\mathbf{A} \leq \mathbf{c}, \qquad \boldsymbol{\pi} \gtrless \mathbf{0}.$$

It is very easy to get a feasible solution to (2) by inspection. For example, if $\mathbf{c} \geq \mathbf{0}$, then $\boldsymbol{\pi} = \mathbf{0}$ is a feasible solution to (2). If $c_j \ngeq 0$ for all j, and a feasible solution to (2) is not readily available, then we can modify problems (1) and (2) slightly as follows. Introduce a nonnegative variable x_{n+1} and add an equation to the constraints in (1). We have

$$x_1 + x_2 + \cdots + x_n + x_{n+1} = b_{m+1} \qquad (x_{n+1} \geq 0),$$

with b_{m+1} a very large positive constant. Clearly such a constraint will not change the solution of the primal problem, but the corresponding dual program becomes

$$\max w' = \pi_1 b_1 + \pi_2 b_2 + \cdots + \pi_m b_m + \pi_{m+1} b_{m+1}$$

subject to

$$\begin{aligned} \pi_1 a_{11} + \pi_2 a_{21} + \cdots + \pi_m a_{m1} + \pi_{m+1} &\leq c_1, \\ \vdots \qquad\qquad\qquad & \quad \vdots \\ \pi_1 a_{1n} + \pi_2 a_{2n} + \cdots + \pi_m a_{mn} + \pi_{m+1} &\leq c_n, \\ \pi_{m+1} &\leq 0. \end{aligned}$$

Then a dual feasible solution is readily available with

$$\pi_{m+1} = \min_j c_j \qquad \text{and} \qquad \pi_i = 0 \qquad (i = 1, \ldots, m).$$

For the purpose of discussion, we shall assume that we have a feasible solution $\boldsymbol{\pi}$ to (2). From the corollary of the theorem on complementary slackness, a pair of solutions $\mathbf{x}$ and $\boldsymbol{\pi}$ are optimum solutions to (1) and (2) if and only if they satisfy

$$(c_j - \pi_i a_{ij}) x_j = 0 \qquad \text{(for all } j\text{)}, \tag{3a}$$

$$\pi_i(a_{ij} x_j - b_i) = 0 \qquad \text{(for all } i\text{)}. \tag{3b}$$

Since the constraints of (1) are equations, (3b) is automatically satisfied when a feasible solution $\mathbf{x}$ to (1) is obtained. Now, assume that we have a current feasible solution $\boldsymbol{\pi}$ of (2). Then some of the constraints of (2) are satisfied as equalities and some are satisfied as inequalities. [Note that π is a feasible but not necessarily a basic feasible solution to (2), so that all constraints may be satisfied as inequalities.] For those constraints which are satisfied as equalities the corresponding x_j can be any positive value and the products $(c_j - \boldsymbol{\pi}\mathbf{a}_j)x_j = 0$. For those constraints which are satisfied as inequalities, i.e., $c_j - \boldsymbol{\pi}\mathbf{a}_j > 0$, then the corresponding x_j have to be zero in order that $(c_j - \boldsymbol{\pi}\mathbf{a}_j)\, x_j = 0$. The question is: How do we find an $\mathbf{x}$ that satisfies (3a) and the constraints of (1)?

Based on the feasible solution π to (2), we will define the index set $J = \{j \mid c_j - \boldsymbol{\pi}\mathbf{a}_j = 0\}$. For $j \in J$ any $x_j \geq 0$ will satisfy (3a). For $j \in N - J$, $c_j - \boldsymbol{\pi}\mathbf{a}_j > 0$; so the only way to satisfy (3a) is to put $x_j = 0$. Thus, if we can find a nonnegative combination of columns $\mathbf{a}_j$ $(j \in J)$ that equals $\mathbf{b}$, then this set of $x_j \geq 0$ $(j \in J)$ together with $x_j = 0$ $(j \in N - J)$ constitute an optimum solution to (1), since they satisfy the complementary slackness condition (3). To find the nonnegative combination of columns $\mathbf{a}_j$ $(j \in J)$, we set up the following program which is called the restricted primal program:

$$\min \xi = \sum_{i=1}^{m} x_i^a$$

subject to (4)

$$\mathbf{a}_{ij}\, x_j + x_i^a = b_i \qquad (j \in J, i = 1, \ldots, m),$$
$$x_j \geq 0, \qquad x_i^a \geq 0,$$

where x_i^a are the artificial variables.

If $\xi = 0$ in (4), it means that $x_i^a = 0$ and a set x_j $(j \in J)$ is found that satisfies (4). This set x_j $(j \in J)$ together with $x_j = 0$ $(j \in N - J)$ will be both feasible and optimum for (1). It is feasible because the constraints of (4) with $x_i^a = 0$ are the same as that of (1) with the columns $\mathbf{a}_j$ $(j \in N - J)$ deleted. (Deleting column $\mathbf{a}_j$ is the same as letting the associated $x_j = 0$).

If $\xi > 0$, then we have to consider two cases. Denote the optimum solution to the dual program of (4) by $\bar{\boldsymbol{\pi}}$.

CASE 1. $\bar{\boldsymbol{\pi}}\, \mathbf{a}_j \leq 0$ for $j \in N - J$. We shall see that in this case, (1) has no feasible solution. To show this, we note that the dual constraints of (4) are

$$\boldsymbol{\pi}\, \mathbf{a}_j \leq 0 \qquad (j \in J),$$
$$\pi_i \leq 1.$$

If $\bar{\boldsymbol{\pi}}$ is the optimum solution to the dual program (4), then $\bar{\boldsymbol{\pi}}\mathbf{a}_j \leq 0\, (j \in J)$. This together with the assumption that $\bar{\boldsymbol{\pi}}\mathbf{a}_j \leq 0$ for $j \in N - J$ implies that $\bar{\boldsymbol{\pi}}\mathbf{a}_j \leq 0$ for all $j \in N$. Let $\boldsymbol{\pi}$ be the feasible solution to (2). Then we shall show that $\boldsymbol{\pi}' = \boldsymbol{\pi} + \theta\bar{\boldsymbol{\pi}}$, $(\theta > 0)$ is also a feasible solution to (2). This is because

$$\boldsymbol{\pi}'\mathbf{a}_j = (\boldsymbol{\pi} + \theta\bar{\boldsymbol{\pi}})\, \mathbf{a}_j = \boldsymbol{\pi}\mathbf{a}_j + \theta\bar{\boldsymbol{\pi}}\mathbf{a}_j \leq c_j + \theta\bar{\boldsymbol{\pi}}\mathbf{a}_j \leq c_j \qquad (\text{as } \bar{\boldsymbol{\pi}}\mathbf{a}_j \leq 0).$$

Furthermore, the value of the objective function in (2) can be made arbitrarily large. This is because $\bar{\boldsymbol{\pi}}\mathbf{b} = \xi > 0$ and $\boldsymbol{\pi}'\mathbf{b} = (\boldsymbol{\pi} + \theta\bar{\boldsymbol{\pi}})\,\mathbf{b} = \boldsymbol{\pi}\mathbf{b} + \theta\bar{\boldsymbol{\pi}}\mathbf{b}$. This value can be made arbitrarily large simply by choosing θ arbitrarily large. From the theorem of duality, this implies that (1) has no feasible solution.

CASE 2. $\bar{\boldsymbol{\pi}}\mathbf{a}_j > 0$ for at least one $j \in N - J$. In this case we shall see that $\boldsymbol{\pi}' = \boldsymbol{\pi} + \theta\bar{\boldsymbol{\pi}}$ is a feasible solution to (2) for some values of θ satisfying $0 \leq \theta \leq \theta_1$. Note that by the definition of the index set J, we have

$$\boldsymbol{\pi}\mathbf{a}_j < c_j \qquad (\text{for all } j \in N - J).$$

Let

$$\theta_1 = \min_j \left[\frac{c_j - \boldsymbol{\pi}\mathbf{a}_j}{\bar{\boldsymbol{\pi}}\mathbf{a}_j}\right] \qquad (j \in N - J,\ \bar{\boldsymbol{\pi}}\mathbf{a}_j > 0). \tag{5}$$

Then $\boldsymbol{\pi}' = \boldsymbol{\pi} + \theta\bar{\boldsymbol{\pi}}$ is a feasible solution to (2) for $0 \leq \theta \leq \theta_1$. This is because

$$\begin{aligned} \boldsymbol{\pi}'\mathbf{a}_j = \boldsymbol{\pi}\mathbf{a}_j + \theta\bar{\boldsymbol{\pi}}\mathbf{a}_j &\leq \boldsymbol{\pi}\mathbf{a}_j + \theta_1\bar{\boldsymbol{\pi}}\mathbf{a}_j \\ &\leq \boldsymbol{\pi}\mathbf{a}_j + c_j - \boldsymbol{\pi}\mathbf{a}_j \qquad (\text{for } \bar{\boldsymbol{\pi}}\mathbf{a}_j > 0) \\ &\leq c_j \end{aligned}$$

$$\boldsymbol{\pi}'\mathbf{a}_j = \boldsymbol{\pi}\mathbf{a}_j + \theta\bar{\boldsymbol{\pi}}\,\mathbf{a}_j \leq \boldsymbol{\pi}\mathbf{a}_j \leq c_j \qquad (\text{for } \bar{\boldsymbol{\pi}}\mathbf{a}_j < 0).$$

Furthermore, this $\boldsymbol{\pi}'$ is a better solution to (2) than the original $\boldsymbol{\pi}$:

$$\boldsymbol{\pi}'\mathbf{b} = \boldsymbol{\pi}\mathbf{b} + \theta\bar{\boldsymbol{\pi}}\mathbf{b} \geq \boldsymbol{\pi}\mathbf{b} \qquad (\text{for } \bar{\boldsymbol{\pi}}\mathbf{b} = \xi > 0, \theta \geq 0).$$

In other words, we have a better feasible solution to (2). Based on this new $\boldsymbol{\pi}'$, we can again define the set J for which $J = \{j \mid \boldsymbol{\pi}'\mathbf{a}_j - c_j = 0\}$. This can be iterated until either the optimum solutions to (1) and (2) are obtained or it reveals that (1) has no feasible solution.

Example 1. Consider

$$\min z = x_1 + x_2 + 2x_3 + 8x_4$$

subject to

$$\begin{aligned} 2x_1 - x_2 + 3x_3 - 2x_4 &= 3, \\ -x_1 + 3x_2 - 4x_3 + 4x_4 &= 1, \\ x_j \geq 0 \quad (j &= 1, 2, 3, 4). \end{aligned} \tag{6}$$

The dual program of (6) is

$$\max w = 3\pi_1 + \pi_2$$

subject to

$$\begin{aligned} 2\pi_1 - \pi_2 &\leq 1, \\ -\pi_1 + 3\pi_2 &\leq 1, \\ 3\pi_1 - 4\pi_2 &\leq 2, \\ -2\pi_1 + 4\pi_2 &\leq 8. \end{aligned} \tag{7}$$

A feasible solution to (7) is $(\pi_1, \pi_2) = (0, 0)$. For this value of $\boldsymbol{\pi}$ all the constraints of (7) are satisfied as strict inequalities so the the index set J is empty. The restricted primal program becomes

$$\min \xi = x_1^a + x_2^a$$

subject to

$$\begin{aligned} x_1^a &= 3, \\ x_2^a &= 1, \\ x_i^a &\geq 0 \qquad (i = 1, 2). \end{aligned} \tag{8}$$

The optimum dual solution $\bar{\boldsymbol{\pi}}$ of (8) is $(\bar{\pi}_1, \bar{\pi}_2) = (1, 1)$ and the objective function $\xi = 4$:

$$\theta_1 = \min_j \left[\frac{c_j - \boldsymbol{\pi}\mathbf{a}_j}{\bar{\boldsymbol{\pi}}\,\mathbf{a}_j}\right] = \frac{c_2 - (0, 0)\,\mathbf{a}_2}{(1, 1)\,\mathbf{a}_2} = \frac{1}{2} \quad (\text{for } \bar{\boldsymbol{\pi}}\,\mathbf{a}_j > 0).$$

Therefore, the new feasible solution $\boldsymbol{\pi}'$ to (7) is

$$\boldsymbol{\pi}' = \boldsymbol{\pi} + \theta_2 \bar{\boldsymbol{\pi}} = (0, 0) + (1/2)(1, 1) = (1/2, 1/2).$$

Substituting this value of $\boldsymbol{\pi}'$ into (7), we see that the second constraint is satisfied as an equation. Thus the restricted primal program becomes

$$\min \xi = x_1^a + x_2^a$$

subject to

$$\begin{aligned} -x_2 + x_1^a \qquad &= 3, \\ +3x_2 \qquad + x_2^a &= 1, \\ x_2, x_1^a, x_2^a &\geq 0. \end{aligned} \tag{9}$$

The optimum dual solution to (9) is $\bar{\boldsymbol{\pi}} = (1, 1/3)$ with $\xi = 10/3$:

$$\theta_1 = \frac{c_1 - (1/2, 1/2)\,\mathbf{a}_1}{(1, 1/3)\,\mathbf{a}_1} = \frac{1 - (1/2)}{5/3} = \frac{3}{10}.$$

Thus the new feasible solution $\boldsymbol{\pi}'$ is $(1/2, 1/2) + (3/10)(1, 1/3) = (4/5, 3/5)$. Based on this new $\boldsymbol{\pi}'$, the tight constraints of (7) are the first and the second; the rest of the constraints are satisfied as strict inequalities. Thus the new restricted primal program becomes

$$\min \xi = +x_1^a + x_2^a$$

subject to

$$\begin{aligned} 2x_1 - x_2 + x_1^a \qquad &= 3, \\ -x_1 + 3x_2 \qquad + x_2^a &= 1, \\ x_1, x_2, x_1^a, x_2^a &\geq 0. \end{aligned} \tag{10}$$

The optimum solution of (10) is $x_1 = 2$, $x_2 = 1$ with $\xi = 0$. This means that

Tableau 6.17

	1	x_1^a	x_2^a	x_1	x_2	x_3	x_4		
$-z$	0			1	1	2	8		
$-\xi$	0	1*	1*	0	0	0	0	π	$\bar{\pi}$
x_1^a	3	1	0	2	−1	3	−2	0	
x_2^a	1	0	1	−1	3	−4	4	0	

Tableau 6.18

	1	x_1^a	x_2^a	x_1	x_2	x_3	x_4		
$-z$	0			1	1	2	8		
$-\xi$	−4	0	0	−1	−2	1	−2	π	$\bar{\pi}$
x_1^a	3	1	0	2	−1	3	−2	0	1
x_2^a	1	0	1	−1	3*	−4	4	0	1

$(x_1, x_2, x_3, x_4) = (2, 1, 0, 0)$ is an optimum solution to (6). Note that the complementary slackness conditions are satisfied:

$$(c_1 - \boldsymbol{\pi}\mathbf{a}_1)\,x_1 = (1 - (4/5, 3/5)\,[2, -1])\cdot 2 = 0,$$
$$(c_2 - \boldsymbol{\pi}\mathbf{a}_2)\,x_2 = (1 - (4/5, 3/5)\,[-1, 3])\cdot 1 = 0,$$
$$(c_3 - \boldsymbol{\pi}\mathbf{a}_3)\,x_3 = (2 - (4/5, 3/5)\,[3, -4])\cdot 0 = 0,$$
$$(c_4 - \boldsymbol{\pi}\mathbf{a}_4)\,x_4 = (8 - (4/5, 3/5)\,[-2, 4])\cdot 0 = 0.$$

Knowing the idea behind the method, we shall do the preceding numerical example again in a tableau similar to that of the simplex tableau. Tableau 6.17 includes the original objective function z in (6) as well as the function ξ which expresses the degree of primal infeasibility. Note that we have marked two positions with * in the ξ-row which are above the identity matrix. The numbers that appear in these positions in later tableaux will be the values of $1 - \bar{\pi}_1$ and $1 - \bar{\pi}_2$.

Substracting from the ξ-row, the third, and the fourth row, we have Tableau 6.18, which is in the standard form for minimizing ξ with x_1^a and x_2^a as the starting basic variables. Since all the coefficients in the z-row are nonnegative, $\boldsymbol{\pi} = (0, 0)$ is a feasible solution to (7). Multiplying the third row and the fourth row by (0, 0) respectively and subtracting them from the z-row, we have the same z-row. (In these subtractions we do not include the entries corresponding to artificial variables.) The result of subtraction does not change Tableau 6.18 in any way. As all coefficients in the z-row are nonnegative, none of the columns under x_1, x_2, x_3, and x_4 can be used

Tableau 6.19

	1	x_1^a	x_2^a	x_1	x_2	x_3	x_4	π	$\bar{\pi}$
$-z$	-2			1/2	0	5/2	7		
$-\xi$	-4	0	0	-1	-2	1	-2		
x_1^a	3	1	0	2	-1	3	-2	1/2	1
x_2^a	1	0	1	-1	3*	-4	4	1/2	1

Tableau 6.20

	1	x_1^a	x_2^a	x_1	x_2	x_3	x_4	π	$\bar{\pi}$
$-z$	-2			1/2	0	5/2	7		
$-\xi$	$-10/3$	0	2/3	$-5/3$	0	$-5/3$	2/3		
x_1^a	10/3	1	1/3	5/3	0	5/3	$-2/3$	1/2	1
x_2	1/3	0	1/3	$-1/3$	1	$-4/3$	4/3	1/2	1/3

in the restricted primal program. The first restricted primal program then consists of the first three columns of Tableau 6.18 and the last three rows of Tableau 6.18. From this subtableau we have $\xi = 4$ and $1 - \bar{\pi}_1 = 0$, $1 - \bar{\pi}_2 = 0$ or $\bar{\pi}_1 = 1$, $\bar{\pi}_2 = 1$. Note that the results of $-\bar{\boldsymbol{\pi}}\mathbf{a}_j$ are recorded in the entries of the ξ-row and the results of $c_j - \boldsymbol{\pi}\mathbf{a}_j$ are recorded in the entries of the z-row. Thus the value of θ_1 is determined by

$$\theta_1 = \min_j \frac{c_j - \boldsymbol{\pi}\mathbf{a}_j}{\bar{\boldsymbol{\pi}}\mathbf{a}_j} = \min\left(\left|\frac{1}{-1}\right|, \left|\frac{1}{-2}\right|\right) = \frac{1}{2}.$$

Multiplying the ξ-row by 1/2 and adding it to the z-row, we get Tableau 6.19 (the addition excludes the entries corresponding to x_1^a and x_2^a). This operation is equivalent to $c_j - \boldsymbol{\pi}\mathbf{a}_j + \theta_1(-\bar{\boldsymbol{\pi}}\mathbf{a}_j)$ or $c_j - (\boldsymbol{\pi} + \theta_1\bar{\boldsymbol{\pi}})\,\mathbf{a}_j$ or $c_j - \boldsymbol{\pi}'\,\mathbf{a}_j$.

Now since the coefficient in the z-row under x_2 is zero, this column can be used in the restricted primal program. Performing the pivot step on the last three rows of Tableau 6.19, we get Tableau 6.20.

Since all the coefficients in the ξ-row under x_1^a, x_2^a, and x_2 are nonnegative, it signals the completion of the restricted primal program with $\xi = 10/3$ and the optimum dual solution $\bar{\boldsymbol{\pi}}$ given by $1 - \bar{\pi}_1 = 0$ and $1 - \bar{\pi}_2 = 2/3$. This means that $\bar{\pi}_1 = 1$ and $\bar{\pi}_2 = 1/3$. The value of θ_1 is determined by

$$\theta_1 = \min\left(\left|\frac{1/2}{-5/3}\right|, \left|\frac{3/2}{-5/3}\right|\right) = \frac{3}{10}.$$

Thus $(\pi_1', \pi_2') = (1/2, 1/2) + (3/10)(1, 1/3) = (4/5, 3/5)$. Adding 3/10 of

Tableau 6.21

	1	x_1^a	x_2^a	x_1 ↓	x_2 ↓	x_3	x_4	π	$\bar{\pi}$
$-z$	-3			0	0	2	36/5		
$-\xi$	$-10/3$	0	2/3	$-5/3$	0	$-5/3$	2/3		
x_1^a	10/3	1	1/3	5/3*	0	5/3	$-2/3$	4/5	1
x_2	1/3	0	1/3	$-1/3$	1	$-4/3$	4/3	3/5	1/3

Tableau 6.22

	1	x_1^a	x_2^a	x_1	x_2	x_3	x_4	π	$\bar{\pi}$
$-z$	-3			0	0	2	36/5		
$-\xi$	0	1	1	0	0	0	0		
x_1	2	3/5	1/5	1	0	1	$-2/5$	4/5	0
x_2	1	1/5	2/5	0	1	-1	18/15	3/5	0

the ξ -row to the z-row (omitting the entries corresponding to the artificial variables), we get Tableau 6.21. Now since the coefficients in the z-equation under x_1 and x_2 are both zero, these columns can be used in the restricted primal program. These are indicated by the arrows above x_1 and x_2. Performing a pivot step on the last three rows of Tableau 6.21, we get Tableau 6.22. Since $\xi = 0$, it is the optimum tableau, with $z = 3$ and $x_1 = 2$, $x_2 = 1$, $x_3 = 0$, $x_4 = 0$.

DECOMPOSITION PRINCIPLE 7

7.1 DECOMPOSITION PRINCIPLE (Dantzig and Wolfe [46], [47])

In matrix calculations it is customary to partition a large matrix into several blocks and then do some calculations on each of the blocks. This approach is especially advantageous if some of the submatrices have special structures, for example, identity or zero. This is also true in linear programming when the matrix **A** has certain special structures. It should be emphasized that the decomposition principle described below can be used for any matrix **A** but the merit of this approach is more vividly revealed when the matrix **A** has a special structure. Consider a linear program

$$\min z = \mathbf{cx}$$

subject to

$$\mathbf{Ax} = \mathbf{b}, \qquad \mathbf{x} \geq \mathbf{0}. \tag{1}$$

It happens often that the matrix **A** has the special structure shown in Fig. 7.1, where coefficients not in any blocks are zero.

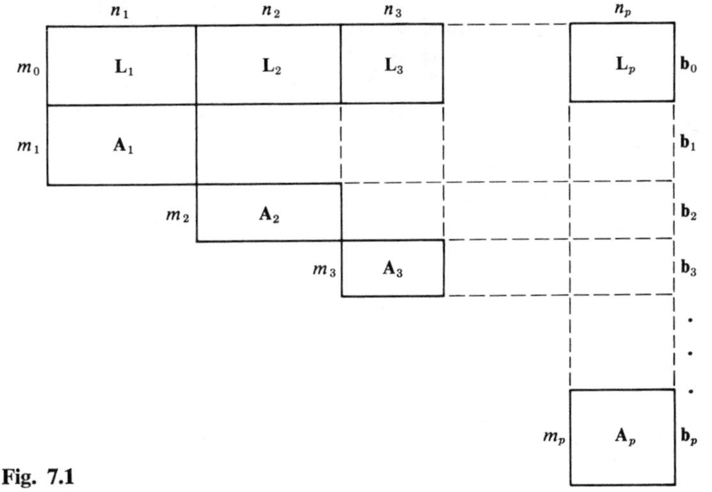

Fig. 7.1

The linear program for a big company with several branch offices may be of this structure. Each branch office is faced with a linear program of its own, i.e., $\mathbf{A}_i \mathbf{x}_i = \mathbf{b}_i$, say, and the headquarters of the company has a constraint matrix involving all its branch offices. Some of the matrices $\mathbf{A}_i$ may be empty; this may be the case if a company has an office such as the personnel office which is nonproductive (hence $\mathbf{A}_i$ is empty), but which is in the constraint matrix of the whole company. Note that the vector $\mathbf{b}$ in (1) is also partitioned into $p + 1$ vectors $\mathbf{b}_0, \mathbf{b}_1, \ldots, \mathbf{b}_p$. Similarly, the vector $\mathbf{c}$ is partitioned into p row vectors $\mathbf{c}_1, \mathbf{c}_2, \ldots, \mathbf{c}_p$. Therefore, we can rewrite (1) as

$$\min z = \sum_{j=1}^{p} \mathbf{c}_j \mathbf{x}_j$$

subject to

$$\begin{aligned} \sum_{j=1}^{p} \mathbf{L}_j \mathbf{x}_j &= \mathbf{b}_0, \\ \mathbf{A}_{(j)} \mathbf{x}_{(j)} &= \mathbf{b}_j \qquad (j = 1, \ldots, p), \\ \mathbf{x}_j &\geq \mathbf{0}. \end{aligned} \tag{2}$$

Each of the subset of constraints $\mathbf{A}_{(j)} \mathbf{x}_{(j)} = \mathbf{b}_j$ defines a convex polytope S_j. Let $\mathbf{x}_{ij}$ be the extreme points of the convex polytope. Then any solution $\mathbf{x}_j$ can be written as

$$\mathbf{x}_j = \sum_{i=1}^{s_j} \lambda_{ij} \mathbf{x}_{ij}, \tag{3}$$

with

$$\sum_{i=1}^{s_j} \lambda_{ij} = 1, \qquad \lambda_{ij} \geq 0,$$

where the polytope S_j is assumed to have s_j vertices and is bounded. Assume for the moment that we know all $\mathbf{x}_{ij}$. Let

$$\mathbf{l}_{ij} = \mathbf{L}_j \mathbf{x}_{ij}, \qquad c_{ij} = \mathbf{c}_j \mathbf{x}_{ij}. \tag{4}$$

Then (2) becomes

$$\min z = \sum_{j=1}^{p} \sum_{i=1}^{s_j} c_{ij} \lambda_{ij}$$

subject to

$$\sum_{j=1}^{p} \sum_{i=1}^{s_j} \lambda_{ij} \mathbf{l}_{ij} = \mathbf{b}_0, \tag{5}$$

with

$$\begin{aligned} \sum_{i=1}^{s_j} \lambda_{ij} &= 1 \qquad (j = 1, \ldots, p), \\ \lambda_{ij} &\geq 0 \qquad (i = 1, \ldots, s_j). \end{aligned}$$

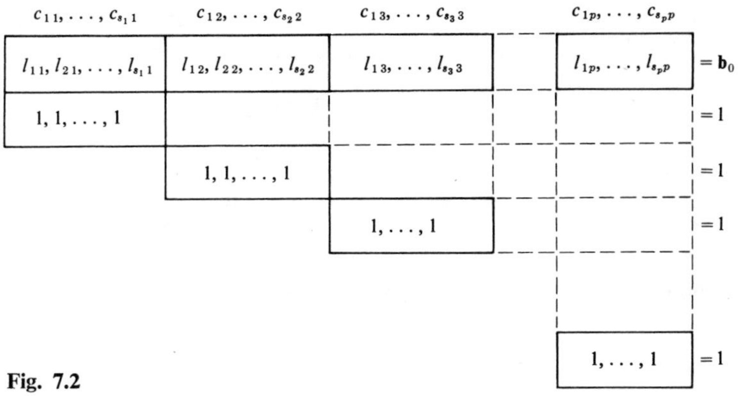

Fig. 7.2

If the unknown λ_{ij} in (5) are found, we then get $\mathbf{x}_j$ from (3) provided that all $\mathbf{x}_{ij}$ are known. The problem (5) can be systematically displayed as in Fig. 7.2.

The transformation from (2) to (5) has reduced the number of rows from $m_0 + \sum_{j=1}^{p} m_j$ to $m_0 + p$ rows. On the other hand, it has greatly increased the number of variables from $\sum_{j=1}^{p} n_j$ to $\sum_{j=1}^{p} s_j$. Fortunately, we do not have to deal with all the variables λ_{ij} and we do not need to know all $\mathbf{x}_{ij}$.

Since the matrix in Fig. 7.2 has $m_0 + p$ rows, $m_0 + p$ vectors are needed to form a basic feasible solution. Let us assume that we do have a starting basic feasible solution and have used the revised simplex method. This will generate prices for each row. Let the price vector be $(\boldsymbol{\pi}, \bar{\boldsymbol{\pi}})$, where $\boldsymbol{\pi}$ is a m_0 component vector and $\bar{\boldsymbol{\pi}}$ is a p component vector. Note that a typical column vector in Fig. 7.2 is $[\mathbf{l}_{ij}, \mathbf{e}_j]$. According to the simplex method, a vector not in the basis should be brought into the basis if its relative cost is negative, i.e., if

$$\bar{c}_{ij} = c_{ij} - (\boldsymbol{\pi}, \bar{\boldsymbol{\pi}})\,[\mathbf{l}_{ij}, \mathbf{e}_j] < 0.$$

Let

$$\bar{\boldsymbol{\pi}} = (\bar{\pi}_1, \bar{\pi}_2, \ldots, \bar{\pi}_p).$$

Then

$$\bar{c}_{ij} = c_{ij} - \boldsymbol{\pi}\mathbf{l}_{ij} - \bar{\pi}_j.$$

Now among the vectors not in the basis, some are in S_1, some are in S_2, etc. If the minimum of the relative costs of vectors in each S_j is nonnegative, i.e., $\min_i \bar{c}_{ij} \geq 0$, then the current solution is optimum. Therefore, we shall search in each S_j for the vector with the minimum relative cost. Since in a given S_j, $\bar{\pi}_j$ is the same for all vectors, we solve

$$\min_i (c_{ij} - \boldsymbol{\pi}\mathbf{l}_{ij}) = \min_i (\mathbf{c}_j - \boldsymbol{\pi}\mathbf{L}_j)\,\mathbf{x}_{ij},$$

subject to $\mathbf{x}_{ij} \in S_j$. (That is, we pick the minimum vertex in the convex polytope S_j.) But this is a linear program, namely

$$\min (\mathbf{c}_j - \boldsymbol{\pi} \mathbf{L}_j) \mathbf{x}_j$$

subject to

$$\mathbf{A}_{(j)} \mathbf{x}_{(j)} = \mathbf{b}_j, \qquad \mathbf{x}_j \geq \mathbf{0}. \tag{6}$$

Since the objective function in (6) is linear, the minimum of the objective function is always at a vertex, i.e., $\mathbf{x}_{ij}$.

If

$$(\mathbf{c}_j - \boldsymbol{\pi} \mathbf{L}_j) \mathbf{x}_{ij} - \bar{\pi}_j < 0,^*$$

then the vector $[\mathbf{l}_{ij}, \mathbf{e}_j]$ should be brought into the basis, and the usual simplex step of changing basic and nonbasic variables is performed. One thing should be emphasized. When we bring the vector $[\mathbf{l}_{ij}, \mathbf{e}_j]$ into the basis, we should multiply it by the current $\mathbf{B}^{-1}$ before we perform the pivot operation. Because when $(\boldsymbol{\pi}, \bar{\boldsymbol{\pi}})$ was obtained in (5), the matrix in (5) had been multiplied by $\mathbf{B}^{-1}$. Had this $[\mathbf{l}_{ij}, \mathbf{e}_j]$ been present in (5), it would have been multiplied on the left by $\mathbf{B}^{-1}$ just as the rest of the column vectors in (5). The operation of multiplying a column vector in the starting tableau by the current $\mathbf{B}^{-1}$ is called *updating*.

If after solving p small linear programs

$$\min_i (\mathbf{c}_j - \boldsymbol{\pi}\mathbf{L}_j) \mathbf{x}_{ij} - \bar{\pi}_j \geq 0 \qquad (\text{for } j = 1, \ldots, p),$$

then the current solution is optimum.

7.2 EXAMPLE

Consider the linear program

$$\min x_1 + 8x_2 + 5x_1' + 6x_2' + x_3'$$

subject to

$$\begin{aligned} x_1 + 4x_2 + (1/4)x_1' + 2x_2' + (5/4)x_3' &= 7, \\ 2x_1 + 3x_2 &= 5, \\ 5x_1 + x_2 &= 6, \\ 3x_1' + 4x_2' + 3x_3' &= 12, \\ x_1, x_2, x_1', x_2', x_3' &\geq 0. \end{aligned} \tag{1}$$

* $\mathbf{x}_{ij}$ is the optimal solution to (6).

Note in problem (1) that

$$\mathbf{L}_1 = (1, 4), \qquad \mathbf{L}_2 = (1/4, 2, 5/4),$$
$$\mathbf{b}_0 = 7, \qquad \mathbf{b}_1 = [5, 6], \qquad \mathbf{b}_2 = 12,$$
$$\mathbf{A}_1 = \begin{bmatrix} 2 & 3 \\ 5 & 1 \end{bmatrix}, \qquad \mathbf{A}_2 = (3, 4, 3),$$
$$\mathbf{c}_1 = (1, 8), \qquad \mathbf{c}_2 = (5, 6, 1).$$

The convex set S_1 is a single point with $\mathbf{x}_{11} = [1, 1]$. The convex set S_2 is a plane triangle with $\mathbf{x}_{12} = [4, 0, 0]$, $\mathbf{x}_{22} = [0, 3, 0]$, and $\mathbf{x}_{32} = [0, 0, 4]$ as vertices. In order to have a starting basic solution, we need $m_0 + p = 1 + 2$ vectors. Therefore we shall assume that we start with $\mathbf{x}_{11}$, $\mathbf{x}_{12}$, and $\mathbf{x}_{22}$ (note that we do not need to know $\mathbf{x}_{32}$):

$$l_{11} = \mathbf{L}_1 \mathbf{x}_{11} = (1, 4)[1, 1] = 5, \qquad c_{11} = (1, 8)[1, 1] = 9,$$
$$l_{12} = \mathbf{L}_2 \mathbf{x}_{12} = (1/4, 2, 5/4)[4, 0, 0] = 1, \qquad c_{12} = (5, 6, 1)[4, 0, 0] = 20,$$
$$l_{22} = \mathbf{L}_2 \mathbf{x}_{22} = (1/4, 2, 5/4)[0, 3, 0] = 6, \qquad c_{22} = (5, 6, 1)[0, 3, 0] = 18.$$

Therefore, the problem becomes

$$\min 9\lambda_{11} + 20\lambda_{12} + 18\lambda_{22} + \cdots$$

subject to

$$\begin{aligned} 5\lambda_{11} + \lambda_{12} + 6\lambda_{22} + \cdots &= 7, \\ \lambda_{11} \qquad\qquad\qquad &= 1, \\ \lambda_{12} + \lambda_{22} + \cdots &= 1. \end{aligned} \tag{2}$$

This is a standard linear program with unknown λ_{ij}. If we use the penalty method (see Section 2.3), then we should associate with every artificial variable a large positive constant as its cost. However, in Tableau 7.1 we give zero cost to every artificial variable with the understanding that when the relative cost associated with the artificial variable becomes negative or positive, it does not affect the termination of the simplex algorithm. The dotted part in Tableau 7.1 indicates that there may be many columns that have not been included.

Tableau 7.1

	1	x_1^a	x_2^a	x_3^a	λ_{11}	λ_{12}	λ_{22}		Constant
$-z$	1	0	0	0	9	20	18	...	0
x_1^a		1			5	1	6	...	7
x_2^a			1		1	0	0	...	1
x_3^a				1	0	1	1	...	1

Tableau 7.2

	1	x_1^a	x_2^a	x_3^a	λ_{11}	λ_{12}	λ_{22}		Constant
$-z$	1	2/5	−11	−20.4	0	0	0	...	−28.6
λ_{11}	0	0	1	0	1	0	0	...	1
λ_{12}	0	−1/5	1	6/5	0	1	0	...	4/5
λ_{22}	0	1/5	−1	−1/5	0	0	1	...	1/5

After introducing $\lambda_{11}, \lambda_{12}, \lambda_{22}$ into the basis, we have Tableau 7.2. From Tableau 7.2 we see that $(\boldsymbol{\pi}, \bar{\pi}_1, \bar{\pi}_2) = (-2/5, 11, 20.4)$.

$$(\mathbf{c}_1 - \boldsymbol{\pi}\mathbf{L}_1)\,\mathbf{x}_1 = \{(1, 8) - (-2/5)(1, 4)\}\,[x_1, x_2] = \frac{7}{5}x_1 + \frac{48}{5}x_2.$$

Therefore, in S_1 we have

$$\min \frac{7}{5}x_1 + \frac{48}{5}x_2$$

subject to

$$\begin{aligned} 2x_1 + 3x_2 &= 5, \\ 5x_1 + x_2 &= 6, \\ x_1, x_2 &\geq 0. \end{aligned} \tag{3}$$

The solution is $x_1 = 1$, $x_2 = 1$ with

$$(\mathbf{c}_1 - \boldsymbol{\pi}\mathbf{L}_1)\,\mathbf{x}_1 - \bar{\pi}_1 = \frac{7}{5} \times 1 + \frac{48}{5} \times 1 - 11 = 0.$$

Similarly in S_2

$$\begin{aligned}(\mathbf{c}_2 - \boldsymbol{\pi}\mathbf{L}_2)\,\mathbf{x}_2 &= \left((5, 6, 1) - \left(-\frac{2}{5}\right)\left(\frac{1}{4}, 2, \frac{5}{4}\right)\right)[x_1', x_2', x_3'] \\ &= 5.1x_1' + 6.8x_2' + 1.5x_3',\end{aligned}$$

so the linear program becomes

$$\min 5.1x_1' + 6.8x_2' + 1.5x_3'$$

subject to

$$3x_1' + 4x_2' + 3x_3' = 12$$

The solution is $x_1' = 0$, $x_2' = 0$, $x_3' = 4$:

$$\begin{aligned}(\mathbf{c}_2 - \boldsymbol{\pi}\mathbf{L}_2)\,\mathbf{x}_2 - \bar{\pi}_2 &= 5.1 \times 0 + 6.8 \times 0 + 1.5 \times 4 - \frac{102}{5} \\ &= 6 - 20.4 = -14.4 < 0,\end{aligned}$$

$$l_{32} = \mathbf{L}_2\mathbf{x}_{32} = \left(\frac{1}{4}, 2, \frac{5}{4}\right)[0, 0, 4] = 5.$$

Thus $[\mathbf{l}_{32}, \mathbf{e}_2] = [5, 0, 1]$. Before adding this vector to Tableau 7.2, we should multiply it by the current $\mathbf{B}^{-1}$, namely

$$\begin{bmatrix} 0 & 1 & 0 \\ -1/5 & 1 & 6/5 \\ 1/5 & -1 & -1/5 \end{bmatrix} \begin{bmatrix} 5 \\ 0 \\ 1 \end{bmatrix} = \begin{bmatrix} 0 \\ 1/5 \\ 4/5 \end{bmatrix}.$$

This vector [0, 1/5, 4/5] together with its relative cost -14.4 is added to Tableau 7.2 and is shown in Tableau 7.3. A pivot step on Tableau 7.3 leads to Tableau 7.4, which is optimum with

$$\lambda_{11} = 1, \quad \lambda_{12} = 3/4$$

and

$$\lambda_{32} = 1/4.$$

Thus

$$\mathbf{x}_1 = \lambda_{11}\,[1, 1] = [1, 1],$$

$$\mathbf{x}_2 = \frac{3}{4}\,[4, 0, 0] + \frac{1}{4}\,[0, 0, 4] = [3, 0, 1].$$

As a check, we find that constraints of (1) are satisfied and

$$z = 1 + 8 \times 1 + 5 \times 3 + 6 \times 0 + 1 \times 1 = 25.$$

Tableau 7.3

	1	x_1^a	x_2^a	x_3^a	λ_{11}	λ_{12}	λ_{22}	λ_{32}		Constant
$-z$	1	2/5	-11	-20.4	0	0	0	-14.4	...	-28.6
λ_{11}	0	0	1	0	1	0	0	0	...	1
λ_{12}	0	$-1/5$	1	6/5	0	1	0	1/5	...	4/5
λ_{22}	0	1/5	-1	$-1/5$	0	0	1	4/5*	...	1/5

Tableau 7.4

	1	x_1^a	x_2^a	x_3^a	λ_{11}	λ_{12}	λ_{22}	λ_{32}		Constant
$-z$	1	4	-29	-24	0	0	18	0	...	-25
λ_{11}	0	0	1	0	1	0	0	0	...	1
λ_{12}	0	$-1/4$	5/4	5/4	0	1	$-1/4$	0	...	3/4
λ_{32}	0	1/4	$-5/4$	$-1/4$	0	0	5/4	1	...	1/4

EXERCISE

Consider the program

$$\min z = 5x_1 + x_2 + x_3 + 6x_1' + 2x_2' + x_3'$$

subject to

$$
\begin{aligned}
x_1 + x_2 + \ \ x_3 + \ \ x_1' + x_2' + x_3' &= 6, \\
x_1 \qquad + \ \ x_3 \qquad\qquad\qquad\qquad &= 1, \\
x_2 + 2x_3 \qquad\qquad\qquad\qquad &= 3, \\
+ 2x_1' + x_2' + x_3' &= 4, \\
x_i \geq 0, \qquad x_i' \geq 0 \qquad (i = 1, 2, 3).&
\end{aligned}
$$

Use the decomposition algorithm of Dantzig and Wolfe. Use λ_{11} (which corresponds to $x_1 = 1$, $x_2 = 3$) and λ_{12} λ_{22} (which corresponds to $x_1' = 2$, $x_2' = 4$) as the starting basic variables.

SUGGESTED READING

In this chapter, we have transformed a large linear program, shown in Figure 7.1 (which has a large number of rows and columns), into a linear program, shown in Figure 7.2, which has a large number of columns. To solve the linear program in Figure 7.2, we do not have to write down all the columns. We use a few columns as the starting basis and generate the column which is to enter the basis. The problem of generating the best column is another linear program. In general, a large linear program is solved by splitting the linear program into two parts (a main part and an auxiliary part). The main part is a linear program which has many rows or many columns. Neither these rows nor these columns are explicitly written down. The auxiliary part is another optimization problem which supplies the best row or the best column for the main part. Many examples like this are given in Chapter 11. The reader should also read Gomory [82].

MAXIMAL FLOW 8

8.1 INTRODUCTION

In this chapter we shall study so-called network flow theory. Problems in network flow can be formulated as linear programs. However, due to the special structure of these problems, a sufficient number of efficient algorithms and elegant theorems have been developed to warrant separate study of the problems. In most of the problems the optimum solutions are always integers, a fact which is not true in linear programs.

We shall first define a network. A *network* consists of a set of nodes (vertices, points) and a set of arcs (edges, links, lines, branches) connecting these *nodes*. It is always assumed in this book that there is a finite number of nodes and arcs. If an arc has a direction, then it is called a *directed arc;* otherwise, it is called an *undirected arc*. Circles are used to represent nodes, lines with arrows to represent directed arcs, and lines without arrows to represent undirected arcs. In Fig. 8.1 we have a network with four nodes and six directed arcs.

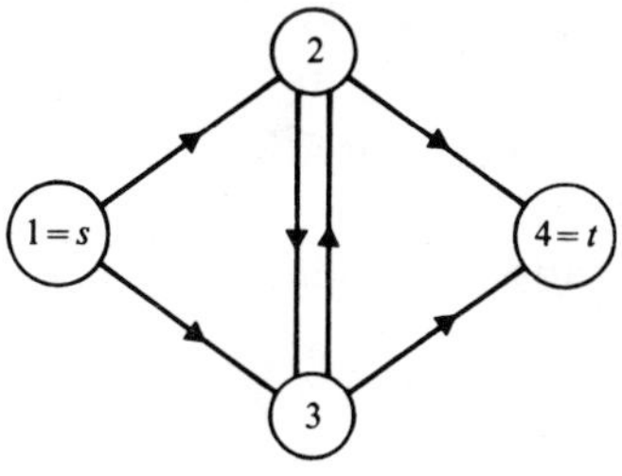

Fig. 8.1

We shall use N_i to indicate the node i and A_{ij} to indicate the directed arc leading from N_i to N_j. If the arc between nodes N_i and N_j is an undirected arc, then either A_{ij} or A_{ji} can be used. A network is connected if for every partitioning of the nodes of the network into subsets X and $\bar{X}$, there is either an arc A_{ij} or A_{ji} with $N_i \in X$ and $N_j \in \bar{X}$. The word "network" will be used to denote a connected network throughout this book. For convenience we shall assume that between any two nodes N_i and N_j there is at most one directed arc A_{ij} and one directed arc A_{ji} or there is only one undirected arc A_{ij}. In most cases we can replace an undirected arc by a pair of directed arcs. Also, we can rule out the possibility of having an arc leading from one node to itself.

Let $N_1, A_{12}, N_2, A_{23}, \ldots, N_{k-1}, A_{k-1,k}, N_k$ be a sequence of nodes and arcs. Then this sequence of nodes and arcs is called a *chain* leading from N_1 to N_k, or a *directed chain.* If $N_1 = N_k$, then it is called a *directed cycle.* For example, in Fig. 8.1 the sequence $N_s, A_{12}, N_2, A_{2t}, N_t$ is a chain from N_s to N_t; so is the sequence $N_s, A_{12}, N_2, A_{23}, N_3, A_{32}, N_2, A_{24}, N_t$ a chain from N_s to N_t. The sequence $N_2, A_{23}, N_3, A_{32}, N_2$ is a cycle. A chain is called a *simple chain* if it does not contain any cycles. From now on, the word chain is used to mean a simple chain.

A *path,* like a chain, is also a sequence of nodes and arcs but the arcs can be directed in either direction or they can be undirected arcs. For example, in Fig. 8.1 $N_s, A_{13}, N_3, A_{23}, N_2, A_{24}, N_t$ is a path. If A_{23} is replaced by A_{32}, then it is a chain.

So far, the definition of a network is just the definition of a graph. We use the word "network" because there will be many numbers associated with every arc, while in graph theory an arc just indicates the connection between the nodes. Let every arc A_{ij} have an associated *positive integer* b_{ij} called the capacity of the arc. (Arc capacity and branch capacity are also commonly used.) There are two special nodes in a network. One is called the *source,* denoted by N_s, and one is called the *sink*, denoted by N_t. The network can be considered as a pipeline system with the arcs representing pipelines, the source being the inlet of the water, the sink being the outlet of the water, and all other nodes just being junctions between pipelines. The capacity of each arc can be considered to indicate the cross sectional area of the pipeline. With such a pipeline system, we are interested in the maximum flow that can be put through it from the source to the sink.

In order to make the above intuitive problem precise, we shall first define a flow in the network. A set of nonnegative integers x_{ij} is called a *flow* in a network if they satisfy the following constraints:

$$\sum_i x_{ij} - \sum_k x_{jk} = \begin{cases} -v & \text{if } j = s, \\ 0 & \text{if } j \neq s, t, \\ v & \text{if } j = t, \end{cases} \tag{1}$$

$$0 \leq x_{ij} \leq b_{ij} \qquad \text{(for all } i, j). \tag{2}$$

The v which appears in (1) is a nonnegative number called the value of the flow. Note that (1) expresses the fact that flow is conserved at every node except the source and the sink. Constraint (2) means that the arc flow x_{ij} is always bounded by the capacity of the arc b_{ij}. Constraints (1) and (2) do resemble the laws governing water flow in pipelines. But there is no liquid in the world that is governed by (1) and (2). To illustrate this point, consider the network in Fig. 8.1 with N_1 as the source and N_4 as the sink. Assume that every arc has capacity of one unit. Then the set $x_{12} = 1$, $x_{24} = 1$, $x_{ij} = 0$, otherwise, is a set of nonnegative integers which satisfy (1) and (2). But any liquid in a pipeline system like Fig. 8.1 will have $x_{13} \neq 0$ if $x_{12} = 1$. To make the analogy complete, we have to think that the pipeline system has many *valves* at every node that can keep the liquid from going to any of the arcs that are incident to that node.

To find the maximum flow value in any network is obviously a linear program with the objective function $v = \sum_j x_{sj}$ and the constraints (1) and (2). However, as this is a very special case of a linear program, we shall develop algorithms more efficient than the simplex method, which is for general linear programs.

If the network is a chain $N_1, A_{12}, N_2, A_{23}, \ldots, N_k$ with N_1 the source and N_k the sink, then the maximum amount of flow that can be put through the network is obviously limited by the arc with the minimum capacity of all the arcs in the chain. Here the arc with the minimum capacity is the bottleneck of the network. We shall now define the general notion of a bottleneck in an arbitrary network.

A cut is denoted by $(X, \bar{X})$, where X is a subset of nodes of the network and $\bar{X}$ is its complement. A *cut* $(X, \bar{X})$ is a set of all arcs A_{ij} with either $N_i \in X$ and $N_j \in \bar{X}$ or $N_j \in X$ and $N_i \in \bar{X}$. A cut is therefore a set of arcs the removal of which will disconnect the network. A cut separating N_s and N_t is a cut $(X, \bar{X})$ with $N_s \in X$ and $N_t \in \bar{X}$.

The *capacity* or *value* of a cut $(X, \bar{X})$, denoted by $c(X, \bar{X})$, is $\sum_{i,j} b_{ij}$ with $N_i \in X$ and $N_j \in \bar{X}$. Note that in defining a cut, we count all the arcs that are between the set X and the set $\bar{X}$, but in calculating its capacity, we count the capacity only of arcs from X to $\bar{X}$, but not the directed arcs from $\bar{X}$ to X. Therefore, $c(X, \bar{X}) \neq c(\bar{X}, X)$ in general.

A cut $(X, \bar{X})$ separating N_s and N_t is then an analogy of a bottleneck. Clearly due to the constraints (1) and (2) the maximum flow value v is less than or equal to the capacity of any cut separating N_s and N_t. What is surprising, perhaps, is that the maximum flow value is *always* equal to the minimum capacity of all cuts separating N_s and N_t. A cut separating N_s and N_t with minimum capacity is called a *minimum cut*. (For simplicity, we will sometimes omit the phrase separating N_s and N_t in describing a cut.) The fact that the maximum flow value is always equal to the capacity of a minimum cut was proved first by Ford and Fulkerson [64] under the theorem of *max-flow min-cut*. This is the central theorem in network flow theory.

We shall give a constructive proof of the theorem (see Ford and Fulkerson [65]), which constructs a maximal flow and locates a minimum cut. The proof is to show that there always exists a flow with value equal to the capacity of a cut. Since the maximum flow is always equal to or less than the capacity of any cut, in particular, the minimum cut, this will prove the theorem.

Theorem 8.1. *Max-Flow Min-Cut Theorem* [64]. For any network the maximal flow value from the source to the sink is equal to the capacity of a minimum cut separating the source and the sink.

Proof. Given any set of nonnegative integers x_{ij} satisfying (1) and (2). If the value of the flow is equal to the capacity of a cut, then the theorem is proved. If not, we can always increase the value of the flow by the following rule until the value of the flow is equal to the capacity of a cut: [$x_{ij} = 0$ for all i and j is a set of nonnegative integers satisfying (1) and (2)].

Based on the current flow in the network we shall define a subset X of the nodes recursively by the following rules.

0. $N_s \in X$.
1. If $N_i \in X$ and $x_{ij} < b_{ij}$, then $N_j \in X$.
2. If $N_i \in X$ and $x_{ji} > 0$, then $N_j \in X$.

Any node not in X then belongs to $\bar{X}$. Using these rules to define the set X, we have two possible outcomes.

CASE 1. N_t is in $\bar{X}$. This implies that in all arcs from X to $\bar{X}$ we have $x_{ij} = b_{ij}$ (due to rule 1) and there is no arc flow x_{ji} from $\bar{X}$ to X (due to rule 2). Then

$$\sum_{\substack{i \in X, \\ j \in \bar{X}}} x_{ij} = \sum_{\substack{i \in X, \\ j \in \bar{X}}} b_{ij} \qquad \text{and} \qquad \sum_{\substack{i \in X, \\ j \in \bar{X}}} x_{ji} = 0.$$

Hence we have a flow with value equal to $c\,(X, \bar{X})$.

CASE 2. N_t is in X. If we follow the rules that make N_t in X, there is always a path from N_s to N_t, say $N_s, \ldots, N_i, A_{i,i+1}, \ldots, N_t$ for which, in every arc, either $x_{i,i+1} < b_{i,i+1}$ or $x_{i+1,i} > 0$. An arc $A_{i,i+1}$ of the path is called a forward arc if $x_{i,i+1} \geq 0$ and is called a backward arc if $x_{i+1,i} > 0$.

Let ϵ_1 = minimum of all differences $b_{i,i+1} - x_{i,i+1}$ in the path, let ϵ_2 = minimum of $x_{i+1,i}$ in the path, and let $\epsilon = \min(\epsilon_1, \epsilon_2)$ = positive integer. Then we can increase the arc flows by ϵ on all forward arcs of the path and decrease the arc flows by ϵ on all backward arcs of the path. In this way the value of the flow is increased by ϵ and the new x_{ij} satisfies all the constraints (1) and (2). Now we can redefine the set X again based on the new flow. If N_t is still in X, we can again increase the flow value by ϵ. Since the capacity of a minimum cut is a finite number and we increase the value of the flow by at least one unit, after a finite number of steps we always obtain the maximum flow. Q.E.D.

Let us call the path in which $x_{ij} < b_{ij}$ on all forward arcs and $x_{ji} > 0$ on all backward arcs a *flow augmenting path* with respect to a flow. We shall use F_{st} to denote the totality of nonnegative integers x_{ij} satisfying (1) and (2). Then we have the following corollary.

Corollary 8.1. A flow F_{st} is maximum if and only if there is no flow augmenting path with respect to F_{st}.

Several comments are in order. The value of a maximum flow is certainly unique in any network, but there may be many flows that give the same maximum flow value. Also there may be many minimum cuts in the network. For example, consider the network in Fig. 8.2.

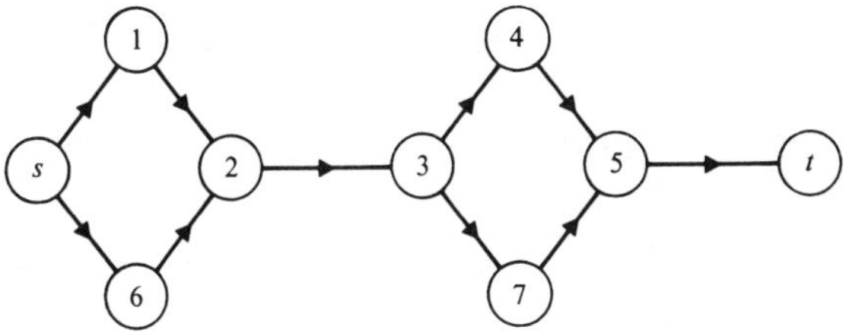

Fig. 8.2

Assume that every arc has a capacity of one unit. Then both the arc A_{23} and the arc A_{5t} are minimum cuts. The maximum flow value is certainly 1, but the maximum flow can be $x_{s1} = x_{12} = x_{23} = x_{34} = x_{45} = x_{5t} = 1$ or $x_{s6} = x_{62} = x_{23} = x_{37} = x_{75} = x_{5t} = 1$.

Theorem 8.2. Let $(X, \bar{X})$ and $(Y, \bar{Y})$ be minimum cuts. Then $(X \cup Y, \overline{X \cup Y})$ and $(X \cap Y, \overline{X \cap Y})$ are also minimum cuts.

Proof. If $X \subset Y$, then $X \cup Y = Y$ and $X \cap Y = X$, so

$$(X \cup Y, \overline{X \cup Y}) = (Y, \bar{Y}) \qquad \text{and} \qquad (X \cap Y, \overline{X \cap Y}) = (X, \bar{X}).$$

Now consider Fig 8.3 and let $N_s \in Q$ and $N_t \in R$,

$$X = Q \cup S, \qquad \bar{X} = P \cup R,$$
$$Y = P \cup Q, \qquad \bar{Y} = R \cup S,$$

so that

$$X \cap Y = Q, \qquad X \cap \bar{Y} = S,$$
$$\bar{X} \cap Y = P, \qquad \bar{X} \cap \bar{Y} = R.$$

Let $c(P, Q) = \sum b_{ij}$ for all $i \in P, j \in Q$, and similarly for other notations. Since $(X, \bar{X})$ is a minimum cut separating N_s and N_t and $(Q, P \cup R \cup S)$ is also a cut separating N_s and N_t,

$$c(X, \bar{X}) \leq c(Q, P \cup R \cup S),$$

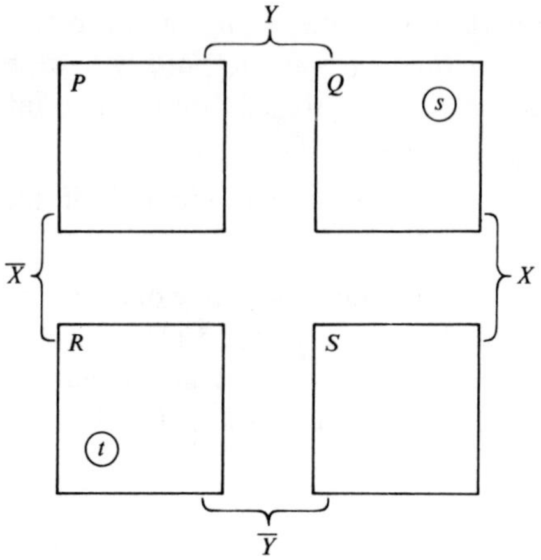

Fig. 8.3

or, alternatively,

$$c(Q, P) + c(Q, R) + c(S, P) + c(S, R) \leq c(Q, P) + c(Q, R) + c(Q, S),$$

or

$$c(S, P) + c(S, R) \leq c(Q, S). \tag{3}$$

Since

$$c(X, \bar{X}) \leq c(P \cup Q \cup S, R),$$

or

$$c(Q, P) + c(Q, R) + c(S, P) + c(S, R) \leq c(P, R) + c(Q, R) + c(S, R),$$

we have

$$c(Q, P) + c(S, P) \leq c(P, R). \tag{4}$$

Similarly

$$c(Y, \bar{Y}) \leq c(Q, P \cup R \cup S)$$

implies

$$c(P, R) + c(P, S) \leq c(Q, P) \tag{5}$$

and

$$c(Y, \bar{Y}) \leq c(P \cup Q \cup S, R)$$

implies

$$c(P, S) + c(Q, S) \leq c(S, R). \tag{6}$$

Adding (3), (4), (5), and (6), we have

$$2c(S, P) + 2c(P, S) \leq 0,$$

and since $b_{ij} \geq 0$, then

$$c(S, P) = c(P, S) = 0. \tag{7}$$

Substituting (7) into (3), (4), (5), and (6), we have

$$c(S, R) \leq c(Q, S),$$
$$c(Q, P) \leq c(P, R),$$
$$c(P, R) \leq c(Q, P),$$
$$c(Q, S) \leq c(S, R),$$

or

$$c(S, R) = c(Q, S), \tag{8}$$
$$c(Q, P) = c(P, R). \tag{9}$$

From (7), (8), and (9) we have

$$\begin{aligned} c(X, \bar{X}) &= c(Q, P) + c(Q, R) + c(S, R) \\ &= c(Q, P) + c(Q, R) + c(Q, S) = c(X \cap Y, \overline{X \cap Y}), \end{aligned}$$

$$\begin{aligned} c(X, \bar{X}) &= c(Q, P) + c(Q, R) + c(S, R) \\ &= c(P, R) + c(Q, R) + c(S, R) = c(X \cup Y, \overline{X \cup Y}). \text{ Q.E.D.} \end{aligned}$$

Since there are many minimum cuts, the question naturally arises as to which minimum cut is obtained in the constructive proof of the max-flow min-cut theorem. Let $(X_i, \bar{X}_i)$, $(i = 1, \ldots, m)$ be *all* the minimum cuts separating N_s and N_t and let $(X, \bar{X})$ be the minimum cut picked out in the proof. Then $X = \cap_i X_i$. To see this, first we prove that $(X, \bar{X})$ is indeed a minimum cut. Let $(X_1, \bar{X}_1)$ and $(X_2, \bar{X}_2)$ be any two minimum cuts. Then from Theorem 8.2 $(X_1 \cap X_2, \overline{X_1 \cap X_2})$ is also a minimum cut. Let $(X_3, \bar{X}_3)$ be another minimum cut. Using Theorem 8.2 again, we know that $(X_1 \cap X_2 \cap X_3, \overline{X_1 \cap X_2 \cap X_3})$ is also a minimum cut. If this process is repeated $m - 1$ times, then it shows that

$$(X_1 \cap \cdots \cap X_m, \overline{X_1 \cap \cdots \cap X_m}) = (X, \bar{X})$$

is a minimum cut. Secondly, it is clear that the set X does not contain any proper subset X_i for which $(X_i, \bar{X}_i)$ is a minimum cut as $X = \cap_i X_i$. Since the recursive definition of X cannot be used to label a node in $\bar{X}$ once the maximal flow value is equal to $c(X, \bar{X})$, this means that $(X, \bar{X})$ is the minimum cut picked out in the constructive proof of the max-flow min-cut theorem.

8.2 THE LABELING METHOD FOR GETTING MAXIMUM FLOW

We have already given a constructive proof of the max-flow min-cut theorem. Now we shall describe in detail the algorithm for getting the maximum flow. As was pointed out in Section 8.1, any network flow problem can be formulated as a linear program. The labeling method is not, however, a special case of the simplex method. The simplex method moves from one vertex of the polytope to another until the optimum vertex is reached. The labeling method is not such a method, as will be made clear later.

The labeling method starts with any arbitrary flow (zero flow may be used as the starting flow) and then tries to increase the flow value. The algorithm terminates if the flow value cannot be increased. The algorithm is a systematic way of searching all possible flow augmenting paths from N_s to N_t. This is done by giving labels to nodes to indicate the direction that flow in an arc may be increased. Once a flow augmenting path is found, the flow is increased to its maximum capacity along the path and all the labels on the nodes are erased. We then start to assign new labels to nodes based on the new flow.

The algorithm consists of two steps: step 1 is the labeling process, which assigns labels to nodes, and step 2 is flow change. Steps 1 and 2 are iterated until the increase of flow becomes impossible.

STEP 1. *Labeling Process.* Every node is always in one of the three states, labeled and scanned, labeled and unscanned, or unlabeled. A node is labeled and scanned if it has a label and we have inspected all its neighboring nodes. (Two nodes are neighbors if both are connected by one arc.) A node is labeled and unscanned if it has a label but not all its neighbors have been inspected. A node is unlabeled if it has no label.

Initially, all nodes are unlabeled. A label for a node N_j always has two parts. The first part is the index of a node N_i, which indicates that we can send flow from N_i to N_j, and the second part is a number which indicates the maximum amount of flow we can send from the source to N_j without violating the capacity restrictions. We first assign the label $[s^+, \epsilon(s) = \infty]$ to N_s. The first label simply says that we can send flow from N_s to itself; the number ∞ indicates that there is no upper bound on how much can be sent. The node N_s is now labeled and unscanned and all other nodes are unlabeled. In general, select a node N_j which is labeled and unscanned. Assume N_j has a label of the form $[i^+, \epsilon(j)]$ or $[i^-, \epsilon(j)]$. To all neighboring nodes N_k of N_j which are unlabeled and for which $0 \leq x_{jk} < b_{jk}$ assign the label $[j^+, \epsilon(k)]$ to N_k, where

$$\epsilon(k) = \min\,[\epsilon(j), b_{jk} - x_{jk}].$$

To all neighboring nodes N_k which are unlabeled and for which $x_{kj} > 0$ assign the label $[j^-, \epsilon(k)]$, where

$$\epsilon(k) = \min\,[\epsilon(j), x_{kj}].^*$$

The $+$ and the $-$ signs in the first label indicate how the flow should be changed in step 2. Now all the neighboring nodes of N_j have labels; N_j

---

* For an undirected arc we could define $\epsilon(k) = \min\,[\epsilon(j), x_{kj} + b_{jk}]$. This would increase the capacity of the flow augmenting path. If this procedure is adopted, a negative arc flow in the flow change routine means that the arc flow is in the direction opposite to the original arc flow.

is considered to be labeled and scanned and may be disregarded during the rest of this step. (If one inspects all the neighbors of N_j and cannot label the neighbors, then N_j is also considered to be a labeled and scanned node.) All the nodes N_k are now labeled and unscanned.

Continue to assign labels to neighbors of labeled and unscanned nodes until either N_t is labeled or no more labels can be assigned and N_t is unlabeled. If N_t cannot be labeled, no flow augmenting path exists and, hence, the flow is maximal. If N_t is labeled, a flow augmenting path can be found using step 2.

STEP 2. *Flow Change*. Assume that N_t is labeled $[k^+, \epsilon(t)]$. Replace x_{kt} by $x_{kt} + \epsilon(t)$ and turn to N_k. If N_k is labeled $[j^+, \epsilon(k)]$, replace x_{jk} by $x_{jk} + \epsilon(t)$ and turn to N_j. If N_k is labeled $[j^-, \epsilon(k)]$, replace x_{kj} by $x_{kj} - \epsilon(t)$ and turn to N_j. Continue until N_s is reached. Erase the labels on all the nodes and go back to step 1.

When the algorithm terminates at step 1, there is a set X of labeled nodes and arcs A_{ij} with $N_i \in X$ and $N_j \in \bar{X}$ for which $x_{ij} = b_{ij}$ and there is no arc flow $x_{ji} > 0$. This implies that $(X, \bar{X})$ is a minimum cut with a flow equal to its capacity. Therefore, maximal flow is obtained. On the other hand, each time step 2 increases the value of the flow by at least one unit (the arc capacities are integers, and we start with integer flow.) As the maximal flow value is bounded from above by the minimum cut capacity, which is an integer, the algorithm is a finite process.

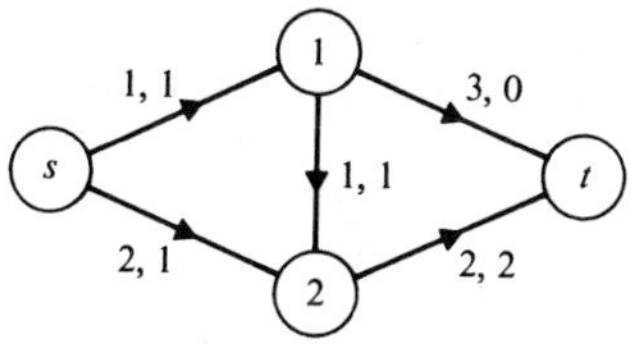

Fig. 8.4

Consider the network shown in Fig. 8.4 with two numbers associated with each directed arc. The first number is the arc capacity and the second number is the initial arc flow. [We may use any flow satisfying (1) and (2) as the initial flow. For example, $x_{ij} = 0$ for all i, j.]

STEP 1. Assign N_s the label $[s^+, \infty]$. There are two neighboring nodes of N_s. It is not possible to label Node N_1 at this point because $b_{s1} - x_{s1} = 1 - 1 = 0$ and there is no arc flow $x_{1s} > 0$. Assign N_2 the label $[s^+, 1]$ since $b_{s2} - x_{s2} = 2 - 1 = 1$, and

$$\epsilon(2) = \min [\epsilon(s), b_{s2} - x_{s2}] = \min [\infty, 1] = 1.$$

Now N_s is labeled and scanned, and N_2 is labeled and unscanned. There are two unlabeled neighboring nodes of N_2, namely, N_1 and N_t. Node N_t

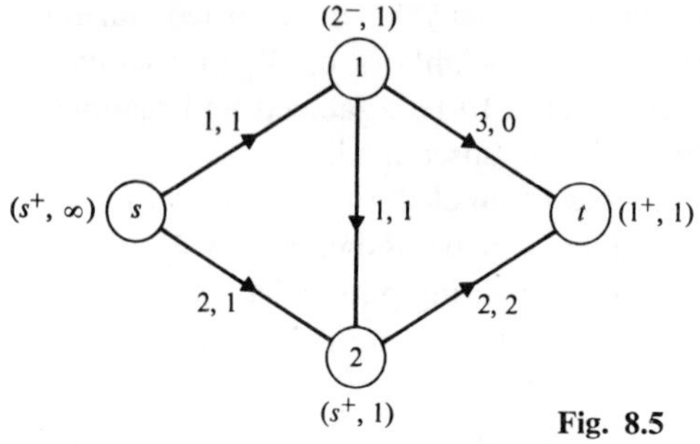

Fig. 8.5

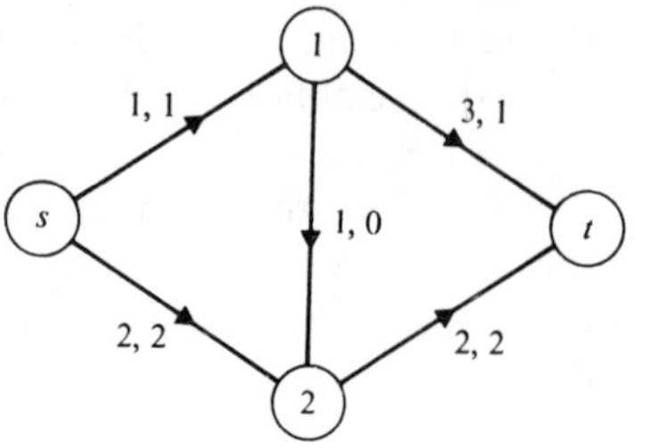

Fig. 8.6

cannot be labeled at this point, but N_1 can be labeled $[2^-, 1]$, because $x_{12} = 1 > 0$ and $\epsilon(1) = \min [\epsilon(2), x_{12}] = \min [1, 1] = 1$. Now N_2 is labeled and scanned, and N_1 is labeled and unscanned. There is only one unlabeled neighboring node of N_1, namely N_t. Node N_t should receive the label $[1^+, 1]$ since

$$\epsilon(t) = \min [\epsilon(1), b_{1t} - x_{1t}] = \min [1, 3 - 0] = 1.$$

The result of the labeling process is shown in Fig. 8.5. Since N_t is labeled, we go to step 2.

STEP 2. As the label of N_t is $[1^+, 1]$, add 1 to x_{1t}, so that, as a result, $x'_{1t} = x_{1t} + 1 = 0 + 1 = 1$. Turn to N_1 with label $[2^-, 1]$ and subtract 1 unit from x_{12}, so that $x'_{12} = x_{12} - 1 = 1 - 1 = 0$. Turn to N_2 with label $[s^+, 1]$. Add one unit to x_{s2}, so that $x'_{s2} = x_{s2} + 1 = 1 + 1 = 2$. The result of the flow change is shown in Fig. 8.6.

STEP 1. Assign $[s^+, \infty]$ to N_s. Now N_1 and N_2 both cannot be labeled, and N_t is unlabeled. Stop.

There are two things to be noted. First, we increase the flow in Fig. 8.4 by sending one unit of flow along the flow augmenting path $N_s, A_{s2}, N_2, A_{12}, N_1, A_{1t}, N_t$. Normally we cannot send flow from N_2 to N_1 because A_{12} is a directed arc, but when there is an arc flow in A_{12} already, we can send flow from N_2 to N_1 and the result simply cancels the existing arc flow. Second, the minimum cut obtained is $(X, \bar{X})$, where X is the single node N_s and $\bar{X}$ is the three nodes N_1, N_2, and N_t. Note that $(Y, \bar{Y})$ with $Y = \{N_s, N_2\}$ is also a minimum cut with capacity equal to $b_{s1} + b_{21} + b_{2t} = 1 + 0 + 2 = 3$. But $X \subset Y$ and the algorithm always selects the minimum cut $(X, \bar{X})$ with X the smallest subset, as mentioned before.

If the arc capacities b_{ij} are not all integers, then the algorithm may not be a finite one and also may converge to a wrong limit. Such an example is shown in Ford and Fulkerson [67]. This shows that the labeling method is not equivalent to the simplex method for linear programs. Since the network flow problem is a special case of a linear program and the simplex method works for real numbers, we should have an algorithm that works for real arc capacities. The following modification of the labeling algorithm will work for any undirected network with real arc capacities.

STEP 1. Delete all arcs that are saturated with flow, i.e., $x_{ij} = b_{ij}$. (At the start no arc is saturated since $x_{ij} = 0$.) Go to step 2.

STEP 2. Using whatever arcs are available, find a flow augmenting path by the labeling method and send as much flow as possible along that path. If a flow augmenting path is found, go to step 1; if not, go to step 3.

STEP 3. Put back all arcs that have been deleted, i.e., all saturated arcs are now available. Find a flow augmenting path from N_s to N_t and send as much flow as possible along that path. If such a path is found, go to step 1; if not, stop. The current flow is maximal.

Let us prove that it is a finite algorithm that does give the maximum flow. Each flow change in step 2 will make *at least one more arc saturated with flow*. After a finite number of iterations between step 1 and step 2, enough saturated arcs will be deleted to make it impossible to increase the flow value in step 2. If we use the labeling method in step 2, we will label a set X, and all arcs A_{ij} with $N_i \in X$ and $N_j \in \bar{X}$ will be saturated. (They may be saturated in either direction.) The flow value at this time is equal to

$$\sum x_{ij} - \sum x_{kl} \quad \text{or} \quad \sum b_{ij} - \sum b_{kl} \, (N_i \in X, N_j \in \bar{X}, N_l \in X, N_k \in \bar{X}).$$

Now we go to step 3 and put back all saturated arcs. This time, we can label a node which belonged to $\bar{X}$ in step 2, if there is an arc with $x_{kl} > 0$. This will make $N_t \in X$ and the flow value will be increased. We return to step 1. Therefore, when we are forced to use a saturated arc in step 3 again, the flow value is again equal to the sum of a set of arc capacities minus the sum of some arc capacities. But this set of arcs will always be different from the last set or differ in the directions in which the arcs are saturated, since the flow value is different. As there is a finite number of arcs in the network and there are only two directions of an arc that can be saturated, there is a finite number of the values $\sum b_{ij} - \sum b_{kl}$. Each time we go to step 3, the flow value is one of these values $\sum b_{ij} - \sum b_{kl}$. Each time the flow value is increased, so none of these values can repeatedly be the flow value in step 3. Thus the algorithm is a finite one.

The same process works also for networks with directed arcs, but the proof is a bit tedious. The difficulty is that the arc flow of a directed arc may be canceled in step 2 and no other arc saturated in the flow change process. Then we cannot say that at least one more arc is saturated in step 2.

Now we shall discuss a new result on the number of labeling processes required to achieve the maximal flow.

Every flow augmenting path increases the maximal flow value by at least one unit. If the maximal flow value is v, then we need at most v labeling processes to achieve the maximal flow. Suppose that we multiply all arc capacities by 10. Then the maximal flow value of the new network would be $10v$. This would mean that we need at most $10v$ labeling processes to achieve the maximal flow. Therefore, it is nice to have an upper bound on the number of labeling processes, which is independent of the maximal flow value, which is unknown at the beginning of the computation. Edmonds and Karp [58] have obtained such an upper bound. This upper bound is valid even when all arc capacities are real numbers. We shall now explore their results. First we have to introduce some notions and modify the labeling method. For convenience, we always consider an n-node network with $n(n - 1)$ arcs, although some of the arc capacities may be zero. For a given flow F in a network, we shall use $N(F)$ to denote the network with the flow F. In $N(F)$, an arc A_{ij} may be saturated, i.e. $x_{ij} = b_{ij}$, and we can consider the arc A_{ij} nonexistent, since we cannot send any flow from N_i to N_j along the arc A_{ij}. Because we can send flow from N_j to N_i in $N(F)$, we can consider that there is an arc A_{ji} with arc capacity $b_{ji} = x_{ij}$. For example, in Fig. 8.4 we can consider the arc A_{12} nonexistent and there is an arc A_{21} with capacity equal to 1. From now on, when we talk about a network $N(F)$, we are thinking about a network which is different from the original network without any arc flows. The labeling method generates a sequence of networks $N(F_1), N(F_2), \ldots, N(F_k)$, where F_k is the maximal flow The flow F_{i+1} is obtained from F_i by superimposing a flow augmenting path.

In the labeling method described earlier in this chapter, we did not prescribe the order in which labeled nodes are scanned. Now we want to follow the first-labeled first-scanned rule. For example, in Fig. 8.4 since we label N_2 before we label N_1, then we should scan N_2 before we scan N_1. In this first-labeled first-scanned labeling method, we will always get a flow augmenting path which contains the minimum number of arcs if the flow is not already maximum. Another refinement of the labeling method is necessary. If $A_{s1}, A_{12}, A_{23}, \ldots, A_{k,t}$ is a flow augmenting path, we define

$$\epsilon(j + 1) = \min [\epsilon(j), b_{j,j+1} - x_{j,j+1} + x_{j+1,j}].$$

If this way of defining $\epsilon(j + 1)$ is adopted, we will always saturate at least one arc in the flow augmenting path. Consider the network shown in Fig. 8.7, where the numbers beside the arcs are their arc capacities. We can consider this network as $N(F_0)$. Assume that we send one unit of flow along A_{s1}, A_{13}, A_{3t}; this will saturate the arc A_{13}, and we obtain $N(F_1)$, as shown in Fig. 8.8. In Fig. 8.8 we consider the arc A_{13} nonexistent and there is an arc A_{31} with arc capacity equal to 1. If we send one unit of flow along the flow augmenting path $A_{s2}, A_{23}, A_{31}, A_{14}, A_{4t}$, then we have the network $N(F_2)$ shown in Fig. 8.9. In Fig. 8.9 the arc A_{31} is nonexistent and A_{13} reappears as an arc with arc capacity equal to 1. We may consider that we

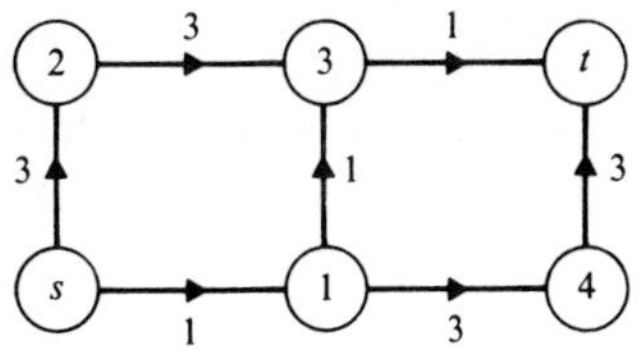

Fig. 8.7

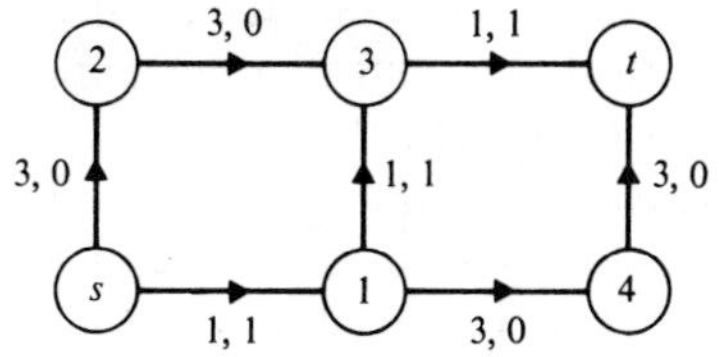

Fig. 8.8

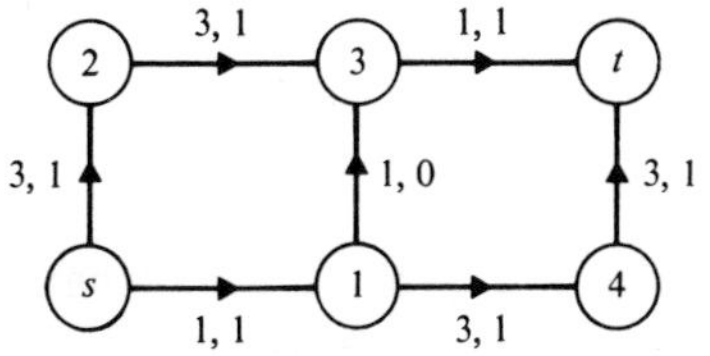

Fig. 8.9

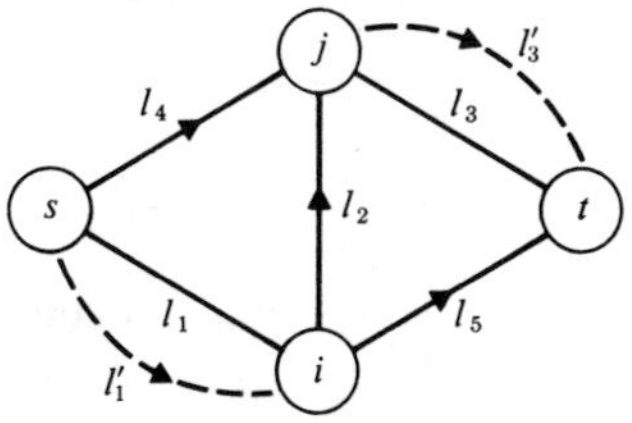

Fig. 8.10

have saturated A_{31} of $N(F_2)$ in Fig. 8.8. We have seen that each time a flow augmenting path saturates at least one arc of $N(F)$. We can summarize this result as a lemma.

Lemma 8.1. For any sequence of networks $N(F_0), N(F_1), \ldots, N(F_k)$ there is at least one arc of $N(F_i)$ which is not an arc of $N(F_{i+1})$, where F_{i+1} is obtained from F_i by adding a flow augmenting path using

$$\epsilon(j + 1) = \min\,[\epsilon\,(j), b_{j,j+1} - x_{j,j+1} + x_{j+1,j}].$$

We define the cardinal length of a path as the number of arcs in that path. We define the cardinal distance of N_s to N_t in the network $N(F)$ as the cardinal length of the shortest flow augmenting path from N_s to N_t in $N(F)$. If there exists no flow augmenting path from N_s to N_t, then we define the cardinal distance of N_s to N_t to be ∞. We shall use l_{st} for the cardinal distance from N_s to N_t.

One thing should be emphasized. The cardinal distance of a network $N(F)$ is the cardinal length of the shortest flow augmenting path in the network $N(F)$. This distance is ∞ if F is already the maximal flow. This is to be distinguished from the shortest flow chain existing in the network. For example, in Fig. 8.8 the shortest flow chain N_s, N_1, N_3, N_t is of length 3 while the cardinal distance from N_s to N_t is 5, since the flow augmenting path is $N_s, N_2, N_3, N_1, N_4, N_t$. In Fig. 8.9 the shortest flow chain is of length 3, while the cardinal distance from N_s to N_t is ∞.

Lemma 8.2. The length of the shortest flow chain and the cardinal distance from N_s to N_t in $N(F_i)$ are not greater than the length of the shortest flow chain and the cardinal distance from N_s to N_t in $N(F_{i+1})$, respectively.

Since the first-labeled first-scanned labeling method always finds the shortest flow augmenting path, it is clear that the length of the shortest flow chain and the cardinal distance from N_s to N_t are monotonically increasing if every flow augmenting path does not contain a backward arc. Now we want to prove that this lemma is true even if the flow augmenting path contains backward arcs. Without loss of generality, we can assume that the network in Fig. 8.10 is a part of an arbitrary network.

Each line in Fig. 8.10 may represent a path and l_i is the cardinal length of that path. Let us assume that the shortest flow augmenting path is of length $l_1 + l_2 + l_3$. This implies that

$$l_1 + l_2 \leq l_4,$$

$$l_2 + l_3 \leq l_5,$$

Of course, there may be many other flow augmenting paths with length equal to $l_1 + l_2 + l_3$, but we can consider that all these paths have been used and the path from N_s to N_i, N_i to N_j, N_j to N_t is the only one left which is of length $l_1 + l_2 + l_3$.

Table 8.1

	$N(F_{i-1})$	$N(F_i)$	$N(F_j)$	$N(F_p)$
Cardinal distance from N_s to N_t	$l_1 + l_2 + l_3$	At least $l_1 + l_2 + l_3$	At least $l_1 + l_2 + l_3 + 2$	At least $l_1 + l_2 + l_3 + 2$
Length of shortest flow chain	k $(k \leq l_1 + l_2 + l_3)$	At least k	At least k	At least k

$j \geq i+1$, $p \geq j+1$

Now we shall consider four networks $N(F_{i-1})$, $N(F_i)$, $N(F_j)$, and $N(F_p)$, which may be any four networks that achieve the maximal flow. $N(F_{i-1})$ is the network before the flow augmenting path of length $l_1 + l_2 + l_3$ is used. $N(F_i)$ is the network after the flow augmenting path is used. (Let us assume that the subpath l_2 is saturated.) $N(F_j)$ is the network after a flow augmenting path such as N_s, N_j, N_i, N_t is used. $N(F_p)$ is the network after a flow augmenting path, which again saturates the subpath l_2, is used. The results that we want to prove can be summarized in Table 8.1. The cardinal distance from N_s to N_t in a network is monotonically increasing. If an arc is saturated the second time, then the cardinal distance from N_s to N_t is increased by at least two units. Furthermore, canceling arc flow of an arc in a flow augmenting chain will not create a flow chain of shorter distance. (The above will not be true unless we have used the refinement in the labeling.)

The network $N(F_{i-1})$ may be the first network in the sequence such that no arc flow has ever been canceled. If we assume that the shortest flow chain is of length k, then $l_1 + l_2 + l_3 \geq k$, since the first-labeled first scanned labeling method always locates the flow augmenting path of minimal cardinal distance. The transition from $N(F_{i-1})$ to $N(F_i)$ is obvious. Now let us consider a network $N(F_j)$ $(j \geq i+1)$. If we have to use the flow augmenting path N_s, N_j, N_i, N_t, then it is of cardinal length $l_4 + l_2 + l_5$. Because $l_4 \geq l_1 + l_2$ and $l_5 \geq l_2 + l_3$, we have $l_4 + l_2 + l_5 \geq l_1 + 3l_2 + l_3 \geq l_1 + l_2 + l_3 + 2$. Canceling the arc flow in the subpath l_2 will create two flow chains of length $l_4 + l_3$ and $l_1 + l_5$, both of which are of length at least $l_1 + l_2 + l_3$. Since we assume $l_1 + l_2 + l_3 \geq k$, the shortest flow chain is still of length k. If we had to cancel an arc flow in a path of length k, then the cardinal distance from N_s to N_t is at least $k + 2$. Note that $k + 2$ is not less than $l_1 + l_2 + l_3$; otherwise the path of length $k + 2$ will be used before the path $l_1 + l_2 + l_3$ is used. If $k + 2 = l_1 + l_2 + l_3 + 1$, then that path of length $k + 2$ will be used before the path of length $l_1 + l_2 + l_3 + 2$ is used. This is possible and that is why we did not specify $j = i + 1$.

Our assumptions that the path of length l_2 is saturated in $N(F_j)$ and that the path N_s, N_j, N_i, N_t is a flow augmenting path, imply that the paths of length l_4 and l_5 are not saturated in $N(F_j)$. If there existed a path from N_s to N_i of l'_1 or a path from N_j to N_t of length l'_3, then $l'_1 \geq l_1 + 1$ and $l'_3 \geq l_3 + 1$. Otherwise the path N_s, N_i, N_t or the path N_s, N_j, N_t will be less than $l_1 + l_2 + l_3 + 2$ in length, and these paths will be used before the flow augmenting path N_s, N_j, N_i, N_t is used. When we have used the flow augmenting path N_s, N_j, N_i, N_t, then any other flow augmenting path which contains the subpath from N_i to N_j is of length at least $l'_1 + l_2 + l'_3 \geq l_1 + l_2 + l_3 + 2$. Now, not only have we proved the results in Table 8.1 hence Lemma 8.2, but also we have proved something else, i.e., if any arc is saturated twice, then the cardinal distance from N_s to N_t is increased by at least two. This is now stated as a lemma.

Lemma 8.3. Let $x_{ij} = b_{ij}$ in $N(F_p)$, $x_{ij} < b_{ij}$ in $N(F_q)$, and $x_{ij} = b_{ij}$ in $N(F_r)$. Then the cardinal distance from N_s to N_t in $N(F_r)$ is at least two greater than the cardinal distance from N_s to N_t in $N(F_p)$; $(p < q < r)$.

Having proved Lemmas 8.1, 8.2, and 8.3, we can now state the theorem.

Theorem 8.3. If in the labeling method for finding a maximal flow in a network with n nodes, each flow augmenting path is the one having fewest arcs and with $\epsilon(j) = \min\,[\epsilon(i), b_{ij} - x_{ij} + x_{ji}]$, then the maximal flow will be obtained after at most n^3 flow augmenting paths.

Proof. If the maximal flow is not obtained, then the longest flow augmenting path is of cardinal length $n - 1$. If we can show that the cardinal distance from N_s to N_t has to be greater than $n - 1$ before n^3 flow augmenting paths are located, then we have proved the correctness of the theorem.

From Lemma 8.3 an arc can be saturated in one network but not the next network for at most $(n - 1)/2$ times. Each flow augmenting path saturates at least one arc in $N(F)$, and there are $n(n - 1)$ arcs in the network. Therefore the total number of flow augmenting paths must be at most $n(n - 1)[(n - 1)/2] + 1 \leq n^3$.

It is clear that the above upper bound can be improved by noting that every arc of the form A_{si} or A_{jt} can be saturated only once. But there currently exists no augment that will reduce the upper bound to $O(n^2)$.

8.3 APPLICATIONS

There are extensions of the simple network flow problem that can be reduced to finding the maximal flow in a network and many applications of network flow to problems of combinatorial analysis. In each of these extensions or applications, the technique is to construct a network such that the problem of finding maximum flow in the network is equivalent to the problem that we want to solve. We shall describe a few of these constructions and mention some known results.

One problem involves having multiple sources and multiple sinks with limited supplies and demands at the sources and sinks. The question is, can these demands be satisfied by the supplies given? If we allow flow from any of the sources to go to any of the sinks, then this problem can be easily reduced to the one source and one sink situation by simply creating a "supersource" and a "supersink". From the supersource we create a directed arc leading to each of the original sources with capacity equal to the amount of supply limited to the corresponding sources. A similar thing is done at the supersink. This is shown in Fig. 8.11. Then the problem of whether supply and demand can be met in the original network is reduced to a maximal flow problem in the new network.

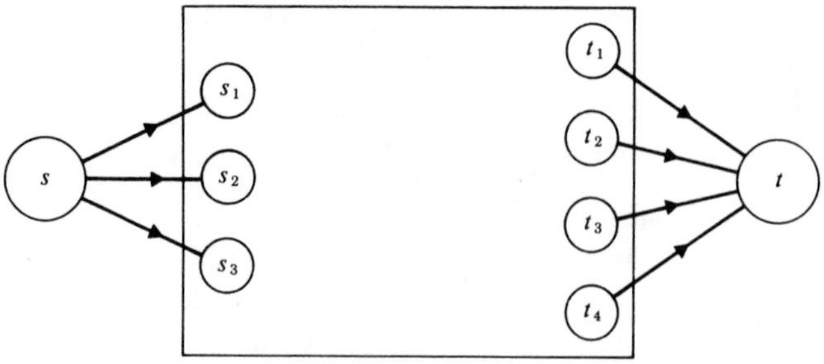

Fig. 8.11

If there are many sources and many sinks in which certain sinks can be satisfied only by certain sources, then this becomes a problem of multicommodity flows in a network. Such problems will be treated in Chapter 11.

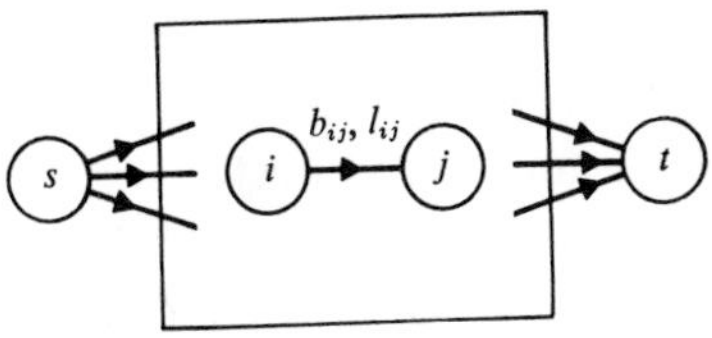

Fig. 8.12

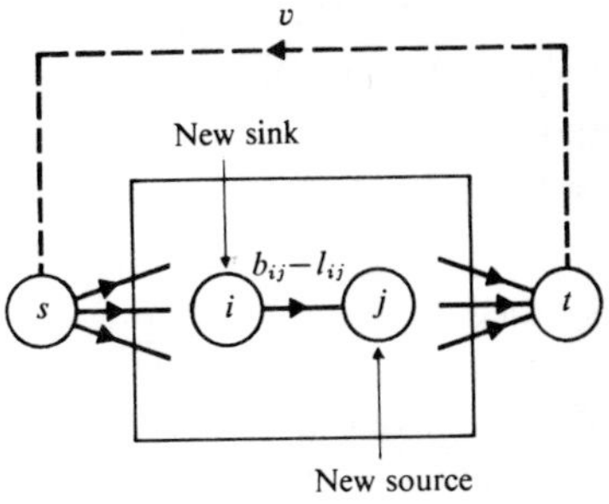

Fig. 8.13

Another generalization allows positive integers instead of zero as lower bounds on arc capacities, i.e., for any arc, we will have the constraint $0 \leq l_{ij} \leq x_{ij} \leq b_{ij}$. The question is whether there is a flow from N_s to N_t with all the lower and upper bounds satisfied. We shall first answer this question with only one directed arc having a lower bound. Let this arc be A_{ij} with lower bound l_{ij}. Then we shall create an artificial source of amount l_{ij} at node N_j, and an artificial sink at N_i of amount l_{ij} and change the capacity of the arc A_{ij} from b_{ij} to $b_{ij} - l_{ij}$. Also we shall add a directed arc of infinite capacity from N_t to N_s. In this new network we do a maximum flow computation using N_j as the source and N_i as the sink. If the flow value is l_{ij} or greater with the arc flow x_{ts} in the arc A_{ts}, then there is a flow of value $v = x_{ts}$ in the original network with $l_{ij} \leq x_{ij}$. The original network and the new network are shown in Figs. 8.12 and 8.13, respectively.

If there are many arcs with lower bounds, then we have to create many artificial sources and sinks and reduce the case of multiple sources and sinks to one supersource and one supersink as was done in the preceding problem.

The following are some well-known theorems which can be converted into the max-flow min-cut theorem. The reader can refer to Ford and Fulkerson [67] for all these conversions.

A graph is called a *bipartite graph* if the nodes can be partitioned into two sets S and T, $S = \{S_i\}$ $(i = 1, \ldots, m)$ and $T = \{T_j\}$ $(j = 1, \ldots, n)$, such that all arcs of the graph connect some member of S to some member of T. Two arcs in a graph are said to be *node disjoint* if they are not incident upon the same node. A S, T disconnecting set of nodes is the set of nodes the removal of which together with their incident arcs will disconnect every pair of nodes S_i and T_j.

Theorem 8.4. *Konig and Egervary.* The maximum number of arcs that are pairwise disjoint in a bipartite graph G is equal to the minimum number of nodes in an S, T disconnecting set of nodes.

Theorem 8.5. *Menger.* Let S and T be two disjoint subsets of nodes of a graph. The maximum number of chains from S to T which are pairwise node disjoint is equal to the minimum number of nodes in a S, T disconnecting set of nodes.

A graph is a directed graph if it consists of directed arcs only. A graph is called *acyclic* if it contains no cycles. Let G be an acyclic directed graph. To decompose G into chains is to select a set of chains such that every node of G is in one and only one chain (or the set of chains cover the graph). We say that N_i is greater than N_j if there is a chain leading from N_i to N_j. This is written as $N_i > N_j$. Two nodes of an acyclic graph are said to be *unrelated* if neither $N_i > N_j$ nor $N_i < N_j$.

Theorem 8.6. *Dilworth.* The maximum number of unrelated nodes in an acyclic directed graph is equal to the minimum number of chains necessary to cover the graph.

Let N be a set of elements $\{N_1, N_2, \ldots, N_n\}$; let $S = \{S_1, S_2, \ldots, S_m\}$ be a family of subsets of these elements. For example, $S_1 = \{N_1, N_7\}$, $S_2 = \{N_1, N_2, N_4\}$, etc. A subset of elements of N

$$R = \{N_{j1}, N_{j2}, \ldots, N_{jm}\}$$

is said to be a system of distinct representatives for S if

$$N_{ji} \in S_i \qquad (\text{for } i = 1, \ldots, m).$$

Theorem 8.7. *Hall.* A system of distinct representatives exists for S if and only if every union of k sets of S contains at least k distinct elements.

8.4 RELATION BETWEEN LINEAR PROGRAMMING AND NETWORK FLOWS

We shall first introduce some elementary notions in graph theory. A *tree* is an undirected, connected graph that contains no cycles. Therefore between any two nodes of the tree there is a unique chain joining the two nodes. For a graph with n nodes any two of the following three conditions will serve as a definition of a tree:

1. It is connected.
2. It has no cycles.
3. The number of arcs is $n - 1$.

A *spanning tree* of a graph G is a subgraph of G such that every node of G is in the tree. If G is a graph with n nodes, a tree with n nodes is a spanning tree. So far, we are dealing with notions of graph theory. If we associate with each arc of the graph or the network a number d_{ij}, then we have the notion of a minimum or a maximum spanning tree. A *minimum* (or *maximum*) *spanning tree* of a network is a spanning tree such that the sum of the

d_{ij} of arcs in the tree is minimum (or maximum) with respect to all spanning trees of the network.

Let us now return to the problem of maximal flow. In Section 8.1 we treated the maximal flow problem independently of concepts in linear programming. Actually, network flow problems belong to a special class of linear programming problems and every network flow problem can be formulated as a linear program. Also many algorithms in network flow theory use duality concepts in linear programming. Take the network in Fig. 8.1, for example. We have six variables $x_{s2}, x_{s3}, \ldots, x_{3t}$, the arc flows. Although $v = x_{s2} + x_{s3}$, we shall treat v as a variable. The maximum flow problem can be formulated as a linear program with

$$\max z = \mathbf{cx}$$

subject to

$$\mathbf{Ax} = \mathbf{0}, \qquad \mathbf{A'x} \leq \mathbf{b}, \qquad \mathbf{x} \geq \mathbf{0}, \tag{1}$$

where

$$\mathbf{x} = [v, x_{s2}, x_{s3}, x_{23}, x_{32}, x_{2t}, x_{3t}],$$

$$\mathbf{c} = (1, 0, 0, 0, 0, 0, 0),$$

$$\mathbf{A} = \begin{bmatrix} -1 & 1 & 1 & 0 & 0 & 0 & 0 \\ 0 & -1 & 0 & 1 & -1 & 1 & 0 \\ 0 & 0 & -1 & -1 & 1 & 0 & 1 \\ 1 & 0 & 0 & 0 & 0 & -1 & -1 \end{bmatrix} \qquad [\mathbf{A} \text{ is } n \times (m+1)],$$

$$\mathbf{A'} = \begin{bmatrix} 0 & 1 & 0 & 0 & 0 & 0 & 0 \\ 0 & 0 & 1 & 0 & 0 & 0 & 0 \\ 0 & 0 & 0 & 1 & 0 & 0 & 0 \\ 0 & 0 & 0 & 0 & 1 & 0 & 0 \\ 0 & 0 & 0 & 0 & 0 & 1 & 0 \\ 0 & 0 & 0 & 0 & 0 & 0 & 1 \end{bmatrix} \qquad [\mathbf{A'} \text{ is } m \times (m+1)],$$

$$\mathbf{b} = [b_{s2}, b_{s3}, b_{23}, b_{32}, b_{2t}, b_{3t}],$$

and n is the number of nodes, and m is the number of arcs.

Of particular interest is the structure of **A**. Each column of **A** has two nonzero entries, $+1$ and -1, and because of its structure, the n-row matrix **A** is of rank $n - 1$. Physically, every row of **A** corresponds to the flow conservation equation at a certain node. The balance of flow at $n - 1$ nodes plus the knowledge that input equals output imply the balance of flow at the remaining node. Another property of **A** is not so apparent. Every subdeterminant of **A** is of value ± 1 or 0. This called the *totally unimodular property*. It is this totally unimodular property that guarantees an integer optimum solution if the vector **b** is an all-integer vector.

In a linear program variables associated with some columns of the constraint matrix are called nonbasic variables or independent variables, because their values can be assigned arbitrarily. The values of the basic variables are then determined uniquely by the nonbasic variables. If we arbitrarily assign the arc flows in a network without capacity constraints, then the conservation equation at each node may not be satisfied. Therefore, among all arcs incident to a node, the arc flow in one arc may not be arbitrarily assigned but is determined from the conservation equation. If we consider all the arcs whose arc flows are determined uniquely by the rest of the arc flows, then all these arcs will form a spanning tree. To see that it is a spanning tree, we argue as follows. Among all arc flows incident to a node, one arc flow must be determined from the rest of the arc flows in order to satisfy the flow conservation equation at that node. Since there are $n-1$ independent flow conservation equations, there are $n-1$ such arcs. These $n-1$ arcs cannot form any cycles because one can add flows in the cycle without violating the flow conservation equations of the nodes in the cycle. This would contradict that the values of these $n-1$ arcs are uniquely determined. Therefore, for a network without arc capacities, the arc flows in a spanning tree are the basic variables.

Consider a network without arc capacities, i.e., we demand only that $\mathbf{Ax} = \mathbf{0}$ and $\mathbf{x} \geq \mathbf{0}$ in (1). Let every arc have associated with it a cost which is the cost of shipping one unit of flow along that arc. If we want to ship a given amount of flow from the source to the sink, at minimum cost, then it is clear that we shall ship all the flow along a *single* route—the route of minimum cost. Since a route from the source to the sink generally contains less than $n-1$ arcs, the number of nonzero basic variables is less than $n-1$. This means that the problem has a basic optimum solution which is highly degenerate. For a network with capacity constraints, we have to convert the inequality constraints $\mathbf{A}'\mathbf{x} \leq \mathbf{b}$ in (1) into equations. This will introduce m slack variables, where m is the number of arcs in the network. Now we have $n-1+m$ independent equations. If we now try to ship a given amount of flow from the source to the sink, at minimum cost, we may not be able to ship all flow along a single route. But the number of nonzero basic variables is always less than $n-1+m$. This means it is also a highly degenerate problem.

8.5 UNIMODULAR PROPERTY (Hoffman and Kruskal [103], Veinott and Dantzig [199])

We have shown that any network flow problem can be formulated as a linear program such as

$$\max z = \mathbf{cx}$$

subject to

$$\mathbf{Ax} = \mathbf{b}, \qquad \mathbf{x} \geq \mathbf{0}. \tag{1}$$

The maximal flow problem discussed in this chapter and the minimal cost flow problem discussed in Chapter 10 both can be cast into the form (1). We have shown that there always exists an integer optimum solution to the network flow problem provided that the arc capacities are integers. For a general linear program we cannot expect that there always exists an integer optimum solution. Thus we like to investigate the subclass of linear programs that will ensure the existence of an integer optimum solution. Hoffman and Kruskal [103] have shown that a linear program with the constraint $\mathbf{Ax} \leq \mathbf{b}$ and $\mathbf{x} \geq \mathbf{0}$ always has an integer optimum solution for any arbitrary integer vector $\mathbf{b}$ provided that the matrix $\mathbf{A}$ is a totally unimodular matrix. A matrix is said to be *totally unimodular* if and only if every subdeterminant of $\mathbf{A}$ equals $+1$, -1, or 0. This means that the convex polytope defined by $\mathbf{Ax} \leq \mathbf{b}$ has integer extreme points for any arbitrary integer vector $\mathbf{b}$ provided that $\mathbf{A}$ is totally unimodular. The condition that $\mathbf{A}$ is totally unimodular is clearly sufficient for the existence of an integer optimum solution. The difficulty is to show that the condition is also necessary. The proof by Hoffman and Kruskal [103] is long and we shall follow the simpler proof of Veinott and Dantzig [199].

Theorem 8.8. Let a linear program have the constraints $\mathbf{Ax} = \mathbf{b}$, $\mathbf{x} \geq \mathbf{0}$. The matrix $\mathbf{A}$ is an integer matrix having linearly independent rows and $\mathbf{b}$ is an integer vector. Then the following three conditions are equivalent.

CONDITION 1. The determinant of every basis $\mathbf{B}$ of $\mathbf{A}$ equals $+1$ or -1.

CONDITION 2. The extreme points of the convex polytope C defined by $\mathbf{Ax} = \mathbf{b}$, $\mathbf{x} \geq \mathbf{0}$ are all with integer components for all integer vectors $\mathbf{b}$.

CONDITION 3. The inverse $\mathbf{B}^{-1}$ of every basis $\mathbf{B}$ is an integer matrix.

Proof.

Condition 1 implies Condition 2. Let $\mathbf{x}$ be an extreme point of the convex polytope C and $\mathbf{B}$ the associated basis. Then $\mathbf{x} = [\mathbf{x}_B, \mathbf{x}_N]$, where $\mathbf{Bx}_B = \mathbf{b}$ and $\mathbf{x}_N = \mathbf{0}$. But $\mathbf{b}$ is an integer vector by assumption and $\det \mathbf{B} = \pm 1$ by Condition 1. It follows from Cramer's rule that $\mathbf{x}_B$ is an integer vector. This means that the extreme point $\mathbf{x} = [\mathbf{x}_B, \mathbf{x}_N]$ has all integer components.

Condition 2 implies Condition 3. Let $\mathbf{B}$ be a basis, and $\mathbf{y}$ be any integer vector such that $\mathbf{y} + \mathbf{B}^{-1}\mathbf{e}_i \geq \mathbf{0}$, where $\mathbf{e}_i$ is the ith unit column vector. Let $\mathbf{z} = \mathbf{y} + \mathbf{B}^{-1}\mathbf{e}_i \geq \mathbf{0}$. Then $\mathbf{Bz} = \mathbf{By} + \mathbf{e}_i$ is an integer vector since $\mathbf{B}$, $\mathbf{y}$, and $\mathbf{e}_i$ are all with integer entries. Because $\mathbf{b}$ can be any integer vector, we shall let $\mathbf{Bz} = \mathbf{b}$. Now $\mathbf{Bz} = \mathbf{b}$ and $\mathbf{z} \geq \mathbf{0}$, which shows that $\mathbf{z}$ is the extreme point of a convex polytope C defined by $\mathbf{Ax} = \mathbf{b}$, $\mathbf{x} \geq \mathbf{0}$. By Condition 2, $\mathbf{z}$ is an integer vector. But $\mathbf{z} - \mathbf{y} = \mathbf{B}^{-1}\mathbf{e}_i$, which shows that $\mathbf{B}^{-1}\mathbf{e}_i$ is an integer vector because it is the difference of two integer vectors $\mathbf{z}$ and $\mathbf{y}$. The vector $\mathbf{B}^{-1}\mathbf{e}_i$ is the ith column vector of $\mathbf{B}^{-1}$, which means that the ith column of $\mathbf{B}^{-1}$ is an integer vector. We can repeat the argument for $\mathbf{e}_i$ $(i = 1, \ldots, m)$. Then it shows that $\mathbf{B}^{-1}$ is an integer matrix.

Condition 3 implies Condition 1. Let **B** be a basis. By assumption, **B** is an integer matrix and det **B** is a nonzero integer. By Condition 3, $\mathbf{B}^{-1}$ is an integer matrix; det $\mathbf{B}^{-1}$ is also a nonzero integer. But (det **B**) (det $\mathbf{B}^{-1}$)= 1, which implies that det **B** = det $\mathbf{B}^{-1} = \pm 1$. Having proved Theorem 8.8 about the convex polytope defined by $\mathbf{Ax} = \mathbf{b}$, $\mathbf{x} \geq \mathbf{0}$, we can easily prove the similar results about the convex polytope C' defined by $\mathbf{Ax} \leq \mathbf{b}$, $\mathbf{x} \geq \mathbf{0}$.

Corollary. Consider the convex polytope C' defined by $\mathbf{A}'\mathbf{x} \leq \mathbf{b}$, $\mathbf{x} \geq \mathbf{0}$, where $\mathbf{A}'$ is an integer matrix. Then the following three conditions are equivalent.

CONDITION 1′. $\mathbf{A}'$ is totally unimodular.

CONDITION 2′. The extreme points of C' are all with integer components for any arbitrary vector **b**.

CONDITION 3′. Every nonsingular submatrix of $\mathbf{A}'$ has an integer inverse.

Let $\mathbf{A} = (\mathbf{A}', \mathbf{I})$. We can easily prove the equivalence of Condition 1 to Condition 1′, Condition 2 to Condition 2′, and Condition 3 to Condition 3′. For example, if **M** is any nonsingular submatrix of $\mathbf{A}'$ of rank $m - k$, then a basis in **A** can be found, after permuting rows, of the form

$$\mathbf{B} = \begin{pmatrix} \mathbf{M} & \mathbf{0} \\ \mathbf{N} & \mathbf{I}_k \end{pmatrix},$$

where $\mathbf{I}_k$ is a $k \times k$ identity matrix. Then det **B** = det **M**, so that det **B** $= \pm 1$. By other similar transformations we can get other results first proved in Hoffman and Kruskal [103]. We remark here that if any one of the matrices $\mathbf{A}$, $\mathbf{A}^T$, $-\mathbf{A}$, $(\mathbf{A}, \mathbf{A})$, or $(\mathbf{A}, \mathbf{I})$ is totally unimodular, then so are all the others. The reader can study references [103] and [199] to find out more about these transformations.

To test whether a matrix **A** has the unimodular property is a difficult job if every basis of **A** has to be tested. There is, however, a sufficient (but not necessary) condition for a matrix to be unimodular which is more easily tested.

Theorem 8.9. A matrix is unimodular if the following four conditions are satisfied.

CONDITION 1. Every column contains at most two nonzero entries.

CONDITION 2. Every entry is $0, \pm 1$. The matrix **A** can be partitioned into two disjoint sets of rows R_1 and R_2 such that:

2a) Two nonzero entries in a column with the same sign are not contained in the same set of rows.

2b) Two nonzero entries in a column with different signs are contained in the same set of rows.

Proof. A proof is given by Hoffman in the appendix of Heller and Tompkins [99]. It is sufficient to prove that any square matrix **A** satisfying the above four conditions has determinant 0, ± 1. The proof is by induction on the size of the matrix. For a one by one matrix the theorem follows from Condition 2. Assume now that the theorem is true for an $(n-1) \times (n-1)$ matrix, and **A** is an $n \times n$ matrix. If some column of **A** has all zero entries, then $|\mathbf{A}| = 0$. If some column has exactly one nonzero entry, then expand by that column $|\mathbf{A}| = \pm|\mathbf{A}'|$, where $\mathbf{A}'$ is the cofactor of the nonzero entry and has determinant ± 1 or zero by the induction hypothesis. Thus we shall assume that every column of the matrix **A** contains exactly two nonzero entries. It follows from Conditions 1, and 2 that

$$\sum_{i \in R_1} a_{ij} = \sum_{i \in R_2} a_{ij} \qquad (\text{for } j = 1, \ldots, n).$$

This implies that $|\mathbf{A}| = 0$. Note that the argument is true even if one of the subsets R_i is empty. This completes the proof of the theorem.

EXERCISES

1. Use the labeling method to find the maximal flow from N_s to N_t in the network in Fig. 8.14, starting with $x_{s1} = x_{12} = x_{23} = x_{3t} = 2$. (The numbers beside the arcs are the arc capacities.)

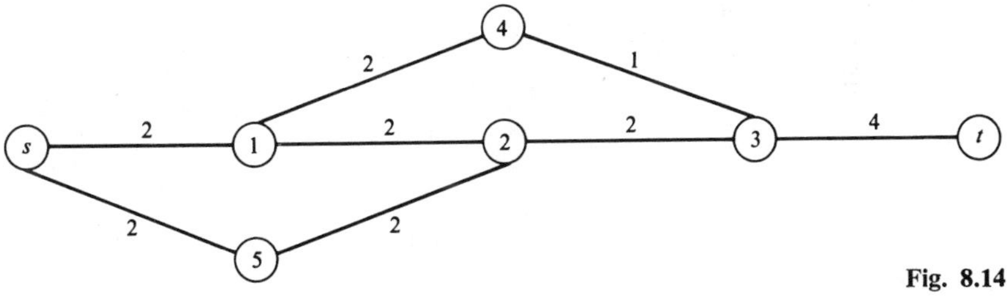

Fig. 8.14

2. If we consider the arc capacities as numbers associated with the arcs, what is a minimum spanning tree of the network (considered as a graph) in Exercise 1?
3. In proving the max-flow min-cut theorem, we define $N_s \in X$.

$$\text{If } N_i \in X,\ x_{ij} < b_{ij}, \text{ then } N_j \in X.$$

$$\text{If } N_i \in X, x_{ji} > 0, \text{ then } N_j \in X.$$

   Write an analogous recursive definition starting with $N_t \in \bar{X}$ in terms of the existing flow from N_s to N_t.
4. Given a network with directed and undirected arcs and the maximum flow value of N_s to N_t is v. If we replace every undirected arc with capacity b by two directed arcs of opposite directions, each with capacity equal to b, would the maximal flow value in this new network be v? Why?

5. Consider a network with the maximum flow value v from N_s to N_t. If an undirected arc of capacity b is added to the network, what are the possible maximal flow values of the new network? What if an arc of capacity b is removed instead of added to the original network?

SUGGESTED READING

1. In the labeling method for getting the maximal flow, all labels are erased once a flow augmenting path is found. A different labeling procedure is developed by Scoins [177] and Johnson [119] where each node receives three labels. If a flow augmenting path is found, only the branch of the tree that contains the flow augmenting path is erased. In Johnson's paper, there is also discussion of basic solution in terms of the network.
2. In the papers of Minty [151], [152], [153], [154], there is ample discussion of results in electrical networks with their relation to network flows.
3. A network can be described by a node-arc incidence matrix. Thus, we can define a cut of a node-arc incidence matrix. Suppose that we are given an arbitrary real matrix. Can we define a cut of this real matrix? The generalization of the notions in networks to more abstract and general systems is studied in Fulkerson [69] and Edmonds and Fulkerson [57].

MULTITERMINAL MAXIMAL FLOWS 9

9.1 PROBLEMS

In the previous chapter we were interested in the maximal flow from a source to a sink in a network; all other nodes in the network were merely intermediate points where the flow is conserved, or merely like relay stations in the language of electrical engineering. In this chapter we are interested in finding maximal flows between all pairs of nodes in a network, i.e., any pair of nodes can serve as the source and the sink while all other nodes are intermediate nodes. *In this chapter we shall consider only undirected networks,* i.e., $b_{ij} = b_{ji}$ for all i,j. Only in this case are there simple and elegant answers. (There is a recent paper [95] which replaces the condition $b_{ij} = b_{ji}$ by a weaker condition.)

There are several questions that we shall ask:

1. *Realization Condition.* If the maximal flow values between N_i and N_j are denoted by f_{ij} $(i,j = 1, \ldots, n; i \neq j)$, is there any relation between these numbers? What are the necessary and sufficient conditions for a set of $n(n-1)/2$ numbers to represent maximum flow values between pairs of nodes in some network?
2. *Analysis.* What are the maximal flow values between all pairs of nodes in a network? This question can certainly be solved by doing a maximal flow algorithm for each pair of nodes, but something better can be done.
3. *Synthesis.* What network will meet prescribed lower bounds on all maximum flow values and at minimum total arc capacity?

9.2 REALIZABILITY (Gomory and Hu [89])

Realization Condition. For a given undirected network with arc capacities $b_{ij} = b_{ji}$, the maximal flow values f_{ij} are certainly symmetric, i.e., $f_{ij} = f_{ji}$. (For convenience, we shall let $f_{ii} = \infty$ for all i.) We now have the following theorem.

Theorem 9.1. *Realizability*. The necessary and sufficient condition for a set of nonnegative numbers $f_{ij} = f_{ji}$ $(i, j = 1, \ldots, n)$ to be the maximal flow values of a network is that

$$f_{ik} \geq \min (f_{ij}, f_{jk}) \qquad \text{(for all } i, j, k). \tag{1}$$

Proof.

Necessity. By considering N_i and N_k as the source and the sink, then from the max-flow min-cut theorem, we have

$$f_{ik} = c(X, \bar{X}), \tag{2}$$

where $N_i \in X$ and $N_k \in \bar{X}$. Now N_j either belongs to X or to $\bar{X}$. If $N_j \in X$, then $(X, \bar{X})$ is a cut separating N_j and N_k; hence

$$f_{jk} \leq c(X, \bar{X}) = f_{ik}. \tag{3}$$

If N_j belongs to $\bar{X}$, then $(X, \bar{X})$ is a cut separating N_i from N_j; hence

$$f_{ij} \leq c(X, \bar{X}) = f_{ik}. \tag{4}$$

Since at least one of the two conditions (3) and (4) must hold, we have

$$f_{ik} \geq \min (f_{ij}, f_{jk}). \qquad \text{Q.E.D.}$$

It follows from (1) by induction that

$$f_{1,n} \geq \min (f_{12}, f_{23}, \ldots, f_{n-1,n}), \tag{5}$$

where $N_1, N_2, \ldots, N_n$ is any sequence of nodes of the network.

Several comments are now in order. Take any three nodes of the network and consider the maximal flow values f_{ij}, f_{jk}, and f_{ik} between them. (Recall that $f_{ij} = f_{ji}$) We claim that at least two of the flow values must be equal. For if these three values are distinct, putting the smallest value on the left-hand side of (1) will contradict (1). Furthermore, the flow value which is not equal to the other two flow values must be the largest; otherwise, (1) will again be contradicted. If we were to draw $n(n - 1)/2$ links between nodes of the network with lengths of the link proportional to the maximal flow values, then each triangle would have two equal sides with the other side longer or of the same length. Therefore (1) is like a "triangular inequality" which limits severely the values that can be maximal flow values of a network.

It follows from (5) that among the $n(n - 1)/2$ flow values $f_{ij} = f_{ji}$, there exist at most $n - 1$ distinct flow values. This can be seen as follows. Consider the complete graph with $n(n - 1)/2$ links with lengths proportional to their maximal flow values and select those links which will form a maximum spanning tree. We claim that each of the $n(n - 1)/2$ flow values must be equal to one of the $(n - 1)$ values associated with the spanning tree. Let f_{1n} be one of the $n(n - 1)/2$ flow values not associated with the maximum spanning tree. There is a unique path from N_1 to N_n consisting of links of the maximum spanning tree. From (5), f_{1n} must be greater than or equal to the minimum value in this unique path. If it is greater, we can replace the minimum link in the path by f_{1n} and get another spanning tree with total value greater than the original maximum spanning tree, which is a contradiction.

Sufficiency. This is proved by constructing a network which has the numbers n_{ij} satisfying (1) as its maximum flow values. To do this, consider the numbers n_{ij} *satisfying (1)* for $j > i$ as lengths of links of a graph and select among the links a maximum spanning tree. Now consider a network which is of the same structure as the maximum spanning tree and with arc capacities $b_{ij} = n_{ij}$, where n_{ij} are the given numbers which are to be realized as the flow values of some network. We claim that this tree network has $f_{ij} = n_{ij}$. For any pair of nodes of the network, we have

$$\begin{aligned} f_{ij} &= \min(b_{i1}, b_{12}, \ldots, b_{qj}) \\ &= \min(n_{i1}, n_{12}, \ldots, n_{qj}) \\ &= n_{ij}, \end{aligned}$$

where $b_{i1}, b_{12}, \ldots, b_{qj}$ are the capacities of arcs which form the unique path from N_i to N_j. Note that in proving the sufficiency of (1), we have shown that there is *always a tree network* that will do the job. Q.E.D.

9.3 ANALYSIS (Gomory and Hu [89])

The problem here is: if we want maximal flow values between several nodes instead of between one pair, can we somehow reduce the amount of computation? Assume that we are interested in finding maximal flow values between p nodes where $2 \leq p \leq n$. Then instead of doing $p(p-1)/2$ maximum flow computations, *we need to do only $p - 1$ maximum flow computations*. Furthermore, each of the flow computations is done on a simplified network.

First we shall describe a process called "condensing a subset of nodes into a single node." The process regards a subset of nodes of the network as a single node, i.e., between every pair of two nodes of the subset an arc of infinite capacity is added. (Consider the network shown in Fig. 9.1.) The

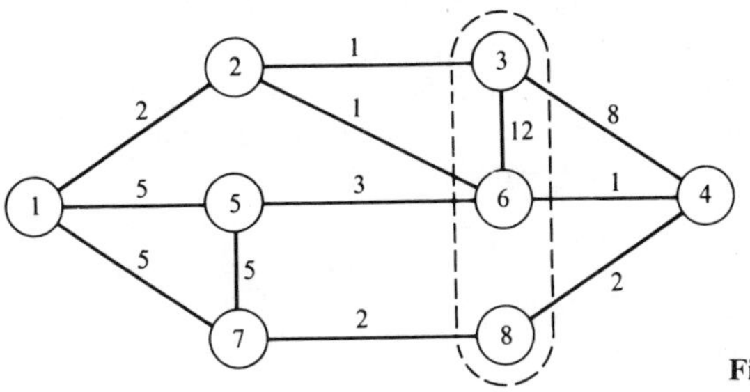

Fig. 9.1

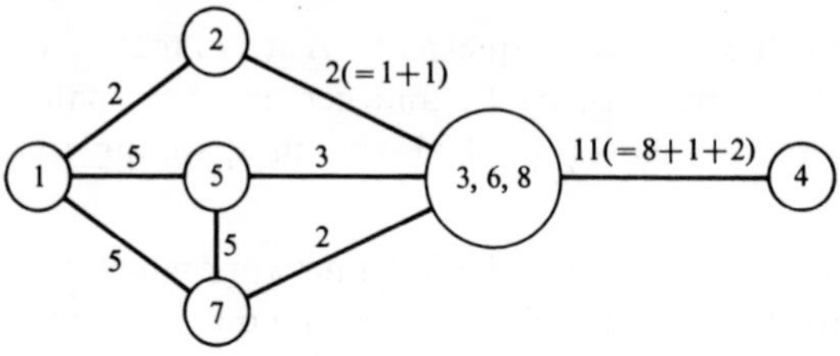

Fig. 9.2

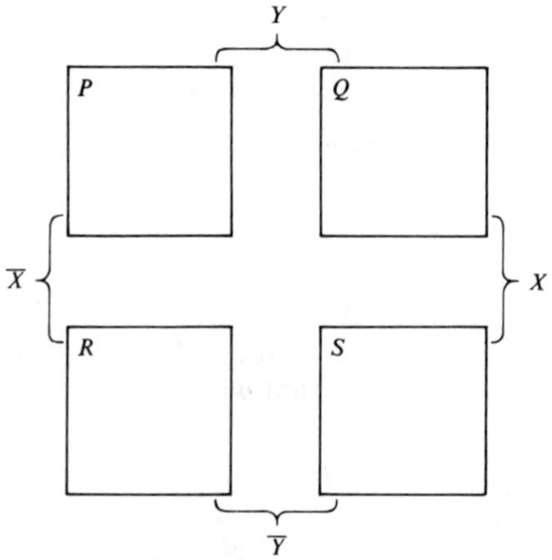

Fig. 9.3

arcs directly connecting a node N_i, *not* in the subset, to any nodes in the subset are replaced by a single arc having a capacity equal to the sum of the capacities of the connecting arcs.

If we condense the nodes N_3, N_6, and N_8 into a single node, then the resulting network is as shown in Fig. 9.2.

In the network of Fig. 9.1, the maximal flow $f_{27} = c(Y, \bar{Y}) = 4$ and the minimum cut $(Y, \bar{Y}) = (2|1, 3, 4, 5, 6, 7, 8)$ consists of the arcs b_{21}, b_{23}, and b_{26}. *Increasing* arc capacities of arcs *not* in the minimum cut $(Y, \bar{Y})$ will not affect the value of $c(Y, \bar{Y})$ and, furthermore, may only *increase* the capacity of other cuts separating N_2 and N_7. Thus $(Y, \bar{Y})$ will remain as a minimum cut separating N_2 and N_7. Therefore, so far as calculating the maximal flow value f_{27} is concerned, we may, for example, condense $\{N_3, N_6, N_8\}$ into a single node and do the calculation in the network of Fig. 9.2. To use this idea more fully, let us study some properties of minimum cuts in a network.

Two cuts $(X, \bar{X})$ *and* $(Y, \bar{Y})$ *are said to cross each other* if and only if each of the four sets $X \cap Y$, $X \cap \bar{Y}$, $\bar{X} \cap Y$, and $\bar{X} \cap \bar{Y}$ contains at least one node.

Lemma 9.1. Let $(X, \bar{X})$ be a minimum cut separating $N_i \in X$ and some other node, and let N_e and N_k be any two nodes contained in $\bar{X}$. Then there exists a minimum cut $(Z, \bar{Z})$ separating N_e and N_k such that $(Z, \bar{Z})$ and $(X, \bar{X})$ do not cross each other.

Proof. Assume that there is a minimum cut $(Y, \bar{Y})$ separating N_e and N_k which does cross $(X, \bar{X})$. Let

$$X \cap Y = Q, \qquad X \cap \bar{Y} = S,$$

$$\bar{X} \cap Y = P, \qquad \bar{X} \cap \bar{Y} = R,$$

as shown in Fig. 9.3.

CASE 1. Let $N_i \in Q$, let $N_e \in P$, and let $N_k \in R$. Since $(X, \bar{X})$ is a minimum cut, we have

$$c(Q, P) + c(S, P) + c(Q, R) + c(S, R) \leq c(Q, P) + c(Q, R) + c(Q, S)$$

or, since $c(S, P) \geq 0$, (1)

$$c(S, R) \leq c(Q, S). \tag{2}$$

Since

$$c(P, R) + c(Q, R) = c(P, R) + c(Q, R) \tag{3}$$

and

$$0 \leq c(P, S), \tag{4}$$

adding both sides of (2), (3), and (4), we have

$$c(P, R) + c(Q, R) + c(S, R) \leq c(P, R) + c(Q, R) + c(Q, S) + c(P, S). \tag{5}$$

But the left-hand side of (5) is the value of a cut $(P \cup Q \cup S, R)$, which is a cut separating N_e and N_k that does not cross $(X, \bar{X})$, and the right-hand side of (5) is the minimum cut $(Y, \bar{Y})$. Thus $(P \cup Q \cup S, R)$ is the required $(Z, \bar{Z})$.

CASE 2. $N_i \in S$. Similarly we can show that $(P, Q \cup R \cup S)$ is a cut separating N_e and N_k with a value not greater than that of $(Y, \bar{Y})$. Thus either $(P \cup Q \cup S, R)$ or $(P, Q \cup R \cup S)$ is the required minimum cut $(Z, \bar{Z})$ that does not cross $(X, \bar{X})$. This means that if $(X, \bar{X})$ is a minimum cut, we can condense X into a single node in calculating the maximum flow values between two nodes in $\bar{X}$.

Lemma 9.2. Let $(X, \bar{X})$ be a minimum cut separating N_i and some other nodes, and let N_e be any node that belongs to $\bar{X}$. Then there exists a minimum cut $(Z, \bar{Z})$ separating N_i and N_e such that $(X, \bar{X})$ and $(Z, \bar{Z})$ do not cross each other.

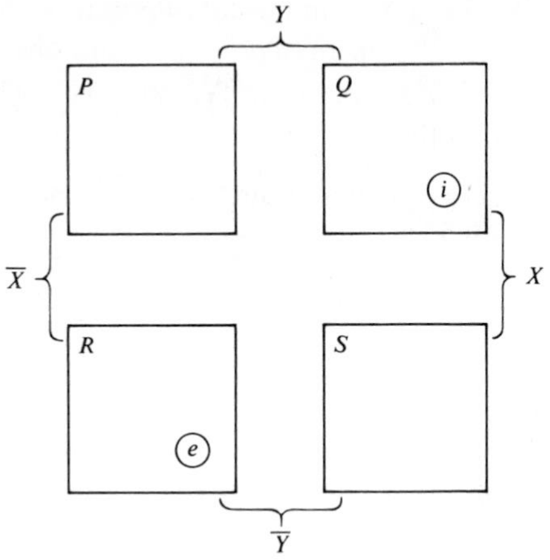

Fig. 9.4

Proof. Assume that there is a minimum cut $(Y, \bar{Y})$ separating N_i and N_e which does cross $(X, \bar{X})$ and let (as before)

$$X \cap Y = Q, \qquad X \cap \bar{Y} = S,$$
$$\bar{X} \cap Y = P, \qquad \bar{X} \cap \bar{Y} = R,$$

where $N_e \in R$ and $N_i \in Q$ (see Fig. 9.4).

Since $(X, \bar{X})$ is a minimum cut, by exactly the same argument, we have (5). But then the left-hand side of (5) is the value of a cut $(P \cup Q \cup S, R)$ which separates N_i and N_e and has a value not greater than that of $(Y, \bar{Y})$ whose capacity is the right-hand side of (5). Thus, $(P \cup Q \cup S, R)$ is the required $(Z, \bar{Z})$.

This means that if $(X, \bar{X})$ is a minimum cut separating N_i and some other node and we want to find f_{ie}, where N_e is any node in $\bar{X}$, we can condense X into a single node.

Lemma 9.3. Let $f_{ab} = c(X, \bar{X})$ and N_i and N_j be any two nodes with $N_i \in X$, $N_j \in \bar{X}$. Then there exists a minimum cut $(Z, \bar{Z})$ with $c(Z, \bar{Z}) = f_{ij}$ such that $(Z, \bar{Z})$ does not cross $(X, \bar{X})$.

Proof. Assume that $(Y, \bar{Y})$ is a minimum cut separating N_i and N_j that does cross $(X, \bar{X})$ so that

$$f_{ij} = c(Y, \bar{Y})$$

and (see Fig. 9.5)

$$X \cap Y = Q, \qquad X \cap \bar{Y} = S,$$
$$\bar{X} \cap Y = P, \qquad \bar{X} \cap \bar{Y} = R.$$

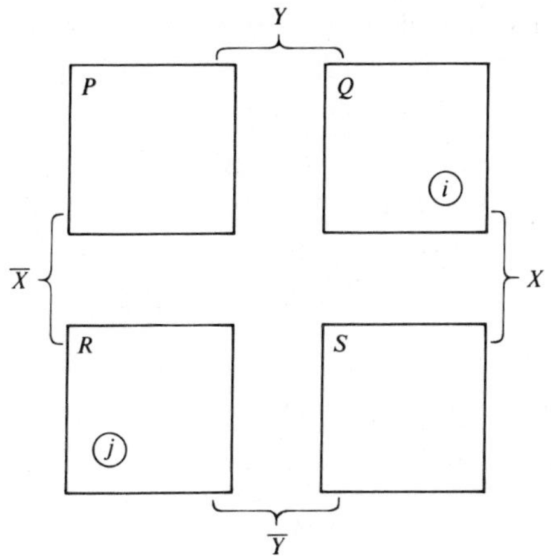

Fig. 9.5

CASE 1. $N_a \in Q$, $N_i \in Q$, $N_b \in R$, and $N_j \in R$. Then it follows from (1), (2), (3), (4), and (5) that $c(P \cup Q \cup S, R)$ is the desired $(Z, \bar{Z})$ with $f_{ij} = c(Z, \bar{Z})$.

CASE 2. $N_a \in S$, $N_i \in Q$, $N_b \in P$, and $N_j \in R$. Since $(X, \bar{X})$ is a minimum cut separating N_a and N_b and $(S, P \cup Q \cup R)$ is a cut separating N_a and N_b,

$$c(Q, P) + c(Q, R) + c(S, P) + c(S, R) \leq c(S, Q) + c(S, P) + c(S, R).$$

As $c(Q, R) \geq 0$, we have

$$c(Q, P) \geq c(S, Q) = c(Q, S). \tag{6}$$

Since $(P, Q \cup S \cup R)$ is a cut separating N_a and N_b,

$$\begin{aligned} c(X, \bar{X}) &= c(Q, P) + c(Q, R) + c(S, P) + c(S, R) \\ &\leq c(Q, P) + c(S, P) + c(R, P). \end{aligned}$$

As $c(Q, R) \geq 0$,

$$c(S, R) \leq c(R, P) = c(P, R), \tag{7}$$

$$c(P, R) + 2c(Q, R) + c(Q, S) \leq c(P, R) + 2c(Q, R) + c(Q, S) + 2c(P, S). \tag{8}$$

Adding (6), (7), and (8), we have

$$\begin{aligned} &[c(Q, P) + c(Q, R) + c(Q, S)] + [c(P, R) + c(Q, R) + c(S, R)] \\ &\qquad \leq 2[c(P, R) + c(P, S) + c(Q, R) + c(Q, S)] \end{aligned} \tag{9}$$

or

$$c(Q, P \cup R \cup S) + c(P \cup Q \cup S, R) \leq 2c(Y, \bar{Y}). \tag{10}$$

The two cuts on the left side of (10) are of less capacity than $(Y, \bar{Y})$. Therefore either $(Q, P \cup R \cup S)$ or $(P \cup Q \cup S, R)$ is the desired $(Z, \bar{Z})$ which separates N_i and N_j and does not cross $(X, \bar{X})$.

CASE 3. $N_a \in Q$, $N_i \in Q$, $N_b \in P$, and $N_j \in R$. Lemma 2 is a special case of this. Since $(X, \bar{X})$ is a minimum cut separating N_a and N_b and $(Q, P \cup R \cup S)$ is a cut separating N_a and N_b,

$$c(X, \bar{X}) \leq c(Q, P \cup R \cup S)$$

or

$$c(Q, P) + c(S, P) + c(Q, R) + c(S, R) \leq c(Q, P) + c(Q, R) + c(Q, S).$$

As $c(S, P) \geq 0$, we have

$$c(S, R) \leq c(Q, S), \tag{11}$$

$$c(P, R) + c(Q, R) \leq c(P, R) + c(Q, R) + c(P, S). \tag{12}$$

Adding (11) and (12), we have

$$c(P, R) + c(Q, R) + c(S, R) \leq c(P, R) + c(Q, R) + c(P, S) + c(Q, S)$$

or

$$c(P \cup Q \cup S, R) \leq c(Y, \bar{Y}). \tag{13}$$

Thus $(P \cup Q \cup S, R)$ is the desired $(Z, \bar{Z})$ which separates N_i and N_j and does not cross $(X, \bar{X})$.

Now we try to find the maximum flow values between nodes of a subset of the network N. Let us call those nodes *terminal* nodes, and assume there are p terminal nodes and $n - p$ ordinary nodes or intermediate nodes. Suppose there is another network N' which consists of p nodes, and the maximum flow values between the p terminal nodes of N are the same as the maximum flow values of the network N'. (Two networks with the same maximal flow values between a set of nodes are said to be flow equivalent to each other with respect to that set of nodes.) Then we can get all the maximum flow values of the p nodes from the network N'. It turns out that there always exists an N' which is a tree. The algorithm described below constructs from a network N the tree N' which has the same maximal flow values. The algorithm of finding maximum flow values between p terminal nodes in an n-node network consists of two steps which are iterated until the tree network N' (which is flow equivalent to the original network N) is constructed. Let us first outline the algorithm before giving the detailed description.

STEP 1. Do a maximal flow computation for two terminal nodes on a network which is usually smaller than the original network, since subsets are condensed into single nodes. Based on the flow computation, we get a minimum cut. Go to step 2.

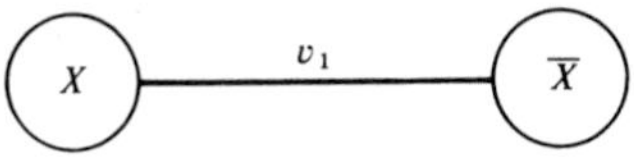

Fig. 9.6

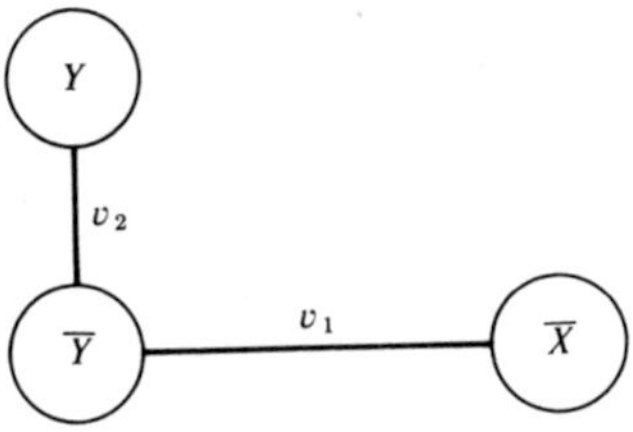

Fig. 9.7

STEP 2. Use the minimum cut just obtained in step 1 and construct a link of the tree network N'. The algorithm ends when $p - 1$ links are constructed. Select a pair of nodes, which will serve as the source and the sink in step 1, and condense certain subsets of the original network into single nodes. This is the network that will be used to do the maximal flow computation in step 1. Go to step 1.

Now, we give the detailed description. First select two terminal nodes arbitrarily and do a maximum flow computation on the original network. This gives a minimum cut $(X, \bar{X})$, which is represented symbolically by two circles connected by a link as in Fig. 9.6. This is the first link of the tree network N'. The value v_1 written beside the link is the value of the minimum cut $(X, \bar{X})$. In one circle all the nodes of X are listed; in the other, those nodes of $\bar{X}$.

Second, from the tree diagram obtained so far, select any circle which contains two or more terminal nodes and do a maximum flow computation between the two terminal nodes on a network in which X or $\bar{X}$ is condensed. Let us say the two terminal nodes selected are in X. Then $\bar{X}$ is condensed into a single node. This will give another minimum cut. This is represented symbolically as in Fig. 9.7, where v_2 is the value of the minimum cut just obtained.

Note that $\textcircled{\bar{X}}$ is attached to $\textcircled{\bar{Y}}$ if $\bar{X}$ and $\bar{Y}$ are in the same part of the minimum cut with value v_2; $\textcircled{\bar{X}}$ is attached to $\textcircled{Y}$ if $\bar{X}$ and Y are in the same part of the minimum cut with value v_2. The process of dividing a circle is continued. At any stage of the construction, we choose a circle $\textcircled{Y}$ which contains two or more terminal nodes as shown in Fig. 9.8. If $\textcircled{Y}$ is removed from the tree diagram, the tree becomes several disconnected components. In doing a maximal flow for two terminal nodes in $\textcircled{Y}$, all the nodes located in one component of the diagram are condensed into a single node. After $p - 1$ maximal flow computations, a tree diagram is obtained in which each circle contains exactly one terminal node and possibly several other intermediate nodes. (Note that in doing the maximal flow computation, we are doing it on a network usually simpler than that of the original network due to condensation of nodes.)

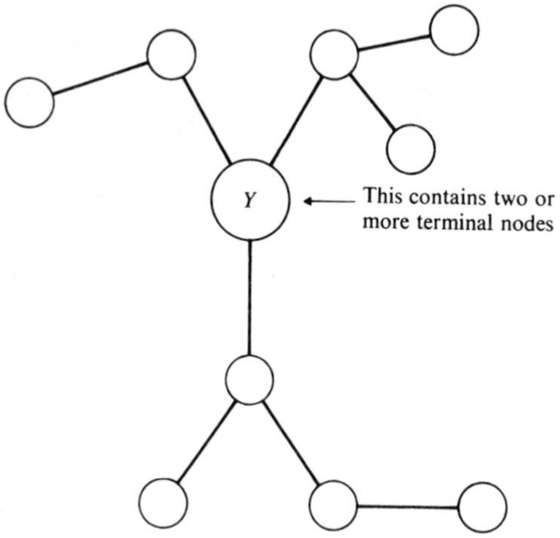
Y
This contains two or more terminal nodes

Fig. 9.8

We assert that if we consider the tree diagram as a network with branch capacities equal to the value associated with the links in the diagram, then the tree network will have the same maximal flow values as the original network.

Theorem 9.2. The maximum flow value between any two terminal nodes N_i and N_j of the original network is equal to

$$\min (v_{ia}, v_{ab}, \ldots, v_{dj}), \tag{14}$$

where $v_{ia}, v_{ab}, \ldots, v_{dj}$ are values associated with links of the tree which form a unique path from N_i to N_j.

Proof. Note that all links connecting circles in the tree diagram represent minimum cuts separating certain pairs of terminal nodes of the network. We shall show that the value associated with a link is the maximum flow value between the two terminal nodes in the two neighboring circles. Consider a link connecting two circles with one circle containing the terminal node N_a and one circle containing the terminal node N_b. Let us call the set of nodes on the same side as N_a the set X and the set of nodes on the same side as N_b the set $\bar{X}$. Then the value associated with this link is $c(X, \bar{X})$, which will be shown later to be equal to the maximum flow value f_{ab}. At this moment, let us assume that the minimum cut $(X, \bar{X})$ is for $N_i \in X$ and $N_j \in \bar{X}$. The maximum flow value f_{ab} is equal to the value of a minimum cut $(Z, \bar{Z})$ in the original network, say $N_a \in Z$ and $N_b \in \bar{Z}$. This $(Z, \bar{Z})$ is a minimum cut separating N_a and N_b. By Lemma 9.3, there exists a $(Z, \bar{Z})$ which does not cross $(X, \bar{X})$. Let $Z \subset X$ and $\bar{Z} \supset \bar{X}$, as shown in Fig. 9.9. (The case $Z \subset \bar{X}$ and $\bar{Z} \supset X$ is similar.)

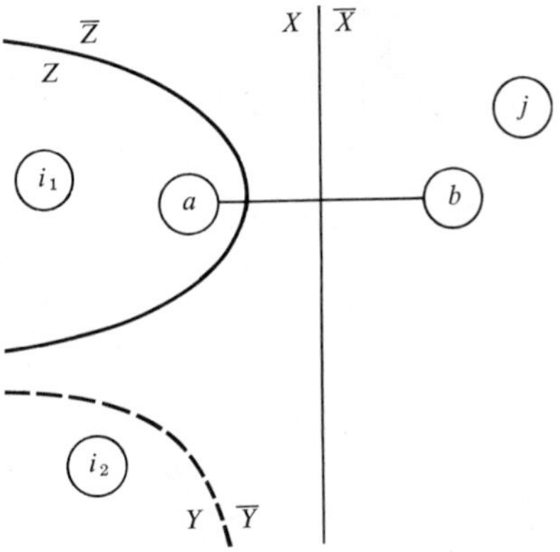

Fig. 9.9

CASE 1. Let $N_i \in Z$. This is shown in Fig. 9.9 as (i_1). Then $(Z, \bar{Z})$ separates N_i and N_j, $c(Z, \bar{Z}) \geq f_{ij} = c(X, \bar{X})$; otherwise it would contradict the fact that $(X, \bar{X})$ is a minimum cut separating N_i and N_j.

CASE 2. $N_i \in \bar{Z} \cap X$. This is shown in Fig. 9.9 as (i_2). Let $f_{ia} = c(Y, \bar{Y})$. By Lemma 9.1 and Theorem 8.2, there is a $(Y, \bar{Y})$* which does not cross $(X, \bar{X})$ and $(Z, \bar{Z})$. Furthermore, N_a, N_b, and N_j all belong to $\bar{Y}$ (as we have assumed that (a)(b) are neighboring circles and (i) is on the side of (a)). Then $(Y, \bar{Y})$ is a cut separating N_i and N_j:

$$c(Y, \bar{Y}) \geq f_{ij} = c(X, \bar{X}). \tag{15}$$

Also, as $(Z, \bar{Z})$ is a cut separating N_a and N_i, we have from (15)

$$c(Z, \bar{Z}) \geq f_{ia} = c(Y, \bar{Y}) \geq c(X, \bar{X}). \tag{16}$$

Therefore, in both Case 1 and Case 2 we have

$$c(Z, \bar{Z}) \geq c(X, \bar{X}). \tag{17}$$

Note that $(X, \bar{X})$ is a cut separating N_a and N_b; hence

$$c(X, \bar{X}) \geq f_{ab} = c(Z, \bar{Z}). \tag{18}$$

(17) and (18) imply that $c(Z, \bar{Z}) = c(X, \bar{X}) = f_{ab}$.

Having established that the neighboring terminal nodes have a maximum flow value equal to the value of the connecting link, we have, from (5) of Section 9.2, for any two terminal nodes connected by a series of links

---

* Let $(Y_1, \bar{Y}_1)$ be the minimum cut that does not cross $(X, \bar{X})$ and $(Y_2, \bar{Y}_2)$ be the minimum cut that does not cross $(Z, \bar{Z})$. Then $(Y, \bar{Y}) = (Y_1 \cap Y_1, \overline{Y_1 \cap Y_2})$ is the minimum cut that does not cross $(X, \bar{X})$ and $(Z, \bar{Z})$.

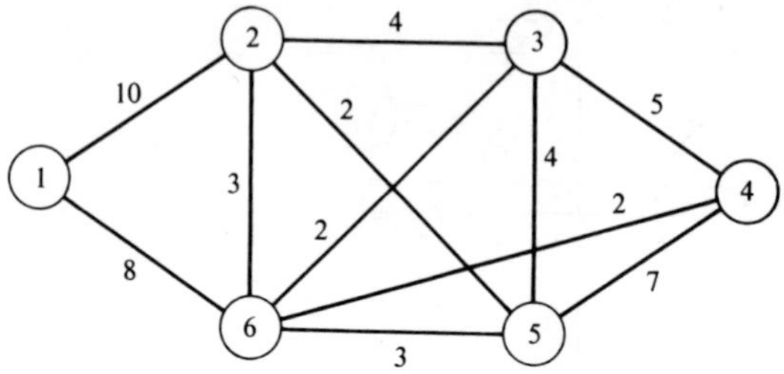

Fig. 9.10

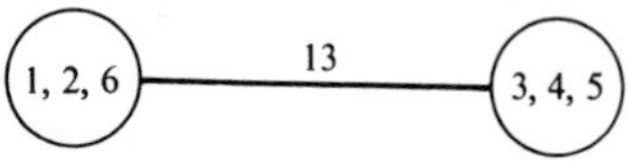

Fig. 9.11

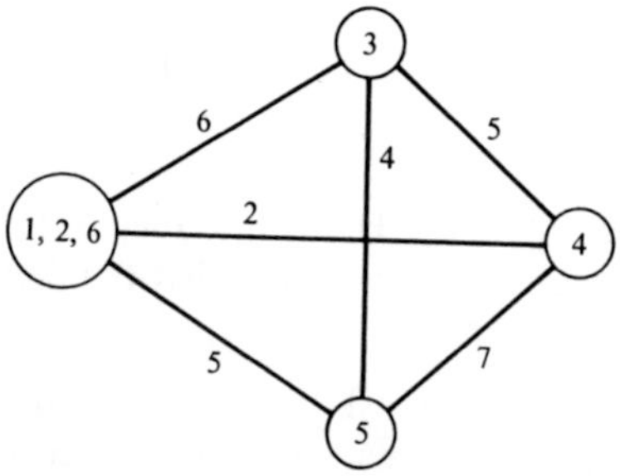

Fig. 9.12

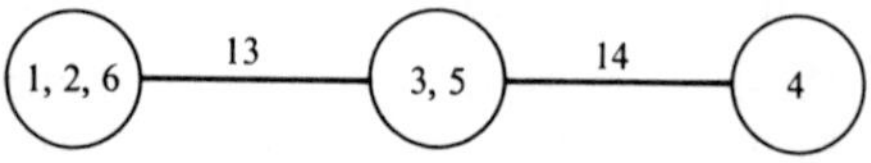

Fig. 9.13

in the tree

$$f_{ij} \geq \min (f_{ia}, f_{ab}, \ldots, f_{dj}) = \min (v_{ia}, v_{ab}, \ldots, v_{dj}), \tag{19}$$

where N_i and N_j are not neighboring terminal nodes in the tree.

Because the value of every link in the right-hand side of (19) represents the capacity of a cut separating N_i and N_j, we have

$$f_{ij} \leq \min (v_{ia}, v_{ab}, \ldots, v_{dj}). \tag{20}$$

(19) and (20) establish the desired result of the theorem.

Let us do a numerical example illustrating the analysis technique. Consider the network in Fig. 9.10, where the numbers besides the arcs denote arc capacities. Assume that we are interested in the maximal flows between N_1, N_3, N_4, and N_5. First let us arbitrarily select N_1 and N_3 and do a maximum flow computation. We get a minimum cut $(N_1, N_2, N_6 \mid N_3, N_4, N_5)$ with value 13. This is indicated symbolically by Fig. 9.11.

Now, we do a maximum flow computation between N_3 and N_4 in the network shown in Fig. 9.12. We get the network in Fig. 9.12. by condensing N_1, N_2, and N_6 in Fig. 9.10 into a single node. The result of this computation is a minimum cut $(N_1, N_2, N_6, N_3, N_5 \mid N_4)$ with value 14 which is shown in Fig. 9.13. Note that (3, 5) is attached to (1, 2, 6) because they are on one

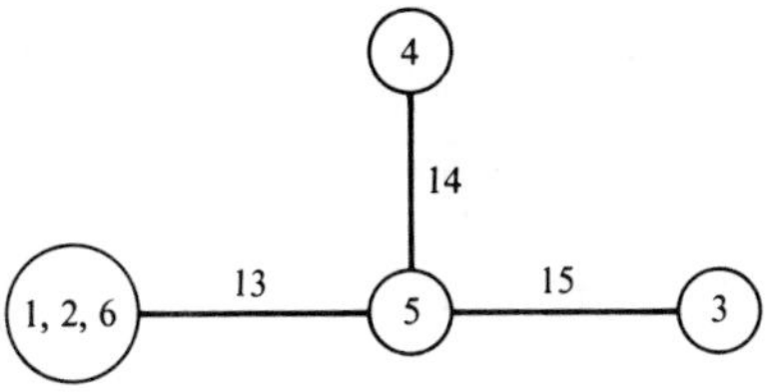

Fig. 9.14

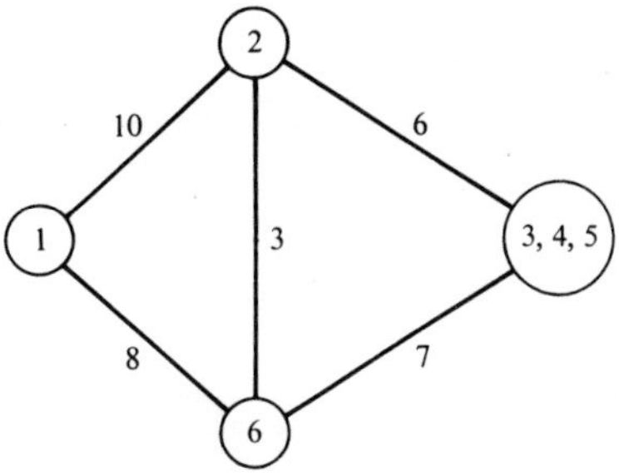

Fig. 9.15

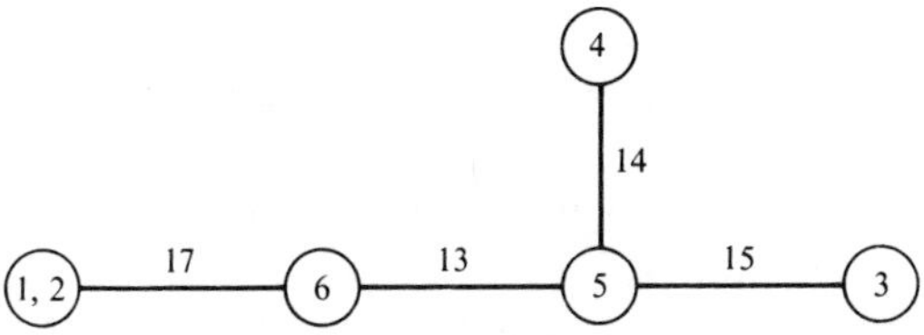

Fig. 9.16

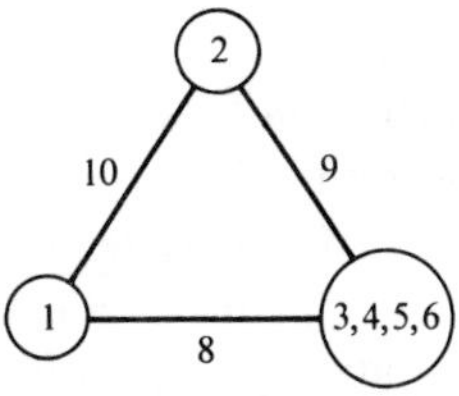

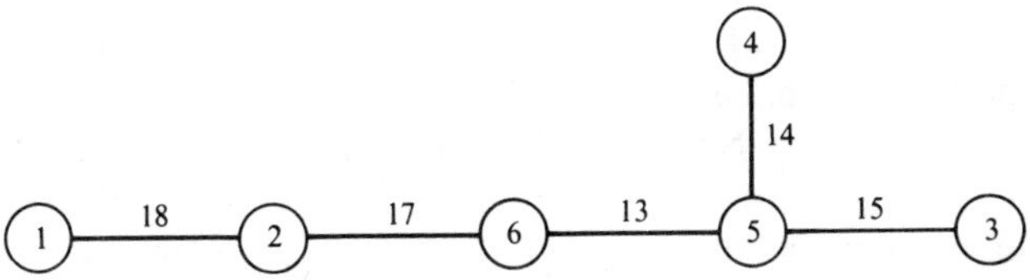

Fig. 9.18

side of the minimum cut separating N_3 and N_4. Now, we do a maximum flow computation between N_3 and N_5, which again should be done on the network shown in Fig. 9.12. As a result of this, we have a minimum cut $(N_1, N_2, N_6, N_5, N_4 \mid N_3)$ with value 15. This is shown symbolically in Fig. 9.14.

Now since each circle in the diagram contains only one terminal node, we can stop. The flow values are $f_{13} = f_{14} = f_{15} = 13$, $f_{34} = f_{45} = 14$, and $f_{35} = 15$. This network then has the same maximum flow values f_{13}, f_{14}, f_{15} f_{34}, f_{35}, and f_{45} as the original network in Fig. 9.10.

If we are interested in maximum flow values between all pairs of nodes, we simply continue the process and choose N_1 and N_6, say, and do the maximum flow computation on the network in Fig. 9.15. The result is a minimum cut $(N_1, N_2 \mid N_6, N_3, N_4, N_5)$ with value 17, which is shown in Fig. 9.16.

Now, we choose N_1 and N_2 and do a maximum flow computation on the network in Fig. 9.17. The result is a minimum cut $(N_1 \mid N_2, N_6, N_3, N_4, N_5)$ with value 18. This is shown in Fig. 9.18. From Fig. 9.18 we can easily

Table 9.1

	①	②	③	④	⑤	⑥
①	∞	18	13	13	13	17
②	18	∞	13	13	13	17
③	13	13	∞	14	15	13
④	13	13	14	∞	14	13
⑤	13	13	15	14	∞	13
⑥	17	17	13	13	13	∞

reach the maximal flow values between all pairs of nodes, and they are listed in Table 9.1.

We have seen that the networks in Figs 9.18 and 9.10 have the same maximal flow values for all pairs of nodes. Two networks with the same f_{ij} are *flow equivalent* to each other. If the maximum flow values are the same for pairs in a subset of nodes, then they are flow equivalent with respect to that set of nodes. Thus the network in Fig. 9.14 and the network in Fig. 9.10 are flow equivalent with respect to N_1, N_3, N_4, and N_5.

The method of analysis described above constructs a flow equivalent network which is a tree. Note that there are many trees that are flow equivalent to a given network. But the flow equivalent tree constructed above has another property, namely, each link of the tree represents a minimum cut of the original network. Therefore, it is called a *cut tree* by Gomory and Hu [89]. A cut tree of n-nodes shows the $n - 1$ minimum cuts of the original network which do not cross each other. The $n - 1$ cuts are shown in dotted lines in Fig. 9.19.

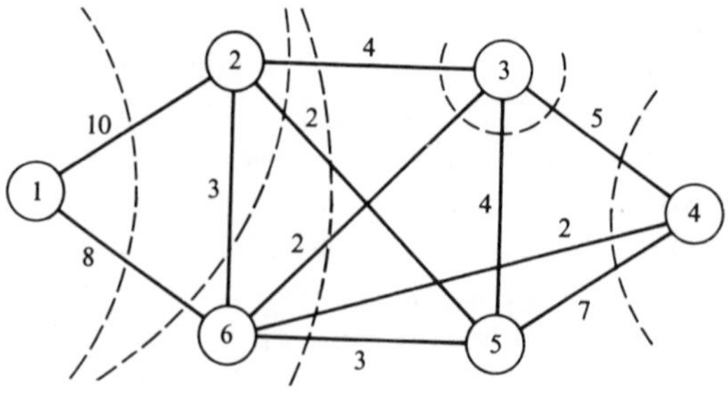

Fig. 9.19

9.4 SYNTHESIS (Gomory and Hu [89])

In the previous section we have shown how to find maximal flow values of a given network. Now we shall study the inverse problem, i.e., given

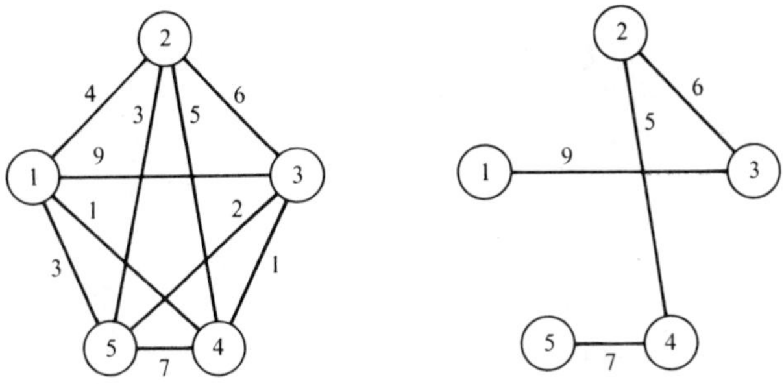

(a) (b) Fig. 9.20

$n(n-1)/2$ numbers r_{ij} which represent the lower bounds on maximal flow between N_i and N_j, what is the undirected network that will have $f_{ij} \geq r_{ij}$ and a minimum total arc capacity?

Let the $n(n-1)/2$ r_{ij} be given. They may be drawn as a complete graph with n nodes. If we consider the r_{ij} as lengths of the links of the graph, we can form a maximum spanning tree of the graph. The requirements r_{ij} associated with the maximum spanning tree are called the *dominant requirements*. The maximum spanning tree is called the *dominant requirement tree*. If Fig. 9.20(a) represents the required flow values in the network, then its dominant requirement tree is shown in Fig. 9.20 (b).

For any network to have $f_{ij} \geq r_{ij}$ for all i, j, it is necessary and sufficient to have $f_{ij} \geq r_{ij}$ for $r_{ij} \in T$, the dominant requirement tree. It is clearly necessary to have $f_{ij} \geq r_{ij}$ for $r_{ij} \in T$, since these are a subset of the original requirements. It is also sufficient since the missing r_{ip} satisfy the following relation, because T is a maximum spanning tree:

$$r_{ip} \leq \min (r_{ij}, r_{jk}, \ldots, r_{op}), \tag{1}$$

where r_{ij}, r_{jk}, etc., on the right-hand side of (1) are associated with the links forming the unique path in T from N_i to N_p. In any network satisfying the dominant requirements, any flow f_{ip} must automatically satisfy

$$f_{ip} \geq \min (f_{ij}, f_{jk}, \ldots, f_{op}) \geq \min (r_{ij}, r_{jk}, \ldots, r_{op}) \geq r_{ip}, \tag{2}$$

and so all requirements are satisfied. Therefore, for the sake of convenience we shall consider only the dominant requirements.

The total arc capacity for any undirected network is $\frac{1}{2} \sum_{i \neq j} b_{ij}$. We now introduce a lower bound C_L for this quantity. Consider any node N_i of the network. Let $u_i = \max_j r_{ij}$, i.e., u_i is the largest flow requirement among those involving N_i. Any satisfactory network must have at least that much b_{ij} to allow the flow out of N_i, i.e., $\sum_j b_{ij} \geq u_i$. Since an arc is counted once in each of its two end nodes, a lower bound to the total arc capacity is then

$$C_L = \frac{1}{2} \sum_i u_i \leq \frac{1}{2} \sum_{i \neq j} b_{ij}.$$

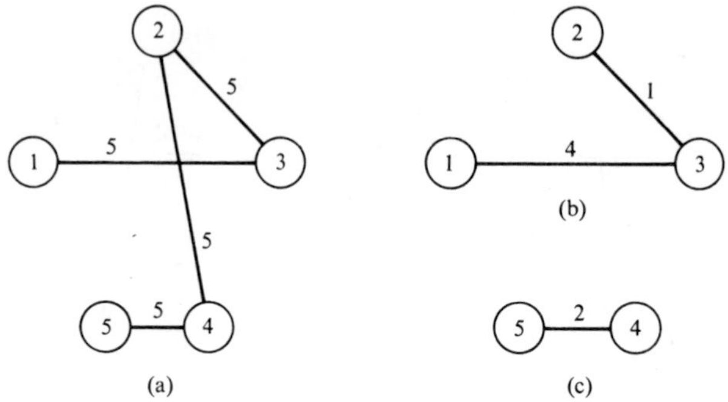

Fig. 9.21

We shall now describe the synthesis procedure (Gomory and Hu [89]) for getting a satisfactory network at this lower bound. Note first that these u_i can be obtained by considering only the dominant requirements, i.e., selecting $\max_j r_{ij}$ for $r_{ij} \in T$ and adjacent to N_i. Now consider a fixed tree T with attached requirements r_{ij} and resulting lower bound C_L. If the r_{ij} are replaced by a new set of r'_{ij}, we get a new bound C'_L. Let us now use $r''_{ij} = r_{ij} + r'_{ij}$ as the requirements associated with the same tree and get a lower bound C''_L. Then, in general, we have

$$C''_L \leq C_L + C'_L,$$

since the $\max_j r_{ij}$ and $\max_j r'_{ij}$ may not coincide on every node N_i. But if r_{ij} (or r'_{ij}) are uniform requirements, i.e., $r_{ij} = r$ for all r_{ij} in T, then

$$C''_L = C_L + C'_L. \tag{3}$$

Now consider two networks, one with arc capacity b_{ij} and maximal flows f_{ij}, the other with b'_{ij} and f'_{ij}. If we form a third network having arc capacities $b''_{ij} = b_{ij} + b'_{ij}$, then the maximal flows f''_{ij} of the third network clearly satisfy

$$f''_{ij} \geq f_{ij} + f'_{ij}. \tag{4}$$

Now let T be the dominant requirement tree which we want to satisfy. Let $r_{\min}$ be the smallest in the tree and write any r_{ij} as $r_{\min} + (r_{ij} - r_{\min})$. We can then consider the original tree as the superposition of two trees, one with uniform requirements $r_{\min}$; one with $r_{ij} - r_{\min}$. (The tree with $r_{ij} - r_{\min}$ may consist of two or more parts due to $r_{ij} - r_{\min} = 0$, or we can still consider it as one tree with some requirements zero.) Note that the tree with $r_{\min}$ is connected; otherwise (3) does not apply. For example, the tree T in Fig. 9.20(b) can be considered as the superposition of Fig. 9.21. For any part without uniform requirements, the decomposition procedure can be continued until each part has uniform requirements. For example, Fig. 9.21 can be further decomposed into Fig. 9.22.

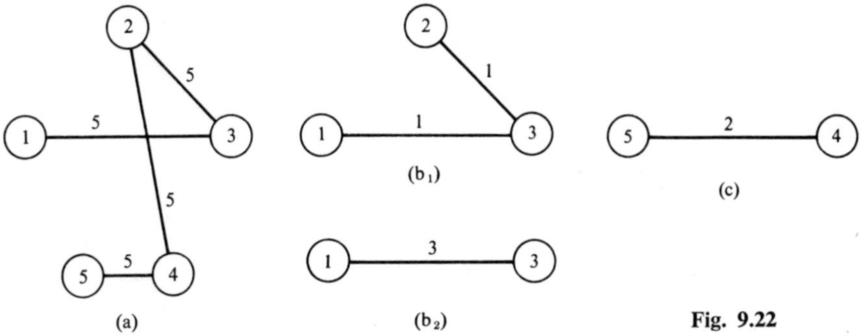

Fig. 9.22

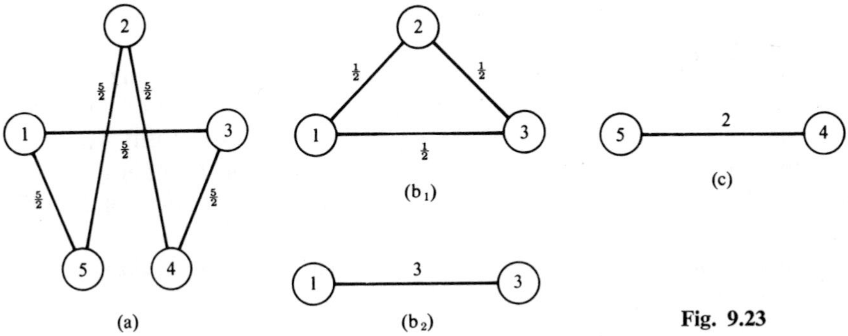

Fig. 9.23

Let us use the phrase "synthesizing a tree" to mean "constructing a network with maximal flows greater than or equal to the requirements in the tree." After a tree is decomposed into a sum of uniform trees, we can synthesize each uniform tree individually. If each uniform tree can be synthesized at its lower bound C_L, then the superposition of each satisfactory network will give a network capable of satisfying the original requirements, due to (4), and which is of minimum total arc capacity, due to (3).

Therefore, the problem is reduced to synthesizing a uniform tree with requirements all equal to r. This can be done by drawing any loop through the nodes and then assigning $r/2$ to each of the arcs of the loop. (When there are only two nodes, a single arc of capacity r is used.) Clearly such a network will meet the flow requirements and, furthermore, is of the total minimal capacity. (The total capacity is $nr/2$ for a network of n nodes, and the lower bound is $\frac{1}{2}\sum_i u_i = \frac{1}{2}nr$.)

Take Fig. 9.22 for example. Each of the uniform trees can be synthesized as shown in Fig. 9.23. Upon superimposing the networks in Fig. 9.23, we obtain Fig. 9.24, which is a network satisfying all requirements of Fig. 9.20(a) and is of minimum total arc capacity.

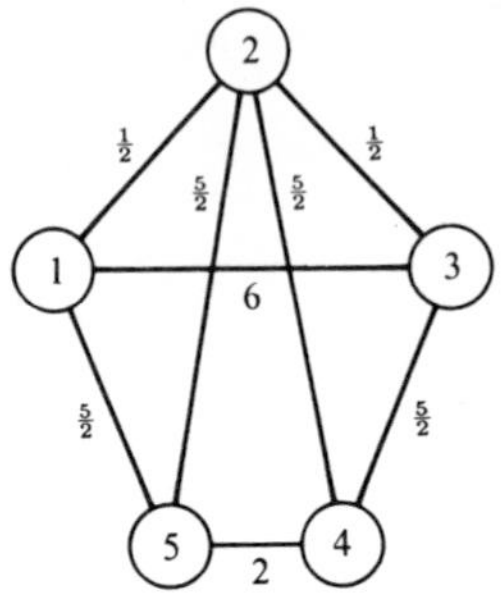

Fig. 9.24

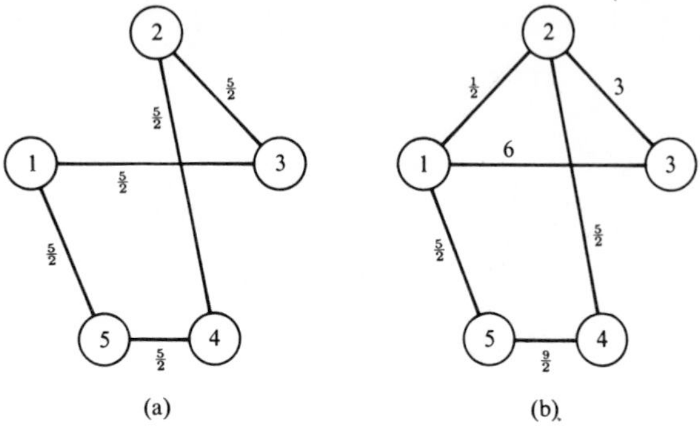

Fig. 9.25

In synthesizing a uniform tree, we have the freedom of passing through the nodes in any order. For example, the loop in Fig. 9.23(a) could be replaced by Fig. 9.25(a), with the resulting network Fig. 9.25(b). If we check the flows in Fig. 9.25(b) we find that $f_{ij} = r_{ij}$ for all $i, j \in T$, but in Fig. 9.24 we find that $f_{ij} > r_{ij}$ for some i, j, although both have the same total minimum arc capacity.

We shall first study the problem of getting as much flow as possible and then study the problem of meeting all r_{ij} in the dominant requirement tree exactly. Of course, in both cases we want the total arc capacity to be minimum.

First, the total minimum arc capacity C_L is determined by the u_i, not the r_{ij}. Therefore, after the u_i are found, we can raise r_{ij} to $r^*_{ij} = \min(u_i, u_j)$ without changing the u_i or the lower bound C_L. Any further increase of r^*_{ij} would certainly change the lower bound. Now by a procedure described later we are able to synthesize the new tree T^* with resulting maximal flows $f^*_{ij} = r^*_{ij}$. We claim that this network N^* in some sense is a *uniformly dominant network*. This is summarized in the following theorem.

Theorem 9.3. Given the requirements r_{ij}, there is a satisfactory network N^* having capacity C^*_L ($C^*_L = \frac{1}{2}\sum_i u_i$) with maximal flows

$$f^*_{ij} = \min(u_i, u_j). \tag{5}$$

Let N' be any other network with $f'_{ij} \geq r_{ij}$, with at least one inequality being a strict inequality, and with total capacity C'. Then either

$$C' > C^*_L \tag{6}$$

or

$$f'_{ij} \leq f^*_{ij}. \tag{7}$$

Proof. There is no need to prove the case (6); the only thing needed is that if $f'_{ij} \geq r_{ij}$ and $C' \leq C^*_L$, then $f'_{ij} \leq f^*_{ij}$. If $f'_{ij} \geq r_{ij}$, then

$$\sum_j b'_{ij} \geq u_i = \max_j r_{ij}$$

for each i. Since

$$\tfrac{1}{2} \sum_{i,j} b'_{ij} = C' \leq C^*_L = \tfrac{1}{2} \sum_i u_i,$$

we actually have $\sum_j b'_{ij} = u_i$. This implies that

$$f'_{ij} \leq \min\left(\sum_j b'_{ij}, \sum_i b'_{ij}\right) = \min(u_i, u_j) = f^*_{ij}.$$

Now we attack the problem of synthesizing the flow requirements in the tree exactly, at minimal total capacity. The reason for getting excess flows is due to the superposition of networks which may not have the same partition of nodes as their minimum cuts. Therefore, in synthesizing a uniform tree, we want the loop network to have the same capacities of cuts as that represented by the links of the uniform tree. For example, in the loop network of Fig. 9.23(a) the cut $(N_1, N_2, N_3 \mid N_4, N_5)$ is of capacity 10, while the link between N_2 and N_4 in Fig. 9.22(a) represents a cut of capacity 5. But in the loop network of Fig. 9.25(a) the cut $(N_1, N_2, N_3 \mid N_4, N_5)$ is also of capacity 5. If we synthesize trees so that the tree becomes a cut tree of the constructed loop network, then in superimposing the loop networks, minimum cuts are also superimposed to form minimum cuts and the original dominant requirement tree becomes a cut tree of the synthesized network. Hence the flow f_{ip} of two nodes N_i and N_p satisfies

$$f_{ip} \leq \min(r_{ij}, r_{jk}, \ldots, r_{op}). \tag{8}$$

Inequalities (2) and (8) imply

$$f_{ip} = \min(r_{ij}, r_{jk}, \ldots, r_{op}), \tag{9}$$

so that all requirements are met exactly.

To synthesize a loop network with the uniform tree as its cut tree, we have to have two arcs of capacities $r/2$ corresponding to each link of the tree. The following labeling procedure will construct such a loop network from a given tree T:

STEP 1. Label any node of T with the number 1.

STEP 2. Check if there is any unlabeled node adjacent to the current largest labeled node, which is node k. If yes, label it $k + 1$. If there is more than one unlabeled node adjacent to the node k, then any of the nodes can be labeled $k + 1$. If there is no unlabeled node adjacent to node k, check if there is any unlabeled node adjacent to node $k - 1$. If yes, label it $k + 1$; if not check any unlabeled node adjacent to $k - 2$, etc.

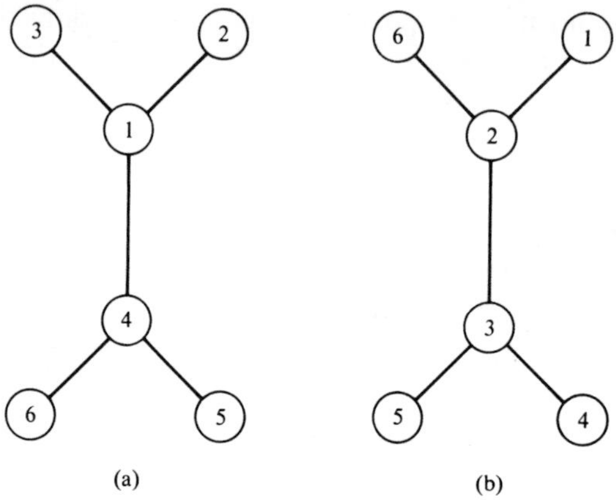

Fig. 9.26

STEP 3. When the nodes of T are all labeled, construct a loop from node 1 to node 2, ... to node n and then back to node 1. This is the loop network desired.

In Fig. 9.26 we give two possible labelings of an n-node tree by the procedure just mentioned. To prove that this procedure gives a loop network with T as its cut tree, we consider any link l_{ij} of the tree such as the link between N_1 and N_4 in Fig. 9.26(a) or the link between N_2 and N_3 in Fig. 9.26(b). Let the two nodes adjacent to the link be labeled i and j with $i < j$. If the link l_{ij} is removed, then the tree is disconnected into two components; one component contains N_i and one component contains N_j. Let k be the largest label which occurs in the component which contains j. Then the node with label $k + 1$ must be in the component which contains i. (If $k = n$, then $k + 1$ means 1.) Since $i < j$, the node with the label $j - 1$ must be also in the component which contains i. Then the two arcs of the loop network from $j - 1$ to j and from k to $k + 1$ correspond to l_{ij}.

EXERCISES

1. Find the flow equivalent tree to the network shown in Fig. 9.1.
2. Describe an algorithm that would convert any flow equivalent tree to a flow equivalent path. For example, the tree in Fig. 9.18 is flow equivalent to the tree in Fig. 9.27.

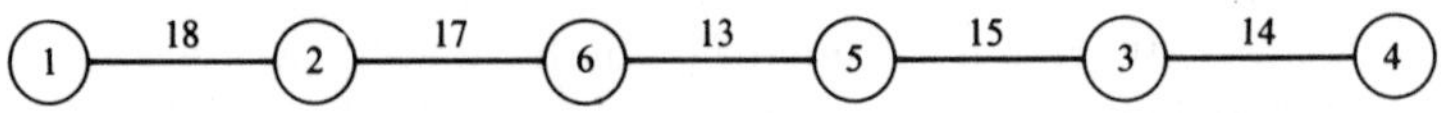

Fig. 9.27

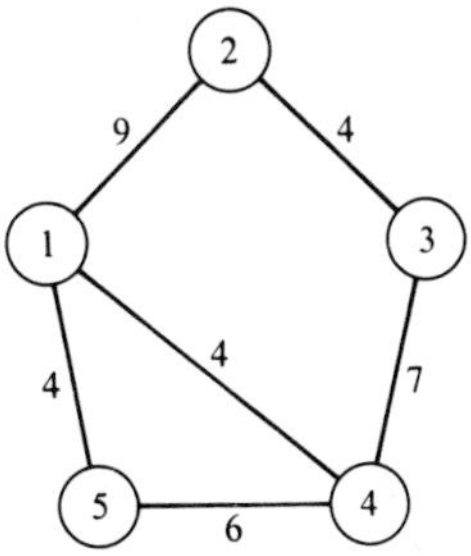

Fig. 9.28

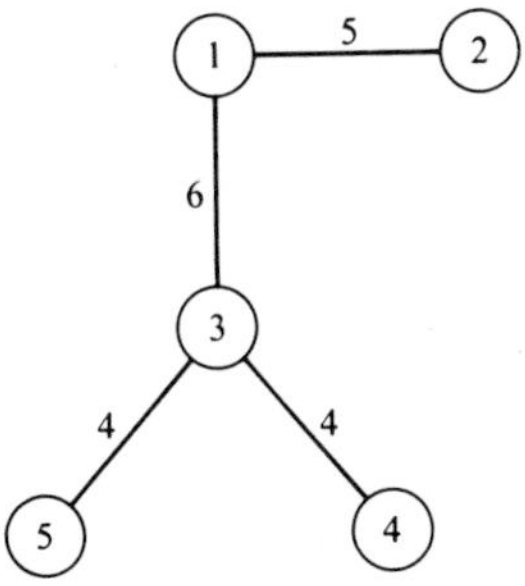

Fig. 9.29

3. Synthesize the following requirements, shown in Fig. 9.28, with a minimum capacity network:
   (a) Find the uniformly dominant network.
   (b) All requirements have to be satisfied exactly.
4. If all the b_{ij} of a network are distinct, is the cut tree unique?
5. For a network with directed arcs, show that the condition $f_{ik} \geq \min(f_{ij}, f_{jk})$ is necessary but not sufficient for realizability.
6. Given the tree requirement of Fig. 9.29. Synthesize a multiterminal network with minimum capacity which satisfies these requirements exactly.

SUGGESTED READING

1. Assume that there are n nodes in an undirected network and we want to find the maximal flows between nodes in a subset. Let there be p nodes in the subset. The algorithm by Ackers [2] is to simplify the network while still keeping the simplified network flow equivalent to the original network with respect to the subset. Let N_i be a node *not* in the subset which is incident to three other nodes as shown in Fig. 9.30 (a). Then the node N_i can be eliminated and the configuration is changed to Fig. 9.30 (b). By a sequence of changes between (a) and (b) the network can usually be simplified a great deal.

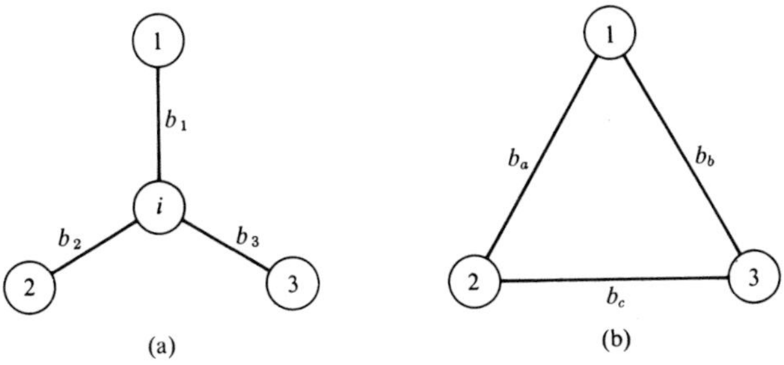

Fig. 9.30

2. If cost c_{ij} are given for building one unit of arc capacity between N_i and N_j, what is the minimum cost network that will satisfy all the flow requirements? See Gomory and Hu [90].

OPEN QUESTIONS

1. If the arc capacities are restricted to be 0 or 1, what are the necessary and sufficient conditions on the entries of a square matrix such that it represents the maximal flow values of some network? (Note that the triangular inequality is still necessary but no longer sufficient.)
2. In the minimum synthesis of a network, the arc capacity may be $\frac{1}{2}$. If all arc capacities are restricted to be integers, what would be the minimum capacity network?
3. Given a network with capacities associated with arcs and k pairs of nodes $N_1, N_{1'}; N_2, N_{2'}; \ldots; N_k, N_{k'}$. Find the capacity of a minimum disconnecting set $c(1, 2, \ldots, k; 1', 2', \ldots, k')$.
4. Given an undirected network with capacities associated with arcs. Find a subset of arcs such that its removal will disconnect the n-node network into k parts, and the total capacity of all arcs in the subset is a minimum. (Note that the problem is trivial for $k = 2$ and $k = n - 1$.)
5. If all arcs have infinite capacities and all nodes have finite capacities, what are the corresponding results in realization, analysis, and synthesis?

SHORTEST CHAINS AND MINIMAL COST FLOWS 10

10.1 SHORTEST CHAINS (Dijkstra [49])

In this section we shall treat one fundamental problem in network theory, i.e., the problem of finding a shortest chain from a given starting node to another node in the network. This problem arises very frequently as a subproblem in other problems of optimization and also has a practical interest of its own. Every arc A_{ij} of the network has associated with it a distance d_{ij}. The problem is to find a chain from N_s to N_t with the sum of the distances d_{ij} of arcs in the chain a minimum. If nodes are interpreted as cities and d_{ij} as the cost of traveling from city i to city j, then a shortest chain represents a cheapest route. There are many other practical problems in which one wants to find an optimum route under other criteria of optimality. But the shortest chain is the most frequently discussed and serves as an example.

We shall in *this section* assume that all d_{ij} are positive. If a pair of nodes is not connected by an arc, the distance between the pair of nodes is defined as ∞. Note that the distances d_{ij} are arbitrary and do not have to satisfy the triangular inequality $d_{ij} + d_{jk} \geq d_{ik}$. Otherwise, the problem would be trivial since then the arc A_{st} would be the shortest chain from N_s to N_t. Also we do not assume $d_{ij} = d_{ji}$.

Instead of finding the shortest chain from N_s to N_t, let us find the shortest chain from N_s to all other nodes N_i in the network.

The reason for doing this is that any node N_i may be an intermediate node on the shortest chain from N_s to N_t. If a node N_i is on the shortest chain from N_s to N_t, then the subchain from N_s to N_i must be a shortest chain from N_s to N_i. Otherwise we would replace the subchain from N_s to N_i by another chain of shorter distance to form a shorter chain from N_s to N_t. This new chain would be of shorter distance than the original chain from N_s to N_t and would contradict the fact that the original chain from N_s to N_t is a shortest chain.

Consider all the arcs used in all the shortest chains from N_s to all the other nodes N_i. These arcs will form a graph. Let us try to delete from the graph as many arcs as possible and still maintain one chain from N_s to each node N_i. (If there exists a unique shortest chain from N_s to every node N_i, then no deletion is possible.) If there are two shortest chains from N_s to N_i, say, then some arc on one of the two chains to N_i can be deleted. The resulting graph after all deletions will then form a tree. Therefore, if A_{ij} is an arc in the tree, the shortest chain from N_i to N_j must be the arc A_{ij} itself. The algorithm that will be presented later obtains such a tree.

As we have said before, we want to obtain a tree which contains shortest chains from N_s to all the nodes in the network. We shall call arcs in the tree, *tree arcs*, and arcs not in the tree, *nontree arcs*. After the tree is obtained, every shortest chain consists of tree arcs. At the beginning, every arc is considered to be a nontree arc. The algorithm tries to increase the membership of tree arcs from zero to $n - 1$, where n is the number of nodes in the network.

To begin, N_s must be a node in the tree. Now assume that we have m tree arcs ($m = 0, \ldots, n - 2$). Let L_{sk} be the true shortest distance from N_s to N_k and L'_{sk} be the shortest distance from N_s to N_k using tree arcs and *at most* one nontree arc. If all chains from N_s to N_k need more than one nontree arc, then $L'_{sk} = \infty$. Note that L'_{sk} depends on m; it changes as m increases. In general, $L'_{sk} \geq L_{sk}$. Assume that part of the tree is obtained and consider all the neighboring nodes of the current tree. N_k is a neighbor of the tree if there is an arc A_{ik} or A_{ki}, where N_i is any node in the current tree. Then $L'_{si} = L_{si}$ (here L'_{si} uses only tree arcs). For the neighboring node N_k, we set

$$L'_{sk} = \min_i \, (L_{si} + d_{ik}).$$

Now if we let

$$L'_{sr} = \min_k L'_{sk},$$

then we claim $L'_{sr} = L_{sr} = L_{si} + d_{ir}$ and the arc A_{ir} should be changed into a tree arc. We see this as follows.

As $L'_{sr} \leq L'_{sk}$, any chain passing k and then going to r would have greater distance than L'_{sk}; hence is greater than L'_{sr}. (Here we use the assumption $d_{ij} \geq 0$; otherwise the distance from N_k to N_r may be negative.) Since N_k represents all the neighboring nodes of the present tree (N_s is in the tree), any chain from N_s to N_r, if it does not lie entirely in the tree, will contain a first node not in the tree, which is N_k. Thus, any such chain will have distance greater than L'_{sk}. (It is impossible for L'_{sk} to become smaller than L_{sr} in a later step.)

As the membership of tree arcs is increased by one, we have to recalculate L'_{sk} for all neighboring nodes of the new tree. To do this, we compare L'_{sk} obtained earlier with $L_{sr} + d_{rk}$. If $L_{sr} + d_{rk}$ is smaller, then L'_{sk} is replaced by this smaller value. If $L_{sr} + d_{rk}$ is larger, L'_{sk} remains unchanged.

This is indicated symbolically by

$$L'_{sk} := \min(L'_{sk}, L_{sr} + d_{rk}),$$

where := means to be replaced by.

Now we briefly outline the algorithm.

STEP 0. $L'_{sk} = d_{sk}$. In the beginning, N_s is the only node in the tree, and for step 1, we let $L_{ss} = 0$.

STEP 1. $L_{sr} = \min_k L'_{sk} = L_{sj} + d_{jr}$. The N_k are neighboring nodes of the current tree.

STEP 2. Change the arc A_{jr} into a tree arc.

STEP 3. If the number of tree arcs is $n - 1$, stop. If not, go to step 4.

STEP 4. $L'_{sk} := \min(L'_{sk}, L_{sr} + d_{rk})$. Return to step 1.

This algorithm may be carried out by labeling the nodes. Each node N_k will receive a label of the form (L, i). The first part of the label is the value L'_{sk} or L_{sk} and the second part indicates the last node on the shortest chain from N_s to N_k. A label is called a *temporary label* if it is (L'_{sk}, i), and is called a *permanent label* if it is (L_{sk}, i). At the beginning, let N_k be the neighboring nodes of N_s. Then every N_k has $(d_{sk}, s) = (L'_{sk}, s)$. Let $L_{sr} = \min_k L'_{sk}$. Then $(L'_{sr}, s) = (L_{sr}, s)$, and it becomes a permanent label.

Let N_r be the latest node that is added to the tree and let N_k be the set of neighboring nodes of the tree. (Note that the membership of N_k changes as the tree enlarges.) Let us count the number of additions and comparisons needed to complete the algorithm, using the replacement

$$L'_{sk} := \min(L'_{sk}, L_{sr} + d_{rk}). \tag{1}$$

We need at most n additions in (1). On the right-hand side we need at most n comparisons and another n comparisons on the left-hand side to get a permanent label. Therefore, we need $3n$ operations to get a permanent label. As we have n nodes, we need *at most* $3n^2$ operations.

Consider the network in Fig. 10.1, where the numbers beside the arcs are the distances. Arcs without arrows are undirected arcs and their distances are symmetric.

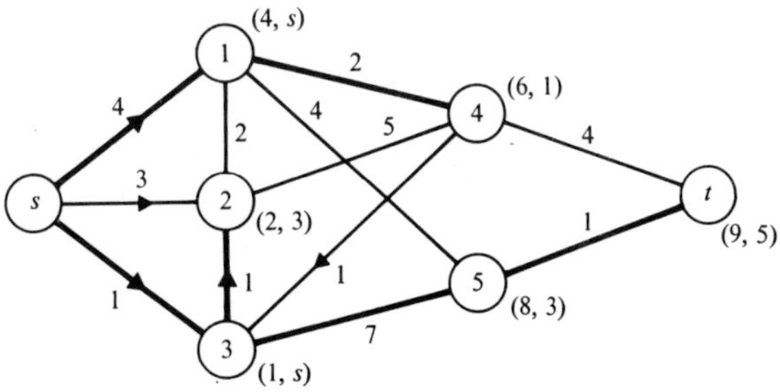

Fig. 10.1

In the beginning, there is not a single tree arc and N_1, N_2, and N_3 are neighboring nodes of N_s. We give temporary labels $(L'_{s1}, s) = (4, s)$ to N_1, $(3, s)$ to N_2, and $(1, s)$ to N_3. As $\min\{4, 3, 1\} = 1$, $(1, s)$ becomes a permanent label of N_3 and A_{s3} becomes a tree arc. The tree now consists of A_{s3} only.

Now the neighboring nodes of the tree are N_1, N_2, N_4, and N_5:

$$L'_{s1} := \min(L'_{s1}, L_{s3} + d_{31}) = \min(4, 1 + \infty) = 4,$$
$$L'_{s2} := \min(L'_{s2}, L_{s3} + d_{32}) = \min(3, 1 + 1) = 2,$$
$$L'_{s4} := \min(L'_{s4}, L_{s3} + d_{34}) = \min(\infty, 1 + \infty) = \infty,$$
$$L'_{s5} := \min(L'_{s5}, L_{s3} + d_{35}) = \min(\infty, 8) = 8.$$

Since L'_{s2} is the smallest, it becomes a permanent label and A_{32} becomes a tree arc. Now the tree consists of two tree arcs. Continuing,

$$L'_{s1} := \min(L'_{s1}, L_{s2} + d_{21}) = \min(4, 2 + 2) = 4,$$
$$L'_{s4} := \min(L'_{s4}, L_{s2} + d_{24}) = \min(\infty, 2 + 5) = 7,$$
$$L'_{s5} := \min(L'_{s5}, L_{s2} + d_{25}) = \min(8, 2 + \infty) = 8.$$

Since L'_{s1} is the smallest, it now becomes a permanent label and A_{s1} becomes a tree arc. Proceeding,

$$L'_{s4} := \min(L'_{s4}, L_{s1} + d_{14}) = \min(7, 4 + 2) = 6,$$
$$L'_{s5} := \min(L'_{s5}, L_{s1} + d_{15}) = \min(8, 4 + 4) = 8.$$

Since L'_{s4} is the smallest, it now becomes a permanent label and A_{14} becomes a tree arc. Continuing,

$$L'_{st} := \min(L'_{st}, L_{s4} + d_{4t}) = \min(\infty, 6 + 4) = 10,$$
$$L'_{s5} := \min(L'_{s5}, L_{s4} + d_{45}) = \min(8, 6 + \infty) = 8.$$

Since L'_{s5} is the smallest, it becomes a permanent label and A_{15} or A_{35} becomes a tree arc. We choose A_{35} as the tree arc. Then

$$L'_{st} := \min(L'_{st}, L_{s5} + d_{5t}) = \min(10, 8 + 1) = 9.$$

So A_{5t} becomes a tree arc and the computation is completed. In Fig. 10.1 all tree arcs are drawn as heavy lines and the labels of nodes are enclosed in parentheses.

The algorithm given above can also be used to find other optimum routes under other criteria of optimality. Therefore, it is desirable to know what other problems this algorithm can handle. We associate an arbitrary number g_{ij} with the arc A_{ij}. Let $A_{i1}, A_{12}, \ldots, A_{pj}, A_{jk}$ be a sequence of arcs which forms a chain, let $G_{ij}(g_{i1}, \ldots, g_{pj})$ be the value associated with the chain from N_i to N_j, and let $G_{ik}(g_{i1}, \ldots, g_{pj}, g_{jk})$ be the value associated with the chain from N_i to N_k. Then we require

$$G_{ij} \leq G_{ik} \qquad \text{(if we want to minimize)}, \tag{2a}$$

$$G_{ij} \geq G_{ik} \qquad \text{(if we want to maximize)}. \tag{2b}$$

For example, if g_{ij} are the distances d_{ij} and the problem is the shortest chain problem, then

$$G_{ij}(g_{i1}, \ldots, g_{pj}) = g_{i1} + g_{12} + \cdots + g_{pj}, \tag{3}$$

$$G_{ik}(g_{i1}, \ldots, g_{pj}, g_{jk}) = g_{i1} + g_{12} + \cdots + g_{pj} + g_{jk}. \tag{4}$$

Since we require distances to be nonnegative, comparison of (3) and (4) shows that condition (2a) is satisfied.

Now suppose that g_{ij} are the arc capacities b_{ij} and the problem is to find a chain which can carry a maximum amount of flow (this is called the maximum capacity route problem; see Hu [104]:

$$G_{ij}(g_{i1}, \ldots, g_{pj}) = \min(g_{i1}, g_{12}, \ldots, g_{pj}),$$

$$G_{ik}(g_{i1}, \ldots, g_{pj}, g_{jk}) = \min(g_{i1}, g_{12}, \ldots, g_{pj}, g_{jk}).$$

Condition (2b) is satisfied. To use the algorithm, we simply let L'_{sk} be the maximum amount of flow that can be shipped from N_s to N_k and change (1) to

$$L'_{sk} := \max\{L'_{sk}, \min(L_{sr}, b_{rk})\}. \tag{5}$$

Among the temporary labels the maximum one becomes the permanent label. The reader can use the same algorithm to solve many other problems by simply changing (1). It should be emphasized that (2a) and (2b) are sufficient conditions for applying an analogous algorithm to (1).

There is another interesting application of the shortest chain problem, which may not be so obvious, i.e., to find the minimum cut of an $s - t$ planar network. (See Ford and Fulkerson [64].)

An undirected network is an *$s - t$ planar network* if by adding an arc from N_s to N_t, the resulting network is planar. (A network is planar if all the arcs connecting the nodes can be drawn in the plane such that no two arcs cross each other.) For example, Fig. 10.2 is a planar network, but not an $s - t$ planar network. However, if we should omit the arc A_{23}, say,

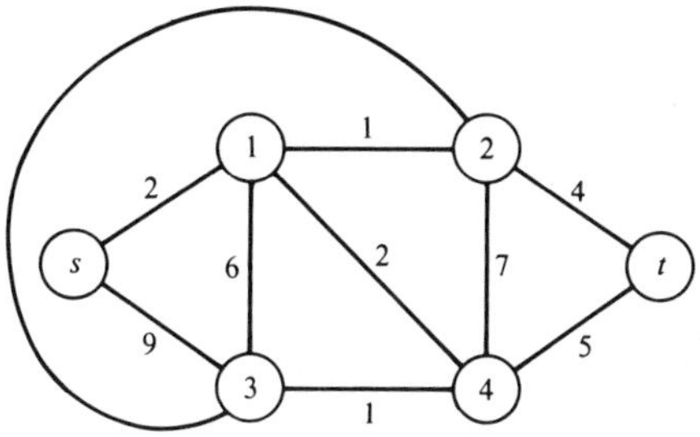

Fig. 10.2

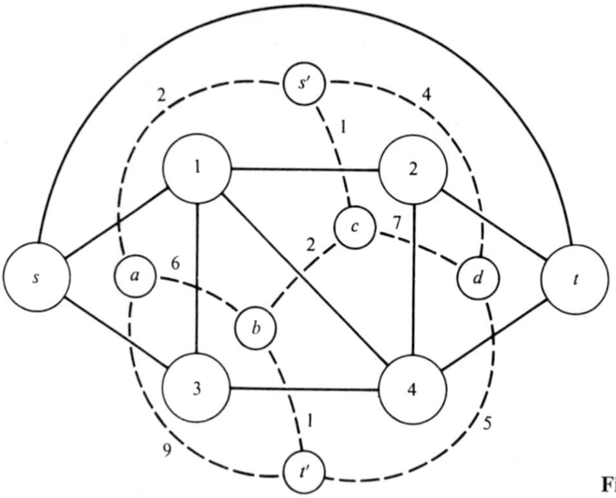

Fig. 10.3

then the new network will become an $s - t$ planar network. Let us remove the arc A_{23} from Fig. 10.2 so that it becomes an $s - t$ planar network. Let the numbers beside the arcs represent arc capacities. What is the minimum cut separating N_s and N_t? This can certainly be found by a maximal flow computation. However, let us find a dual network so that the shortest chain in the dual network corresponds to the minimum cut of the original network.

The dual network is constructed as follows. First draw the arc from N_s to N_t if there does not already exist such an arc. Because the n-node network is $s - t$ planar, the plane is partitioned into n regions after the arc A_{st} is added. There are two regions which use the arc from N_s to N_t as a boundary arc. Let us draw a node in each of the regions and call the two nodes in the two regions near A_{st}, N'_s and N'_t. For each arc A_{ij} of the original network, we shall draw an arc A'_{ij} which connects N'_i and N'_j, where N'_i and N'_j are in the two regions using A_{ij} as a boundary arc. Now every chain from N'_s to N'_t corresponds to a cut separating N_s and N_t of the original network. If we let b_{ij} of A_{ij} become the distances d_{ij} of A'_{ij}, then the shortest chain from N'_s to N'_t corresponds to the minimum cut separating N_s from N_t. Fig. 10.3 shows such a construction.

10.2 MULTITERMINAL SHORTEST CHAINS (Floyed [63], Hu [111], Murchland [158], Warshall [209])

In this section we are interested in finding shortest chains between all pairs of nodes. As before all d_{ij} do not satisfy the triangular inequality or the symmetric relations. Furthermore, *we shall not restrict the d_{ij} to be nonnegative*. However, the total distance of any cycle must be nonnegative; otherwise, the shortest chain problem is not well defined. *The nonexistence* *of a negative cycle rules out an undirected arc having a negative distance*, since we regard an undirected arc as two opposite directed arcs both with the same distance as the undirected arc.

As we pointed out in the last section, the whole problem lies in the fact that $d_{ij} + d_{jk} \not\geq d_{ik}$; otherwise, the shortest chain between every pair of nodes N_i and N_j would be the arc A_{ij}. However, there must be some arcs A_{ij} for which the shortest chain from N_i to N_j is the arc A_{ij}. Let us call these arcs *basic arcs*. Note in Section 10.1 that all tree arcs are basic arcs but not vice versa.

Suppose that we know the shortest chain from N_p to N_q, say. Then this chain must contain only basic arcs; otherwise the fact that the chain from N_p to N_q is a shortest chain will be contradicted. Now if we create an arc A_{pq} with distance equal to the shortest chain, then A_{pq} becomes a basic arc. This problem of multiterminal shortest chains is solved by creating a basic arc (if no such arc already exists) between every pair of nodes. The distance associated with the newly created basic arc is, of course, equal to the shortest chain formed by basic arcs of the original network.

Consider the following operations defined for a *given node* N_j:

$$d_{ik} := \min(d_{ik}, d_{ij} + d_{jk}) \qquad (\text{for all } i \neq k \neq j). \tag{1}$$

This is called a *triple operation*.

The operation (1) compares the distance of an arc d_{ik} with the distance of a chain consisting of two arcs with the intermediate node N_j and changes the original distance of the arc if it is the larger of the two distances. If we do this operation (1) for every node N_j ($j = 1, \ldots, n$), then we claim that the new d_{ik} are lengths of the shortest chains between every pair of nodes. Note in this algorithm that the amount of computation is $n(n-1)(n-2)$ additions and comparisons.

The proof of this algorithm is very easy. Any shortest chain must consist of basic arcs of the original network. The proof shows that at the end of computation, a basic arc of distance equal to the sum of the distances of the basic arcs in the shortest chain is created. To prove this, consider any arbitrary shortest chain such as the shortest chain in Fig. 10.4. The operation (1) will create basic arcs successively as shown by dashed lines. For a network without negative cycles, the shortest distance between any two

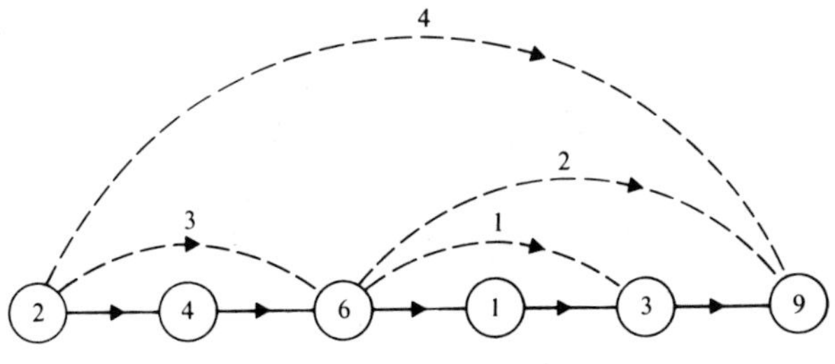

Fig. 10.4

nodes is well defined. If the operation (1) creates an arc A_{29} that is not equal to the true shortest distance, then that distance will be replaced by the true shortest distance at some later step. Once the true shortest distance is created, then it cannot be replaced, since it is the minimum. In Fig. 10.4 we show an arbitrary shortest chain with basic arcs A_{24}, A_{46}, A_{61}, A_{13}, and A_{39}. Since in the operation (1) j is successively fixed at $1, 2, \ldots, 9, \ldots$, we create successively the new basic arcs A_{63}, A_{69}, A_{26}, and A_{29}.

It also can be seen from the proof that $n(n-1)(n-2)$ additions and comparisons are the minimum that can be expected for a network with arbitrarily defined distances.

To keep track of the arcs that make up the shortest chain, we use the following bookkeeping. In a table whose entries are calculated along with (1), the entry in row i and column k indicates the first intermediate node on the shortest chain from N_i to N_k if there is such an intermediate node. Let k be the entry if there is no intermediate node. At the start all entries of the table in the (i, k) positions are set to k. Then

$$(i, k) = \begin{cases} (i, j) & \text{if } d_{ik} > d_{ij} + d_{jk}, \\ \text{remains the same} & \text{if } d_{ik} \leq d_{ij} + d_{jk}. \end{cases} \tag{2}$$

In all the previous calculations we have defined $d_{ii} = 0$ for all i. If we define $d_{ii} = \infty$ for all i, then the operation (1) allowing $i = k$ will provide a technique for finding minimum cycles containing N_i. In many applications we are interested in finding negative cycles, and if d_{ii} becomes negative, it shows that a negative cycle exists.

Consider the network in Fig. 10.5, where the distances of arcs are shown in Table 10.1. We want to find shortest chains between every pair of nodes.

To apply operation (1), for $j = 1$, we check every entry in Table 10.1 which does not lie in the first column or in the first row. Thus

$$d_{23} := \min(d_{23}, d_{21} + d_{13}) = \min(\infty, 11 + 30) = 41,$$
$$d_{32} := \min(d_{32}, d_{31} + d_{12}) = \min(\infty, 30 + 11) = 41.$$

All other entries remain the same. For $j = 2$ we apply the operation (1) to each of the entries in Table 10.1 which does not lie in the second column or the second row. The result is (we have omitted the calculations for

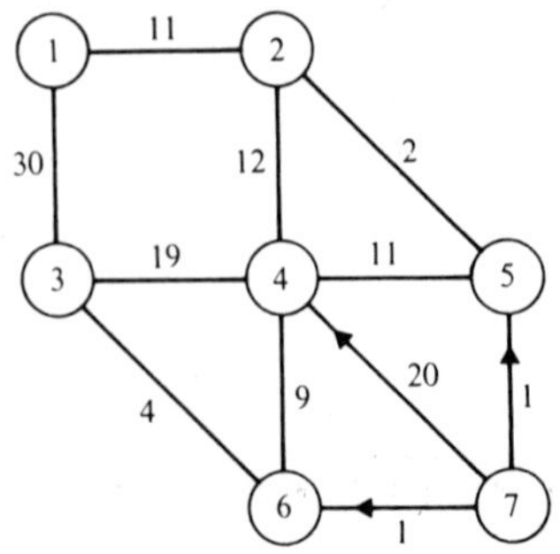

Fig. 10.5

Table 10.1

	①	②	③	④	⑤	⑥	⑦
①	0	11	30	∞	∞	∞	∞
②	11	0	∞	12	2	∞	∞
③	30	∞	0	19	∞	4	∞
④	∞	12	19	0	11	9	∞
⑤	∞	2	∞	11	0	∞	∞
⑥	∞	∞	4	9	∞	0	∞
⑦	∞	∞	∞	20	1	1	0

$d_{43} = d_{34}, d_{41} = d_{14}, d_{51} = d_{15}$, and $d_{53} = d_{35}$)

$$d_{34} := \min(d_{34}, d_{32} + d_{24}) = \min(19, 41 + 12) = 19,$$
$$d_{14} := \min(d_{14}, d_{12} + d_{24}) = \min(\infty, 11 + 12) = 23,$$
$$d_{15} := \min(d_{15}, d_{12} + d_{25}) = \min(\infty, 11 + 2) = 13,$$
$$d_{35} := \min(d_{35}, d_{32} + d_{25}) = \min(\infty, 41 + 2) = 43,$$

and all other entries remain the same. Note that in the above computation for $j = 2$, we have already used the results for $j = 1$. If we carry through the computation, we then get Table 10.2, which shows the shortest distances, and Table 10.3, which shows the actual nodes on the shortest chains. For example, if we want the shortest chain from N_1 to N_6, say, we look at

Table 10.2

	①	②	③	④	⑤	⑥	⑦
①	0	11	30	23	13	32	∞
②	11	0	25	12	2	21	∞
③	30	25	0	13	24	4	∞
④	23	12	13	0	11	9	∞
⑤	13	2	24	11	0	20	∞
⑥	32	21	4	9	20	0	∞
⑦	14	3	5	10	1	1	0

Table 10.3

	①	②	③	④	⑤	⑥	⑦
①	1	2	3	2	2	2	7
②	1	2	4	4	5	4	7
③	1	6	3	6	6	6	7
④	2	2	6	4	5	6	7
⑤	2	2	4	4	5	4	7
⑥	4	4	3	4	4	6	7
⑦	5	5	6	6	5	6	7

Table 10.3, where $(1, 6) = 2$. Then we look at $(2, 6) = 4$, $(4, 6) = 6$. Therefore, the nodes in the shortest chain are successively N_1, N_2, N_4, and N_6.

In finding the intermediate nodes of a shortest chain from N_p to N_q, we first look at the entry $(p, q) = k$, which means that N_k is the first intermediate node in the shortest chain from N_p to N_q. Then we look at (k, q) to find the first intermediate node in the shortest chain from N_k to N_q. This process is repeated until we find the entry $(i, q) = q$ which indicates that we have found all the intermediate nodes in the shortest chain, namely $N_p, N_k, \ldots, N_i, N_q$.

To prove that (2) works, let N_j be the intermediate node with smallest index on a shortest chain from N_p to N_q and N_i and N_k are the two neighboring nodes of N_j on the shortest chain. During the computation, $d^i{}_k > d_{ij} + d_{jk}$, and we set $(i, k) = (i, j) = j$. [Remember that (i, j) was initially set to be j and j is the smallest index on the chain.] Since A_{ij} and A_{jk} are basic arcs, $(i, j) = j$ and $(j, k) = k$ throughout the computation. This proves the correctness of (2) for a shortest chain with one intermediate node. Now the original shortest chain from N_p to N_q is replaced by another, a chain with equal distance but one less intermediate node, since a basic arc A_{ik} with distance equal to $d_{ij} + d_{jk}$ is created. The proof is completed by induction.

Given a network with arc capacities b_{ij}, a route from N_p to N_q is called a maximum capacity route if the minimum arc capacity of this route is not less than the minimum arc capacity of any other route from N_p to N_q. (See Hu [104].) As an application of the triple operations in this chapter, we can use the following operations to get maximum capacity routes between all pairs of nodes in the network:

$$b_{ik} := \max\,[b_{ik}, \min\,(b_{ij}, b_{jk})] \qquad (3)$$

for all $i, k \neq j$ and for $j = 1, \ldots, n$ successively. Another $n \times n$ matrix is calculated along with (3), where entries in the (i, k) position are all set equal to k initially. Then

$$(i, k) = \begin{cases} (i, j) & b_{ik} < \min(b_{ij}, b_{jk}), \\ \text{unchanged} & \text{if } b_{ik} \geq \min(b_{ij}, b_{jk}). \end{cases} \tag{4}$$

10.3 DECOMPOSITION ALGORITHM (Hu [111] and Hu and Torres [113])

In most cases a network has less than $n(n-1)$ arcs and is far from being completely connected. This means that the associated distance matrix has many entries which are infinity. The decomposition algorithm described here takes advantage of this situation. First, let's introduce some new concepts.

Take a subset of nodes in a network and denote it by A. Let X be another subset of nodes. We call the set X a *cut set* of A if it has the following property: If the set X together with its incident arcs are deleted from the network, then the network becomes two disconnected components, one component containing all the nodes of A and no other nodes. A cut set X of A is called a *minimum cut set* if no proper subset of X has this disconnecting property. Clearly, all the neighboring nodes of A constitute a minimum cut set of A. First we shall consider the decomposition algorithm in its simplest form, i.e., how to decompose a network into two parts. Let us assume that the network N is partitioned into three sets of nodes such that $N = A \cup X \cup B$, where X is a minimum cut set of A. If the nodes in set A are assigned with the index $1, 2, \ldots, |A|$* and the nodes in X are assigned the index $|A| + 1, |A| + 2, \ldots, |A| + |X|$, then the associated distance matrix is shown in Table 10.4, where $D_{AA} = [d_{ij}]$ with $N_i \in A$ and $N_j \in A$, $D_{AB} = [d_{ij}]$ with $N_i \in A$ and $N_j \in B$, etc. Initially, all entries in D_{AB} and D_{BA} are infinity.

Table 10.4

D_{AA}	D_{AX}	D_{AB}
D_{XA}	D_{XX}	D_{XB}
D_{BA}	D_{BX}	D_{BB}

We have just introduced the notation $D_{\alpha\beta}$ to be the distance matrix $[d_{ij}]$ with $N_i \in \alpha$ and $N_j \in \beta$. Sometimes it is convenient to use $d_{\alpha\beta}$ to represent one of the entries in $D_{\alpha\beta}$.

Let us introduce a new term, "*a conditional shortest chain.*" A conditional shortest chain is a shortest chain subject to the restriction that nodes in the chain must be in a certain subset of nodes of the network. We shall use d_{ij}^* to denote the shortest distance (using any number of arcs) from N_i to N_j. Now we use $d_{ij}^*(\gamma)$ to denote the distance of the conditional shortest chain from N_i to N_j, where γ is the subset of nodes in which the conditional shortest chain must lie. The matrix of conditional shortest distances $[d_{ij}^*(\gamma)]$

* Here $|A|$ denotes the cardinality of the set A.

with $N_i \in \alpha$ and $N_j \in \beta$ is denoted by $D^*_{\alpha\beta}(\gamma)$, and $d^*_{\alpha\beta}(\gamma)$ represents one of its entries. If N is used to denote the whole network, then $d^*_{ij}(N) = d^*_{ij}$. If we know that the shortest chains lie in the set γ, then

$$d^*_{\alpha\beta}(\gamma) = d^*_{\alpha\beta}(N). \tag{1}$$

Let $\bar{A}$ denote $A \cup X$ and $\bar{B}$ denote $B \cup X$. We consider the original network as two networks overlapping each other. One network, called the $\bar{A}$-network, consists of nodes N_i $(N_i \in \bar{A})$ and arcs A_{ij} $(N_i, N_j \in \bar{A})$. The other network, called the $\bar{B}$-network, consists of nodes N_k $(N_k \in \bar{B})$ and arcs A_{kl} $(N_k, N_l \in \bar{B})$. First, we shall perform the triple operations in the $\bar{A}$-network. This will give the conditional shortest distances between each pair of nodes in the $\bar{A}$-network. In particular, for two nodes in X the conditional shortest distances will replace the original distances between the two nodes. Then we shall do the triple operations on the $\bar{B}$-network, where the distances between nodes in X have been replaced by the conditional shortest distances calculated from the $\bar{A}$-network. After the triple operations in the $\bar{B}$-network, we shall do the triple operation in the $\bar{A}$-network again. The following two theorems give the foundations for the decomposition algorithm for two overlapping networks.

Theorem 10.1. Let $N = A \cup X \cup B$, where the removal of X will make the network disconnected. Then the shortest distances between any two nodes in the $\bar{B}$-network can be obtained by considering only the $\bar{B}$-network, provided that the conditional shortest distances $D^*_{XX}(\bar{A})$ are known. (Note that $\bar{A} = N - B$.)

Proof. If the shortest path lies entirely in $\bar{B}$, then $d^*_{\bar{B}\bar{B}}(N) = d^*_{\bar{B}\bar{B}}(\bar{B})$, which means it is sufficient to do the triple operations on $\bar{B}$-networks. Assume that there are many subpaths, of a shortest path, which contain nodes in $\bar{A}$. This is shown symbolically in Fig. 10.6.

Consider a shortest path from N_1 to N_6. Since both the starting node and the terminal nodes are in $\bar{B}$ and X is a cut set of B, any subpath that contains nodes in A must begin and end in the set X. In Fig. 10.6 the subpath from N_2 to N_3 and the subpath N_4 to N_5 are two such subpaths. If $d_{23}(\bar{A}) = d_{23}(N - B)$ and $d_{45}(N - B) = d_{45}(\bar{A})$ are known, we have effectively in

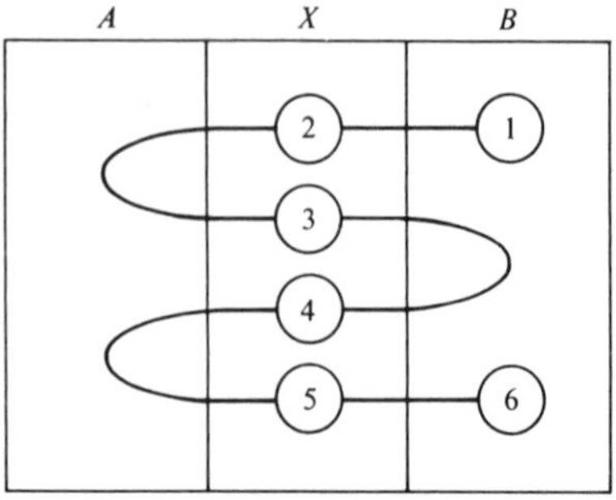

Fig. 10.6

the $\bar{B}$-network, two arcs A_{23} with distance $d_{23}^*(N - B)$ and A_{45} with distance $d_{45}^*(N - B)$.

The shortest path from N_1 to N_6 then consists of the subpath from N_1 to N_2, A_{23}, the subpath from N_3 to N_4, A_{45}, and the subpath from N_5 to N_6, all of which contain arcs in the $\bar{B}$-network. Thus, it is sufficient to consider only the $\bar{B}$-network. Note that the above reasoning is independent of the number of subpaths which contain nodes of $\bar{A}$. Clearly if we interchange A and B, and $\bar{A}$ and $\bar{B}$, then the theorem is also true.

Theorem 10.2. Let $N = A \cup X \cup B$, where the removal of X will make the network disconnected. Then

$$d_{AB}^*(N) = \min_X [d_{AX}^*(N) + d_{XB}^*(N)], \tag{2}$$

$$d_{BA}^*(N) = \min_X [d_{BX}^*(N) + d_{XA}^*(N)]. \tag{3}$$

Proof. To get from any node N_i in A to any node N_k in B we must pass at least one node N_j in X. If the minimum is taken over all N_j in X, then it is certainly the minimum distance. Let the distance matrix $D_{AX}^*(N)$ be $n_a \times p$ and the distance matrix $D_{XB}^*(N)$ be $p \times n_b$. Then the operation as carried out for a given i and k is

$$d_{ik}^* = \min_j (d_{ij}^* + d_{jk}^*) \qquad (j = 1, \ldots, p, N_i \in A, N_k \in B). \tag{4}$$

The total number of additions is then $n_a \times n_b \times p$ with the same number of comparisons. The operation (4) is like an ordinary matrix multiplication with + replacing $\times$ and min replacing summation. We shall refer to (4) as a *matrix minisummation*.

Now we shall state the decomposition algorithm for the two overlapping networks:

STEP 1. Execute the triple operations for each of the entries of the matrix

$$\begin{bmatrix} D_{AA} & D_{AX} \\ D_{XA} & D_{XX} \end{bmatrix}.$$

At the end of the step, we have $D_{AA}^*(\bar{A})$, $D_{AX}^*(\bar{A})$, $D_{XA}^*(\bar{A})$, and $D_{XX}^*(\bar{A})$.

STEP 2. Execute the triple operations on the matrix

$$\begin{bmatrix} D_{XX}^*(\bar{A}) & D_{XB} \\ D_{BX} & D_{BB} \end{bmatrix}.$$

At the end of the step we have, from Theorem 10.1, $D_{XX}^*(N)$, $D_{XB}^*(N)$, $D_{BX}^*(N)$, and $D_{BB}^*(N)$.

STEP 3. Execute the triple operation on the matrix

$$\begin{bmatrix} D_{AA}^*(\bar{A}) & D_{AX}^*(\bar{A}) \\ D_{XA}^*(\bar{A}) & D_{XX}^*(N) \end{bmatrix}.$$

At the end of this step we have, from Theorem 10.1, $D^*_{AA}(N)$, $D^*_{AX}(N)$, $D^*_{XA}(N)$, and $D^*_{XX}(N)$.

STEP 4. Use (4) to obtain $D^*_{AB}(N)$ and $D^*_{BA}(N)$.

Let us calculate the number of additions needed in this algorithm.* (For simplicity, we consider that a matrix of order n requires n^3 additions instead of $n(n-1)(n-2)$. In step 1 $(|A|+|X|)^3$ additions are needed, $(|B|+|X|)^3$ additions in step 2, $(|A|+|X|)^3$ in step 3, and $2|A|\cdot|X|\cdot|B|$ additions are needed in step 4. Thus, total additions needed are

$$2(|A|+|X|)^3 + (|B|+|X|)^3 + 2|A|\cdot|X|\cdot|B|.$$

If the network is calculated as a whole, we need $(|A|+|X|+|B|)^3$ additions. Let $|A|=|B|$. Then the number of additions that can be reduced from decompositions is

$$5|A|^3+|A|^2|X|-3|A||X|^2-2|X|^3.$$

Thus the decomposition reduces computation for $|A|>|X|$. When $|A|\neq |B|$, then the number of additions that can be reduced is

$$3|A|\cdot|B|(|A|+|B|)-|A|^3-3|A|^2|X|+4|A||B||X|$$
$$-3|A||X|^2-2|X|^3.$$

For example if

$$|B|=(5/10)\,n,\qquad |A|=(4/10)\,n,\qquad |X|=(1/10)\,n,$$

the amount of saving is $(494/1{,}000)\,n^3$.

When the network is extremely large and loosely connected, it is advantageous to decompose the network into many overlapping networks. Let the distance matrix of the network be decomposed into four overlapping networks as shown in Table 10.5, where the white areas indicate entries that are all infinity originally.

To construct such a distance matrix like Table 10.5, we proceed as follows. Label any subset of nodes as A. Then its minimum cut set is X_A. Let B be a cut set (not necessarily a minimum cut set) of $A\cup X_A$, and X_B be the minimum cut set of $A\cup X_A\cup B$. (Note that the minimum cut set of B is $X_A\cup X_B$.) Let C be a cut set of $A\cup X_A\cup B\cup X_B$ and X_C be the minimum cut set of $A\cup X_A\cup B\cup X_B\cup C$. Continue until no further decomposition is desired. In Table 10.5, the original network is decomposed into four overlapping ones: $\bar{A}$-network ($\bar{A}=A\cup X_A$), $\bar{B}$-network ($\bar{B}=X_A\cup B\cup X_B$), $\bar{C}$-network ($\bar{C}=X_B\cup C\cup X_C$), and $\bar{D}$-network ($\bar{D}=X_C\cup D$).

We shall state the general decomposition algorithm for m overlapping networks: $\bar{A}$-network, $\bar{B}$-network, ..., $\bar{G}$-networks, $\bar{H}$-networks.

STEP 1. Do the triple operations on the $m-1$ networks $\bar{A}$, $\bar{B}$, ..., $\bar{G}$, successively, where conditional shortest distances obtained in one network

* The number of comparisons needed is the same.

Table 10.5

	A	X_A	B	X_B	C	X_C	D
A	D_{AA}	D_{AX_A}	D_{AB}	D_{AX_B}	D_{AC}	D_{AX_C}	D_{AD}
X_A	D_{X_AA}	$D_{X_AX_A}$	D_{X_AB}	$D_{X_AX_B}$	D_{X_AC}	$D_{X_AX_C}$	D_{X_AD}
B	D_{BA}	D_{BX_A}	D_{BB}	D_{BX_B}	D_{BC}	D_{BX_C}	D_{BD}
X_B	D_{X_BA}	$D_{X_BX_A}$	D_{X_BB}	$D_{X_BX_B}$	D_{X_BC}	$D_{X_BX_C}$	D_{X_BD}
C	D_{CA}	D_{CX_A}	D_{CB}	D_{CX_B}	D_{CC}	D_{CX_C}	D_{CD}
X_C	D_{X_CA}	$D_{X_CX_A}$	D_{X_CB}	$D_{X_CX_B}$	D_{X_CC}	$D_{X_CX_C}$	D_{X_CD}
D	D_{DA}	D_{DX_A}	D_{DB}	D_{DX_B}	D_{DC}	D_{DX_C}	D_{DD}

will replace original distances in the succeeding network. That is to say, $D^*_{X_AX_A}(\bar{A})$ will replace $D_{X_AX_A}$ before we perform the triple operations on $\bar{B} = X_A \cup B \cup X_B$.

(If we consider the sets A, $A \cup X_A \cup B, \ldots$, successively as the set A in Theorem 10.1 and $B \cup X_B \cup \ldots \cup H$, $C \cup X_C \cup \ldots \cup H, \ldots$, correspondingly, as the set B in Theorem 10.1, then we get the following shortest distance matrices $D^*_{\bar{A}\bar{A}}(\bar{A})$, $D^*_{\bar{B}\bar{B}}(\bar{A} \cup \bar{B}), \ldots, D^*_{\bar{G}\bar{G}}(\bar{A} \cup \bar{B} \cup \ldots \cup \bar{G})$.

STEP 2. Perform the triple operation on the m networks, $\bar{H}$, $\bar{G}, \ldots, \bar{B}$, $\bar{A}$, successively, where the distances obtained in one network will replace the distances of the succeeding network, that is, $D^*_{X_GX_G}(N)$ will replace $D^*_{X_GX_G}(N - H)$. From Theorem 10.1, we have

$$D^*_{\bar{H}\bar{H}}(N),\ D^*_{\bar{G}\bar{G}}(N),\ \ldots,\ D^*_{\bar{B}\bar{B}}(N),\ D^*_{\bar{A}\bar{A}}(N).$$

STEP 3. Find the shortest distances between any two nodes which are not both in one of the sets $\bar{A}, \bar{B}, \ldots, \bar{H}$ by minisummation (4). We shall use the notation $A \oplus X_A \oplus B$ to denote the matrix minisummation with $N_i \in A$, $N_j \in X_A$, and $N_k \in B$. Though both $A \oplus X_A \oplus B$ and $B \oplus X_A \oplus A$ should be calculated, for simplicity we shall write only one of them. The order in which the matrix minisummations should be executed is as follows:

$$A \oplus X_A \oplus B \cup X_B,$$
$$A \cup X_A \cup B \oplus X_B \oplus C \cup X_C,$$
$$A \cup X_A \cup B \cup X_B \cup C \oplus X_C \oplus D \cup X_D,$$
$$\vdots$$
$$A \cup X_A \cup \ldots \cup F \oplus X_F \oplus G \cup X_G,$$
$$A \cup X_A \cup \ldots \cup G \oplus X_G \oplus H.$$

In the above matrix minisummation, the $D^*_{AX_B}(N)$ obtained in the first matrix minisummation are used in the second minisummation.

To get some idea of the number of arithmetic operations used in the decomposition algorithm, we assume that $|A| = |B| = \cdots = |H| = t$ and $|X_A| = |X_B| = \cdots = |X_G| = \delta$. We shall calculate only the number of additions, since the number of comparisons needed is the same. In step 1 the number of additions is $(t + \delta)^3 + (m - 2)(t + 2\delta)^3$. In step 2 the number of additions is $2(t + \delta)^3 + (m - 2)(t + 2\delta)^3$. In step 3 the number of additions is

$$2\{t + (2t + \delta) + \cdots + [(m - 2)t + (m - 3)\delta]\}\cdot\delta\cdot(t + \delta) + 2[(m - 1)t + (m - 2)\delta]\cdot\delta\cdot t$$
$$= m(m - 1)t^2\delta + 2(m - 1)(m - 2)t\delta^2 + (m - 2)(m - 3)\delta^3.$$

Therefore, the total number of additions is

$$(2m - 1)t^3 + (m^2 + 11m - 15)t^2\delta + (2m^2 + 18m - 35)t\delta^2 + (m^2 + 11m - 23)\delta^3. \tag{5}$$

If we do not use the decomposition algorithm but perform the triple operations on the entire matrix, the number of additions is

$$[mt + (m - 1)\delta]^3. \tag{6}$$

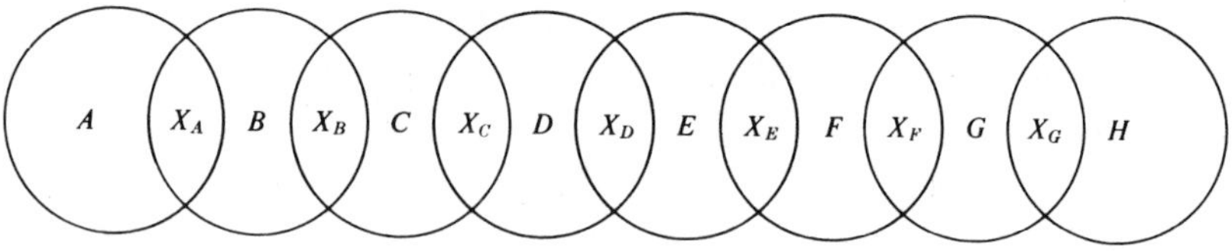

(a)

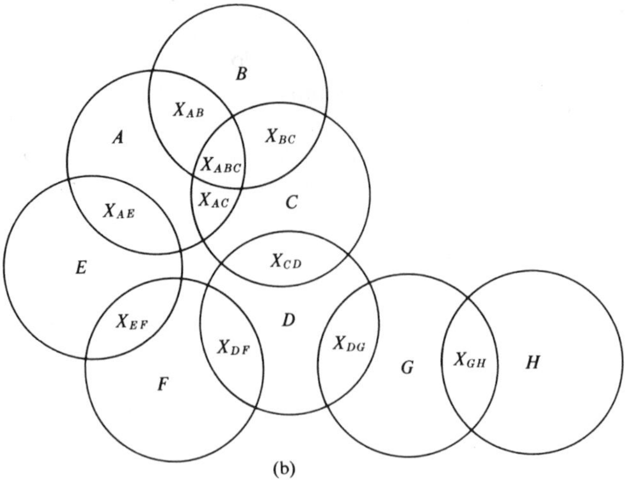

(b)

Fig. 10.7

For larger m (5) approaches $m^2 \delta (t + \delta)^2$ and (6) approaches $m^3(t + \delta)^3$. Thus the ratio of (5) to (6) approaches $[\delta/(t + \delta)]/m$ as $m \to \infty$.

Having prescribed a rule to obtain the distance matrix like Table 10.5, we can certainly decompose each of the networks $\bar{A}, \bar{B}, \ldots, \bar{H}$ as if each of them was the original network. Thus the decomposition algorithm can always be used to decompose a network into finer and finer networks until decomposition no longer pays.

One fact should be emphasized: each of the subsets of nodes like A, X_A, B, X_B, etc., need not be connected. We can take any subset as A. But once A is determined, X_A is uniquely determined. The set B can be any set that will disconnect $A \cup X_A$, but X_B is the minimum cut set that disconnects $A \cup X_A \cup B$.

This decomposition of a network can be classified as a linear decomposition, since the network is partitioned linearly into m overlapping sets as shown Fig. 10.7(a).Consider a network consisting of m overlapping sets which overlap each other arbitrarily as shown for example in Fig. 10.7(b). In this case we may still decompose the network linearly by letting $A^* = \bar{E}$, say, $\bar{B}^* = \bar{A} \cup \bar{F}$, $\bar{C}^* = \bar{B} \cup \bar{C} \cup \bar{D}$, $\bar{D}^* = \bar{G}$, and $\bar{E}^* = H$, for example, and then decompose $\bar{B}^*$ into two small networks and $\bar{C}^*$ into three small networks $\bar{B}$, $\bar{C}$, and $\bar{D}$.

It is possible to decompose the network into the networks $\bar{A}, \bar{B}, \ldots$ directly, but the number of operations needed would be more than the number needed to decompose the network linearly.

We shall now discuss an idea which can be used to explain the decomposition algorithm or can be used together with the decomposition algorithm.

We are given an n-node network for which we want to find the shortest paths between p nodes, $p \leq n$. Then a p-node network is said to be *distance equivalent* to the n-node network if the distances of $p(p-1)$ pairs of shortest paths of the two networks are the same. In Fig. 10.8 the two networks are distance equivalent with respect to the nodes N_1, N_2, N_3, and N_4.

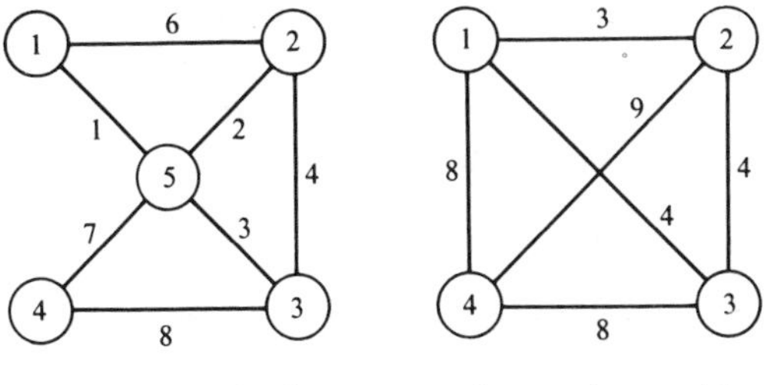

Fig. 10.8

The idea of distance equivalent networks can be used locally to eliminate nodes and arcs which are not of concern to us during a particular phase in the calculations. Simple formulas can be derived to eliminate these nodes and arcs. Some networks and their distance equivalent networks are shown in Fig. 10.9.

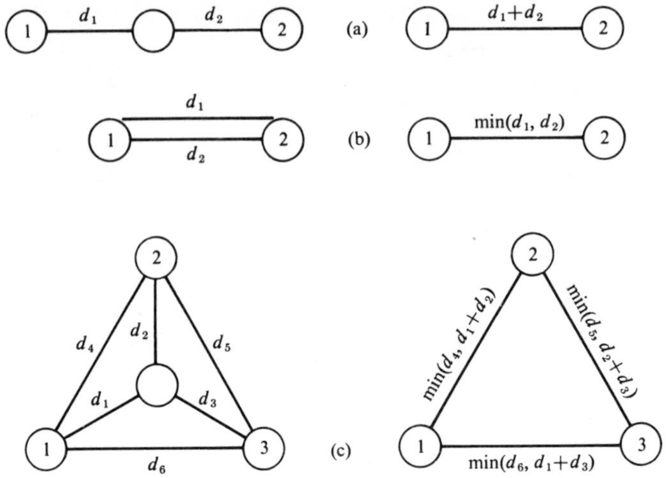

Fig. 10.9

In Fig. 10.9(c) it is possible that the shortest distance from N_2 to N_3 is $d_4 + d_6$ or $d_2 + d_1 + d_6$, but when we convert the four-node network to the triangular network, all shortest distances can be found in the triangular network. If we apply simple transformations such as those shown in Fig. 10.9, we can eliminate $n - p$ nodes and construct the distance equivalent p-node network. Then we can apply the triple operations or use the decomposition algorithm on the p-node network.

The proof of Theorem 10.1 can be thought of as eliminating the set A when we obtain $D^*_{XX}(A \cup X)$.

10.4 MINIMAL COST FLOWS

In Chapter 8 every arc of the network was assigned a given capacity b_{ij} which limits the amount of flow that can pass through the arc. In this chapter every arc is also assigned a cost c_{ij}, or the cost of shipping one unit of flow along that arc. Now we are interested in shipping a given amount of flow from the source to the sink at minimal cost. If there are no capacity restrictions on the arcs, then the problem becomes one of finding a shortest chain from N_s to N_t and then shipping all the flow along that chain. To state the problem formally, we want to

$$\min z = \sum c_{ij}x_{ij}$$

subject to

$$\sum_i x_{ij} - \sum_k x_{jk} = \begin{cases} -v, & j = s, \\ 0, & j \neq s, t, \\ v, & j = t, \end{cases}$$

$$0 \leq x_{ij} \leq b_{ij} \qquad \text{(for all } i, j),$$

where c_{ij} is the cost of shipping one unit of flow along the arc A_{ij}. It is assumed implicitly that v is not greater than the maximum flow from N_s to N_t; otherwise the problem is infeasible.

Most of the algorithms for solving minimal cost flows use the primal-dual approach of linear programming. These are discussed by Ford and Fulkerson[67]. We now give two ways of solving this problem which do not use the linear programming concept and are also quite efficient computationally.

The first algorithm can be stated as follows (Busacker and Gowen [22]):

STEP 0. Start with all arc flows equal to zero and the flow value equals zero.

STEP 1. Define the modified costs c_{ij}^* with respect to the given flow that exists in the network as follows:

$$\begin{aligned} c_{ij}^* &= c_{ij} && \text{if } x_{ij} < b_{ij}\ (0 \le x_{ij}), \\ c_{ij}^* &= \infty && \text{if } x_{ij} = b_{ij}, \\ c_{ij}^* &= -c_{ji} && \text{if } x_{ji} > 0. \end{aligned}$$

STEP 2. Find the shortest chain or the minimal cost chain from N_s to N_t using the current modified costs c_{ij}^* obtained in step 1. Then ship the flow along this chain until the chain is no longer the shortest chain. Replace the old flow value by the old flow value plus the flow along the chain. If the new flow value is v, stop. Otherwise, return to step 1.

This algorithm has the interesting feature that when the flow in step 2 is p, it gives the minimum cost flow of p units from N_s to N_t. Therefore, we get the minimal cost flow for $p = 1, \ldots, v$. This should be classified as a dual algorithm.

The second algorithm can be stated as follows (Klein [130]):

STEP 1. Find any feasible flow of v units from N_s to N_t. This can be done by guessing or using the maximal flow algorithm. We stop when the flow value reaches v.

STEP 2. Define the modified costs c_{ij}^* as follows:

$$\begin{aligned} c_{ij}^* &= c_{ij} && \text{if } x_{ij} < b_{ij}\ (0 \le x_{ij}), \\ c_{ij}^* &= \infty && \text{if } x_{ij} = b_{ij}, \\ c_{ij}^* &= -c_{ji} && \text{if } x_{ji} > 0. \end{aligned}$$

STEP 3. Using the c_{ij}^* as distances, find negative cycles in the network. If none exists, the current flow is optimum. If such a negative cycle exists, superimpose a cycle of flow of amount δ, when $\delta = \min(b_{ij} - x_{ij}, x_{ji})$ in the negative cycle and return to step 2. (If the negative cycles are disjoint, we superimpose flow on each of them.)

Since this algorithm gives a feasible flow of v units to start, it should be classified as a primal algorithm. It is easy to see that both algorithms will give a flow of v units if v is not greater than the maximal flow. It is slightly harder to see that the algorithms will give optimum flow when completed. The proof of the two algorithms depends on the following theorem, which can be considered as the central theorem in minimal cost flow. It is stated in [23] and also implicitly in [67], [108], [117], [151].

Theorem 10.3. A flow with value v is optimum if and only if, based on the modified costs, there exist no negative cycles with respect to the flow.

Proof. The condition is certainly necessary, because if such a negative cycle exists, superimposition of a cycle of flow will keep the flow value at v and yet reduce the total cost.

To see that the condition is sufficient, assume that there exists an optimum flow with less cost than the present flow. We can decompose the optimum flow into v chains, each of unit flow. We can also decompose the present flow into v chains, each of unit flow. Imagine that we remove from the network any arc flow which is common to both the optimum flow and the present flow. The result of the removal is that a remaining arc either contains the optimum flow, as part of a chain of the optimum flow, or the arc contains the present flow and is part of a chain of the present flow. Let us call this network with flows removed the *reduced flow network*. In the original network denote a chain of the optimum flow as o_i and a chain of the present flow as p_i. The two chains o_i and p_i may be (a) completely coincident, (b) completely disjoint, or (c) overlapping each other partially. If case (a) happens for all i ($i = 1, \ldots, v$), the two flows are the same and there is no arc flow in the reduced flow network. If case (b) happens, then there must exist at least one o_i and one p_i such that the cost of o_i is less than the cost of p_i. This means that the cycle of flow from N_s to N_t along o_i and then from N_t to N_s along p_i is of negative modified cost. This will contradict the fact that there are no negative cycles.

In case (c), let N_i be the first node at which the two chains o_i and p_i begin to separate and N_j be the node at which the two chains meet again. This is shown in Fig. 10.10.

There are possibly many such pairs of subchains in the network, but there must exist at least one pair such that the cost of the subchain of o_i is less than the cost of the subchain p_i. Then that pair forms a negative cycle in the modified cost (i.e., we can ship one unit of flow along o_i and send one unit of flow from N_j to N_i along p_i to reduce the cost). Q.E.D.

We shall first do a simple example using the first algorithm. Consider the network of Fig. 10.11 in which the first number on an arc is its capacity, the second, its unit shipping cost. All arcs are undirected and we want two units of flow from N_s to N_t at minimum cost.

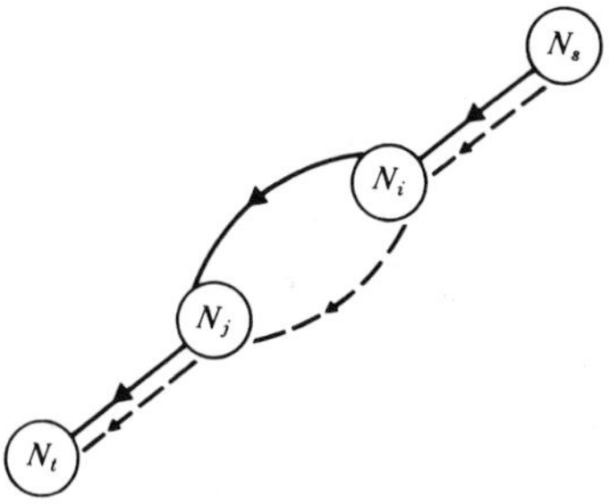

Fig. 10.10

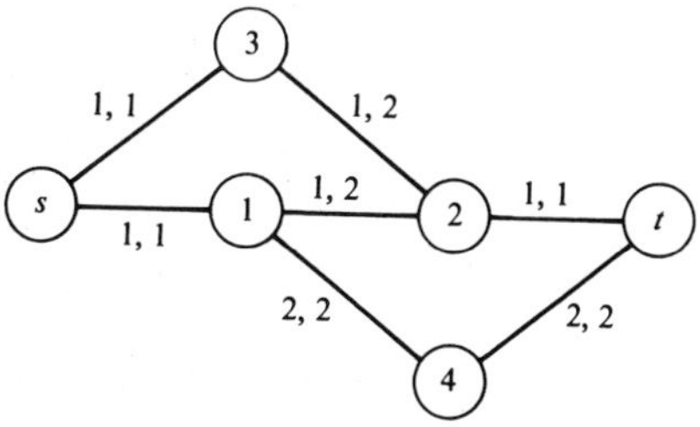

Fig. 10.11

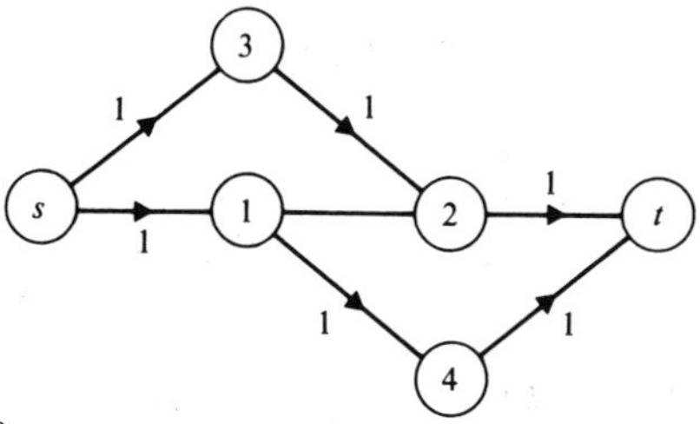

Fig. 10.12

STEP 0. Set $x_{ij} = 0$.

STEP 1. Define $c_{ij}^* = c_{ij}$.

STEP 2. Find the shortest chain from N_s to N_t using $c_{ij}^* = c_{ij}$. This would give the chain N_s, A_{s1}, N_1 A_{12}, N_2, A_{2t}, N_t or the chain N_s, A_{s3}, N_3, A_{32}, N_2, A_{2t}, N_t. Assume that we use the first chain so that $x_{s1} = x_{12} = x_{2t} = 1$.

STEP 1. Define the modified costs c_{ij}^* as follows:

$$
\begin{aligned}
c_{s1}^* &= \infty, &&\text{as } x_{s1} = 1 = b_{s1} = 1,\\
c_{1s}^* &= -1,\\
c_{12}^* &= \infty, &&\text{as } x_{12} = 1 = b_{12},\\
c_{21}^* &= -2,\\
c_{2t}^* &= \infty, &&\text{as } x_{2t} = 1 = b_{2t},\\
c_{t2}^* &= -1,\\
c_{ij}^* &= c_{ij} &&\text{otherwise.}
\end{aligned}
$$

STEP 2. Find the shortest chain using the current modified cost c_{ij}^*. This would be a shortest chain $A_{s3}, A_{32}, A_{21}, A_{14}, A_{4t}$ with total cost $1 + 2 + (-2) + 2 + 2 = 5$. By shipping one unit of flow along this chain, we would get the final flows in the network as in Fig. 10.12, where the numbers indicate arc flows.

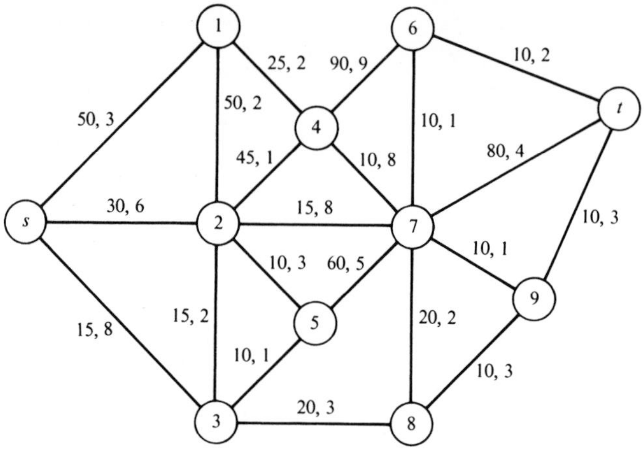

Fig. 10.13

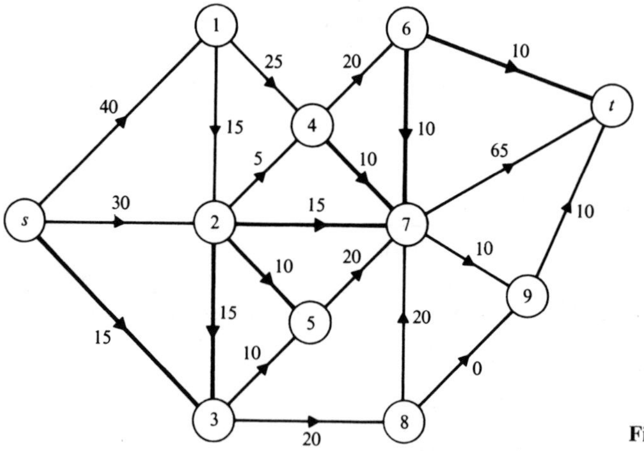

Fig. 10.14

This algorithm is not recommended when v is large. In the case of large v or for finding maximal flow at minimum cost, the second algorithm is recommended.

We shall use the second algorithm to construct a maximum flow at minimum cost for the network of Fig. 10.13 (see Ford and Fulkerson [67]):

STEP 1 Use the maximal flow algorithm to construct the maximum flow. This is shown in Fig. 10.14, where numbers indicate flow. Arcs in the minimum cuts are drawn with heavy lines.

STEP 2. Define the modified costs c_{ij}^*.

STEP 3. Every arc in the minimum cut must be *saturated*, i.e., $c_{ij}^* = \infty$. This implies that none of the arcs in the minimum cut can be in any negative

Table 10.6

	Ⓢ	①	②	④	⑥
Ⓢ	∞	3	∞	∞	∞
①	−3	∞	2	∞	∞
②	−6	−2	∞	1	∞
④	∞	−2	−1	∞	9
⑥	∞	∞	∞	−9	∞

Table 10.7

	③	⑤	⑦	⑧	⑨	ⓣ
③	∞	∞	∞	∞	∞	∞
⑤	−1	∞	5	∞	∞	∞
⑦	∞	−5	∞	−2	∞	4
⑧	−3	∞	∞	∞	3	∞
⑨	∞	∞	−1	3	∞	∞
ⓣ	∞	∞	−4	∞	−3	∞

cycle. Hence we can split the network into two parts and find negative cycles in each of these parts. The modified costs c_{ij}^* for the part of the network containing N_s is listed in Table 10.6, and c_{ij}^* for the other part is listed in Table 10.7.

If we do the triple operations (1) of Section 10.2 for Table 10.6, we will find a negative cycle A_{2s}, A_{s1}, A_{12}. Superposition of $10 = (b_{s1} - x_{s1})$ units of flow will result in the optimum flow in that part. If we do the triple operation (1) of Section 10.2 for Table 10.7, we will find no negative cycles.

10.5 MINIMUM COST IMPROVEMENT OF AN EXISTING NETWORK (Fulkerson [68] and Hu [108])

Suppose that a fixed budget can be allocated among the arcs of an existing network for the purpose of increasing its maximal flow value relative to a given source and sink. How should the money be spent in order to maximize the flow value of the resulting network? If the maximal flow value of a network is required to be v' ($v' > v$ = the maximal flow value of the existing network), how should we increase the arc capacities to achieve this goal at minimal cost? This problem was solved by Fulkerson [68] and it is solved here using an algorithm based on the modified cost concept, proposed by Hu [108]. Assume that the cost of increasing the capacity of an arc is linear, i.e., it costs c_{ij} dollars to increase the arc capacity of A_{ij} by one unit. Let y_{ij} denote the amount of additional arc capacities to be built between N_i and N_j. Then the problem of getting v' units of flow at minimal cost is

$$\min \sum c_{ij} y_{ij}$$

subject to

$$\sum_i x_{ij} - \sum_k x_{jk} = \begin{cases} -v', & j = s, \\ 0, & j \neq s, t, \\ v', & j = t, \end{cases} \tag{1}$$

$$0 \leq x_{ij} \leq b_{ij} + y_{ij}.$$

The problem of maximizing the flow value with a fixed budget c is

$$\max v'$$

subject to

$$\sum c_{ij} y_{ij} = c,$$

$$\sum_i x_{ij} - \sum_k x_{jk} = \begin{cases} -v', & j = s, \\ 0, & j \neq s, t, \\ v', & j = t, \end{cases} \tag{2}$$

$$0 \leq x_{ij} \leq b_{ij} + y_{ij}.$$

The algorithm for solving the problems (1) and (2) can be stated.

STEP 1. Define the modified costs c^*_{ij} based on the current arc flows in the network (we start with $x_{ij} = 0$ for all i, j):

$$\begin{aligned} c^*_{ij} &= 0 && \text{if } x_{ij} < b_{ij}, \\ c^*_{ij} &= c_{ij} && \text{if } x_{ij} \geq b_{ij}, \\ c^*_{ij} &= -c_{ji} && \text{if } x_{ji} > b_{ji} > 0. \end{aligned} \tag{3}$$

STEP 2. Ship the flow along the minimal cost path based on c^*_{ij}. The amount of flow shipped along the minimal cost path is limited by the condition that the c^*_{ij} remain the same as those defined in step 1.

STEP 3. If the total flow is v' or the total cost is c, stop. Otherwise return to step 1.

Consider the network in Fig. 10.15(a), where the numbers beside the arcs are their capacities. The costs c_{ij} of adding unit capacities at the different places are shown in Fig. 10.15(b).

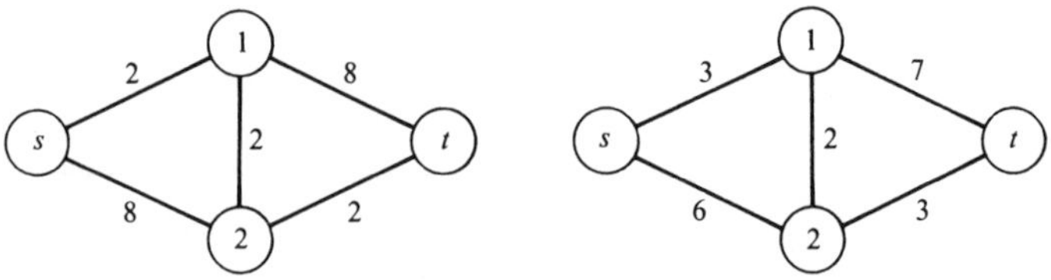

(a) Arc capacities b_{ij}. (b) Unit costs c_{ij}.

Fig. 10.15

We shall solve the problem (1) for $v' = 7$. In step 1, we define the modified cost c^*_{ij}. Since all $x_{ij} = 0$, all $c^*_{ij} = 0$. The iteration of step 1 and step 2 with $c^*_{ij} = 0$ is repeated until the maximal flow value reaches 6. The arc flows corresponding to this maximal flow value are shown in Fig. 10.16, and the modified costs c^*_{ij} are shown in parentheses. (The modified costs are in the same directions as the arc flows; c^*_{ij} are zero in the opposite directions, since no arc flows are greater than their arc capacities.)

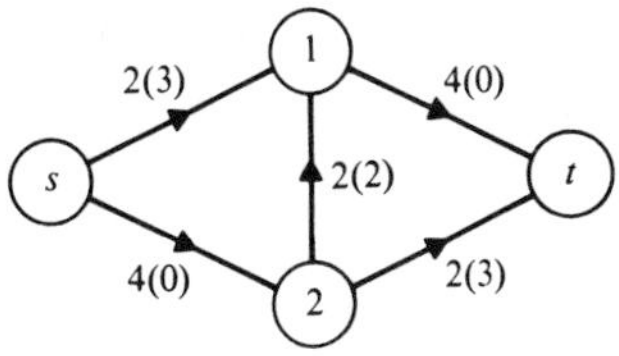

Fig. 10.16

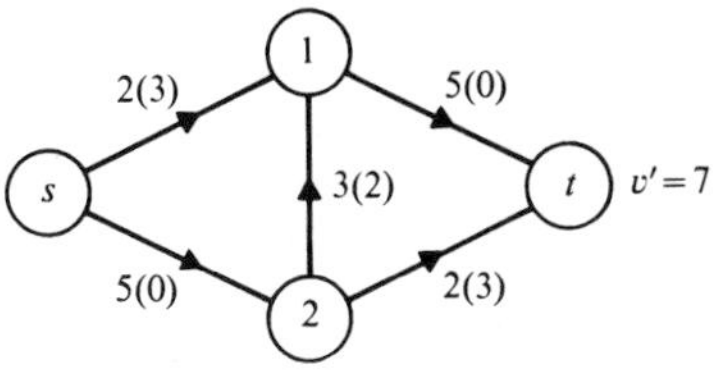

Fig. 10.17

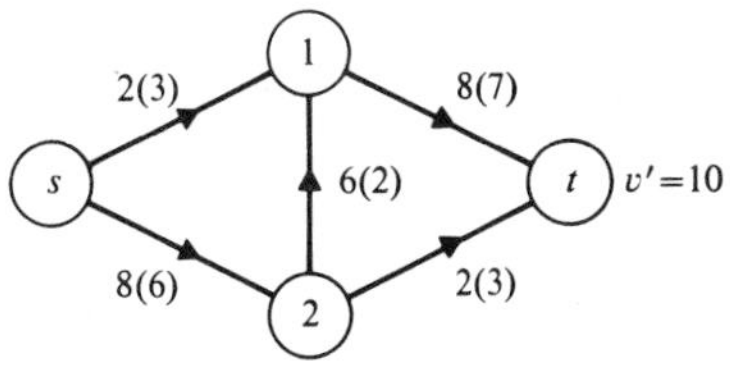

Fig. 10.18

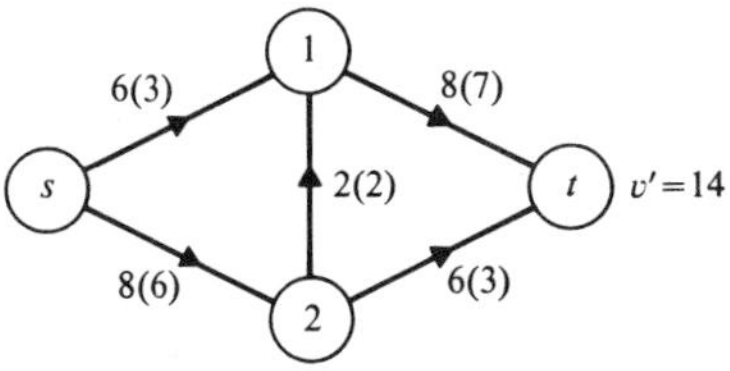

Fig. 10.19

The minimal cost path then consists of the arcs A_{s2}, A_{21}, and A_{1t}. Thus the capacity of arc A_{21} should be increased. The resulting flow is shown in Fig. 10.17 together with the modified costs of arc flows in parentheses.

Note that the modified cost c_{12}^* is -2, since $x_{21} > b_{21} = 2$. If we continue to maximize the flow value v' to 8, 9, . . ., etc., the same modified costs still apply until v' equals 10. This is shown in Fig. 10.18. Now the minimal cost path consists of the arcs A_{s1}, A_{12}, and A_{2t}, since the total cost is $3 + (-2) + 3 = 4$. Assume that we require $v' = 14$. Then we ship four units of flow along this path with the resulting flow pattern shown in Fig. 10.19. Note that when $v' = 7$, we have to increase the capacity of arc A_{12}, but when $v' = 14$, we *do not* have to increase the capacity of arc A_{12}; we increase the capacities of arcs A_{s1} and A_{2t} instead.

EXERCISES

1. Use the tree building algorithm to find the shortest path in the network of Fig. 10.20. Will the algorithm work if some $d_{ij} < 0$? Why? Find a minimum spanning tree in the network. Assume that the numbers in Fig. 10.20 are the capacities of arcs. Find the maximum capacity route from N_s to N_t.
2. Construct a network such that the arc with largest d_{ij} is a part of the shortest path and the arc with the smallest d_{ij} is not a part of the shortest path.
3. Assume that $d_{ij} \geq 0$ in a network, and we use the tree building algorithms described in Section 10.1 from both the source and the sink. Do we have a shortest path if the two trees meet the first time? See Nicholson [164] and Murchland [159].

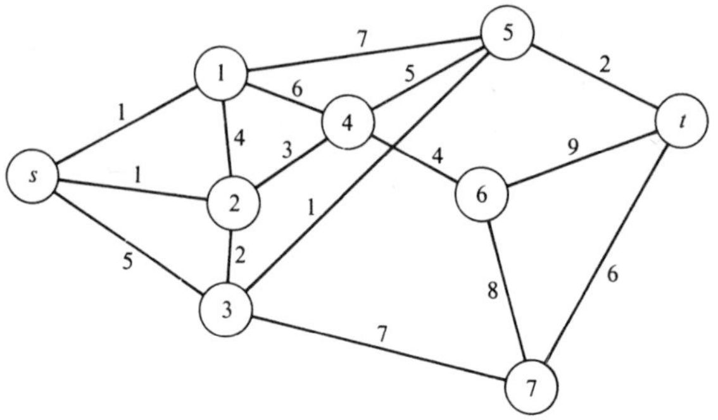

Fig. 10.20

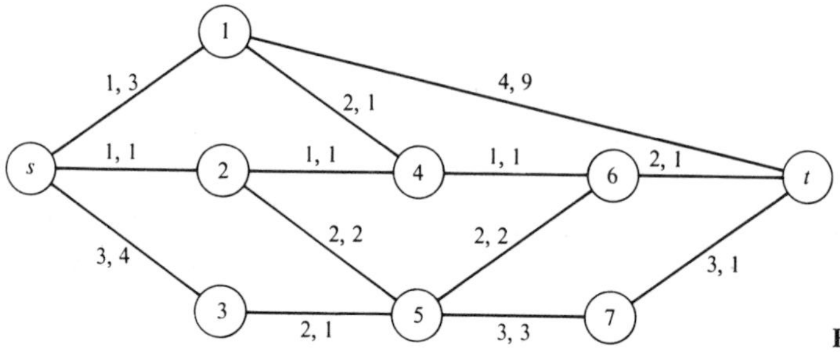

Fig. 10.21

4. Consider the network of Fig. 10.21 with arc capacities and costs written beside the arcs (b_i, c_i). Find the minimal cost flow of four units from N_s to N_t. (a) Use the dual method. (b) Use the primal method.
5. Let b_{ij} be the arc capacity. A route from N_a to N_z is called a maximum capacity route if min $(b_{ab}, b_{bc}, \ldots, b_{yz})$ is a maximum among all routes from N_a to N_z. Write the analogous triple operation to calculate and keep track of the maximum capacity routes between all pairs of nodes.
6. In a minimal cost flow problem, a flow is optimum if and only if there is no negative cycle using the modified costs. If the maximal flow with minimum cost is sought, then we can break the network into two parts in searching the negative cycles. Why?
7. A directed network is called acyclic if it does not contain any cycles. For an acyclic network, we can find the longest chain as well as a shortest chain from N_1 to all the other nodes. Derive algorithms specially for these cases.
8. If a network is s-t planar, is it possible to get the maximal flow without having to cancel any arc flow? See Ford and Fulkerson [64].
9. Use the decomposition idea to find the shortest paths from one node to all the other nodes in a large network by decomposing the network into many overlapping subsets. (Assume $d_{ij} \geq 0$ so that the algorithm in Section 10.1 can be used.)

MULTICOMMODITY FLOW 11

11.1 TWO-COMMODITY FLOWS (Hu [106])

In Chapter 8 the problem was to find maximum flow from the source N_s to the sink N_t without violating the capacity constraints $x_{ij} \leq b_{ij}$ on the arcs. If there are many sources and many sinks and if the flow from any source can be sent to any sink, then this problem can be converted trivially into a one-source and one-sink problem by creating a supersource and a supersink. If we make the restriction that the flow from certain sources must be sent to certain sinks, then the problem is a multicommodity flow problem. Let there be sources N_s and sinks $N_{s'}$ $(s = 1, \ldots, q; s' = 1', \ldots, q')$, where the flow s is from N_s to $N_{s'}$. Let x_{ij}^s be the flow s in the arc A_{ij} and $f(s, s')$ be the value of the flow s from N_s to $N_{s'}$. One of the problems in multicommodity flow is to find

$$\max \sum_{s=1}^{q} f(s; s')$$

subject to

$$\sum_i x_{ij}^s - \sum_k x_{jk}^s = \begin{cases} -f(s, s') & \text{if } j = s, \\ 0 & \text{if } j \neq s, s', \\ f(s, s') & \text{if } j = s', \end{cases}$$

$$\sum_{s=1}^{q} | x_{ij}^s | \leq b_{ij} \qquad \text{(for all } i, j),$$

$$x_{ij}^s \geq 0 \qquad \text{(for all } s, i, j).$$

When there is only one kind of flow, an undirected arc can always be thought of as two directed arcs of opposite direction, and arc flows of opposite directions can be canceled. But, arc flows of different commodities can not cancel each other. This is one of the central difficulties of the multicommodity flow problem.

Another problem of multicommodity flow is the so-called feasibility problem. Given nonnegative integers $r(s; s')$ ($s = 1, \ldots, q$; $s' = 1', \ldots, q'$), can there exist simultaneous flows with

$$f(s; s') \geq r(s; s'),$$

and

$$\sum_i x_{ij}^s - \sum_k x_{jk}^s = \begin{cases} -f(s, s') & \text{if } j = s, \\ 0 & \text{if } j \neq s, s', \\ f(s, s') & \text{if } j = s', \end{cases}$$

$$\sum_{s=1}^{q} | x_{ij}^s | \leq b_{ij} \qquad \text{(for all } i, j),$$

$$x_{ij}^s \geq 0 \qquad \text{(for all } s, i, j).$$

As said before, a single commodity flow problem can always be cast into a linear program with objective function $z = \mathbf{cx}$ subject to the constraint $\mathbf{Ax} = \mathbf{b}$. The matrix $\mathbf{A}$ has the unimodular property, and the optimum solution always has integer components. This is no longer true in the multicommodity flow problem. Most multicommodity flow problems cannot be solved by the labeling method or its variations. The special case that we shall consider first is two-commodity flows in an *undirected* network. In this special case there is a theorem analogous to the max-flow min-cut theorem and also a property analogous to the unimodular property. (Rothschild and Whinston [173] have shown that for a pseudo-symmetric network the result of this section still holds.)

Since the proof of the theorem and the algorithm is very long, we shall first discuss the intuitive idea behind it. There are two kinds of flows in the network. Let us maximize the first kind of flow as if it were a single commodity flow problem. After we have the required amount of the first flow, we have to maintain the amount of the first flow in the network and try to increase the second flow from zero to the required amount. This is done by superimposing a cycle of flow of the first kind in the network. The addition of this cycle of flow of the first kind will increase arc flows of the first kind or decrease them, depending on the direction of the arc flows already in the network. The algorithm presented below searches for a cycle of flow such that after the cycle is added there will exist flow-augmenting paths for the second flow.

It is customary to denote a cut by $(X, \bar{X})$ and the capacity of the cut by $c(X, \bar{X})$. For reasons that will be apparent later, we shall use $(s; t)$ to represent a minimum cut separating N_s and N_t and use $c(s; t)$ to denote the capacity of the minimum cut.

As a cut separates one pair of nodes, we now define the corresponding notion of separating many pairs of nodes. A proper disconnecting set for

m pairs of nodes is a set of arcs the removal of which will make N_i disconnected from $N_{i'}$ $(i = 1, 2, \ldots, m)$ and no proper subset of which will have this property. (Note that N_i may be in the same component as $N_{j'}$ for $i \neq j$.) The phrase "disconnecting set" means a proper disconnecting set through this section. The value of a disconnecting set is the sum of arc capacities of the arcs in the set. A minimum disconnecting set is one whose value is minimum. Let $(1, 2, \ldots, k; 1', 2', \ldots, k')$ denote a minimum disconnecting set which separates N_i from $N_{i'}$ $(i = 1, 2, \ldots, k)$ and let $c(1, 2, \ldots, k; 1', 2', \ldots, k')$ be the value of the minimum disconnecting set.

Lemma 11.1. The removal of a proper disconnecting set for k pairs of nodes will separate the network into at most $k + 1$ components.

Proof. Since every arc connects two nodes, if we remove arcs in the proper disconnecting set one by one, the number of components is increased either by one or not at all. If the number of components is increased by one, at least one pair of nodes is separated. Otherwise, this would contradict the fact that it is a proper disconnecting set. So, when the number of components reaches $k + 1$, all pairs of nodes must already have been separated. This ends the proof.

Let $i - j$ denote the fact that we condense N_i and N_j into one node in the network, i.e., we increase b_{ij} to an arbitrarily large amount.

Lemma 11.2. $c(1, 2; 1', 2') = \min\,[c\,(1 - 2; 1' - 2'), c\,(1 - 2'; 1' - 2)]$.

Proof. By Lemma 11.1 the removal of $(1, 2; 1', 2')$ will separate the network into at most three components. In Fig. 11.1 the rectangles denote components of the network, and the links between rectangles denote the totality of arcs connecting these components.

If the situation is like Fig. 11.1(a), then $c(1, 2; 1', 2') = c(1 - 2; 1' - 2')$. If the situation is like Fig. 11.1(b), then $c(1, 2; 1', 2') = c(1 - 2'; 1' - 2)$. Hence, the lemma.

Lemma 11.2 permits us to get $c(1, 2; 1', 2')$ by doing two maximum flow problems. This lemma means that we can find a minimum disconnecting

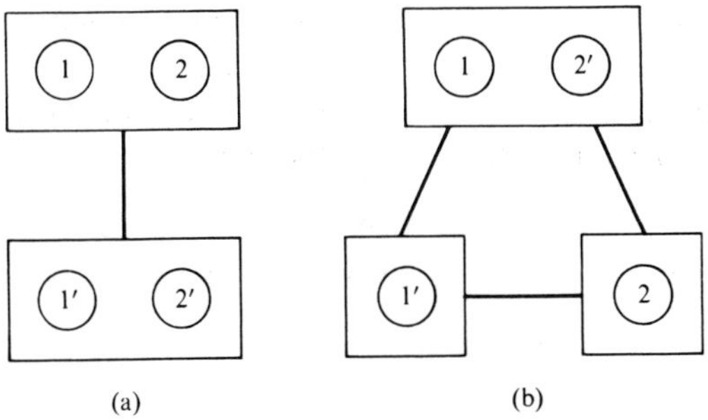

Fig. 11.1

set for two pairs of nodes by considering only partitions of the nodes into a subset and its complement. It is this property which makes the two-commodity flow problem in an undirected network particularly easy. In general, there is no easy way to find a minimum disconnecting set for m pairs of nodes for $m > 2$.

Lemma 11.3. $c(1, \ldots, j; 1', \ldots, j') + c(j+1, \ldots, j+k; j'+1, \ldots, j'+k') \geq c(1, \ldots, j+k; 1', \ldots, j'+k')$.

Proof. This follows directly from the fact that the two sets on the left-hand side will serve as a disconnecting set for $j + k$ pairs of nodes. The sum of their capacities being smaller than the right-hand side would contradict the fact that the right-hand side is the capacity of a minimum disconnecting set. In particular $c(1; 1') + c(2; 2') \geq c(1, 2; 1', 2')$.

We state the theorem of two commodity flows.

Theorem 11.1. *Max Bi-Flows Min-Cut Theorem* (Hu [106]). Two flows $f(1; 1')$ and $f(2; 2')$ are feasible if and only if (1), (2), and (3) are all satisfied, i.e.,

$$f(1; 1') \leq c(1; 1'), \tag{1}$$

$$f(2; 2') \leq c(2; 2'), \tag{2}$$

$$f(1; 1') + f(2; 2') \leq c(1, 2; 1', 2'). \tag{3}$$

The maximum sum of the two flows is equal to the minimum cut capacity of all cuts separating the two pairs of nodes, i.e.,

$$\max\,[f(1; 1') + f(2; 2')] = \min\,[c(1-2; 1'-2'), c(1-2'; 1'-2)]. \tag{4}$$

The necessary part of (1), (2), (3), and (4) is clear. The sufficient part of (1), (2), (3), and (4) is proved by giving an algorithm for constructing the flows.

For any set of arc flows in the network let us define the following sets of nodes:

1. $N_1 \in X_1$: If $N_i \in X_1$ and $x_{ij}^1 + |x_{ij}^2| < b_{ij}$, then $N_j \in X_1$.
2. $N_2 \in X_2$: If $N_i \in X_2$ and $|x_{ij}^1| + x_{ij}^2 < b_{ij}$, then $N_j \in X_2$.
3. $N_2 \in X_{2b}$: If $N_i \in X_{2b}$ and $x_{ij}^1 + x_{ij}^2 < b_{ij}$, then $N_j \in X_{2b}$.
4. $N_2 \in X_{2f}$: If $N_i \in X_{2f}$ and $x_{ji}^1 + x_{ij}^2 < b_{ij}$, then $N_j \in X_{2f}$.

Since arc flows of the same commodity but of opposite directions in an arc can be cancelled without affecting the value of the flow, we can consider the capacity of an arc A_{ij} for flow 1 as follows. If $x_{ij}^1 > 0$ and we want to send flow 1 from N_i to N_j, then the capacity of arc A_{ij} is

$$b_{ij}'' = b_{ij} - |x_{ij}^2| - x_{ij}^1.$$

If we want to send flow 1 from N_j to N_i, then the capacity of arc A_{ij} is

$$b_{ji}'' = b_{ij} - |x_{ij}^2| + x_{ij}^1.$$

Similarly, for flow 2 we have

$$b'_{ij} = b_{ij} - |x^1_{ij}| - x^2_{ij},$$

or

$$b'_{ji} = b_{ij} - |x^1_{ij}| + x^2_{ij},$$

depending in which direction we want to send flow 2. We shall then write $b''_{ij} = b_{ij} - |x^2_{ij}| \pm x^1_{ij}$ and $b'_{ij} = b_{ij} - |x^1_{ij}| \pm x^2_{ij}$ with the understanding that appropriate signs are chosen.

If $N_{1'} \in X_1$, then there exists a chain from N_1 to $N_{1'}$ in which every arc has $b''_{ij} = b_{ij} - |x^2_{ij}| \pm x^1_{ij} > 0$. Hence, we can send more flow 1 along this chain with value equal to min b''_{ij}.

Similarly, if $N_{2'} \in X_2$, we can send more flow 2 along a chain with value equal to min b'_{ij}, where $b'_{ij} = b_{ij} - |x^1_{ij}| \pm x^2_{ij} > 0$. Therefore, if $f(1;1') + f(2;2')$ is a maximum, it is necessary (but not sufficient) that $N_{1'} \in \bar{X}_1$ and $N_{2'} \in \bar{X}_2$.

Let there be a chain of arcs from N_2 to $N_{2'}$. Then all arcs in the chain can be assigned with a positive direction as follows. If an arc A_{ij} is removed from the chain, N_i is connected with N_2 by arcs of the chain, and N_j is connected with $N_{2'}$ by arcs of the chain, then the positive direction of arc A_{ij} is defined as that from N_i to N_j. Note that the assignment of positive direction of an arc is always made with respect to a chain from N_2 to $N_{2'}$. An arc flow is said to be in the forward direction if it is from N_i to N_j and is said to be in the backward direction if it is from N_j to N_i.

Now, if $N_{2'} \in X_{2b}$, then there exists a chain from N_2 to $N_{2'}$ in which every arc A_{ij} has $b_{ij} + x^1_{ji} - x^2_{ij} > 0$, where the positive direction of the arc is from N_i to N_j. This chain is called a backward path from N_2 to $N_{2'}$.

Similarly, if $N_{2'} \in X_{2f}$, then there exists a chain from N_2 to $N_{2'}$ in which every arc A_{ij} has $b_{ij} + x^1_{ij} - x^2_{ij} > 0$, where the positive direction of the arc is from N_i to N_j. This is called a forward path from N_2 to $N_{2'}$. Both forward and backward paths can be found by the labeling method.

For simplicity, we sometimes call these two paths double paths from N_2 to $N_{2'}$. The capacity of a backward path is defined to be

$$\min\,(b_{ij} + x^1_{ji} - x^2_{ij}),$$

where the positive direction of the arc is from N_i to N_j. The capacity of a forward path is defined to be

$$\min\,(b_{ij} + x^1_{ij} - x^2_{ij}).$$

It is understood that by the existence of double paths from N_2 to $N_{2'}$ we mean the existence of a backward path and a forward path, both with positive capacities. It is understood that a backward or a forward path is from N_2 to $N_{2'}$, and we sometimes omit the phrase from N_2 to $N_{2'}$.

Lemma 11.4. If there exists an $(X_{2b}, \bar{X}_{2b})$ with $N_{2'} \in \bar{X}_{2b}$, then there exists no backward path from N_2 to $N_{2'}$. Conversely, if there exists no backward path from N_2 to $N_{2'}$, then there exists an $(X_{2b}, \bar{X}_{2b})$ with $N_{2'} \in \bar{X}_{2b}$.

Proof. If there exists an $(X_{2b}, \bar{X}_{2b})$ with $N_{2'} \in \bar{X}_{2b}$, let A_{ij} be any arc connecting X_{2b} and $\bar{X}_{2b}$ with $N_i \in X_{2b}$ and $N_j \in \bar{X}_{2b}$. By definition, we must have $x_{ij}^1 + x_{ij}^2 = b_{ij}$; otherwise N_j will belong to X_{2b}. As every chain from N_2 to $N_{2'}$ must contain at least one arc of $(X_{2b}, \bar{X}_{2b})$ and now every arc of $(X_{2b}, \bar{X}_{2b})$ has $b_{ij} - x_{ij}^1 - x_{ij}^2 = 0$, then there exists no backward path from N_2 to $N_{2'}$.

Conversely, if there exists no backward path from N_2 to $N_{2'}$, this means that if we start from N_2 and define the set X_{2b} recursively, there always exists an arc with $x_{ij}^1 + x_{ij}^2 = b_{ij}$, where $N_i \in X_{2b}$. The totality of such arcs will form a cut $(X_{2b}, \bar{X}_{2b})$ with $N_{2'} \in \bar{X}_{2b}$.

Let us consider the locations of N_1 and $N_{1'}$. There are two cases. First, in the cut $(X_{2b}, \bar{X}_{2b})$, $x_{ij}^1 \neq 0$. Then it is impossible to have $N_1 \in \bar{X}_{2b}$ and $N_{1'} \in X_{2b}$, because we have at least a chain from N_1 to $N_{1'}$ which contains an arc of $(X_{2b}, \bar{X}_{2b})$. This arc will have $x_{ji}^1 > 0$ with $N_j \in \bar{X}_{2b}$ and $N_i \in X_{2b}$. This will contradict the fact that $b_{ij} - x_{ij}^1 - x_{ij}^2 = b_{ij} + x_{ji}^1 - x_{ij}^2 = 0$. Similarly, if N_1 and $N_{1'}$ are both in X_{2b} or both in $\bar{X}_{2b}$, there must be a chain from N_1 to $N_{1'}$ which contains two arcs of $(X_{2b}, \bar{X}_{2b})$ one of which has $x_{ji}^1 > 0$. So this is also not possible. Therefore, if in the cut $(X_{2b}, \bar{X}_{2b})$, $x_{ij}^1 \neq 0$, then we have $N_1 \in X_{2b}$ and $N_{1'} \in \bar{X}_{2b}$.

Second, in the cut $(X_{2b}, \bar{X}_{2b})$, $x_{ij}^1 = 0$. That is, all arcs in the cut $(X_{2b}, \bar{X}_{2b})$ have $x_{ij}^2 = b_{ij}$. Then there is no restriction on the locations of N_1 and $N_{1'}$ (except that both of them must be contained in X_{2b} or $\bar{X}_{2b}$).

Lemma 11.5. If there exists an $(X_{2f}, \bar{X}_{2f})$ with $N_{2'} \in \bar{X}_{2f}$, then there exists no forward path from N_2 to $N_{2'}$. Conversely, if there exists no forward path from N_2 to $N_{2'}$, there exists an $(X_{2f}, \bar{X}_{2f})$ with $N_{2'} \in \bar{X}_{2f}$.

Proof. The proof is entirely similar to that of Lemma 11.4; hence it is omitted. Also by the same reasoning, if in the cut $(X_{2f}, \bar{X}_{2f})$, $x_{ij}^1 \neq 0$, then $N_1 \in X_{2f}$ and $N_{1'} \in \bar{X}_{2f}$.

By Lemmas 11.4 and 11.5 we have: The existence of either $(X_{2b}, \bar{X}_{2b})$ with $N_{2'} \in \bar{X}_{2b}$ or $(X_{2f}, \bar{X}_{2f})$ with $N_{2'} \in \bar{X}_{2f}$ and the existence of double paths from N_2 to $N_{2'}$ are complementary events.

Let x_f^1 be min (x_{ij}^1), where the x_{ij}^1 are in a forward path with x_{ij}^1 of the forward direction. Let x_b^1 be min (x_{ij}^1), where x_{ij}^1 are in a backward path with x_{ij}^1 of the backward direction.

Denote $b_f = \min(b_{ij} + x_{ij}^1 - x_{ij}^2)$, where A_{ij} are arcs in a forward path with the positive direction from N_i to N_j. Denote $b_b = \min(b_{ij} + x_{ji}^1 - x_{ij}^2)$, where A_{ij} are arcs in a backward path with the positive direction from N_i to N_j.

For a pair of backward and forward paths

$$\min(x_f^1, x_b^1) = x_{bf}^1, \qquad \min(b_b, b_f) = b_{bf}.$$

We shall give an algorithm for deciding whether flows $f(1;1')$ and $f(2;2')$ are feasible and for constructing these flows if they are feasible. The same algorithm can also be used to construct max $[f(1;1') + f(2;2')]$.

Let $r(1;1')$ and $r(2;2')$ be the required flow values of $f(1;1')$ and $f(2;2')$. To ensure that the algorithm is a finite process, we assume that $r(1;1')$, $r(2;2')$, and b_{ij} are all even integers. (In the maximum flow problem of a single commodity it is assumed that b_{ij} are integers.) For computational purposes this is not a restriction because rational branch capacities can be reduced to even integer capacities.

The algorithm for constructing two-commodity flows can be described as follows: Algorithm (cycle flow method, Hu [106]):

STEP 0. Find $f(1;1')$ based on b_{ij}. This is a maximum flow computation of a single commodity and we can use the labeling method of Ford and Fulkerson [65]. If

$$\max f(1;1') < r(1;1'),$$

then the set of flow requirements is not feasible. (If max $[f(1;1')+f(2;2')]$ is required, find max $f(1;1') = c(1;1')$.)

STEP 1. Find $f(2;2')$ based on $b'_{ij} = b_{ij} - |x_{ij}^1| \pm x_{ij}^2$. This is also an ordinary maximum flow problem (i.e., to find out whether $N_{2'} \in \bar{X}_2$ or not). If $f(2;2')$ thus obtained is equal to $r(2;2')$, then the algorithm is completed. If $f(2;2') < r(2;2')$, do step 2.

STEP 2. Locate double paths from N_2 to $N_{2'}$. If double paths do not exist, then the set of flow requirements is not feasible; in other words, max $[f(1;1') + f(2;2')]$ has been obtained. But if double paths do exist, let $\min(x_{bf}^1, 0.5b_{bf}) = h$. If more than one forward and backward path exists, any pair can be chosen.

Since the double paths can be considered a cycle, we send flow 1 of amount h from N_2 to $N_{2'}$ along the backward path and come back from $N_{2'}$ to N_2 on the forward path. Obviously, this operation does not change $f(1;1')$ and keeps $\sum_j x_{ij}^1 = 0$ at every node N_i. But it makes $|x_{ij}^1| + |x_{ij}^2| > b_{ij}$ at certain arcs. (Needless to say, arc flows of the same commodity but of opposite directions are cancelled.)

STEP 3. Increase $f(2;2')$ by $2h$. This is done by sending flow 2 along the forward and backward paths, i.e., h units of flow 2 on each path. After this is completed, $f(2;2')$ is increased by $2h$. We assert that this will also make $|x_{ij}^1| + |x_{ij}^2| \leq b_{ij}$ at every arc.

Steps 1, 2, and 3 are repeated until either the set of flow requirements is found to be infeasible or the set has been constructed.

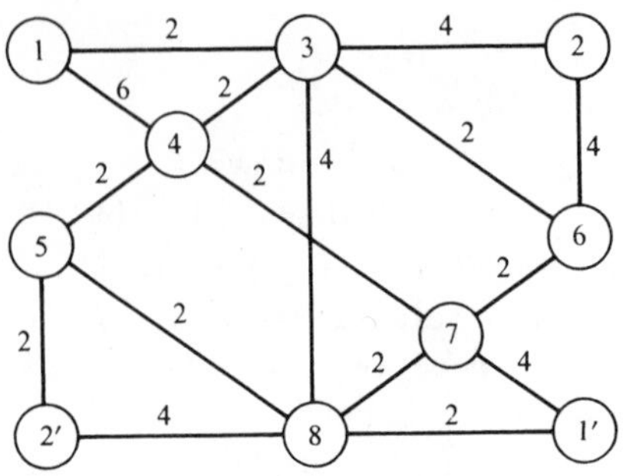

Fig. 11.2

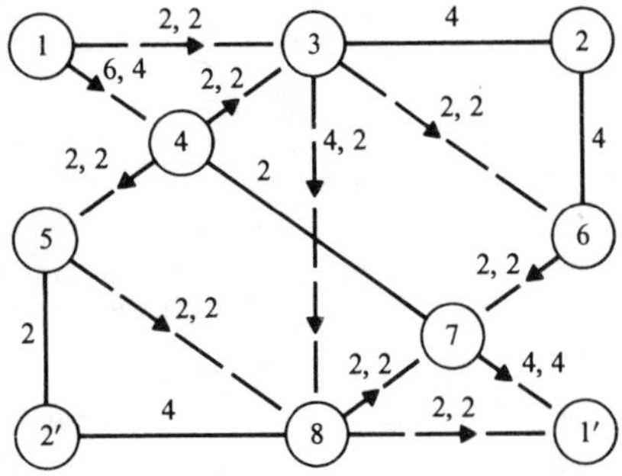

Fig. 11.3

We shall use broken lines of long dashes with arrows to indicate the directions of flow 1, lines of short dashes with arrows to indicate directions of flow 2, and solid lines to indicate an arc with no arc flows. Three numbers are written beside each arc; the first b_{ij}, the second x^1_{ij}, the third x^2_{ij}. When only one or two numbers are written, the remaining numbers are zero.

Consider the network shown in Fig. 11.2, where the numbers written beside the arcs are the b_{ij} of these arcs. We want to find out max $f(1; 1')$ and max $[f(1; 1') + f(2; 2')]$.

STEP 0. We find maximal $f(1; 1') = c(1; 1') = 6$. The flow pattern is shown in Fig. 11.3.

STEP 1. Find $f(2; 2')$ based on $b'_{ij} = b_{ij} - |x^1_{ij}| \pm x^2_{ij}$. We find a flow chain of value 2 which consists of arcs A_{23}, A_{38}, and $A_{82'}$. This is shown in Fig. 11.4.

STEP 2. We locate a backward path from N_2 to $N_{2'}$ which consists of arcs A_{23}, A_{34}, A_{47}, A_{78}, and $A_{82'}$, with

$$x^1_b = \min(x^1_{43}, x^1_{87}) = \min(2, 2) = 2,$$

and

$$b_b = \min(b_{23} - x^2_{23}, b_{34} + x^1_{43}, b_{47}, b_{78} + x^1_{87}, b_{82'} - x^2_{82'})$$
$$= \min(2, 4, 2, 4, 2) = 2.$$

We locate a forward path from N_2 to $N_{2'}$ which consists of arcs A_{23}, A_{36}, A_{67}, A_{74}, A_{45}, and $A_{52'}$, with

$$x^1_f = \min(x^1_{36}, x^1_{67}, x^1_{45}) = \min(2, 2, 2) = 2,$$

and

$$b_f = \min(b_{23} - x^2_{23}, b_{36} + x^1_{36}, b_{67} + x^1_{67}, b_{74}, b_{45} + x^1_{45}, b_{52'})$$
$$= \min(2, 4, 4, 2, 4, 2) = 2.$$

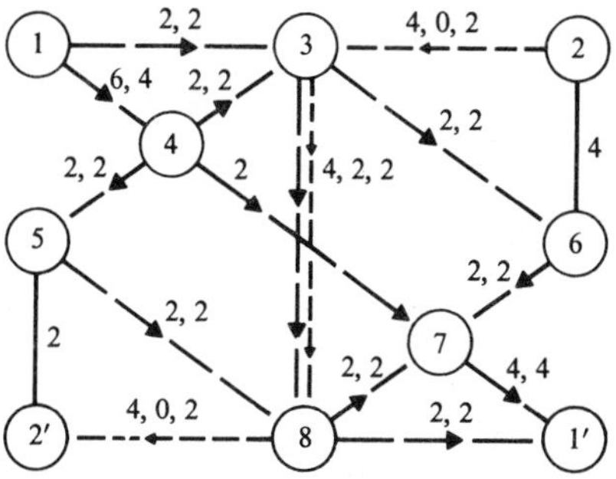

Fig. 11.4

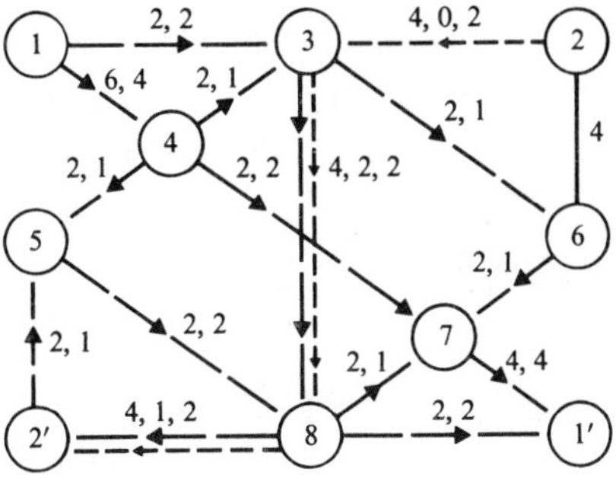

Fig. 11.5

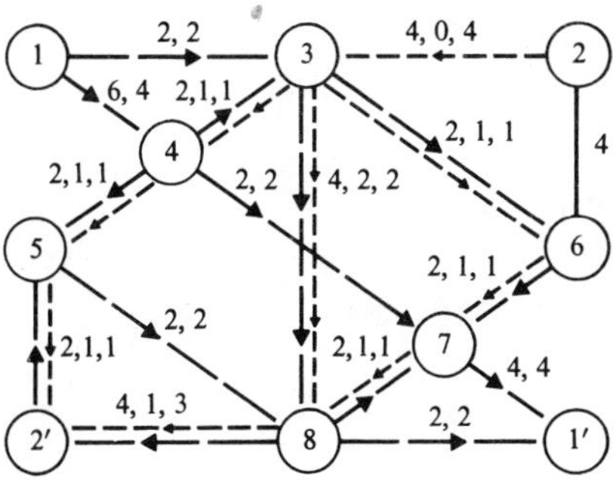

Fig. 11.6

Therefore,

$$x^1_{bf} = 2, \qquad b_{bf} = 2 \qquad \text{and} \qquad h = \min(x^1_{bf}, 0.5b_{bf}) = \min(2, 1) = 1.$$

We send one unit of flow 1 around the cycle formed by the double paths. The result is shown in Fig. 11.5.

STEP 3. $f(2; 2')$ is increased by two units by sending one unit along each path. The result is shown in Fig. 11.6.

Further application of step 1 cannot increase $f(2; 2')$, and application of step 2 cannot locate double paths. Hence, the flows obtained in Fig. 11.6 are maximum, i.e., $f(1; 1') + f(2; 2') = 6 + 4 = 10$ is maximum.

The minimum cut consists of arcs A_{45}, A_{47}, A_{38}, and A_{67}.

To prove that the algorithm works we have to prove the following:

1. After completion of step 3, $|x^1_{ij}| + |x^2_{ij}| \leq b_{ij}$ for all arcs.
2. When the algorithm is completed, max $[f(1; 1') + f(2; 2')]$ is obtained, or the set of flow requirements is already obtained or not feasible.
3. x^1_{ij} and x^2_{ij} are integers.
4. The algorithm is a finite process.

1. We shall prove that every arc in the forward path has

$$|x_{ij}^1| + |x_{ij}^2| \leq b_{ij}$$

after completion of step 3. Let the positive direction be from N_i to N_j. Let A_{ij} be an arc on the forward path. The existence of a forward path implies that

$$b_{ij} + x_{ij}^1 - x_{ij}^2 > 0. \tag{5}$$

Before step 2 is applied, we have

$$b_{ij} - |x_{ij}^1| - |x_{ij}^2| \geq 0. \tag{6}$$

By definition

$$h \leq \min [x_{ij}^1, 0.5(b_{ij} + x_{ij}^1 - x_{ij}^2)]. \tag{7}$$

In step 2 we send h units of flow 1 from N_j to N_i and in step 3, h units of flow 2 from N_i to N_j.

There are four cases:

CASE 1. $x_{ij}^1 \geq 0$ and $x_{ij}^2 \geq 0$ in the arc. Then h units of flow 1 are cancelled in step 2, and h units of flow 2 are added in step 3. From (6) we have

$$b_{ij} - |x_{ij}^1 - h| - |x_{ij}^1 + h| \geq 0.$$

CASE 2. $x_{ji}^1 \geq 0$ and $x_{ij}^2 \geq 0$ in the arc. Inequality (5) becomes

$$b_{ij} - x_{ji}^1 - x_{ij}^2 \geq 0,$$

and (7) becomes

$$h \leq \min [x_{ij}^1, 0.5(b_{ij} - x_{ji}^1 - x_{ij}^2)],$$

or

$$b_{ij} - x_{ji}^1 - x_{ij}^2 - 2h \geq 0. \tag{8}$$

As h units of flow 1 are added in step 2 and h units of flow 2 are added in step 3, from (8) we have

$$b_{ij} - |x_{ji}^1 + h| - |x_{ij}^2 + h| \geq 0.$$

CASE 3. $x_{ij}^1 \geq 0$ and $x_{ji}^2 \geq 0$ in the arc. Then h units of flow 1 are cancelled in step 2, and h units of flow 2 are cancelled in step 3. From (6) we have

$$b_{ij} - |x_{ij}^1 - h| - |x_{ji}^2 - h| \geq 0.$$

CASE 4. $x_{ji}^1 \geq 0$ and $x_{ji}^2 \geq 0$ in the arc. Then h units of flow 1 are added in step 2, and h units of flow 2 are cancelled in step 3. We have

$$b_{ij} - |x_{ji}^1 + h| - |x_{ji}^2 - h| \geq 0.$$

The case of an arc in the backward path is similar and hence omitted.

Note that if an arc is used in both the forward and backward paths in the opposite directions, then in step 2, $2h$ units of flow 1 are added, where in step 3 arc flows of the second commodity will cancel each other. This arc flow will not exceed the arc capacity, because $h = \min(x^1_{bf}, 0.5b_{bf})$. In the example, A_{47} belongs to this case.

Let an arc be used in both the forward and backward paths in the same direction. Then in step 2 arc flows of the first commodity will cancel each other and in step 3, $2h$ units of flow 2 will be added. This arc flow will not exceed the branch capacity, because $h = \min(x^1_{bf}, 0.5b_{bf})$. In the example, A_{23} belongs to this case.

2. Now we prove that the completion of the algorithm implies that

$$\max[f(1;1') + f(2;2')]$$

is obtained or the set of flow requirements is not feasible. The algorithm will terminate only if $r(1;1')$ and $r(2;2')$ have been constructed or when double paths do not exist in step 2. Assume that there does not exist a backward path from N_2 to $N_{2'}$. Then by Lemma 11.4, we have an $(X_{2b}, \bar{X}_{2b})$ with $N_{2'} \in \bar{X}_{2b}$. If in the cut $(X_{2b}, \bar{X}_{2b})$, $x^1_{ij} \neq 0$, then it is shown that $N_1 \in \bar{X}_{2b}$ and $N_{1'} \in \bar{X}_{2b}$. Since all arcs of the cut have $x^1_{ij} + x^2_{ij} = b_{ij}$, where $N_i \in X_{2b}$ and $N_j \in \bar{X}_{2b}$, this means that

$$f(1;1') + f(2;2') = c(X_{2b}, \bar{X}_{2b}). \tag{9}$$

As $(X_{2b}, \bar{X}_{2b})$ is a disconnecting set separating N_1, N_2 and $N_{1'}$, $N_{2'}$, we must have

$$f(1;1') + f(2;2') \leq c(X_{2b}, \bar{X}_{2b}). \tag{10}$$

Equations (9) and (10) imply that $\max f(1;1') + f(2;2')$ has been obtained.

If in the cut $(X_{2b}, \bar{X}_{2b})$, $x^1_{ij} = 0$, i.e., all arcs have $x^2_{ij} = b_{ij}$, where $N_i \in X_{2b}$ and $N_j \in \bar{X}_{2b}$, $\max f(2;2')$ has been obtained. So $f(2;2')$ cannot be increased even if $f(1;1')$ is decreased. If $f(2;2') < r(2;2')$ at this stage, then the set of flow requirements is not feasible. To make $\max[f(1;1') + f(2;2')]$ we have $f(1;1') = c(1;1')$ at step 0 and it remains equal to $c(1;1')$ throughout the algorithm. This means that $f(1;1')$ cannot be increased even if $f(2;2')$ is decreased. Therefore,

$$\max[f(1;1') + f(2;2')]$$

is obtained.

The case in which there is no forward path or there exists an $(X_{2f}, \bar{X}_{2f})$ with $N_{2'} \in \bar{X}_{2f}$ is similar and its proof is omitted. As we have stated before, the nonexistence of double paths implies the existence of either $(X_{2b}, \bar{X}_{2b})$ with $N_{2'} \in \bar{X}_{2b}$ or the existence of $(X_{2f}, \bar{X}_{2f})$ with $N_{2'} \in \bar{X}_{2f}$. The proof is completed.

3. We state the condition 3 as a theorem. (Hu [106])

Theorem 11.2 (*Even Integer*). If $r(1;1')$, $r(2;2')$, and b_{ij} are all even integers with $r(1;1')$ and $r(2;2')$ satisfying Theorem 11.1, then there exists a feasible flow pattern with $f(1;1') = r(1;1')$ and $f(2;2') = r(2;2')$ in which x^1_{ij} and x^2_{ij} are all integers. (If max $[f(1;1') + f(2;2')]$ is required, then we need only assume that the b_{ij} are even integers.)

Proof. In step 0, since $r(1;1')$ is even, by the labeling process we can have $f(1;1') = r(1;1')$ in which the x^1_{ij} are all even. This implies as well that the $b_{ij} - |x^1_{ij}|$ are all even at the end of step 0. Since $r(2;2')$ is also even, at the end of step 1 the x^2_{ij} are also even.

In proving that no arc capacity will be exceeded, we have seen that for an arc A_{ij}, h units of flow 1 are either cancelled or added and h units of flow 2 are either cancelled or added. As we have

$$h = \min(x^1_{bf}, 0.5b_{bf}),$$

h will be nonintegral only when b_{bf} is odd, since x^1_{ij}, x^2_{ij}, and b'_{ij} are even integers in the beginning. Now, $b_{bf} = \min(b_{ij} \pm x^1_{ij} \pm x^2_{ij}) = 0 \pmod 2$ at the end of step 1 the first time.

Consider an arc in which h units of flow 1 are added and h units of flow 2 are cancelled. We have

$$b_{ij} - |x^1_{ij} + h| \pm |x^2_{ij} - h|.$$

If $b_{ij} - |x^1_{ij}| \pm x^2_{ij}$ is even, then $b_{ij} - |x^1_{ij} + h| \pm |x^2_{ij} - h|$ is also even no matter if h is even or odd. This is also true when $2h$ of flow 1 or $2h$ of flow 2 are added. So after completion of step 3 and at the beginning of step 1, every arc has an even capacity for flow 2. After step 1, which increases or decreases x^2_{ij} by even units, we have $b_{ij} \pm x^1_{ij} \pm x^2_{ij}$ still even. Therefore, b_{bf} is never odd or h never becomes a noninteger. This means that x^1_{ij} and x^2_{ij} remain integers throughout the algorithm.

4. To prove the finiteness of this algorithm, it is only necessary to note that $f(2;2')$ has been increased by at least two units ($2x^1_{bf}$ or b_{bf}) while $f(1;1')$ retains its original value obtained in step 0. Since $f(2;2')$ is bounded from above by min $[c(2;2'), c(1,2;1',2') - f(1;1')]$, the algorithm is finite.

Note that the case $N_1 = N_2$ or $N_1 = N_{2'}$ is a special case, and the conditions stated in Theorem 11.1 still hold, because we can consider this case as a network with arbitrarily large b_{12} or $b_{12'}$.

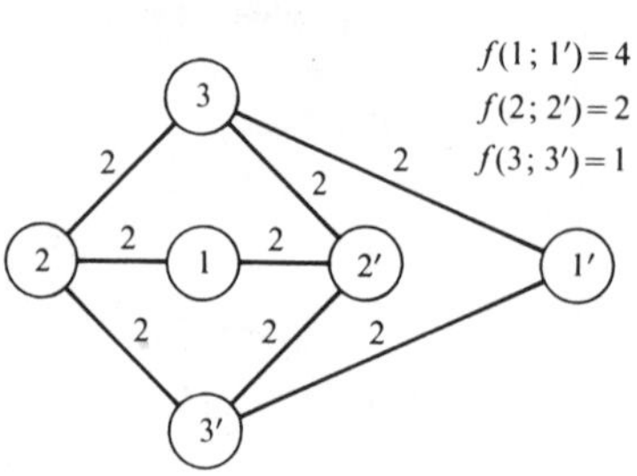

Fig. 11.7

DISCUSSION

It has been a popular conjecture that a set of m-commodity flows is feasible if and only if the following $2^m - 1$ inequalities and their linear combinations are all satisfied, i.e.,

$$f(k; k') \leq c(k; k'), \qquad \binom{m}{1} \text{ of these inequalities,}$$

$$f(i; i') + f(j; j') \leq c(i, j; i', j'), \qquad \binom{m}{2} \text{ of these inequalities,}$$

$$\vdots \qquad\qquad \vdots$$

$$\sum_{k=1}^{k=m} f(k; k') \leq c(1, \ldots, m; 1', \ldots, m'), \qquad \binom{m}{m} \text{ of these inequalities.}$$

A counterexample to the above conjecture was first found by Ford (by private communication) for flows of four commodities. Figure 11.7 shows a counterexample with a set of requirements that cannot be satisfied (see Hu [106]). Since the cycle flow method not only gives the maximum value of $f(1; 1') + f(2; 2')$ but also maximum $f(1; 1')$, this means that we can use the same method to obtain the maximum value of $\alpha_1 f(1; 1') + \alpha_2 f(2; 2')$ with $\alpha_1 \geq \alpha_2 \geq 0$.

11.2 MULTICOMMODITY FLOWS (Ford and Fulkerson [66] and Tomlin [186])

(The reader should reread the first five paragraphs of Section 11.1 before reading this section.) Let us first consider the problem of maximizing the sum of the flows of different commodities. For each commodity there are many chains joining the source to the sink. The problem is to select chains for each commodity such that the arc capacities are not violated and the sum of the flows in all the chains selected is maximum. Assume that there are m arcs in the network with arc capacities $b_1, b_2, \ldots, b_m$. A chain in the network can be represented by an m-vector with 1 in a component if the arc is used and 0 if the arc is not used in the chain. Let us define an arc-chain incidence matrix $\mathbf{A} = [a_{ij}]$ as follows:

$$a_{ij} = \begin{cases} 1, & \text{if the arc } i \text{ is in the chain } j, \\ 0, & \text{otherwise.} \end{cases}$$

If x_j is the amount of flow in chain j, then the problem of maximizing multicommodity flows can be put as

$$\max \sum_j x_j$$

subject to

$$\sum_j a_{ij} x_j + s_i = b_i \qquad (i = 1, \ldots, m), \tag{1}$$

$$x_j, s_i \geq 0,$$

where s_i are slack variables. Note that in this formulation the matrix $[a_{ij}]$ may have millions of columns, one column for each possible chain for each commodity. Fortunately, in order to compute (1), we need only a matrix of size $(m + 1) \times (m + 1)$, as will be shown later. The multicommodity aspect does not appear explicitly in (1), but it is contained in the structure of the matrix $[a_{ij}]$. If we consider only chains of one commodity in the arc-chain incidence matrix, then (1) is simply a maximal flow problem.

Assuming that we have m columns which form a starting basis of (1), we can solve (1) and get the price vector $\boldsymbol{\pi} = (\pi_1, \ldots, \pi_m)$, where each π_i corresponds to a specific row. Note that the relative cost of every nonbasic column $\mathbf{a}_j$ is given by $\bar{c}_j = c_j - \boldsymbol{\pi}\mathbf{a}_j$. If $\bar{c}_j \leq 0$, then the current basis is optimal. If $\bar{c}_j > 0$, then that column should be brought into the basis. The problem of finding $\bar{c}_j$ is a very easy job. If we interpret π_i as the lengths of the arcs, then $\boldsymbol{\pi}\mathbf{a}_j$ is the length of the chain which is represented by the column $\mathbf{a}_j$. Note that $c_j = +1$ for all columns, and if the simplex method is used, $\boldsymbol{\pi}$ will appear in the cost row of the slack variables.* Therefore, we *need not* list all the columns representing chains leading from different sources to different sinks. At each stage of computation we simply use the revised simplex method and keep a matrix of size $(m + 1) \times (m + 1)$. If some π_i is negative, then we choose that column as a pivot column. If all π_i are nonnegative, we consider π_i as the lengths of the arcs and find the shortest chain leading from the source to the sink for each commodity. If the shortest chain of every commodity is of length 1 or more, then the current basis is optimum. (Each column should be updated before adding to the tableau; see Section 7.2 for updating a column.)

In the feasibility problem of multicommodity flows, the flow value of each of the commodities is prescribed, and the question is whether or not all these flow values can be realized simultaneously in a given network. For example, let the network be as shown in Fig. 11.8 and the four flow requirements be as shown in Fig. 11.9 (i.e., we need two units of flow from N_1 to N_2, three units of flow from N_2 to N_4, etc.). We try to ship the four commodities in such a way that no arc capacity of any arc in the original network is exceeded.

Assume that we have a list of feasible networks that satisfy the flow requirements. These feasible networks all have the same number of arcs connecting the same pairs of nodes as the original given network, but every network has different arc capacities. (Some arc capacities may be zero, but we still count them as arcs of that network, so that all feasible networks have the same number of arcs.) These feasible networks are constructed as follows. For each flow requirement we find a chain from the source to the sink of that commodity. Then we assign to each arc of the chain the

* $\boldsymbol{\pi}$ instead of $-\boldsymbol{\pi}$ will appear in the cost row of the slack variables due to the fact that we use $-\mathbf{c}_B$ and $-\mathbf{c}_N$ in the starting tableau.

capacity equal to the flow requirement. Superimposing all the chains for all flow requirements, we have a feasible network. There are millions of such feasible networks, each of which satisfies the prescribed flow requirements. Any linear convex combination of these networks also satisfies the prescribed flow requirements. The approach described below determines if the original network contains a network which is a linear convex combination of these feasible networks.

Let $[a_{ij}]$ be a matrix of m rows, each row corresponding to an arc of the given network. (In the case of Fig. 11.8 the matrix would be of five rows.) A column j of the matrix represents a network which has a_{1j} as the capacity of the first arc, a_{2j} as the capacity of the second arc, etc. Then all the feasible networks mentioned earlier can be represented by columns of the matrix. If the original network represented by $[b_1, \ldots, b_m]$ contains a network $[b'_1, \ldots, b'_m]$ with $b'_i \leq b_i$ $(i = 1, \ldots, m)$, and $[b'_1, \ldots, b'_m]$ is a linear convex combination of the columns of $[a_{ij}]$, then the original network is feasible. Let the coefficient of the convex combination of the column j be x_j. Then the feasibility problem can be formulated as

$$\max \theta = \sum_j x_j$$

subject to

$$a_{ij} x_j + s_i = b_i \qquad (i = 1, \ldots, m; j = 1, \ldots,), \tag{2}$$

$$x_j \geq 0, \qquad s_i \geq 0.$$

If the optimum value of θ is 1, then the original network is feasible. There are millions of columns in $[a_{ij}]$ in this formulation; fortunately, we need not write down all the columns. If we have m columns as the starting basis of (2), then we will get $\boldsymbol{\pi}$ as a result of simplex computation. Using this $\boldsymbol{\pi}$, we can generate a column which increases the objective function as we did in the revised simplex method. Since the relative cost $\bar{c}_j$ of a column j is given by $\bar{c}_j = c_j - \boldsymbol{\pi}\mathbf{a}_j$ and c_j is 1 for all columns, we want to find the minimum of $\boldsymbol{\pi}\mathbf{a}_j$. If for the minimum of $\boldsymbol{\pi}\mathbf{a}_j$ we have $\bar{c}_j = c_j - \boldsymbol{\pi}\mathbf{a}_j \leq 0$, then the current solution is optimum.

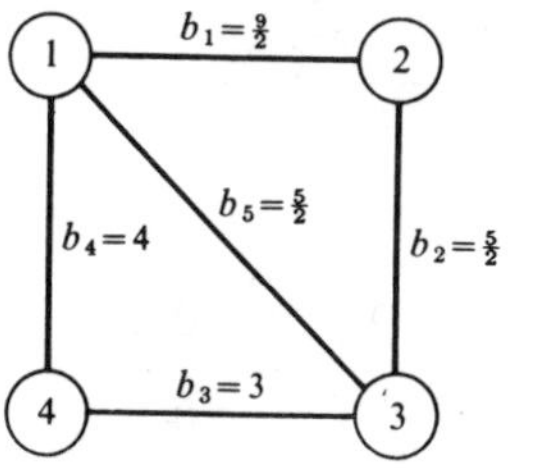

Fig. 11.8 Arc Capacities

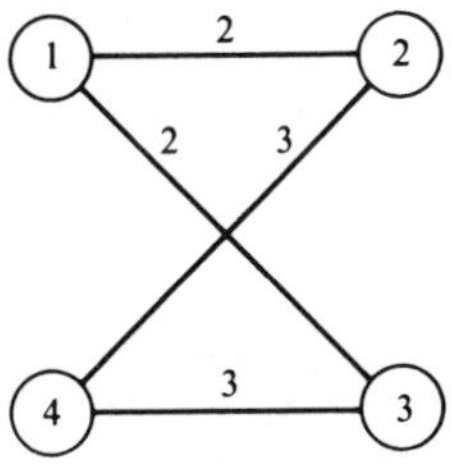

Fig. 11.9 Flow Requirements

For computational purposes we also keep an $(m + 1) \times (m + 1)$ matrix and can interpret π_i as the cost of building the arc i of unit capacity. When all $\pi_i \geq 0$ in the tableau, we try to bring into the basis the column which represents the cheapest network that is capable of carrying the simultaneous flow requirements. If $\theta \geq 1$, then the set of flow requirements is feasible. If $\theta < 1$ and $\boldsymbol{\pi}\mathbf{a}_j \geq 1$ for all j, then the set of flow requirements is infeasible in the existing network. Let us do a numerical example illustrating the feasibility problem of multicommodity flows.

Example. Consider the network shown in Fig. 11.8, where the numbers beside the arcs are their capacities, and the flow requirements of four commodities between the nodes are shown in Fig. 11.9. The question is whether or not the set of flow requirements is feasible in the network. We have Tableau 11.1 which, except the right-most column, expresses the capacities of the network as the sum of slack variables and $\theta = 0$. In this case, $\mathbf{b} = [b_1, b_2, b_3, b_4, b_5] = [9/2, 5/2, 3, 4, 5/2]$. Note the slight change in tabulation in Tableau 11.1 from the revised simplex method discussed in Chapter 5. Here the right-hand side $\mathbf{b}$ appears in the 0th column. The upper left corner is still reserved for the value of the objective function.

Tableau 11.1 *

	1	s_1	s_2	s_3	s_4	s_5	x_1
θ	0						-1
s_1	9/2	1					2
s_2	5/2		1				3
s_3	3			1			6*
s_4	4				1		0
s_5	5/2					1	2

* All the blank spaces in tableaux denote zero.

Tableau 11.2

	1	s_1	s_2	s_3	s_4	s_5	x_2
θ	1/2			1/6			-1
s_1	7/2	1		$-1/3$			5
s_2	1		1	$-1/2$			0
x_1	1/2			1/6			0
s_4	4			0	1		6
s_5	3/2			$-1/3$		1	5*

In Tableau 11.1, $\pi = (0, 0, 0, 0, 0)$, so that any network capable of carrying the flow requirements will be the cheapest. We can consider each arc to be of cost ϵ so that each flow requirement is carried by a single arc and the flow requirement from N_2 to N_4 is carried by b_2 and b_3. This process gives the right-most column in Tableau 11.1. The result of a pivot in Tableau 11.1 is shown in Tableau 11.2 (except the right-most column).

In Tableau 11.2, $\pi = [0, 0, \frac{1}{6}, 0, 0]$, so that the cheapest network is shown in the right-most column of the tableau. (Note that the network [5, 0, 0, 6, 5] should be updated before adding to Tableau 11.2. Here it is the same after updating.) The result of the pivoting of Tableau 11.2 is shown in Tableau 11.3 (except the right-most column). With the $\pi = [0, 0, 1/10, 0, 1/5]$, the cheapest network is [10, 5, 0, 6, 0]. The result of a pivoting of Tableau 11.3 is shown in Tableau 11.4.

With the $\pi = [1/10, 0, 1/10, 0, 1/10]$ there is no network capable of carrying the flow with total cost less than 1. Therefore θ cannot be increased any more. We have $x_1 = 1/2$, $x_2 = 3/10$, $x_3 = 1/5$. To see how the network in Fig. 11.8 can carry the flow requirements, we have $(1/2)[2, 3, 6, 0, 2] = [1, 3/2, 3, 0, 1]$, $(3/10)[5, 0, 0, 6, 5] = [3/2, 0, 0, 9/5, 3/2]$, $(1/5)[10, 5, 0, 6, 0] = [2, 1, 0, 6/5, 0]$. In Fig. 11.10 we show the three networks which are

Tableau 11.3

	1	s_1	s_2	s_3	s_4	s_5	x_3
θ	8/10			1/10		1/5	−1
s_1	2	1		0		−1	10*
s_2	1		1	−1/2		0	5
x_1	1/2			1/6		0	0
s_4	11/5			2/5	1	−6/5	6
x_2	3/10			−1/15		1/5	0

Tableau 11.4

	1	s_1	s_2	s_3	s_4	s_5
θ	1	1/10		1/10		1/10
x_3	1/5	1/10		0		−1/10
s_2	0	−1/2	1	−1/2		1/2
x_1	1/2	0		1/6		0
s_4	1	−6/10		2/5	1	−6/10
x_2	3/10	0		−1/15		1/5

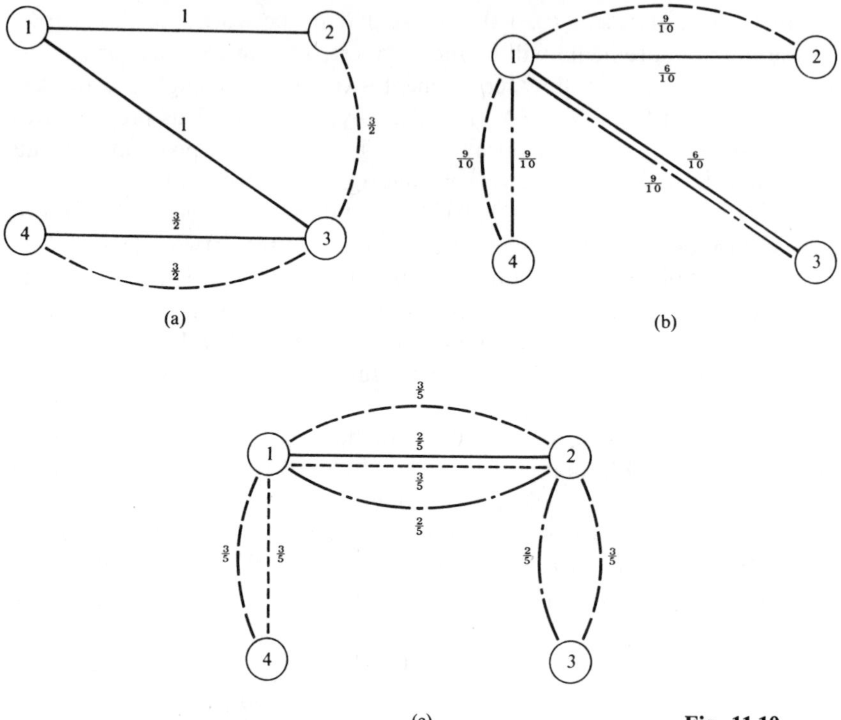

Fig. 11.10

capable of carrying 1/2, 3/10, and 1/5 of the set of flow requirements shown in Fig. 11.9.

There are two problems concerning minimum cost multicommodity network flows. The first problem is like (1) and the second problem is like (2) except that there are costs involved. Associated with every arc of the network there is a cost c_i, which is the shipping cost of one unit of flow through that arc. The first problem requires certain units of flow (no matter what commodity) between sources and sinks with a minimum total cost.

Let b_0 be the required amount of flow. As before we have an arc-chain incidence matrix $[a_{ij}]$, and x_j is used to denote the amount of flow in chain j. Let the cost of shipping one unit of flow in the jth chain be c_j^*. Then the problem is

$$\min z = c_j^* x_j$$

subject to

$$\begin{aligned} &\sum x_j - s_0 = b_0, \\ &\sum a_{ij} x_j + s_i = b_i, \\ &x_j,\ s_0, \qquad s_i \geq 0, \end{aligned} \tag{3}$$

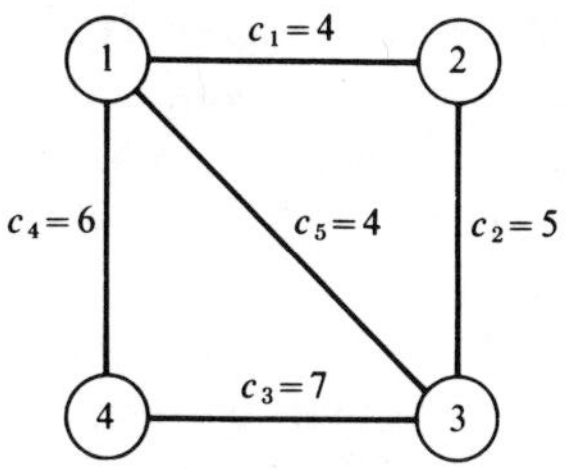

Fig. 11.11

where each column of $[a_{ij}]$ in (3) is a chain leading from a source to a sink of some commodity. Let us associate every arc of Fig. 11.8 with a cost as shown in Fig. 11.11. Let the arc capacity be the same as that of Fig. 11.8 and let us require the sum of flows from N_1 to N_3 and from N_2 to N_4 to be eight units. Then the starting tableau corresponding to (3) is Tableau 11.5 (except the three columns on the right).

Tableau 11.5

	1	s_0	s_1	s_2	s_3	s_4	s_5	x_1	x_2	x_3
$-z$	0							4	10	12
s_0	−8	1						−1	−1	−1
s_1	9/2		1					0	1	0
s_2	5/2			1				0	0	1
s_3	3				1			0	0	1
s_4	4					1		0	1	0
s_5	5/2						1	1	0	0

Tableau 11.6

	1	s_0	s_1	s_2	s_3	s_4	s_5	x_1	x_2	x_3
$-z$	−80	0	0	−12	0	−10	−4	0	0	0
s_0	1	1		1*		1	1	0	0	0
s_1	1/2		1			−1		0	0	0
x_3	5/2			1				0	0	1
s_3	1/2			−1	1			0	0	0
x_2	4					1		0	1	0
x_1	5/2						1	1	0	0

We arbitrarily introduce three columns representing three chains in Tableau 11.5. The first chain uses arc 5, which costs 4. This appears as [4, −1, 0, 0, 0, 0, 1] under x_1. The second component of the vector is −1, which is the coefficient of x_1 in the equation $-\sum x_j + s_0 = -b_0$. The second chain uses arc 1 and arc 4; thus the total cost is $c_1 + c_4 = 4 + 6 = 10$. This is represented by the column [10, −1, 1, 0, 0, 1, 0] under x_2.

Since Tableau 11.5 is not primal feasible, we introduce three chains to reduce its primal infeasibility. The result of pivoting and introducing x_1, x_2, and x_3 successively is shown in Tableau 11.6. Note that the relative cost is $\bar{c}_j^* = c_j^* - \boldsymbol{\pi}\mathbf{a}_j^*$. Here every column is of the form $[-1, \mathbf{a}_j]$. Thus $c_j^* - \boldsymbol{\pi}\mathbf{a}_j^* = c_j^* - (-\pi_0, \boldsymbol{\pi}_1)[-1, \mathbf{a}_j] = -\pi_0 + \sum_i (c_i - \pi_i)a_{ij}$ where π_0 is the price under s_0.

A further pivot on Tableau 11.6 leads to Tableau 11.7 (except the rightmost column). In Tableau 11.7 we can interpret $c_i - \pi_i$ as the length of

Tableau 11.7

	1	s_0	s_1	s_2	s_3	s_4	s_5	x_4
$-z$	−68	12	0	0	0	2	8	−3
s_2	1	1		1		1	1	0
s_1	1/2		1			−1	0	1*
x_3	3/2	−1				−1	−1	1
s_3	3/2	1			1	1	1	−1
x_2	4					1	0	0
x_1	5/2					0	1	0

Tableau 11.8

	1	s_0	s_1	s_2	s_3	s_4	s_5
$-z$	−66.5	12	3			−1	8
s_2	1	1		1		1*	1
x_4	1/2		1			−1	0
x_3	1	−1	−1			0	−1
s_3	2	1	1		1	0	1
x_2	4					1	0
x_1	5/2					0	1

Tableau 11.9

	1	s_0	s_1	s_2	s_3	s_4	s_5
$-z$	-65.5	13	3	1		0	9
s_4	1	1		1		1	1
x_4	3/2	1	1	1		0	0
x_3	1	-1	-1			0	-1
s_3	2	1	1		1	0	1
x_2	3	-1		-1		0	-1
x_1	5/2					0	1

the arc and try to find the shortest chain joining N_1 to N_3 or N_2 to N_4. Here $c_1 - \pi_1 = 4 + 0 = 4$, $c_2 - \pi_2 = 5 + 0 = 5$, $c_3 - \pi_3 = 7 + 0 = 7$, $c_4 - \pi_4 = 6 + 2 = 8$, and $c_5 - \pi_5 = 4 + 8 = 12$. The shortest chain from N_1 to N_3 is therefore of length $4 + 5 = 9$ and the shortest chain from N_2 to N_4 is of length $4 + 8 = 5 + 7 = 12$. Therefore we introduce the column $[9, -1, 1, 1, 0, 0, 0]$. This column, *after updating*, appears as the rightmost column in Tableau 11.7. After a pivot step this becomes Tableau 11.8.

After another pivot step Tableau 11.8 becomes Tableau 11.9. Based on the lengths of arcs in Tableau 11.9, $c_1 - \pi_1 = 4 + 3 = 7$, $c_2 - \pi_2 = 5 + 1 = 6$, $c_3 - \pi_3 = 7 + 0 = 7$, $c_4 - \pi_4 = 6 + 0 = 6$, and $c_5 - \pi_5 = 4 + 9 = 13$, there is no shortest chain from N_1 to N_3 or from N_2 to N_4 of length less than 13. Since $\pi_0 = 13$, $-\pi_0 + \sum_i (c_i - \pi_i)\mathbf{a}_{ij} \geq 0$. Therefore the current solution is optimum.

11.3 SYNTHESIS OF A COMMUNICATION NETWORK (Gomory and Hu [91])

The network considered in this chapter can be thought of as the abstract model of a communication network with the nodes corresponding to stations and the arc capacities corresponding to channel capacities. Flows in a network then may be interpreted as message flows. Since message flows have definite destinations and origins, the message flows are multicommodity flows all sharing the same channel capacities of the network. A communication network must be capable of transmitting simultaneous flows at all times.

Let f_{pq} be the flow value from the source N_p to the sink N_q, and x_{ij}^{pq} be the arc flow in arc A_{ij} with the source N_p and sink N_q. The conservation of flows requires

$$\sum_i x_{ij}^{pq} - \sum_k x_{jk}^{pq} = \begin{cases} -f_{pq}, & j = p, \\ 0, & j \neq p, q, \\ f_{pq}, & j = q. \end{cases} \tag{1}$$

If y_{ij} is the arc capacity of arc A_{ij}, then

$$\sum_{p,q} x_{ij}^{pq} \leq y_{ij} \qquad \text{(for all } i, j). \tag{2}$$

Let $r_{pq}(t)$ be the required flows from N_p to N_q at time t. The fact that the network is capable of handling all the flows at all times is indicated by

$$f_{pq} \geq r_{pq}(t) \qquad \text{(for all } p, q; \text{ for all } t = 1, \ldots, T). \tag{3}$$

As we have mentioned before, there are basically two types of problems. In the problem of analysis, y_{ij} and $r_{pq}(t)$ are given and the problem is to find x_{ij}^{pq} such that (1), (2), and (3) are satisfied. Sometimes costs are associated with arc flows and the problem is to minimize the total cost subject to (1), (2), and (3). In the problem of synthesis, the $r_{pq}(t)$ are given and the problem is to find y_{ij} such that (1), (2), and (3) are satisfied with the total cost $\sum c_{ij} y_{ij}$ minimum. Here the costs are associated with arc capacities that are to be constructed, i.e., c_{ij} is the cost of constructing an arc from N_i to N_j of unit capacity.

In a real communication network, the requirements $r_{pq}(t)$ vary with time. This is due to changing loads on the network. The degree of difficulty of the problems of analysis and synthesis depends on how the $r_{pq}(t)$ are given. There are three cases for the ways in which the $r_{pq}(t)$ may be given.

CASE 1. Time-independent case, i.e., the $r_{pq}(t)$ are independent of t; all requirements are to be met simultaneously.

Analysis. This case is treated in Section 11.2. Basically it is a linear program with many columns, with an auxiliary calculation for generating the columns. The auxiliary calculation is of the shortest path type. Only in the special case of two-commodity flow is the linear programming approach avoided. See Hu [106] or Section 11.1.

Synthesis. This is essentially a multiterminal, shortest path problem (see Hu [111]). Using the costs c_{ij} as lengths, we find the shortest paths for every pair of nodes N_p and N_q. Then we build just enough capacity along each path to carry the required flow. The final network is obtained by superposition of all the previous arc capacities of shortest paths.

CASE 2. Completely time-shared requirements. Here, time is broken up into distinct periods, and during any one period there is a flow between one pair of nodes only.

Analysis. This problem can be solved by doing maximal flow problems, one for each pair of terminal nodes. For the undirected network, much computation can be saved. (See Chapter 9 or Gomory and Hu [89].)

Synthesis. The case of undirected networks with all c_{ij} the same is also treated in Chapter 9 of this book. For the case in which the c_{ij} are not the same, a linear programming approach is used. (See Gomory and Hu [90].) This is a large linear program with many rows. The size of the matrix is reduced by generating only the rows necessary for the computation. Here the auxiliary calculation of generating the rows is of the maximal flow type.

CASE 3. Time varying requirements. This problem is the most general case; cases 1 and 2 can be considered as extreme cases of this one.

Analysis. If we again break time into T distinct periods, then we have T sets of inequalities like (3), one for each time period. For a given period this problem reduces to case 1.

Synthesis. This is the case that we shall treat in detail in this section. Let $\mathbf{y} = [y_1, \ldots, y_m]$ be an m-component vector with each component representing the capacity of an arc in an m-arc network. The vector $\mathbf{y}$ is then a full description of the network to be constructed. Let $\mathbf{N}^t$ be an m-vector representing a network capable of carrying simultaneous flows in the time t. Each component of $\mathbf{N}^t$ is the capacity of an arc of the network. It is clear that such $\mathbf{N}^t$ form a convex (unbounded) polytope in m-space. Let $\mathbf{N}_i^t$ be the extreme points of this convex set, so that there exists at least one optimum $\mathbf{N}^t$ which can be expressed as

$$\mathbf{N}^t = \sum_i \lambda_i^t \mathbf{N}_i^t \qquad (1 \leq \sum \lambda_i^t). \tag{4}$$

If $\mathbf{y}$ is to meet the requirements for each period of time, it is necessary and sufficient for $\mathbf{y}$ to contain a network $\mathbf{N}^t$ for each t. Let $\mathbf{c} = (c_1, \ldots, c_m)$ be the cost vector of the arcs. Then the synthesis problem is

$$\min \mathbf{c} \cdot \mathbf{y}$$

subject to

$$\begin{aligned} \mathbf{y} &\geq \sum_i \lambda_i^t \mathbf{N}_i^t \qquad (t = 1, \ldots, T), \\ 1 &\leq \sum_i \lambda_i^t \qquad [i = 1, \ldots, q(t)]. \end{aligned} \tag{5}$$

In (5) $\mathbf{y}$ and λ_i^t are unknowns. The $\mathbf{N}_i^t$ are assumed to be known and $\mathbf{c}$ is given. This formulation involves $(m + 1)T$ rows and an enormous number of columns, one column for each $\mathbf{N}_i^t$. Rewriting (5), we have

$$\sum_i \lambda_i^t [\mathbf{N}_i^t, -1] \leq [\mathbf{y}, -1]. \tag{6}$$

From Theorem 1.3 (Minkowski-Farkas' lemma) either the inequality $\mathbf{Ax} \leq \mathbf{b}$ has a nonnegative solution or the inequalities $\mathbf{yA} \geq \mathbf{0}$ and $\mathbf{yb} < 0$

have a nonnegative solution. Stated somewhat differently, the inequality $\mathbf{Ax} \leq \mathbf{b}$ has a nonnegative solution if and only if for all $\boldsymbol{\pi} \geq \mathbf{0}$, $\boldsymbol{\pi}\mathbf{A} \geq \mathbf{0}$ implies $\boldsymbol{\pi}\mathbf{b} \geq 0$.* Applying this lemma to (6), we have that (6) has a nonnegative solution λ_i^t for a given $\mathbf{y}$ if and only if there exists nonnegative $(\boldsymbol{\pi}_1^t, \bar{\pi}_0^t)$ such that

$$(\boldsymbol{\pi}_1^t, \bar{\pi}_0^t)[\mathbf{N}_i^t, -1] \geq 0 \qquad \text{(for all } i \text{ and } t). \tag{7}$$

$$(\boldsymbol{\pi}_1^t, \bar{\pi}_0^t)[\mathbf{y}, -1] \geq 0.$$

Let $\bar{\pi}_0^t = -\pi_0^t$, and $\boldsymbol{\pi}^t = (\boldsymbol{\pi}_1^t, \pi_0^t)$. Then (7) is equivalent to

$$(\boldsymbol{\pi}_1^t, \pi_0^t)\ [\mathbf{N}_i^t, 1] \geq 0, \qquad (\boldsymbol{\pi}_1^t, \pi_0^t)\ [\mathbf{y}, 1] \geq 0. \tag{8}$$

Here $\boldsymbol{\pi}_1^t$ is a nonnegative m-vector and π_0^t a nonpositive scalar. The vectors $\boldsymbol{\pi}^t$ satisfying (8) also form a convex (unbounded) polytope so that there is a finite number of vectors $\boldsymbol{\pi}_i^t$ representing extreme points. In any period t, there exists $\boldsymbol{\pi}^t$, which can be expressed as positive combinations of $\boldsymbol{\pi}_i^t$. Therefore, we can reformulate problem (5) as

$$\min \mathbf{c} \cdot \mathbf{y}$$

subject to

$$\boldsymbol{\pi}_i^t[\mathbf{y}, 1] \geq 0 \qquad [t = 1, \ldots, T;\ \mathrm{i} = 1, \ldots, q(t)]. \tag{9}$$

In (9) there are m variables but an enormous number of rows, one for each of the $\boldsymbol{\pi}_i^t$. If we can list all $\boldsymbol{\pi}_i^t$, then (9) can be solved as a linear program. Therefore, the problem is to generate $\boldsymbol{\pi}_i^t$ which represent coefficients of inequalities not satisfied by the current $\mathbf{y}$. There are two ways to solve (9). We shall first discuss the dual approach, which consists of two parts. The main part is a dual simplex tableau, which starts with a dual feasible $\mathbf{y}$ subject to inequalities which are not satisfied by the current $\mathbf{y}$. The auxiliary part supplies the inequalities for the main part. To start the calculation of the main part we can use any dual feasible $\mathbf{y}$, for example, $\mathbf{y} = [0, \ldots, 0]$, which is certainly dual feasible since we assume that $\mathbf{c} > \mathbf{0}$. As there are no inequalities yet generated by the auxiliary part, we cannot do a dual simplex step on the main part. This $\mathbf{y}$ is then sent to the auxiliary part. In the auxiliary part we want

$$\max \theta = \sum \lambda_i^t$$

subject to

$$\mathbf{y} \geq \sum \lambda_i^t \mathbf{N}_i^t \qquad [t = 1, \ldots, T;\ i = 1, \ldots, q(t)]. \tag{10}$$

* This result can also be obtained from the theorem of duality. The fact that $\mathbf{Ax} \leq \mathbf{b}$ has a nonnegative solution is equivalent to the fact that the optimum value of the following linear program is zero: min $\xi = \Sigma x_i^a$ subject to $\mathbf{I}x^a + \mathbf{Ax} + \mathbf{Is} = \mathbf{b}$, $\mathbf{x} \geq \mathbf{0}$. The dual program is then max $\pi'\mathbf{b}$ subject to $\mathbf{I}\pi' \leq \mathbf{1}$, $\pi'\mathbf{A} \leq \mathbf{0}$, $\pi' \leq \mathbf{0}$. Letting $\pi' = -\pi$, we have min $\pi\mathbf{b}$ subject to $\pi\mathbf{A} \geq \mathbf{0}$, $\pi \geq \mathbf{0}$.

In (10) $\mathbf{y}$ is given by the main part; the λ_i^t are the unknowns. To start the calculation we can use any feasible network $\mathbf{N}_i^t$ for a given t.

In solving (10), we have two possible outcomes:

1. $\theta \geq 1$, which means that the current $\mathbf{y}$ is feasible for this period t. If $\theta \geq 1$ for all t, then $\mathbf{y}$ is optimum since the $\mathbf{y}$ in (10) is always a dual feasible $\mathbf{y}$ from the main part.
2. We get a price vector $\boldsymbol{\pi}_1$ such that $\boldsymbol{\pi}_1$ is the solution to the dual of (10):

$$\boldsymbol{\pi}_i^t\,\mathbf{y} = \theta < 1,$$

$$\boldsymbol{\pi}_1\,\mathbf{N}_i^t \geq 1$$

(for all i, since the coefficients of λ_i^t are all one). Let $\boldsymbol{\pi}^t = (\boldsymbol{\pi}_1^t, -1)$. We have

$$\boldsymbol{\pi}^t\,[\mathbf{y}, 1] < 0, \qquad \text{and} \qquad \boldsymbol{\pi}^t[\mathbf{N}_i^t, 1] \geq 0. \tag{11}$$

This $\boldsymbol{\pi}^t[\mathbf{y}, 1] \geq 0$ is then an inequality which is unsatisfied by the current $\mathbf{y}$ and can then be added to the main part.

Note that (10) is a very large linear program, since there is one column for each $\mathbf{N}_i^t$. In order to generate these columns, we use the prices $\boldsymbol{\pi}_i$ of the arcs obtained from (10), say, by taking a few $\mathbf{N}_i^t$, and slack vectors as the basis. The $\mathbf{N}_i^k$ that is not in the basis and should be brought into the basis is the one with $\boldsymbol{\pi}_1 \cdot \mathbf{N}_i^k \leq 1$.

Therefore, we want the column for which $\boldsymbol{\pi}_1\mathbf{N}_i^k$ is minimum. But this is the synthesis problem of case 1 discussed earlier. We can use $\boldsymbol{\pi}_i$ as the lengths of the arcs and use Hu [111] to find the shortest paths between all pairs of nodes to form the column $\mathbf{N}_i^k$.

In summary this dual algorithm consists of two parts: In the main part, a revised dual simplex method is used to solve

$$\min z = \mathbf{c} \cdot \mathbf{y}$$

subject to

$$\boldsymbol{\pi}_1^t\mathbf{y} \geq 1 \qquad [t = 1, \ldots, T;\ i = 1, \ldots, q(t)],$$

$$\mathbf{y} \geq \mathbf{0},$$

where the coefficients of the inequality $\boldsymbol{\pi}_1^t\mathbf{y} \geq 1$ are supplied from the auxiliary part or from other considerations, such as the fact that the total capacity of arcs incident to a node must not be less than the sum of the flow requirements involving that node. After a finite number of duai simplex steps, the $\mathbf{y}$ is both primal and dual feasible with respect to the given set of inequalities. This $\mathbf{y}$ is then transmitted to the auxiliary part. In the auxiliary part, a revised primal simplex method is used to solve (10), where $\mathbf{y}$ is given by the main part. The column $\mathbf{N}_i^t$ that must be generated to increase the value of θ is given by the multiterminal shortest path algorithm using prices obtained in the primal revised simplex method as the lengths of the arcs. If $\theta \geq 1$ for all periods $t = 1, \ldots, T$, then the current network is opti-

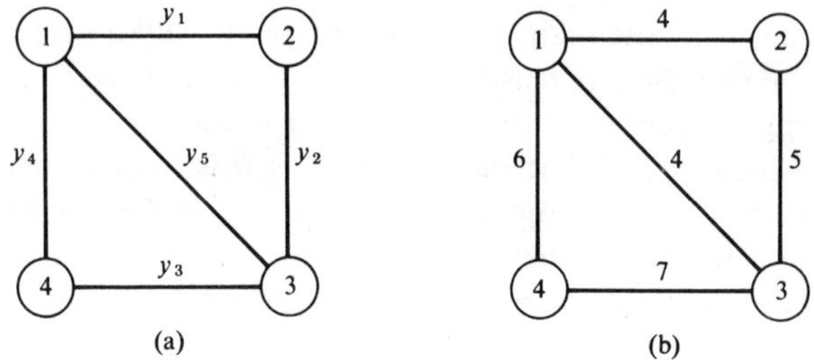

Fig. 11.12

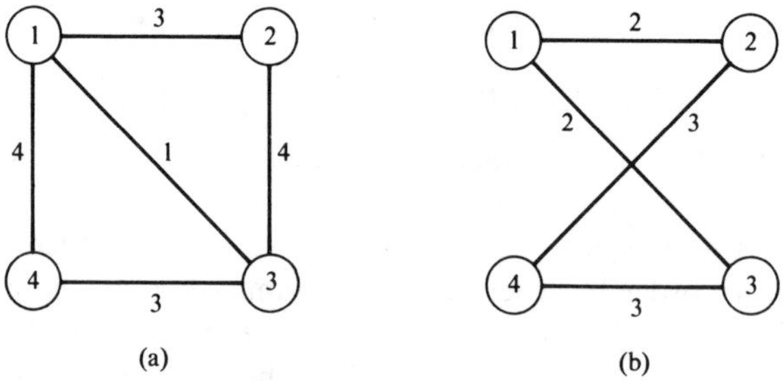

Fig. 11.13

mum. If after a finite number of iterations in the revised simplex method we have $\boldsymbol{\pi}_1\mathbf{y} = \theta < 1$ and $\boldsymbol{\pi}_1\mathbf{N}_i^k \geq 1$ for all $\mathbf{N}_i^k$, then $\boldsymbol{\pi}_1\mathbf{y} \geq 1$ is the desired inequality in the main part. This inequality should be updated before it is added to the tableau of the main part.

Let us give a numerical example. The network with names on each arc is given in Fig. 11.12 (a). The costs of constructing every unit of arc capacity are given in Fig. 11.12 (b). The flow requirements consist of two periods; these are given in Fig. 11.13.

Main Part: We start with Tableau M1 with $\mathbf{y} = [0, 0, 0, 0, 0]$. The inequality that we shall use is that $y_1 + y_4 + y_5 \geq 8$, since the total flow requirements in period 1 involving N_1 are $3 + 1 + 4 = 8$. This inequality is put at the bottom of the tableau. The pivot is indicated by an *. The result of the pivot is shown in Table M2 (except the bottom row). The inequality that is to be added is $-8 + y_2 + y_3 + y_5 = v_2 \geq 0$. This is obtained by considering N_3. To express this inequality in terms of the current nonbasic variables $-v_1$, $-y_2$, $-y_3$, $-y_4$, and $-y_5$, we replace the top row of Tableau M2 by (1, 0, 0, 0, 0, 0) and then multiply the matrix in Tableau M2 on the left by $(-8, 0, 1, 1, 0, 1)$. This gives the inequality $-8 + y_2 + y_3 + y_5 = v_2 \geq 0$, which is added to the bottom of Tableau M2. (Note that in this special case, the updated inequality is the same as the original inequality. This cannot be expected in general.)

We proceed this way, considering nodes N_4 and N_2, with the obvious associated inequalities $y_3 + y_4 - 7 = v_3 \geq 0$ and $y_1 + y_2 - 7 = v_4 \geq 0$ and obtain Tableau M3 (except the bottom row).

Tableau M1

	1	$-y_1$	$-y_2$	$-y_3$	$-y_4$	$-y_5$
$-z$	0	4	5	7	6	4
y_1	0	−1	0	0	0	0
y_2	0	0	−1	0	0	0
y_3	0	0	0	−1	0	0
y_4	0	0	0	0	−1	0
y_5	0	0	0	0	0	−1
v_1	−8	−1*	0	0	−1	−1

Tableau M2

	1	$-v_1$	$-y_2$	$-y_3$	$-y_4$	$-y_5$
$-z$	−32	4	5	7	2	0
y_1	8	−1	0	0	1	1
y_2	0	0	−1	0	0	0
y_3	0	0	0	−1	0	0
y_4	0	0	0	0	−1	0
y_5	0	0	0	0	0	−1
v_2	−8	0	−1	−1	0	−1*

Tableau M3

	1	$-v_1$	$-y_2$	$-v_4$	$-v_3$	$-v_2$
$-z$	−81	3/2	0	5/2	9/2	5/2
y_1	7	0	1	−1	0	0
y_2	0	0	−1	0	0	0
y_3	7	1/2	1	−1/2	−1/2	−1/2
y_4	0	−1/2	−1	1/2	−1/2	1/2
y_5	1	−1/2	0	1/2	1/2	−1/2
v_5	−8	−1	−2*	1	0	0

Tableau A1

	1	s_1	s_2	s_3	s_4	s_5	λ_1^t	...	λ_i^t
θ	0	0	0	0	0	0	−1	...	−1
s_1	7	1					3		
s_2	0		1				4*		
s_3	7			1			3		
s_4	0				1		4		
s_5	1					1	1		

Tableau A2

	1	s_1	s_2	s_3	s_4	s_5	λ_2^t
θ	0	0	1/4	0	0	0	−1
s_1	7	1	−3/4	0	0	0	7
λ_1^t	0	0	1/4	0	0	0	0
s_3	7	0	−3/4	1	0	0	3
s_4	0	0	−1	0	1	0	4*
s_5	1	0	−1/4	0	0	1	5

At this point all the simple inequalities are satisfied and we must go through the auxiliary part to generate additional inequalities. The auxiliary part begins with Tableau A1, where slack vectors are used to form a starting basis. Initially the prices (which appear in the top row under $s_1, \ldots, s_5$) are all zero, so that any feasible network provides an improving column, such as the one headed by λ_1^t. After pivoting we have a nonzero price which appears in the top row of Tableau A2. Based on this price vector [0, 1/4, 0, 0, 0], the cheapest network is then [7, 0, 3, 4, 5], which expressed in terms of current variables is shown as the right-most column in Tableau A2.

We proceed through another pivot step and two more improving networks as shown in Tableaux A3 and A4 before reaching Tableau A5. Note that the column under λ_3^t was updated before it was added to Tableau A3.

$$\begin{bmatrix} 1 & 0 & 0 & 0 & 1/4 & 0 \\ 0 & 1 & 1 & 0 & -7/4 & 0 \\ 0 & 0 & 1/4 & 0 & 0 & 0 \\ 0 & 0 & 0 & 1 & -3/4 & 0 \\ 0 & 0 & -1/4 & 0 & 1/4 & 0 \\ 0 & 0 & 1 & 0 & -5/4 & 1 \end{bmatrix} \begin{bmatrix} -1 \\ 3 \\ 4 \\ 7 \\ 0 \\ 5 \end{bmatrix} = \begin{bmatrix} -1 \\ 7 \\ 1 \\ 7 \\ -1 \\ 9 \end{bmatrix}.$$

Tableau A3

	1	s_1	s_2	s_3	s_4	s_5	λ_3^t
θ	0	0	0	0	1/4	0	−1
s_1	7	1	1	0	−7/4	0	7
λ_1^t	0	0	1/4	0	0	0	1*
s_3	7	0	0	1	−3/4	0	7
λ_2^t	0	0	−1/4	0	1/4	0	−1
s_5	1	0	1	0	−5/4	1	9

Tableau A4

	1	s_1	s_2	s_3	s_4	s_5	λ_4^t
θ	0	0	1/4	0	1/4	0	−1
s_1	7	1	−3/4	0	−7/4	0	7
λ_3^t	0	0	1/4	0	0	0	0
s_3	7	0	−7/4	1	−3/4	0	7
λ_2^t	0	0	0	0	1/4	0	0
s_5	1	0	−5/4	0	−5/4	1	9*

Tableau A5

	1	s_1	s_2	s_3	s_4	s_5
θ	1/9	0	1/9	0	1/9	1/9
s_1	56/9	1	2/9	0	−7/9	−7/9
λ_3^t	0	0	1/4	0	0	0
s_3	56/9	0	−7/9	1	2/9	−7/9
λ_2^t	0	0	0	0	1/4	0
λ_4^t	1/9	0	−5/36	0	−5/36	1/9

In Tableau A5 the price vector is (0, 1/9, 0, 1/9, 1/9,). Based on this price vector, there is no $\mathbf{N}_i^t$ for which $\boldsymbol{\pi}\mathbf{N}_i^t < 1$ and yet $\boldsymbol{\pi}\mathbf{y} = (0, 1/9, 0, 1/9, 1/9)\cdot[7, 0, 7, 0, 1] = \theta = 1/9$. Therefore $\boldsymbol{\pi}\mathbf{y} = (1/9)y_2 + (1/9)y_4 + (1/9)y_5 \geq 1$ is an unsatisfied inequality for the current **y**. This is shown as

$$v_5 = -9 + y_2 + y_4 + y_5 \geq 0.$$

This is updated to become the bottom row of Tableau M3. After pivoting we obtain Tableau M4.

Tableau M4

	1	$-v_1$	$-v_5$	$-v_4$	$-v_3$	$-v_2$
$-z$	-81	3/2	0	5/2	9/2	5/2
y_1	3	$-1/2$	1/2	$-1/2$	0	0
y_2	4	1/2	$-1/2$	$-1/2$	0	0
y_3	3	0	1/2	0	$-1/2$	$-1/2$
y_4	4	0	$-1/2$	0	$-1/2$	1/2
y_5	1	$-1/2$	0	1/2	1/2	$-1/2$
v_6	-3	-1*	1	0	0	-1

Tableau M5

	1	$-v_6$	$-v_5$	$-v_4$	$-v_3$	$-v_2$
$-z$	-85.5	3/2	3/2	5/2	9/2	5/2
y_1	9/2	$-1/2$	0	$-1/2$	0	1/2
y_2	5/2	1/2	0	$-1/2$	0	$-1/2$
y_3	3	0	1/2	0	$-1/2$	$-1/2$
y_4	4	0	$-1/2$	0	$-1/2$	1/2
y_5	5/2	$-1/2$	$-1/2$	1/2	1/2	0

The network in Tableau M4 [3, 4, 3, 4, 1] satisfies the requirements in period 1. We know this by going through the auxiliary calculation. We must check whether it also meets the requirements for the second period. Note that the network [3, 4, 3, 4, 1] satisfying the first period requirements can be easily obtained by using the costs in Fig. 11.12(b) and doing a multiterminal, shortest path calculation. However, it is necessary to obtain Tableau M4 to satisfy requirements of more than one period. Using $\mathbf{y} = [3, 4, 3, 4, 1]$, we do another auxiliary calculation like those shown in Tableaux A1 to A5. At the end of the computation we get $\boldsymbol{\pi} = (1/10, 0, 1/10, 0, 1/10)$ and $\theta = 7/10$. Hence the inequality

$$v_6 = -10 + y_1 + y_3 + y_5 \geq 0$$

is updated and put at the bottom of Tableau M4. A pivot step in Tableau M4 leads to Tableau M5.

In Tableau M5 we have $\mathbf{y} = [9/2, 5/2, 3, 4, 5/2]$. Based on this $\mathbf{y}$, we go through auxiliary calculations for both the first and the second period of requirements and obtain $\theta \geq 1$, so this $\mathbf{y}$ is the optimum network with total cost 85.5 as shown in Tableau M5.

The method for synthesizing a communication network discussed above is essentially a dual method, since a feasible network is not obtained until the end of the computation. Now we shall discuss a primal method. A primal simplex method consists of the following steps (we need a starting basis and a primal feasible network):

STEP 1. *Column selection.* Choose a column that will bring an improvement in the cost.

STEP 2. *Row selection.* This is accomplished by the primal simplex rule.

STEP 3. *Gaussian elimination on an inverse matrix.*

Steps (1) and (3) are routine steps. Step (2) is the difficult one since it involves finding out which of the enormous list of inequalities of (9) will be violated first when a currently nonbasic variable is increased from its present level of zero.

Let us assume that $\mathbf{y}_0$ is a primal feasible network, and $\mathbf{y}_1$ is a column which would improve the dual infeasibility if brought into the basis. If θ is the level on which the column will be brought in, then we must have $\mathbf{y}_0 + \theta\mathbf{y}_1$ still a primal feasible network. This means that we want to maximize θ:

$$\max\ \theta$$

subject to

$$\mathbf{y}_0 + \theta\mathbf{y}_1 \geq \sum \lambda_i^t \mathbf{N}_i^t \qquad [t = 1, \ldots, T;\ i = 1, \ldots, q(t)]$$
$$1 \leq \sum \lambda_i^t.$$

This can be rewritten as

$$\max\ \theta' = \theta$$

subject to

$$\begin{aligned} -\theta\mathbf{y}_1 + \sum \lambda_i^t \mathbf{N}_i^t &\leq \mathbf{y}_0, \\ -\sum \lambda_i^t &\leq -1. \end{aligned} \tag{12}$$

First, (12) will always have a bounded maximum, because an unbounded θ would give a feasible network with negative total cost. Let us solve (12) for a period t and get the $\theta_{\max}^t$. Then the prices on the rows $(\boldsymbol{\pi}_1^t, \bar{\pi}_0^t)$ will satisfy

$$(\boldsymbol{\pi}_1^t, \bar{\pi}_0^t)\cdot[\mathbf{y}_0, -1] = \theta_{\max}^t \tag{13}$$

and $(\boldsymbol{\pi}_1^t, \bar{\pi}_0^t)$ times each column in the left-hand side of (12) will be greater than the coefficient of the variable corresponding to that column. In particular, for the first column we have

$$(\boldsymbol{\pi}_1^t, \bar{\pi}_0^t)\cdot[-\mathbf{y}_1, 0] \geq 1. \tag{14}$$

Multiplying (14) by θ and subtracting it from (13), we have

$$(\boldsymbol{\pi}_1^t, \bar{\pi}_0^t)[[\mathbf{y}_0, -1] + \theta\,[\mathbf{y}_1, 0]] \leq \theta_{\max}^t - \theta,$$

or, alternatively,

$$(\boldsymbol{\pi}_1^t, \bar{\pi}_0^t)[\mathbf{y}_0 + \theta \mathbf{y}_1, -1] \leq \theta_{\max}^t - \theta. \tag{15}$$

If $\theta_{\max}^t$ is obtained from (12), then $\mathbf{y}_0 + \theta \mathbf{y}_1$ is a primal feasible network for $0 \leq \theta \leq \theta_{\max}^t$. Therefore if $\theta_{\max}^t$ is the value obtained from (12) by considering the tth period of requirements, then the maximum value of θ is certainly

$$\theta_{\max} = \min_t \theta_{\max}^t.$$

On the other hand, we want to show that there exists a price vector $\boldsymbol{\pi}$ such that $\boldsymbol{\pi}\,[\mathbf{y}_0 + \theta \mathbf{y}_1, -1] < 0$ for $\theta > \theta_{\max}$. Since we have shown in (7) that $\boldsymbol{\pi}[\mathbf{N}_i^t, -1] \geq 0$ for all feasible networks $\mathbf{N}_i^t$, this means that $\boldsymbol{\pi}[\mathbf{y}, -1] \geq 0$ is the binding inequality on the current solution. From (15) we see that $(\boldsymbol{\pi}_1^t, \bar{\pi}_0^t)$ is the desired price vector since the right-hand side of (15) is negative for $\theta > \theta_{\max}$.

In the primal approach, the calculation is divided into two parts. The main part is a revised primal tableau with inequalities to be supplied by the auxiliary part. The auxiliary part solves (12) with $\mathbf{y}_0$ and $\mathbf{y}_1$ given by the main part. At the end of the auxiliary calculation, we obtain a $\theta_{\max}^t$ and a price vector $\boldsymbol{\pi}^t$. If the auxiliary calculation is repeated for requirements of all time periods, we get a $\theta_{\max}$ and a price vector $\boldsymbol{\pi}$. The binding inequality $\boldsymbol{\pi}[\mathbf{y}, -1] \geq 0$ is then added to the main part. The algorithm is completed if there is no improving column left in the main part.

We will do again the numerical example using the primal method. This primal method has the advantage of giving a feasible network at all times, so that calculation can be stopped if progress is too slow.

A primal feasible network is easily obtained by letting $y_{ij} = \max_t r_{ij}(t)$ for all i, j. In our example $r_6 = 3$ is converted into $r_1 = 3$ and $r_4 = 3$. Therefore the starting feasible network is $\mathbf{y}_0 = [5, 4, 3, 4, 2]$. To obtain a starting basis we introduce the variables u_i $(i = 1, \ldots, 5)$ which are unrestricted in size and are defined by

$$y_1 = 5 - u_1, \qquad y_2 = 4 - u_2, \qquad y_3 = 3 - u_3,$$
$$y_4 = 4 - u_4, \qquad \text{and} \qquad y_5 = 2 - u_5.$$

This transformation then gives the starting tableau for the main part, Tableau P1. Clearly any of the u_i if increased from zero level would improve the cost. We put an $\downarrow$ at u_3 to indicate that it is chosen. Therefore, we have to solve (12) with $\mathbf{y}_0 = [5, 4, 3, 4, 2]$ and $\mathbf{y}_1 = [0, 0, 1, 0, 0]$. Instead of using $[\mathbf{y}_0, -1]$, we shall use $[\mathbf{y}_0, 1]$. This will introduce -1 in the column under s_6 and we have Tableau AP1 (except the right-most column). In Tableau AP1, all prices are zero and we get the network [3, 4, 3, 4, 1] as the cheapest network for the first period. This is enlarged to [0, 3, 4, 3, 4, 1, 1] and added to Tableau AP1. Since in Tableau AP1 there is a -1 in the column under s_6, the tableau is not in a starting position. A pivot on the starred element will put the tableau in a starting position. This is shown in Tableau AP2.

Tableau P1

	1	$-u_1$	$-u_2$	↓ $-u_3$	$-u_4$	$-u_5$
$-z$	-93	-4	-5	-7	-6	-4
y_1	5	1	0	0	0	0
y_2	4	0	1	0	0	0
y_3	3	0	0	1	0	0
y_4	4	0	0	0	1	0
y_5	2	0	0	0	0	1

Tableau AP1

	1	θ	s_1	s_2	s_3	s_4	s_5	s_6	λ_1^t
θ'	0	-1							0
s_1	5	0	1						3
s_2	4	0		1					4
s_3	3	1			1				3
s_4	4	0				1			4
s_5	2	0					1		1
1	1	0						-1	1*

Tableau AP2

	1	θ	s_1	s_2	s_3	s_4	s_5	s_6	λ_1^t
θ'	0	-1						0	0
s_1	2	0	1					3	0
s_2	0	0		1				4	0
s_3	0	1*			1			3	0
s_4	0	0				1		4	0
s_5	1	0					1	1	0
λ_1^t	1	0						-1	1

In Tableau AP2 the column under θ is an improving column, because it has negative cost. Pivoting on the starred element leads to Tableau AP3 (except the right-most column).

Tableau AP3

	1	θ	s_1	s_2	s_3	s_4	s_5	s_6	λ_2^t
θ'	0	0			1			3	-3
s_1	2	0	1		0			3	0
s_2	0	0		1	0			4	0
θ	0	1			1			3	-3
s_4	0	0			0	1		4	3*
s_5	1	0			0		1	1	3
λ_1^t	1	0			0			-1	1

Tableau AP4

	1	θ	s_1	s_2	s_3	s_4	s_5	s_6	λ_2^t
θ'	0	0	0	0	1	1	0	7	0
s_1	2	0	1			0		3	0
s_2	0	0		1		0		4	0
θ	0	1			1	1		7	0
λ_2^t	0	0				1/3		4/3	1
s_5	1	0				-1	1	-3	0
λ_1^t	1	0				1/3		$-7/3$	0

Using the prices in Tableau AP3, i.e., (0, 0, 1, 0, 0), we find the cheapest network that will fulfill the first period requirements, namely [3, 4, 0, 7, 4]. This is enlarged to [0, 3, 4, 0, 7 4, 1] and updated before being added to the right-most column of Tableau AP3. A pivot on Tableau AP3 leads to Tableau AP4.

Basing our conclusions on the prices in Tableau AP4, there is no network $\mathbf{y}$ with (0, 0, 1, 1, 0, 7) $[\mathbf{y}, -1] < 0$. Therefore, the binding inequality is $y_3 + y_4 - 7 = v_1 \geq 0$ and $\theta'_{\max} = 0$.

Ordinarily, we would repeat the calculation Tableaux AP1–4 for the second period requirement so as to find the binding inequality and the $\theta^2_{\max}$. Then we would choose $\theta_{\max} = \min\ (\theta^1_{\max}, \theta^2_{\max})$ and its corresponding binding inequality. However, in this case since $\theta^1_{\max} = 0$, we need not repeat the calculation. Now $y_3 + y_4 - 7 = v_1 \geq 0$ is added to the bottom of Tableau P1. This becomes Tableau P2. The result of a pivot step on Tableau P2 is shown in Tableau P3 (except the bottom row).

Tableau P2

	1	$-u_1$	$-u_2$	$-u_3$	$-u_4$	$-u_5$
$-z$	−93	−4	−5	−7	−6	−4
y_1	5	1				
y_2	4		1			
y_3	3			1		
y_4	4				1	
y_5	2					1
v_1	0	0	0	1*	1	0

Tableau P3

	1	$-u_1$	↓ $-u_2$	$-v_1$	$-u_4$	$-u_5$
$-z$	−93	−4	−5	7	1	−4
y_1	5	1				0
y_2	4		1			0
y_3	3			−1	−1	0
y_4	4				1	0
y_5	2					1
v_2	1	0	1*	−1	−1	1

Now the column under u_2 is an improving column, i.e., [0, 1, 0, 0, 0]. To find θ_{max} and the binding inequality, the auxiliary calculation of (12) is repeated with $\mathbf{y}_0 = [5, 4, 3, 4, 2]$ and $\mathbf{y}_1 = [0, 1, 0, 0, 0]$. This time both periods are considered and the binding inequality, which comes from the first period requirement, is

$$v_2 = -8 + y_2 + y_3 + y_5 \geq 0$$

with $\theta_{max} = 1$.

This inequality $v_2 \geq 0$ is updated and added to the bottom of Tableau P3, and a primal pivot step produces a new network [5, 3, 3, 4, 2]. This is shown in Tableau P4 (except the bottom row). The auxiliary calculation is repeated with

$$v_3 = -9 + y_2 + y_3 + y_5 \geq 0,$$

which after updating becomes the bottom row of Tableau P4.

Tableau P4

	1	$-u_1$	$-v_2$	$-v_1$	↓ $-u_4$	$-u_5$
$-z$	-88	-4	5	2	-4	1
y_1	5	1	0	0	0	0
y_2	3	0	-1	1	1	-1
y	3	0	0	-1	-1	0
y_4	4	0	0	0	1	0
y_5	2	0	0	0	0	1
v_3	0	0	-1	1	2*	0

Tableau P5

	1	↓ $-u_1$	$-v_2$	$-v_1$	$-v_3$	$-u_5$
$-z$	-88	-4	3	4	2	1
y_1	5	1	0	0	0	0
y_2	3	0	$-1/2$	$1/2$	$-1/2$	-1
y_3	3	0	$-1/2$	$-1/2$	$1/2$	0
y_4	4	0	$1/2$	$-1/2$	$-1/2$	0
y_5	2	0	0	0	0	1
v_4	0	1*	$1/2$	$-1/2$	$1/2$	1

Tableau P6

	1	$-v_4$	$-v_2$	$-v_1$	$-v_3$	↓ $+u_5$
$-z$	-88	4	1	2	4	-5
y_1	5	-1	$1/2$	$1/2$	$-1/2$	1
y_2	3	0	$-1/2$	$1/2$	$-1/2$	1
y_3	3	0	$-1/2$	$-1/2$	$1/2$	0
y_4	4	0	$1/2$	$-1/2$	$-1/2$	0
y_5	2	0	0	0	0	-1
v_5	1	-1	0	1	-1	2*

Tableau P7

	1	$-v_4$	$-v_2$	$-v_1$	$-v_3$	$-v_5$
$-z$	-85.5	$-3/2$	1	9/2	3/2	5/2
y_1	9/2	$-1/2$	1/2	0	0	$-1/2$
y_2	5/2	1/2	$-1/2$	0	0	$-1/2$
y_3	3	0	$-1/2$	$-1/2$	1/2	0
y_4	4	0	1/2	$-1/2$	$-1/2$	0
y_5	5/2	$-1/2$	0	1/2	1/2	1/2
v_5	0	0	0	0	0	-1

After pivoting Tableau P4 becomes Tableau P5 and the auxiliary calculation gives $v_4 = -10 + y_1 + y_3 + y_5 \geq 0$, which after updating appears in the bottom row of Tableau P5.

The pivot step on Tableau P5 leads to Tableau P6 with the auxiliary calculation giving $v_5 = -7 + y_1 + y_2 \geq 0$, which after updating becomes the bottom row of Tableau P6. In transforming Tableau P5 to Tableau P6, we have changed $-u_5$ to u_5 (since the u_i are unrestricted in sign).

A pivot on Tableau P6 leads to Tableau P7, where there is no improving column. Therefore, the optimum network is obtained.

FLOWS IN CONTINUA 12

The contents of this chapter are the joint work of Dr. R. E. Gomory and the author. The writing was done by the author. Because the ideas are new and seem to be of interest, they are reported here in their most preliminary form. Credits, if any, should be given to Dr. Gomory and the author, but the author is wholly responsible for errors and mistakes in this chapter. For readers interested in functional analysis, it may be better to read Section 12.3 briefly before reading Sections 12.1 and 12.2.

12.1 RELATIVE MINIMUM CUTS

In this chapter we shall introduce some new concepts which have not appeared in the literature. These concepts are important especially for the approximation of a continuous medium by a finite network, which will be discussed in Section 12.3.

Throughout this chapter we shall consider only undirected networks. Two arcs are said to be *neighboring arcs* if they have an end node in common. Two cuts $(X, \bar{X})$ and $(Y, \bar{Y})$ are said to be *neighboring cuts* if every arc of $(X, \bar{X})$ either also belongs to $(Y, \bar{Y})$ or is a neighboring arc of an arc that belongs to $(Y, \bar{Y})$, and the same relation is true for every arc of $(Y, \bar{Y})$.

Consider the network in Fig. 12.1 with the cuts represented by dashed lines:

$$(X, \bar{X}) = \{A_{14}, A_{12}, A_{s2}, A_{s3}\},$$
$$(Y, \bar{Y}) = \{A_{14}, A_{23}, A_{s3}\},$$
$$(Z, \bar{Z}) = \{A_{14}, A_{35}\},$$
$$(W, \bar{W}) = \{A_{23}, A_{s3}, A_{35}\}.$$

We shall use the symbol $\sim$ to indicate that two arcs are neighbors.

Cuts $(X, \bar{X})$ and $(Y, \bar{Y})$ are neighbors because:

1. A_{14} and A_{s3} are in both cuts.
2. $A_{12} \sim A_{23}$ and $A_{s2} \sim A_{23}$ where A_{12} and A_{s2} belong to $(X, \bar{X})$ and A_{23} belongs to $(Y, \bar{Y})$.

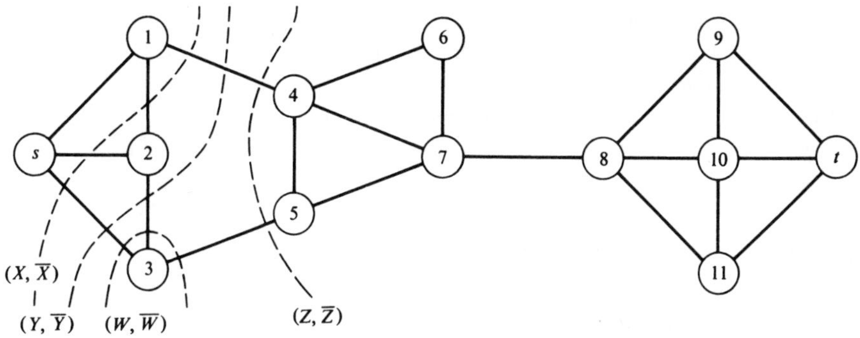

Fig. 12.1

Cuts $(Y, \bar{Y})$ and $(W, \bar{W})$ are not neighbors because A_{14} of $(Y, \bar{Y})$ is not a neighbor of an arc which belongs to $(W, \bar{W})$. Similarly, the reader can verify that $(Y, \bar{Y})$ and $(Z, \bar{Z})$ are neighbors, $(X, \bar{X})$ and $(Z, \bar{Z})$ are not neighbors, $(X, \bar{X})$ and $(W, \bar{W})$ are not neighbors, and $(Z, \bar{Z})$ and $(W, \bar{W})$ are not neighbors.

In the following we shall discuss cuts that separate N_s and N_t. A cut such as $(W, \bar{W})$ will not be of interest. Therefore, we shall use the word "cut" to mean "cut separating N_s and N_t."

A cut is called a *relative minimum cut* if its capacity is less than or equal to the capacity of all of its neighboring cuts. For example, let every arc in Fig. 12.1 have the same arc capacity. Then $(Z, \bar{Z})$ is a relative minimum cut; so is the cut which consists of the single arc A_{78}.

A minimum cut as defined in Chapter 8 is certainly a relative minimum cut but the converse is not true. For example, A_{78} is clearly the minimum cut separating N_s and N_t. $(Z, \bar{Z})$ is a relative minimum cut but not a minimum cut. Therefore, a minimum cut in our terminology is really an absolute minimum cut in a sense. For a cut to be a minimum cut, it is necessary but not sufficient that it be a relative minimum cut. Consider all the cuts separating N_s and N_t in a network. The neighboring relation between cuts is analogous to the distance between points in a plane. For a given point a there are points within distance ϵ to that given point a; these points are said to be in the ϵ-neighborhood of a. Similarly, for a given cut there are cuts which are neighboring cuts of the given cut. In order for a function $f(x)$ to be an absolute minimum at a point a, it is necessary that $f(x) - f(a) \geq 0$ for $|x - a| < \epsilon$, say. Here, in order for a cut to be a minimum cut, it is necessary that it be a relative minimum cut.

In calculus, or in functional analysis, a local minimum is obtained. If a global minimum of the function is desired, we have to compare all the local minima. In network flow theory we are interested in minimum cuts separating the source and the sink. Take the network in Fig. 12.1 for example;

$(Z, \bar{Z})$ and A_{78} are not neighboring cuts, and we want an absolute minimum cut among all cuts separating N_s and N_t. Thus *the labeling method for getting the maximal flow (hence locating the minimum cut) is therefore a technique which locates an absolute minimum which is not implied by a local minimum condition.* We shall explore this aspect in more detail in later sections.

12.2 NODE-CONSTRAINT NETWORKS

In Chapter 8 we associated with every arc of the network an arc capacity which indicates the maximum amount of flow that can pass through the arc. There is no limitation on the amount of flow that can pass a node except that flow must be conserved at every node. Now we shall let the nodes have capacity restrictions and the arcs have no capacity restrictions. We develop this model mostly for use in Section 12.3.

We consider a network consisting of nodes N_i and arcs A connecting N_i and N_j. Each node N_i has associated with it a node capacity w_i, which indicates the maximum amount of flow that can pass through the node. Let x_{ij} be the flow from N_i to N_j in the arc A_{ij}. Since the flow is conserved at every node, the amount of flow passing a node N_j is $\frac{1}{2}\sum_i |x_{ij}|$; this is denoted by x_j. The maximal flow problem for a node-constraint network is therefore

$$\max v$$

subject to

$$\sum_i x_{ij} - \sum_k x_{jk} = \begin{cases} -v, & j = s, \\ 0, & j \neq s, t, \\ v, & j = t, \end{cases}$$

$$x_{ij} \geq 0, \qquad 0 \leq x_j \leq w_j \qquad \text{(for all } i, j), \tag{1}$$

$$\frac{1}{2} \sum_i |x_{ij}| = x_j.$$

Note that we put an absolute value sign on x_{ij} because some of the arc flows are going into the node N_j and some of the arc flows are leaving the node N_j.

A cut separating N_s and N_t in the node-constraint network will be a set of nodes the removal of which will disconnect the network into *two or more parts*, one part containing N_s, another part containing N_t, and no proper subset of which should have this property.

Two nodes are said to be neighbors if there is an arc connecting them. Although the removal of the cut will separate the network into more than two parts, in general, we can still use the notation $(X, \bar{X})$ to denote a cut. Then X denotes all nodes in the part of the network containing N_s and

$(X, \bar{X})$ will be all the neighboring nodes of X. A cut with the sum of the node capacities a minimum is called a *minimum cut*. Just as in the max-flow min-cut theorem in Chapter 8, we can prove an analogous theorem for the node-constraint network. It is true that a node-constraint network can be converted into an arc-constraint network (see Ford and Fulkerson [67]), but this greatly increases the number of arcs. We shall deal with the node-constraint network directly.

Max-Flow Min-Cut Theorem. *Node-Constraint Case.* For a node-constraint network, the maximal flow value from N_s to N_t is equal to the capacity of a minimum cut separating N_s and N_t.

Proof. Assume that all node capacities w_i are positive integers and let F_{st} be any flow, not necessarily maximum. If the value of the flow is equal to the capacity of a cut, the theorem is proved. Otherwise, we shall search for a chain along which the flow value can be increased. This is done by defining a subset X such that flow can be sent to any node in X.

Based on the current flow, we shall define the set X recursively as follows [let $w_{ij} = \min(w_i, w_j)$]

RULE 0. $N_s \in X$.

RULE 1. If $N_i \in X$, $x_{ij} < w_{ij}$, and $x_j < w_j$, then $N_j \in X$.

RULE 2. If $N_i \in X$ and $x_{ji} > 0$, then $N_j \in X$.

RULE 3. If $N_i \in X$ and $x_{ij} < w_{ij}$, $x_j = w_j$, and $x_{kj} > 0$, then $N_k \in X$.

Based on this recursive definition, N_t is either in X or in $\bar{X}$.

CASE 1. N_t is in X. We have to show that the flow value can be increased. Since N_t is in X, there must be a chain from N_s to N_t along which one of the above rules must be true. If Rule 1 or Rule 2 holds then we can clearly send flow along the chain. If Rule 3 holds, let $\epsilon = \min(w_{ij} - x_{ij}, x_{kj})$. Then we can add ϵ to x_{ij} and subtract ϵ from x_{kj}. This is equivalent to sending flow to N_k and keeping N_j saturated with flow. Since w_j are integers, ϵ will be an integer. As the maximal flow is bounded from above, this case cannot be repeated indefinitely.

CASE 2. N_t is in $\bar{X}$. We have to show that the value of the present flow is equal to the capacity of a cut. Let the neighboring nodes of X be called γ-nodes. We have to show the following:

1. There is no arc flow from a γ-node to a node in X.
2. There is no arc flow from $\bar{X} - \gamma$ to γ.
3. There is no arc flow from one γ node to another γ node.
4. All γ-nodes are saturated.

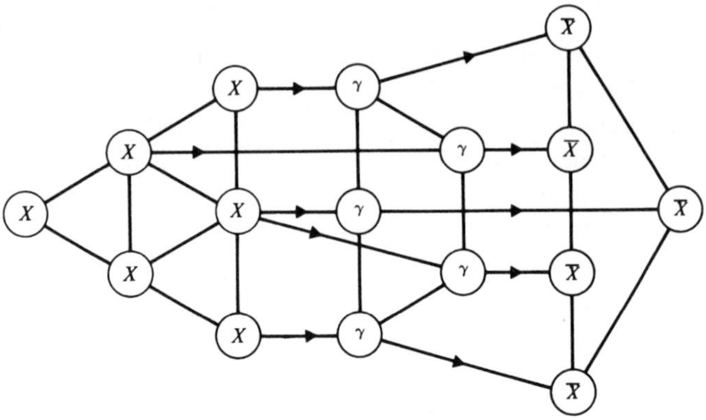

Fig. 12.2

Each of the above can be proved as follows (See Fig. 12.2).

1. There is no $x_{ji} > 0$ with $N_i \in X$ and $N_j \in \gamma$ because Rule 2 would then label N_j to be in X.

2. There is no $x_{kj} > 0$ with $N_j \in \gamma$ and N_k in $\bar{X} - \gamma$, because Rule 3 would then label N_k to be in X.

3. There is no $x_{jk} > 0$ with N_j, $N_k \in \gamma$, because Rule 3 would then label N_j to be in X.

4. Let N_i be in X and N_j be a γ-node and a neighbor of N_i. If N_i is saturated and all the arc flows out of N_i are to γ-nodes, then N_i could not be in X. If there is an $N_k \in X$ and $x_{jk} > 0$, then it follows that the node $N_j \in \gamma$ would be labeled as an X-node from N_k by Rule 3. If N_i is not saturated and if $x_{ij} < w_{ij}$, then N_j will be in X unless N_j is saturated. Therefore all γ-nodes are saturated.

The value of the flow is therefore $\sum x_{ij}$, $N_i \in X$, and $N_j \in \gamma$, which is equal to $\sum w_j$ $(N_j \in \gamma)$. Because γ-nodes are all the neighboring nodes of X, it is a cut. This completes the proof of the theorem.

We can clearly develop a labeling method analogous to the one in Chapter 8 and based on the three rules. However, the third rule requires that not only do we have to look at all neighboring nodes of a node but also at all neighboring nodes of the neighboring nodes. This greatly increases the amount of computation. The following is a labeling procedure which uses only the first and second rules plus minor modifications. Nodes will be classified into five types:

L-nodes: labeled nodes,
LS-nodes: labeled and scanned nodes,
R-nodes: rejected nodes,
RS-nodes: rejected and scanned nodes,
U-nodes: unlabeled nodes.

L-node. A node N_i is an L-node if using the first and second rules we label it to be in X.

LS-node. A node N_i is an LS-node if it is an L-node and we have looked at all neighboring nodes N_j of N_i.

R-node. A node N_j is an R-node if it is looked at and found to be at its capacity, i.e., $x_j = w_j$.

RS-node. A node N_j is an RS-node if it is an R-node and we have looked at all neighboring R-nodes N_k (of N_j) and found that there is no arc flow $x_{kj} > 0$.

U-node. A node N_j is a U-node if it is not any of the above types.

The labeling procedure is done as follows. We first label a node to be in X only if it belongs to X due to the first and second rule. A node is labeled an R-node if it is saturated. If breakthrough occurs, then we increase the flow, erase all labels, and start a new cycle. If a nonbreakthrough occurs, then we look at all R-nodes N_j one by one. For a given R-node N_j, if there is no $x_{kj} > 0$ with N_k an R-node, then N_j is labeled an RS-node. If there is an R-node N_k with $x_{kj} > 0$, then that R-node N_k is changed into an L-node and we search all neighboring nodes of N_k to see if any more nodes can be labeled. If there is no L-node among the R-nodes and the nonbreakthrough occurs, then the present flow is already maximum. In this labeling procedure a node N_j may be first an R-node because $x_j = w_j$ and second become an RS-node due to nonexistence of an R-node N_k with $x_{kj} > 0$. Let us assume that $x_{jk} > 0$ for an R-node N_k. Later the R-nodes N_k may become an L-node and that node N_j will be changed into an L-node also as $x_{jk} > 0$. Therefore, the longest sequence of changing labels that can happen to a node is indicated by

$$R \to RS \to L \to LS.$$

Therefore, a node together with its neighbors is looked at at most twice during this labeling method.

12.3 FLOWS IN A CONTINUOUS MEDIUM

Let us consider a special problem of the calculus of variations. Consider the rectangular region with four sides A, S, B, and T in Fig. 12.3. A bounded continuous weighting function $w(x, y) > 0$ is defined on the rectangular region. We want to find a curve from the side A to the side B such that the line integral

$$\int w(x, y)\, dc$$

is a minimum.

This is a problem of the calculus of variations and can be solved by the usual technique if the weighting function $w(x, y)$ is sufficiently smooth. As

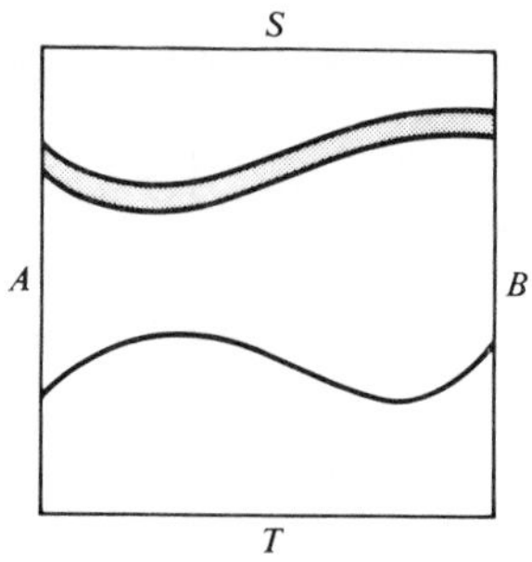

Fig. 12.3

with all problems of the calculus of variations, the minimum, if obtained, is a local minimum which may not imply a global minimum.

Assume that the problem is an abstraction of a practical problem which is to locate a cheapest path for an automobile to go from side A to side B. The weighting function $w(x, y)$ may indicate the amount of fuel consumption at the point $w(x, y)$. There are two reasons that the curve with the line integral $\int w(x, y)\, dc$ a minimum is not what we really want. The first reason is that the weighting function may be very small on the optimum curve but may be very large near the curve. This means that if the automobile should deviate slightly from its prescribed optimum curve, it is very expensive. Since no automobile can be controlled with 100% precision, it is better to locate a strip with width ϵ in which the weighting function $w(x, y)$ is small. The second reason is that the locus of an automobile, unlike the locus of a point, is not a curve but a strip. Thus, in practice, we would rather get a strip with width ϵ from A to B such that

$$\iint w(x, y)\, dA$$

is a minimum. (Furthermore, we want the integral to be a global minimum compared with the integrals of other strips of width ϵ from side A to side B.) It is very easy to construct an example in which, for a given ϵ, the strip with $\iint w(x, y)\, dA$ minimum does not contain the optimum curve with $\int w(x, y)\, dc$ minimum. However, if we let ϵ go to zero, then the optimum strip will approach the optimum curve as the limit. We shall describe a technique which will give a strip of width ϵ with $\iint w(x,y)\, dA$ a global minimum, and if ϵ goes to zero, the strip will approach the optimum curve as a limit.

Note that any continuous curve Γ from A to B will separate the rectangular region into two parts, one part containing the side S and one part containing the side T, and any curve from S to T will meet the curve Γ. In anology to a network with a finite number of nodes, we may think of the rectangular region as a network with the side S as the source and the side T as the sink. The weighting function $w(x, y)$ can be thought of as the capacity function of the medium at the point (x, y). Any curve from A to B corresponds to a cut, and the line integral is the capacity of a cut. If we can define flows in the continuous medium and locate the minimum cut using the maximum-flow minimum-cut theorem, then the minimum cut will be the curve with $\int w(x, y)\, dc$ a global minimum. The approach described below approximates the continuous medium by a finite network.

The finite network consists of many nodes, each node representing a small square of the rectangular region. Each node has a capacity which equals the weight of the small square it represents. The node capacity network will have a set of nodes as its minimum cut. If the approximation is a good one, the set of small squares corresponding to the nodes should resemble a strip of width ϵ.

Thus we have to keep three things in mind: First, in the network with prescribed connection between nodes, a minimum cut is a subset of the nodes. Second, the rectangular region is partitioned into small squares. The union of the small squares, which are represented by the nodes of the minimum cut, is a subregion. Third, the subregion should approach a strip of width ϵ which separates the rectangular region.

The nodes and the small squares are in one-to-one correspondence. For the node capacity network there always exists a minimum cut, and hence we can always get a set of small squares which are represented by the nodes. As the size of the squares goes to zero, the subregion should approach a strip of width ϵ.

Let us first try the most straightforward way of approximating the continuous medium and see what difficulties would arise. Let the rectangular region in Fig. 12.3 be divided into uniform small squares of side h. At the center of every square we put a node with the capacity of the node equal to the total weight of the square. (See Section 12.2 for the definition of a network with node capacity and without arc capacity.) Every node is connected by an arc to its neighboring nodes of distance h apart. Such a network is shown in Fig. 12.4.

The boundary squares touching the side S are represented by sources with limited supply. The amount of supply of a source is the total weight of the square. Similarly, the boundary squares near the side T become sinks with limited demand. This many-source and many-sink network can be converted into a one-source and one-sink network by the technique of Section 8.3. A cut of the network in Fig. 12.4 will be a set of nodes the removal of which together with its incident arcs will disconnect the network into two parts, one part containing all the sources and one part containing all the sinks. The set of squares represented by the set of nodes should look like a strip with the total weight a minimum. It seems plausible that as h approaches zero, the strip will approach the optimum curve as the limit. Unfortunately, the network described above cannot do the job.

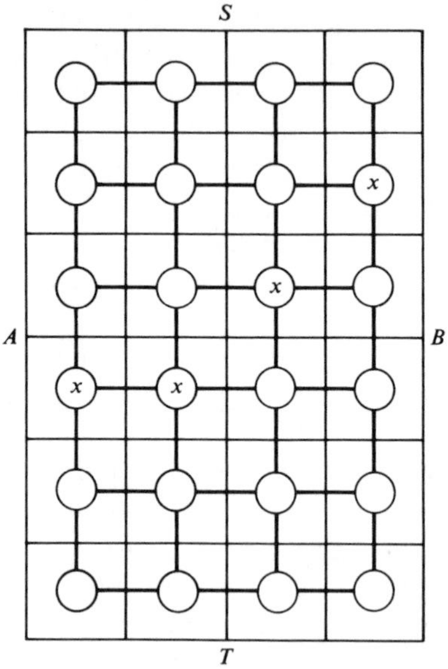

Fig. 12.4

The first difficulty of the approach is that if one connects the set of nodes in the minimum cut, the curve will always consist of horizontal straight lines, vertical straight lines, and lines with 45° angles with the horizontal or vertical lines. One such set of nodes is marked with x in Fig. 12.4. Consequently, the strip which is the union of the squares represented by the nodes will consist of a horizontal strip, a vertical strip, and a 45° strip. This is not desirable, as we need a smooth strip which will approach a smooth optimum curve as h goes to zero.

The second difficulty is that the total weight of the set of nodes may not be equal to the strip which the set of nodes should represent.

If the set of nodes in the minimum cut all lie in a horizontal line, say, then the weight of the set of nodes is equal to the weight of the horizontal strip of width h (see Fig. 12.5a). If the set of nodes in the minimum cut should all lie in a 45° line, say, then the total weight of the set of nodes does not equal the weight of the strip of width h inclined at 45°. This is shown in Fig. 12.5(b).

In order to overcome the difficulties just mentioned, we shall construct a different network as follows. The rectangular region is again divided uniformly into small squares of side h. At the center of each square we put a node with its capacity equal to the total weight of the square. Now we connect any two nodes with an arc if the distance between the two nodes is equal to or less than r ($r \gg h$). *This network is called an r-connected network*. The minimum cut of this network is then a set of nodes which looks

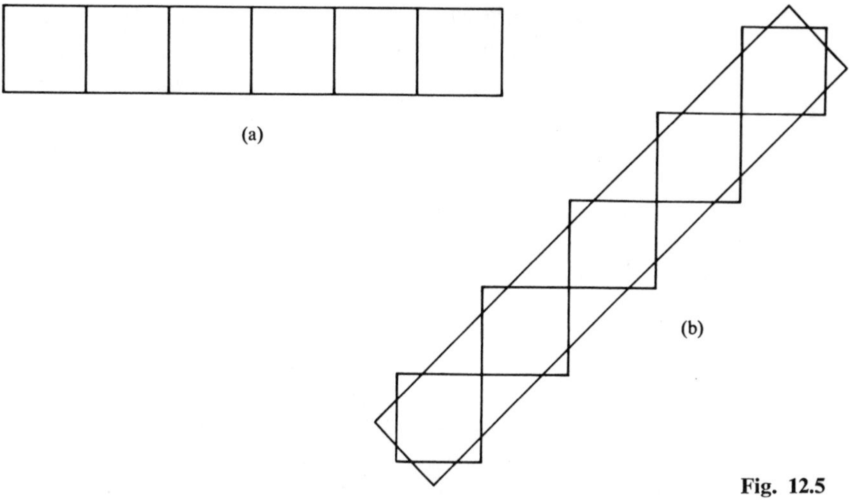

Fig. 12.5

like the lattice points in a strip with width r, and the total weight of the set of nodes is equal to the total weight of the strip.

Furthermore, if h goes to zero, r goes to zero, and h/r goes to zero, then the limit of the strip will be the curve with $\int w(x, y)\, dc$ minimum.

In this r-connecting network, removing a set of nodes in a horizontal row will not disconnect the network into two parts, since there can be two nodes one above and one below the horizontal row, which are connected. In order to block the flow from S to T we have to remove $\langle r/h \rangle$ rows of nodes, for example. The labeling method for a node capacity constraint network will pick out the set of nodes of the minimum cut. Since it is a cut, the network should be separated into two parts once the minimum cut is removed. Since it is a *minimum* cut, no proper subset of nodes should have the separating properties.

Since the small squares are in one-to-one correspondence with the nodes, the subregion, which is the union of small squares, should have the analogous properties of a minimum cut, namely, it separates the rectangular region into two parts and any single small square of the subregion if removed from the subregion will destroy the separating property of the subregion. Now the region containing S and the region containing T both are unions of squares. The two regions are considered to be separated if there exist no two small squares, one in each region, with the distance between the two centers of the squares less than or equal to r.

The question now is, if $h \to 0$, $r \to 0$, $h/r \to 0$, what should the subregion approach as a limit? Briefly, the subregion will approach a strip of width r from A to B.

Since r is comparatively larger than h, there are many more squares completely inside the strip of width r than squares which are partially in the strip. The squares completely inside the strip are called the *interior* squares, and the squares partially in the strip are called the *boundary* squares. For the weighting function to satisfy conditions in Section 12.4 the total weight of the interior squares is always of an order of magnitude greater than that of the total weight of the boundary squares, and the total weight of the subregion or that of the nodes in the minimum cut approaches the weight of the strip as $h/r \to 0$.

12.4 *R*-SEPARATING SET

In this section we discuss some properties of the continuous minimum cut (see Gomory and Hu [92]). First, we shall restrict ourselves to points in the two-dimensional projective plane R_2. Two points a and b in a set P are said to be r-connected if there is a finite sequence of points $p_0, p_1, \ldots, p_n$ with $p_i \in P$ and the distance $\rho(p_i, p_{i+1}) \leq r$ $(i = 0, \ldots, n-1;\ p_0 = a;\ p_n = b)$. See for example Newman [162]. On the other hand, two points a and b in a set P are said to be r-separated if they are not r-connected. We are interested in a set C whose removal from the plane R_2 will r-separate two points in $R_2 - C$. More precisely, we will say that a set $C \subset R_2$ r-separates a and b if:

1. C is closed and bounded.
2. $a, b \notin C$.
3. a and b are not r-connected in $R_2 - C$.

With these definitions, any sufficiently large set will r-separate a and b. However, if we require C to be irreducible, i.e., no proper subset of C will also r-separate a and b, then C is highly structured. In the following, we shall use C to denote an irreducible r-separating set. Note that an irreducible r-separating set is analogous to a cut in the continuous medium and a and b are analogous to the source and the sink. We shall state the theorems and lemmas about the irreducible r-separating set. The proofs will appear in Gomory and Hu [92]. We shall use the following notations:

C: irreducible r-separating set, which is closed by definition.
A: points r-connected to a, which is an open set.
B: points r-connected to b, which is an open set.
D: $R_2 - A - B - C$, which is an open set.

Theorem 12.1 Every r-separating set contains an irreducible r-separating set.

Theorem 12.2 Let p be a point of C. Then $\rho(p, A) \leq r$ and $\rho(p, B) \leq r$.

Lemma 12.1 Let $\overline{p_1 p_2}$ and $\overline{q_1 q_2}$ be two line segments of length less than or equal to r that intersect at some point p. In other words, $\overline{p_1 p_2}$ and $\overline{q_1 q_2}$ are the diagonal lines of a quadrangle. Then there is a vertex of the quadrangle (p_1, p_2, q_1 or q_2) that has its two adjacent sides both less than or equal to r.

Let $p_1, p_2, \ldots, p_n$ be a sequence of points such that $\rho(p_i, p_{i+1}) \leq r$. Then the sequence of line segments $\overline{p_1p_2}, \overline{p_2p_3}, \ldots$ are said to form an r-connecting chain. An r-connecting chain is said to be *simple* if every vertex p_i belongs to only two line segments $\overline{p_{i-1}p_i}$ and $\overline{p_ip_{i+1}}$ (except p_1 and p_n) and every other point is contained in one line segment.

Lemma 12.2 If there exists an r-connecting chain, there exists a simple r-connecting chain.

Theorem 12.3 If C is an irreducible r-separating set, then $R_2 - C = A \cup B$. In other words, D is empty.

(Note that theorem 12.3 is very much like the *Jordan curve theorem* which states that a simple closed curve separates R_2 into two simply connected open sets. Here, an irreducible r-separating set r-separates R_2 into two r-connected open sets A and B.)

Since A or B may consist of many simply connected open sets, we shall call each simply connected set a component of A or B.

Theorem 12.4 Each component of A or B is uniformly locally connected and the boundary of each component of A or B is a simple Jordan curve.

Therefore, the boundary of C is a union of simple Jordan curves. Roughly speaking it can be shown that C splits into sections of two types. The first type are the tubelike sections of width r, like C_1 and C_2 in Fig. 12.6. The second are convex polyhedra with an even number of sides, all sides being of length exactly r (see P in Fig. 12.6). These polyhedra are, intuitively speaking, the areas in which the strip overlaps itself in such a way as to maintain its irreducibility. It can be shown that any C is the union of section of these two types.

If the weighting function $w(x, y)$ is arbitrary, then any irreducible r-separating set can be a minimum weight separating set simply by defining $w(x, y) = \epsilon$ in the irreducible set and $w(x, y)$ large elsewhere.

Note in Fig. 12.6 that $\overline{p_2p_4} < r$. Thus both A_1 and A_2 are r-connected to a and $A = A_1 \cup A_2$. The set of points B including b consists of points enclosed by the strip.

The strip in Fig. 12.6 can be a minimum weight strip, provided that the weighting function is large in A and B and small in the strip. Another irreducible separating strip is shown in Fig. 12.7.

Thus whether the strip in Fig.12.6 or Fig.12.7 is the minimum strip depends on whether the total weight of the strip from p_1p_4 to p_3p_4 in Fig. 12.6 or the total weight on the area in $p_1p_4p_3p'_4$ in Fig. 12.7 is smaller.

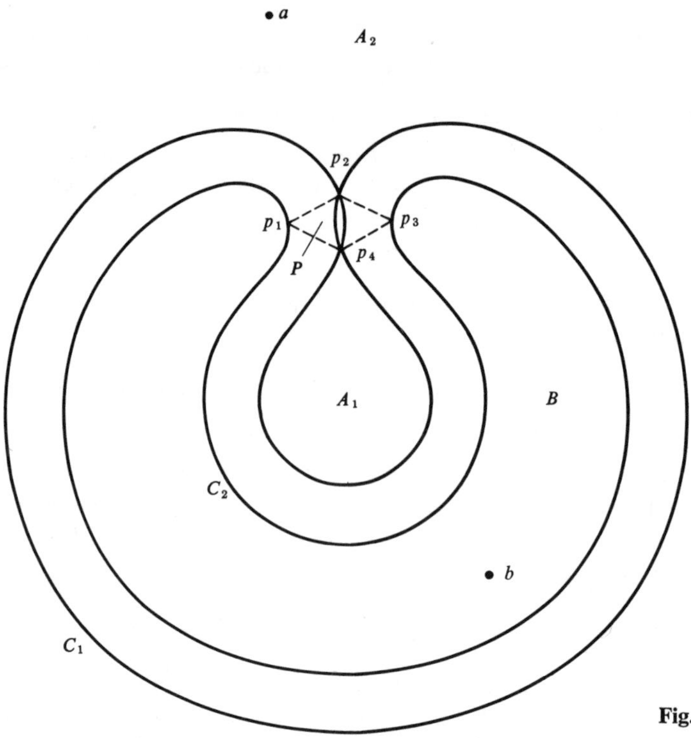

Fig. 12.6

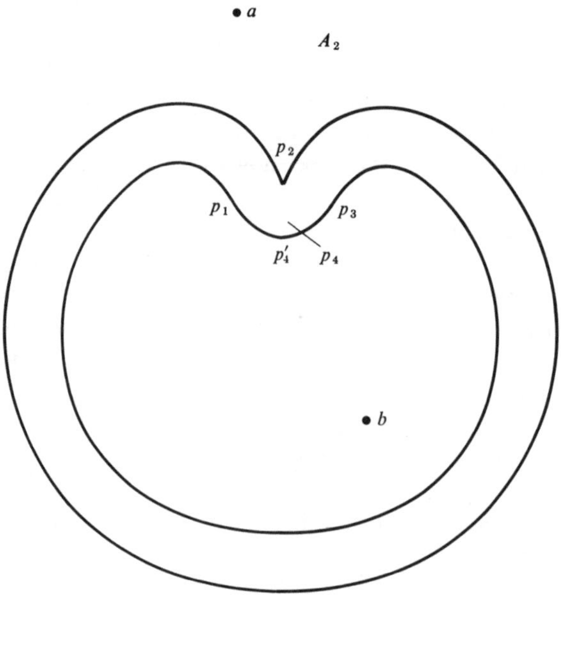

Fig. 12.7

Let the area of the strip from p_1p_4 to p_3p_4 in Fig. 12.6 be Q_1^* and let the area of $p_1p_4p_3p_4'$ in Fig. 12.7 be Q_2^*. Then the ratio Q_2^*/Q_1^* is bounded from above, since it takes a certain area to bend the strip from p_1p_4 to p_3p_4. Let this upper bound be k_1. In general, the area of the irreducible strip overlapping itself is always larger than the irreducible strip not overlapping itself, although the total weight of the former may not be larger than that of the latter. For certain weighting functions, say *a* constant, any minimum weight separating strip will not overlap itself. Therefore, we are interested in finding out the restriction on the weighting function such that the minimum weight separating strip will not overlap itself.

Let Q_1 and Q_2 be the two areas that have nonempty intersections. Let $w(Q_1)$ and $w(Q_2)$ denote the total weights on the area Q_1 and Q_2, respectively. If $Q_2/Q_1 \leq k_1$ implies $w(Q_2) \leq w(Q_1)$, then no minimum weight strip will overlap itself. In order that $w(Q_2) \leq w(Q_1)$, it is necessary to require $w(x, y) \geq c$, where c is a positive constant. Otherwise, $w(x, y) = 0$ in Q_1 and $w(x, y) \neq 0$ in Q_2 will violate the inequality $w(Q_2) \leq w(Q_1)$. Furthermore, it is necessary that the total weight on any area be bounded from above so that $w(Q_2)$ cannot be infinity. The following is a set of sufficient conditions that will ensure nonoverlapping of the mimimum weight strip:

1. $w(x, y) \geq c$, c is a positive constant.
2. The weighting function satisfies the Lipschitz condition with constant K.
3. The constant K satisfies $K \leq 6c/r$, where c is the positive constant in 1 and r is the width of the minimum separating strip. (Note that if $r \to 0$, K can be arbitrarily large).

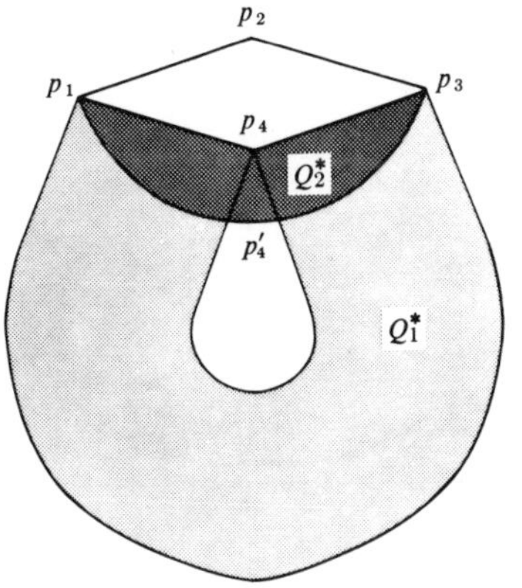

Fig. 12.8

In Fig. 12.8 we show the enlarged picture of the portion of an overlapping strip superposed together with the nonoverlapping one. The heavily shaded area is Q_2^* and the lightly shaded area is Q_1^*. The lower bound on the total weight of Q_1^* is obtained by letting $w(x, y) = c$ throughout Q_1^*. The upper bound on the total weight on Q_2^* is obtained by letting the weighting function grow as large as possible from the intersection point of Q_1^* and Q_2^*.

The idea of a separating strip can be generalized to the case where we want to separate two sets of points instead of two points. In the rectangular region in Section 12.1, we want to separate the line S and the line T. This is equivalent to r-separating in R_2 if we define $w(x, y)$ to be zero outside the rectangular region.

If we trust our intuition in three-dimensional space, the corresponding r-separating set in R_3 is a surface of thickness r, and this leads us to Plateau's problem.

Plateau's problem is to find the surface of least area spanned in a given closed Jordan curve Γ. Related problems are to find minimal surfaces of least area when the whole boundary or part of it is not prescribed but left free on a given manifold. If we define a weighting function at every point of the space, we can ask for the minimum weight surface spanned in a given closed Jordan curve Γ. The weight of a surface is defined to be the integral of the function w on the surface.

We shall first consider the problem of minimum weight surface with free boundary. Consider a surface P which is topologically equivalent to a sphere. The inside open region is denoted by R, where the open region plus the boundary surface P is denoted by $\bar{R}$. On the surface P we have two special subsurfaces Γ_s and Γ_t. If a weighting function is defined on $\bar{R}$ and, say, zero elsewhere, then we can ask for the minimum weight surface separating Γ_s and Γ_t. If $P - \Gamma_s - \Gamma_t$ is a curve Γ and the weighting function is a constant in $\bar{R}$, the problem of finding a separating surface of minimum weight becomes Plateau's problem. In the approximation by a finite network, we first find a minimum weight surface with thickness r and then let r go to zero.

FRACTIONAL INTEGER PROGRAMMING ALGORITHM 13

13.1 INTRODUCTION (Gomory [79])

Consider a linear program

$$\max x_0 = a_{00} - a_{01}x_1 - a_{02}x_2 - \cdots - a_{0n}x_n$$

subject to

$$\begin{aligned} x_{n+1} &= a_{n+1,0} - a_{n+1,1}x_1 - a_{n+1,2}\,x_2 - \cdots - a_{n+1,n}x_n, \\ &\vdots \\ x_{n+m} &= a_{n+m,0} - a_{n+m,1}x_1 - a_{n+m,2}x_2 - \cdots - a_{n+m,n}x_n, \\ x_j &\geq 0 \qquad (j = 1, \ldots, n, n+1, \ldots, n+m). \end{aligned} \tag{1}$$

Note that $x_{n+1}, \ldots, x_{n+m}$ are slack variables and $x_1, \ldots, x_n$ are the original variables of (1). If we require, in addition to the constraints in (1), that all variables x_j $(j = 1, \ldots, n)$ must be integers, then the program is called an *integer program*. There are many problems, especially combinatorial problems, which can be formulated as integer programs. For a brief survey see Dantzig [34], Balinski [6], and Section 15.3.

The constraints in (1) define a convex region of n dimensions. This is shown in Fig. 13.1 in which $OABCD$ is the convex region. The dots in Fig. 13.1 represent lattice points with integer components. Those lattice points within $OABCD$ are then feasible solutions to the integer program. Since optimum solutions to a linear program always occur on the boundary of its solution space and none of the boundary points on $ABCD$ are with integer components, they are not even feasible solutions of the integer program. Suppose that the feasible region of the linear program can be shrunk to the convex hull of its feasible lattice points inside the feasible region. This convex hull is shown as the shaded area $OEFGH$. This shaded area can be thought of as a feasible region of some other linear program. In fact, if the linear program that defines the feasible region $OABCD$ is restricted by more constraints such as RR' as shown in Fig. 13.1, then the modified linear program can have as a feasible region the shaded area. This new feasible region shown

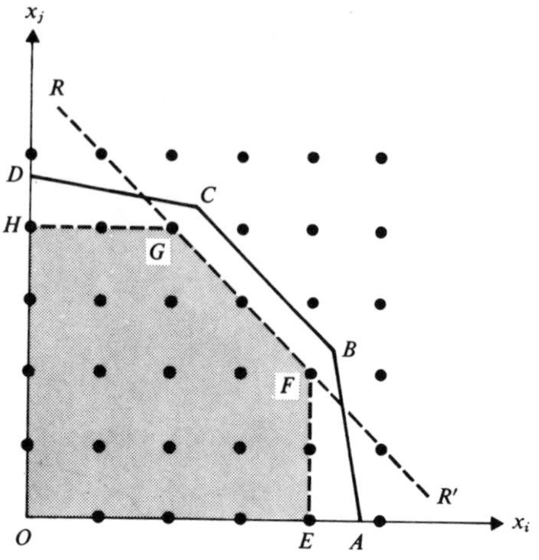

Fig. 13.1. Solution spaces in basic variables of the optimum tableau.

in the shaded area has two important features: First, it contains every feasible point with integer components of the original linear program (since it is the convex hull of those points). Second, all the extreme points of this new feasible region have integer components. Therefore any basic optimum solution of the *modified linear program* has integer components and it is also the optimum solution to the *original integer program.*

The integer programming algorithms that will be presented below are just methods of systematically generating additional constraints to cut the feasible region down to the convex hull of its integer feasible points.

Once this is done, we can solve the modified linear program by any existing method, and its basic optimum solution will automatically be an integer solution. The integer algorithm presented below will have the following properties: 1. Generated constraints never exclude from the new feasible region an integer feasible point of the original integer program. 2. In a finite number of steps, enough constraints will be generated to cut the feasible region of the original linear program so that the optimum solution of the modified linear program has integer components. 3. The generated constraints (or hyperplanes) pass through at least one integer point, although not necessarily an integer point inside the convex hull. 4. Each new constraint will reduce the feasible region of the original linear program. It should be emphasized at this point that before the feasible region of the original linear program is cut to its convex hull, we may already obtain the optimum solution to the original integer program. Also since the optimum integer solution can be defined as the intersection of n hyperplanes, these n hyperplanes are actually the only ones that are really needed; some of these may be constraints of the original problem.

Tableau 13.1

		1	$-x_1$	$\dots$	$-x_n$
x_0	=	a_{00}	a_{01}	$\dots$	a_{0n}
x_1	=	0	-1		
		0	$\cdot$		
$\vdots$		$\vdots$		$\cdot$	
				$\cdot$	
x_n	=	0			-1
x_{n+1}	=	$a_{n+1,0}$	$a_{n+1,1}$	$\dots$	$a_{n+1,n}$
$\vdots$		$\vdots$			
x_{n+m}	=	$a_{n+m,1}$	$a_{n+m,1}$	$\dots$	$a_{n+m,n}$

We usually introduce n trivial equations $x_j = -(-x_j)$ $(j = 1, \dots, n)$ as part of the constraints of (1) and then write the integer program in a matrix form as

$$\mathbf{x} = \mathbf{A}(-\mathbf{x}_n), \tag{2}$$

where $\mathbf{x}$ is a column vector with $x_0, x_1, \dots, x_n, x_{n+1}, \dots, x_{n+m}$ as components, $\mathbf{A}$ is a matrix of $(n + m + 1) \times (n + 1)$, and $(-\mathbf{x}_n)$ is the vector with its components $(1, -x_1, -x_2, \dots, -x_n)$, where $x_1, x_2, \dots, x_n$ are the nonbasic variables in the starting tableau. The integer program also can be put in the form of Tableau 13.1.

The reason for expressing every variable in terms of $(-x_1), (-x_2), \dots, (-x_n)$ is purely historical, but it has become the standard practice in integer programming. We shall use $\boldsymbol{\alpha}_j$ $(j = 0, 1, \dots, n)$ to denote the column vector with all its components in the jth column of the current tableau and a_{ij} $(i = 0, 1, \dots, n + m; j = 0, 1, \dots, n)$ the coefficients in the ith row and jth column of the tableau. We shall assume that all a_{ij} are integers in the starting tableau. This implies that the slack variables $x_{n+1}, \dots, x_{n+m}$ should also be nonnegative integers.

We shall describe an algorithm due to Gomory [79] for solving integer programs. The algorithm first treats the integer program as a linear program and solves it by the primal or dual simplex method. At the end of the computation, we have $a_{i0} \geq 0$ $(i = 1, \dots, n + m)$ and $a_{0j} \geq 0$ $(j = 1, \dots, n)$. (The technique for getting a starting dual feasible solution is to add an additional constraint $x_{n+m+1} = M - x_1 - x_2 - \cdots - x_n \geq 0$, where M is an arbitrarily large constant, and pivot on this row with the lexicographically smallest column as the pivot column.) If $a_{i0} \geq 0$ and are all integers, then this is obviously also the optimum solution to the integer program, as the integer constraints were neglected in obtaining the solution. If $a_{i0} \geq 0$ but not all integers, we add a constraint in addition to (1). The constraint is added to the bottom of the tableau so as to make the tableau not primal feasible, i.e., $a_{i0} < 0$ for $i = n + m + 1$. Then the dual simplex method is used to make $a_{i0} \geq 0$. If a_{i0} are still not integers, more constraints are added to the bottom of the tableau. This is repeated until $a_{i0} \geq 0$ ($i = 1, \ldots, n, \ldots, n + m$) and are integers.

If an additional constraint makes the current tableau not primal feasible, it means that the present solution, which represents a vertex of the solution space, does not satisfy this additional constraint. In other words, a certain part of the solution space is cut off by the additional constraint. If the additional constraint has the property that it will never exclude any lattice point of the solution space of the original linear program, then after many such additional constraints are added, it seems plausible that the vertices of the reduced solution space will be of integer components. Then we can use the simplex method to solve it and get an integer solution as our optimum solution. The difficulty is to derive the additional constraints systematically and show that the algorithm is a finite one.

Every time a pivot step is performed, a new set of nonbasic variables is chosen, and the tableau also changes. We use the superscript t to denote the tth tableau, and the matrix equation (2) is written as

$$\mathbf{x}^t = \mathbf{A}^t(-\mathbf{x}_n^t), \tag{3}$$

where $\mathbf{x}^0$ is a column vector with $n + m + 1$ components, $\mathbf{A}$ is a matrix of $(n + m + 1) \times (n + 1)$, and $(-\mathbf{x}_n)$ is the vector with its components $(+1, -x_1, -x_2, \ldots, -x_n)$, the negative of the current nonbasic variables. If the matrix $\mathbf{A}$ has $a_{0j} \geq 0$ ($j = 1, \ldots, n$), $a_{00} \equiv 0$ (mod 1), and the $a_{i0} \geq 0$ ($i = 1, \ldots, n + m$) and are integers, then the optimum solution to the integer program is obtained. If some a_{i0} are not integers, we shall then derive an additional constraint. Consider an equation in (3) where a_{i0} is noninteger. Omitting the row subscript, we have

$$x \equiv a_0 + \sum a_j(-x_j), \tag{4}$$

where the x_j on the right are the current nonbasic variables and a_0 is not an integer. Since x in (4) is required to be an integer, or $x \equiv 0$ (mod 1), where we say that two numbers are congruent ($\equiv$) modulo 1 if they differ by an integer, the right-hand side of (4) must also satisfy

$$0 \equiv a_0 + \sum a_j(-x_j) \qquad \text{(mod 1)}. \tag{5}$$

This is an equation which must be satisfied by every feasible integer solution. Since the x_j are also required to be integers, we can add or subtract the relations $0 \equiv x_j$ and also $0 \equiv 1$* from (5) such that (5) becomes

$$0 \equiv f_0 + \sum f_j(-x_j), \qquad (0 < f_0 < 1,\ 0 \leq f_j < 1). \tag{6}$$

Equation (6) is equivalent to

$$\sum f_j x_j \equiv f_0. \tag{7}$$

---

* Adding or subtracting the relations $0 \equiv x_j$ and $0 \equiv 1$ from (5) corresponds to rotating and translating the hyperplane from which (5) was derived.

In (7) f_0 is a constant less than 1 and the left-hand side of (7) is always positive since $f_j \geq 0$ and $x_j \geq 0$. Since (7) is a congruent relation $\equiv$ (mod 1), the left-hand side must be f_0, $1 + f_0, \ldots$; in other words,

$$\sum f_j x_j \geq f_0. \tag{8}$$

The inequality (8) can be rewritten as an equation by introducing a nonnegative integer slack variable s.

$$s = -f_0 + \sum f_j x_j \geq 0. \tag{9}$$

This then can be added to the bottom of the tableau and used as a pivot row. This means that we introduce s as a basic variable with negative value $-f_0$. After the pivot, the slack variable becomes nonbasic with value zero. The pivot row becomes a trivial relation $s = -1(-s)$ and can be dropped. We shall call the slack variable introduced by (9) the Gomory's slack variable. Later on we shall discuss what will happen if we keep all the additional rows corresponding to Gomory's slack variables.

We shall give a proof that the algorithm is finite. Our proof depends on the assumption that some lower bound is known for the value of x_0, i.e., if an integer solution exists, it is larger than some known lower bound M (which can be a large negative constant). This is not a very restrictive assumption and it is always satisfied if the convex region defined by (2) is bounded. Let us first state the algorithm.

STEP 1. We solve the integer program as if it were a linear program by a primal or dual simplex method. When the optimum solution to the linear program is obtained, we have $a_{i0} \geq 0$ $(i = 1, \ldots, m + n)$ and $a_{0j} \geq 0$, $(j = 1, \ldots, n)$. Also we want $\boldsymbol{\alpha}_j^t \succ \mathbf{0}$ $(j = 1, \ldots, n)$.

STEP 2. If the a_{i0} are integers, then the problem is solved as the solution is obtained without considering the integer requirements. If not, let a_{i0}^t be the *first* noninteger component of $\boldsymbol{\alpha}_0^t$. Then the ith row is called the *generating row* or the *source row*. Add the equation

$$s = -f_{i0}^t - \sum_{j=1}^{n} f_{ij}^t(-x_j^t) \tag{10}$$

to the bottom of the tableau. Equation (10) is called a Gomory's cut or a derived row. Do a dual simplex step using (10) as the pivoting row. This will keep the tableau dual feasible. Repeat until the a_{i0} $(i = 1, \ldots, m + n)$ are all nonnegative integers. If an a_{i0} should become negative in this step, then a dual simplex step is taken without generating a Gomory cut. (If a_{00} becomes negative, the 0th row is not selected as the pivot row. If a_{00} becomes a noninteger, the 0th row is selected as the generating row.)

Each time the a_{ij} $(i = 0, 1, \ldots, n + m; j = 0, \ldots, n)$ change in a tableau, it is called a cycle. The superscript t is used to denote the cycle. The fact that $\boldsymbol{\alpha}_0^t \succ \boldsymbol{\alpha}_0^{t+1}$ and $a_{00} > M$ is not enough for finiteness, since a_{00} may decrease each time by $\epsilon(t)$ and $\sum_{t=1}^{\infty} \epsilon(t) = c$. One such example is $\epsilon(t) = 1/2^t$. Another possibility is that a_{00} remains at a fixed value above the assumed lower bound, and some a_{i0} decreases indefinitely. To see how these difficulties are overcome, we must look into the details of the pivot steps.

The proof consists of showing that after a finite number of steps, all components of the 0th column are nonnegative integers or no integer solution exists. If a_{00} is to remain fixed for all tableaux $t \geq t_0$, then a_{00}^t must be an integer.

Suppose that a_{00}^t is not an integer. Let $a_{00}^t = n_{00}^t + f_{00}^t$, where n_{00}^t is an integer and $0 < f_{00}^t < 1$. Then the 0th equation becomes the generating row and we would add the equation

$$s = -f_{00}^t - \sum_{j=1}^{n} f_{0j}^t(-x_j^t).$$

If the sth column is the pivot column, we have

$$a_{00}^{t+1} = a_{00}^t - a_{0s}^t (f_{00}^t / f_{0s}^t),$$

or

$$a_{00}^{t+1} \leq a_{00}^t - f_{00}^t \qquad \text{as} \qquad a_{0s}^t \geq f_{0s}^t,$$

or

$$a_{00}^{t+1} \leq n_{00}^t.$$

In other words, a_{00} would decrease at least to the next integer. Therefore, it is impossible for a_{00} to decrease by $\epsilon(t)$ with $\sum_{t=1}^{\infty} \epsilon(t) < c$. If each time a_{00} decreases to the next integer or by an integer amount, then after a finite number of decreases it will be below M (the assumed lower bound). If the algorithm is not finite, then a_{00} must remain at some *fixed integer value* for all $t > t_0$. Let us assume that this is the case.

We now fix our attention on a_{10}. Similarly a_{10} cannot remain fixed at some noninteger value. If it does, since a_{00} is now an integer, the first row will become the generating row, and after introducing the derived row and pivoting

$$a_{10}^{t+1} = a_{10}^t - a_{1s}^t \left(\frac{f_{10}^t}{f_{1s}^t}\right),$$

where $0 < f_{10}^t < 1$ and $0 < f_{1s}^t < 1$. Here a_{1s}^t is *nonnegative* and greater than f_{1s}^t. (If a_{1s}^t is negative, $\boldsymbol{\alpha}_s^t$ lexicographically positive implies that a_{0s}^t is positive and the pivot would decrease a_{00}^t, contradicting our assumption that it remains fixed.) Hence

$$a_{10}^{t+1} \leq a_{10}^t - f_{10}^t = [a_{10}^t],$$

and a_{10} will decrease at least to the next integer. Therefore, either a_{10} remains at some fixed integer value or it will become negative after a finite number of steps. If a_1^0 becomes negative, then the first row becomes the pivot row, and we have

$$\boldsymbol{\alpha}_0^{t+1} = \boldsymbol{\alpha}_0^t - \left(\frac{a_{10}}{a_{1s}}\right)\boldsymbol{\alpha}_s^t.$$

Note that $\boldsymbol{\alpha}_s \succ \mathbf{0}$ and $a_{1s} < 0$ implies that $a_{0s} > 0$; this will make a_{00} strictly decrease, which contradicts our assumption that a_{00} remains fixed. If $a_{1j} \geq 0$ for all $j = 1, \ldots, s, \ldots, n$, this indicates that the program is infeasible. (Note that negative elements are candidates for pivots.)

Therefore the only remaining possibility is for a_{10} to remain fixed at certain nonnegative integers after a finite number of steps.

Now we can repeat the same argument to the second, third, etc., until $(n+m)$th component. This completes the proof of finiteness. Note that we need only the first $n + 1$ components of $\boldsymbol{\alpha}_0$ to be nonnegative integers ($a_{00} \gtrless 0$) and a_{i0} $(i = n + 1, \ldots, n + m)$ nonnegative.

In the numerical example that follows, we keep all the additional constraints. We keep them because we want to show that these additional constraints are inequalities with integer coefficients if expressed in terms of the original nonbasic variables.

If we keep all the rows corresponding to Gomory's slack variables, then these Gomory slack variables may become basic variables after being nonbasic. If a Gomory slack variable becomes basic with nonnegative value, then the corresponding row represents an inequality satisfied by the current solution and that row can be dropped. If a Gomory slack variable becomes basic with a negative value, then that row can be used as a pivot row. This saves the trouble of generating an additional Gomory cut; but the trouble of keeping all the rows corresponding to Gomory's slack variables greatly outweighs the saving.

13.2 EXAMPLE (Gomory [79])

We shall give two examples illustrating the algorithm. The source row and the pivot column are marked by an arrow and the pivot by *. In order to speed the algorithm in the particular examples, we do not use the first noninteger row as the source row. To the right of each tableau there are remarks about the cuts, the study of which will be delayed to later chapters. The reader need pay attention only to the tableaux.

Example 1. Consider the integer program

$$\max x_0 = 4x_1 + 5x_2 + x_3$$

subject to

$$\begin{aligned} 3x_1 + 2x_2 \phantom{{}+x_3} &\leq 10, \\ x_1 + 4x_2 \phantom{{}+x_3} &\leq 11, \\ 3x_1 + 3x_2 + x_3 &\leq 13, \\ x_1, x_2, x_3 &\geq 0, \text{integers.} \end{aligned}$$

Introducing slack variables x_4, x_5, and x_6, we have

	1	$-x_1$	$-x_2$	$-x_3$
x_0	0	-4	-5	-1
x_1	0	-1	0	0
x_2	0	0	-1	0
x_3	0	0	0	-1
x_4	10	3	2	0
x_5	11	1	4*	0
x_6	13	3	3	1

$D = 1$

	1	$-x_1$	$-x_5$	$-x_3$
x_0	55/4	$-11/4$	5/4	-1
x_1	0	-1	0	0
x_2	11/4	1/4	1/4	0
x_3	0	0	0	-1
x_4	18/4	10/4*	$-2/4$	0
x_5	0	0	-1	0
x_6	19/4	9/4	$-3/4$	1

$D = 1 \times 4 = 4$

$$B = \begin{vmatrix} -1 & 0 & 0 & 0 \\ 0 & -1 & 0 & 0 \\ 11 & 1 & 4 & 0 \\ 0 & 0 & 0 & -1 \end{vmatrix}$$

	1	$-x_4$	$-x_5$	$-x_3$
x_0	187/10	11/10	$-7/10$	-1
x_1	18/10	4/10	$-2/10$	0
x_2	23/10	$-1/10$	3/10	0
x_3	0	0	0	-1
x_4	0	-1	0	0
x_5	0	0	-1	0
x_6	7/10	$-9/10$	$-3/10$	1*

$D = 4 \times 10/4 = 10$

↓ Pivot column

	1	$-x_4$	$-x_5$	$-x_6$
x_0	194/10	2/10	4/10	1
x_1	18/10	4/10	−2/10	0
x_2	23/10	−1/10	3/10	0
x_3	7/10	−9/10	−3/10	1 ← Source row
x_4	0	−1	0	0
x_5	0	0	−1	0
x_6	0	0	0	−1
s_1	−7/10	−1/10	−7/10*	0

$D = 10 \times 1 = 10$

Inequality group F

$\frac{1}{10}$ (0,0,0,0) (5,5,5,0)
(7,1,7,0) (2,6,2,0)
(4,2,4,0) (9,7,9,0)
(1,3,1,0) (6,8,6,0)
(8,4,8,0) (3,9,3,0)

For example,
$(7,1,7,0) + (4,2,4,0) \equiv (1,3,1,0) \pmod{10}$

Optimum solution to linear programs:
$x_0 = 194/10,\ x_1 = 18/10,\ x_2 = 23/10,\ x_3 = 7/10.$

	1	$-x_4$	$-s_1$	$-x_6$
x_0	19	1/7	4/7	1
x_1	2	3/7	−2/7	0
x_2	2	−1/7	3/7	0
x_3	1	−6/7	−3/7	1
x_4	0	−1	0	0
x_5	1	1/7	−10/7	0
x_6	0	0	0	−1
s_1	0	0	−1	0

$D = 10 \times \frac{7}{10} = 7$

Inequality group F

$\frac{1}{7}$ (0,1,4,0) (0,5,6,0)
(0,2,1,0) (0,6,3,0)
(0,3,5,0) (0,0,0,0)
(0,4,2,0)

Optimum integer solution:
$x_0 = 19,\ x_1 = 2,\ x_2 = 2,\ x_3 = 1.$

Note that if we express x_4, x_5, and x_6 in terms of original nonbasic variables x_1, x_2, and x_3, then the inequality $s_1 \geq 0$ becomes an all-integer inequality in terms of x_1, x_2, and x_3. Thus

$$-(7/10) + (1/10)(10 - 3x_1 - 2x_2) + (7/10)(11 - x_1 - 4x_2) \geq 0$$

or $x_1 + 3x_2 \leq 8$. This is discussed in Section 13.4. To obtain an all-integer matrix, we simply continue to generate cuts:

	1	$-x_4$	$-s_1$	$-x_6$	
x_0	19	1/7	4/7	1	
x_1	2	3/7	−2/7	0	
x_2	2	−1/7	3/7	0	
x_3	1	−6/7	−3/7	1	← Source row
x_4	0	−1	0	0	
x_5	1	1/7	−10/7	0	
x_6	0	0	0	−1	
s_1	0	0	−1	0	
s_2	0	−1/7*	−4/7	0	

	1	$-s_2$	$-s_1$	$-x_6$
x_0	19	1	0	1
x_1	2	3	−2	0
x_2	2	−1	1	0
x_3	1	−6	3	1
x_4	0	−7	4	0
x_5	1	1	−2	0
x_6	0	0	0	−1
s_1	0	0	−1	0
s_2	0	−1	0	0

Example 2. Consider the program max $x_0 = 3x_1 - x_2$ subject to

$$\begin{aligned} 3x_1 - 2x_2 &\le 3, \\ -5x_1 - 4x_2 &\le -10, \\ 2x_1 + x_2 &\le 5, \\ x_1, \quad x_2 &\ge 0, \text{ integers.} \end{aligned}$$

Introducing slack variables x_3, x_4, and x_5, we have the starting tableau

	1	$-x_1$	$-x_2$
x_0	0	-3	1
x_1	0	-1	0
x_2	0	0	-1
x_3	3	3*	-2
x_4	-10	-5	-4
x_5	5	2	1

$D = 1$

	1	$-x_3$	$-x_2$
x_0	3	1	-1
x_1	1	1/3	$-2/3$
x_2	0	0	-1
x_3	0	-1	0
x_4	-5	5/3	$-22/3$
x_5	3	$-2/3$	7/3*

$D = 3$

Inequality group

$\frac{1}{3}$ (0,1,1)
(0,2,2)
(0,0,0)

	1	$-x_3$	$-x_5$
x_0	30/7	5/7	3/7
x_1	13/7	1/7	2/7
x_2	9/7	$-2/7$	3/7
x_3	0	-1	0
x_4	31/7	$-3/7$	22/7
x_5	0	0	-1
s_1	$-6/7$	$-1/7$	$-2/7$*

← Source row (x_1)

$D = 3 \times 7/3 = 7$

Inequality group

$\frac{1}{7}$ (6,1,2) (2,5,3)
(5,2,4) (1,6,5)
(4,3,6) (0,0,0)
(3,4,1)

Optimum solution to linear program:
$x_0 = 30/7$, $x_1 = 13/7$, $x_2 = 9/7$.

	1	$-x_3$	$-s_1$	
x_0	3	1/2	3/2	
x_1	1	0	1	
x_2	0	−1/2	3/2	
x_3	0	−1	0	
x_4	−5	−2*	11	← Pivot row
x_5	3	1/2	−7/2	
s_1	0	0	−1	

$D = 7 \times 2/7 = 2$

Inequality group

$\frac{1}{2}$ (0,1,1)
(0,0,0)

	1	$-x_4$	$-s_1$	
x_0	7/4	1/4	17/4	← Source row
x_1	1	0	1	
x_2	5/4	−1/4	−5/4	
x_3	5/2	−1/2	−11/2	
x_4	0	−1	0	
x_5	7/4	1/4	−3/4	
s_1	0	0	−1	
s_2	−3/4	−1/4*	−1/4	

$D = 2 \times 2 = 4$

Inequality group

$\frac{1}{4}$ (3,1,1)
(2,2,2)
(1,3,3)
(0,0,0)

	1	$-s_2$	$-s_1$
x_0	1	1	4
x_1	1	0	1
x_2	2	−1	−1
x_3	4	−2	−5
x_4	3	−4	1
x_5	1	1	−1
s_1	0	0	−1
s_2	0	−1	0

$D = 4 \times 1/4 = 1$

Optimum integer solution:

$x_0 = 1,\ x_1 = 1,\ x_2 = 2,\ x_j = 0\ (j \neq 1, 2).$

13.3 GEOMETRIC INTERPRETATION

Consider a source row in the tth tableau

$$x = a_0 + \sum a_j(-x_j^t), \tag{1}$$

where x_j^t are the current nonbasic variables, $a_0 = [a_0] + f_0 \geq 0$ ($[a_0]$ denotes the largest integer less than or equal to a_0.) From (1), we obtain the Gomory cut

$$s = -f_0 + \sum f_j x_j^t \geq 0. \tag{2}$$

In the starting tableau, all coefficients a_{ij} are integers, and each variable x (basic or nonbasic) is an integer combination of the original nonbasic variables. This means that the right-hand side of (1) must also be an integer combination of the original nonbasic variables x_j.

Let

$$a_0 + \sum a_j(-x_j^t) = n_0 + \sum n_j x_j, \tag{3}$$

where $n_0 \equiv n_j \equiv 0 \pmod 1$, i.e., the right-hand side of (3) is an integer form in terms of the original nonbasic variables.

In the tth tableau, $x = [a_0] + f_0$. From (1) and (3), we have

$$x = n_0 + \sum n_j x_j = [a_0] + f_0. \tag{4}$$

Equation (4) then defines a hyperplane passing through the optimum vertex of the convex set in the x_j-space. We claim that there is no lattice point between the hyperplane defined by (4) and the hyperplane

$$n_0 + \sum n_j x_j = [a_0]. \tag{5}$$

Because if there is a lattice point, say $x_j^* \equiv 0 \pmod 1$, then $n_0 + \sum n_j x_j^*$ will be an integer. But there is no integral value between $[a_0]$ and $[a_0] + f_0$. Thus the hyperplane (4) can be pushed into the convex set until it reaches the position (5). Thus $n_0 + \sum n_j x_j \leq [a_0]$ is an inequality which will be satisfied by every integer feasible point. In Example 1, we have

$$x_4 = 10 - 3x_1 - 2x_2 \geq 0 \quad \text{and} \quad x_5 = 11 - x_1 - 4x_2 \geq 0.$$

Then $x_4 + 7x_5 = 87 - 10x_1 - 30x_2 \geq 0$ or $x_1 + 3x_2 \leq 8.7$, from which we derive the inequality $x_1 + 3x_2 \leq 8$.

In (1), x could be a slack variable s, but we shall show in the next section that any such variable s is also an integer combination of the original nonbasic variables. Thus, the geometrical interpretation goes through unchanged.

In Fig. 13.2 we show that the cut $s_1 \geq 0$ used in Example 1 is an all-integer inequality in terms of the original nonbasic variables.

One thing should be noted. We can use integer combinations of equations like (1), say 5 times one equation plus -7 times another equation, to produce a new source row. In this way, the left-hand side of the source row may no longer be nonnegative. However, if one examines carefully how in

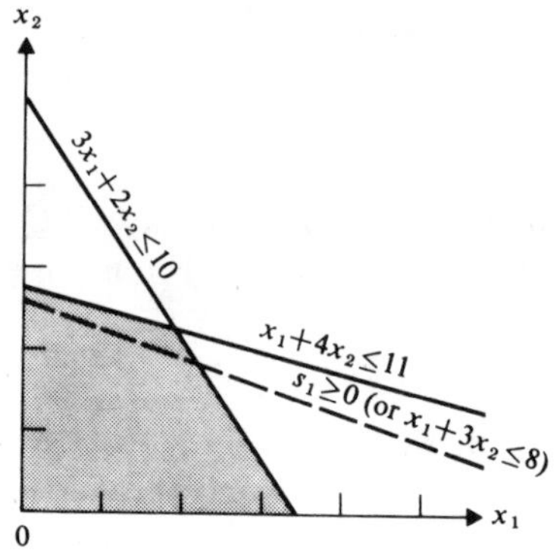

Fig. 13.2

Section 13.1 (9) is derived from Section 13.1 (4), then one finds out that the left-hand side of (4) is required to be *only* an integer. The process of adding or subtracting the relation $0 \equiv x_j$ corresponds to adding or subtracting the unit rows in the tableau.

13.4 PROPERTIES OF ADDED INEQUALITIES (Gomory and Baumol [87])

In this section we shall show some properties of the added inequalities. First, we shall show that an added inequality such as

$$s = -f_0^t + \sum f_j^t x_j^t \geq 0, \tag{1}$$

where x_j^t are the current nonbasic variables, will become an all-integer inequality in the original nonbasic variables. To see this, let us assume that the inequality (1) under consideration is the first added inequality, and the source row is

$$x^t = a_0^t + \sum_j a_j^t (-x_j^t), \tag{2}$$

where x_j^t are either original variables or slack variables of (1) of Section 13.1. For each x_j^t we shall express x_j^t in terms of original nonbasic variables, i.e., either $x_j^t = x_j$ or $x_j^t = a_{n+j,0} - \sum_i a_{n+j,i} x_i$. Thus we will have expressed x^t in (2) in terms of the original nonbasic variables.

As the expression of any variable in terms of the original nonbasic variables is unique, (2) must be either

$$x_j^t = x_j \qquad \text{or} \qquad x_i = a_{n+i,0} - \sum_{j=1}^{n} a_{n+i,j} x_j$$

of (1) of Section 13.1. In both cases the right-hand side of (2) is an all-integer expression. In the derived Gomory cut

$$s_i = -f_0^t - \sum f_j^t (-x_j^t) = \{[a_0^t] + \sum [a_j^t](-x_j^t)\} - \{a_0^t + \sum a_j^t (-x_j^t)\}, \tag{3}$$

where $[a_0^t]$ $[a_j^t]$ are the integer parts of a_0^t and a_j^t. Now the first brace is an all-integer expression and the second brace has just been shown to be an all-integer expression; therefore, the new inequality $s_i \geq 0$ is an all-integer inequality when it is expressed in the original variables. Having shown this for the first added inequality, we can of course consider it as part of the original program. This reasoning then can be continued to the second added inequality.

Therefore, we have proved that the added Gomory cuts are all-integer inequalities if they are expressed in terms of the original nonbasic variables. Examining the expression (1) more closely, we can arrive at other conclusions. Consider the *first* generated Gomory cut like (1). Let us divide x_j^t in (1) into two sets J and $\bar{J}$. The x_j^t in J are original nonbasic variables and those in $\bar{J}$ are the original basic variables. If all x_j^t in (1) are expressed in terms of original nonbasic variables, we have

$$s_i = -f_{i0} + \sum_{j \in J} f_{ij} x_{k(j)} + \sum_{j \in \bar{J}} f_{ij} (a_{ij} - \sum_{k=1}^{n} a_{i(j)k} x_k) \geq 0, \tag{4}$$

where an index is in parentheses if the double summation convention is not applied to that index. Transferring terms in (4), we have

$$-f_{i0} + \sum_{j \in \bar{J}} f_{ij} a_{ij} \geq -\sum_{j \in J} f_{ij} x_{k(j)} + \sum_{k=1}^{n} (\sum_{j \in \bar{J}} f_{ij} a_{i(j)k}) x_k. \tag{5}$$

All terms in the left-hand side of (5) are positive except $-f_{i0}$, where $0 < f_{i0} < 1$. Thus the left-hand side of (5) is *strictly* greater than -1. However, we have just proved that (4) is an all-integer inequality and the left-hand side is all the terms that do not contain any variables; therefore it represents an integer constant. This implies that the left-hand side of (5) is a nonnegative integer.

Looking at the right-hand side, we see that the coefficients of a variable x_k are either

$$\sum_{j \in \bar{J}} f_{ij} a_{i(j)k} \qquad \text{or} \qquad \sum_{j \in \bar{J}} f_{ij} a_{i(j)k} - f_{ij}.$$

Consider the special case that the coefficients in the original tableau are all nonnegative. In the first case, $\sum f_{ij} a_{i(j)k}$ represents a nonnegative quantity. As we have proved that all coefficients must be integers, $\sum f_{ij} a_{i(j)k}$ must be a nonnegative integer such as 0, 1, 2, ...

In the second case, the terms in

$$\sum_{j \in \bar{J}} f_{ij} a_{i(j)k} - f_{ij}$$

are all nonnegative except $-f_{ij}$, which lies between -1 and 0. Thus the expression

$$\sum_{j \in \bar{J}} f_{ij} a_{i(j)k}$$

must be *strictly* greater than -1. But the expression represents the coefficient of a certain variable x_k, so it must be an integer. Therefore, the expression must be a nonnegative integer such as 0, 1, 2, ... This is true for the first added inequality, but once this is proved we can consider the first added inequality as part of the original tableau and apply the reasoning to the second added inequality, etc.

Therefore, we conclude that if all coefficients in the original tableaux are nonnegative integers, so are the added Gomory cuts if they are expressed in terms of the original nonbasic variables.

When the optimum solution to the linear program is obtained, let t_j be the current nonbasic variables. Dual feasibility implies that

$$x_0 = a_{00} + \sum a_{0j}(-t_j),$$

with $a_{0j} \geq 0$ and $t_j \geq 0$. If we consider the t_j-space as shown in Fig. 13.3, the objective function is a supporting hyperplane to the first quadrant, which attains its maximum value in the convex set at the origin ($t_j = 0$). Any point inside the first quarter corresponds to some positive t_j and therefore smaller values of x_0.

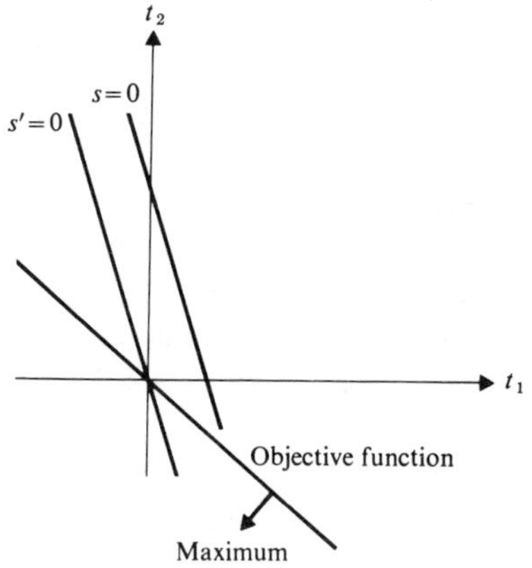

Fig. 13.3

The hyperplane represented by

$$s = -f_0 + \sum f_j t_j = 0.$$

with $t_j \geq 0$, is a hyperplane cutting the first quadrant into two parts with the lower left part containing the origin. This hyperplane is parallel to the hyperplane $s' = \sum f_j t_j$, which is a supporting hyperplane for the first quadrant with the origin as the vertex of intersection. Since we have shown that s is an integer combination of original variables,

$$s = n' + \sum n_i x_i = -f_0 + \sum f_j t_j. \tag{6a}$$

The current solution $t_j = 0$ will give the integer form $n' + \sum n_i x_i$ a noninteger value $-f_0$. Therefore, the supporting hyperplane $s' = f_j t_j = 0$ can be pushed toward the inside of the first quadrant.

Another way to look at the cutting plane is to consider the space of t_j and s ($j = 1, \ldots, n$), with s as the $n + 1$ dimension as shown in Fig. 13.4. Then equation (6a) represents a hyperplane H_1 in $t_j \oplus s$-space. The intersection of hyperplane H_1 with $s = 0$ is

$$0 = -f_0 + \sum f_j t_j. \tag{6b}$$

Equation (6b) then represents a hyperplane H_2 that cuts off the origin of the t_j-space.

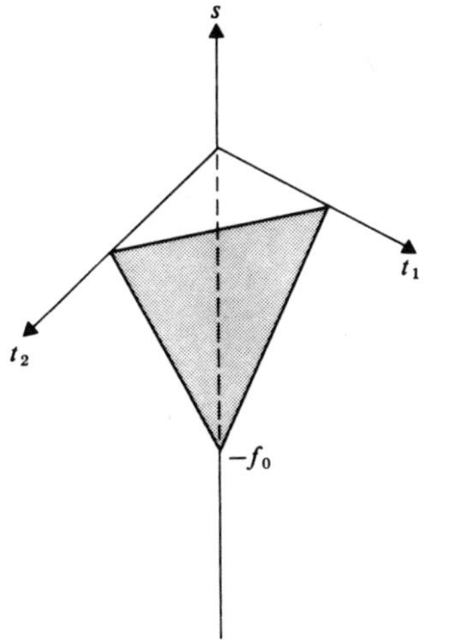

Fig. 13.4

After we cut off the origin which represents the optimum vertex, we will introduce another coordinate system, which uses the new nonbasic variables as its coordinate axis and has the optimum solution to the linear programs as its origin.

ALL-INTEGER ALGORITHM 14

14.1 ALL-INTEGER ALGORITHM (Gomory [80])

In this section, we shall describe another algorithm for solving integer programs. This is called the *all-integer algorithm* because if we start from an original tableau that consists of integers, it retains an all-integer tableau throughout the computation. This algorithm starts with a dual feasible tableau like the dual simplex method for linear programs. If a_{i0} $(i = 1, \ldots, n + m)$ are nonnegative integers, then the problem is solved. If a particular row has $a_{r0} < 0$, then a new equation is derived and added to the bottom of the tableau to be the pivot row. The dual simplex method is then applied. The derived row will consist of all integer coefficients and have the pivot. -1. This keeps the tableau always in integers. Note that in the previous algorithm, a row i becomes the generating row only if a_{i0} is not an integer Now a row i becomes the generating row only if a_{i0} is negative.

Let the integer program be

$$\max x_0 = a_{00} + \sum_{j=1}^{n} a_{0j}(-x_j)$$

subject to

$$\begin{aligned} x_1 &= -1(-x_1) \geq 0, \\ &\vdots \\ x_n &= -1(-x_n) \geq 0, \\ x_{n+1} &= a_{n+1,0} + \sum_{j=1}^{n} a_{n+1,j}(-x_j) \geq 0, \qquad (1) \\ &\vdots \\ x_{n+m} &= a_{n+m,0} + \sum_{j=1}^{n} a_{n+m,j}(-x_j) \geq 0. \end{aligned}$$

This can be written as

$$\mathbf{x}^t = \mathbf{A}^t(-\mathbf{x}_n^t). \qquad (2)$$

We assume that for $t = 0$ (i.e., the starting tableau), all a_{ij} are integers and all columns $\boldsymbol{\alpha}_j$ ($j = 1, \ldots, n$) are lexicographically positive. Then all columns will be maintained lexicographically positive throughout the computation.

Before describing how to get the derived row from the generating row, let us introduce a new way of representing a number. Let us use $[x]$ to denote the largest integer less than or equal to x. If y is any number (positive or negative), and λ is any positive number, then we can write

$$y = [y/\lambda]\lambda + r_y, \tag{3}$$

where $0 \leq r_y < \lambda$ (r_y is the remainder of y divided by λ if we insist that the quotient must always be an integer and the remainder must always be nonnegative). In particular, $1 = [1/\lambda]\lambda + r$; therefore if $\lambda > 1$, $[1/\lambda] = 0$ and $r = 1$. If $\lambda = 1$, then $[1/\lambda] = 1$ and $r = 0$.

Just as before, let us derive an inequality which must be satisfied by any integer solution of (1). Consider an equation in the tth tableau (omitting the row subscript) with $a_0 < 0$:

$$x = a_0 + \sum a_j(-x_j^t), \tag{4}$$

where x is any component of $\mathbf{x}$ and the x_j^t are the current nonbasic variables. We can represent x, a_0, and a_j in terms of λ by substitution in (3), where

$$x = x \times 1 = x\,\{[1/\lambda]\lambda + r\}, \tag{5}$$

$$a_j = [a_j/\lambda]\lambda + r_j \qquad (j = 0, 1, \ldots, n). \tag{6}$$

Substituting (5) and (6) into (4) and transferring terms, we have

$$\sum_{j=1}^{n} r_j x_j^t + rx = r_0 + \lambda\left\{\left[\frac{a_0}{\lambda}\right] + \sum_{j=1}^{n}\left[\frac{a_j}{\lambda}\right](-x_j^t) + \left[\frac{1}{\lambda}\right](-x)\right\}. \tag{7}$$

Since $r_j \geq 0$, $r \geq 0$, and x, x_j^t are all required to be nonnegative, the left-hand side of (7) is always nonnegative. Consider now the terms enclosed by braces on the right-hand side of (7). Every term inside the braces is either an integer or required to be an integer. Therefore, the whole brace is an integer. Let us denote this whole brace by a slack variable s, i.e.,

$$s = \left[\frac{a_0}{\lambda}\right] + \sum_{j=1}^{n}\left[\frac{a_j}{\lambda}\right](-x_j^t) + \left[\frac{1}{\lambda}\right](-x). \tag{8}$$

However, s is not only an integer but is a nonnegative integer. If s were a negative integer such as $-1, -2, \ldots$, etc., multiplication by λ ($\lambda > r_0$) would make the right-hand side of (7) negative while the left-hand side of (7) is nonnegative.

Now we consider two cases $\lambda = 1$ and $\lambda > 1$. For $\lambda = 1$, $[a_j/\lambda] = [a_j]$ and $[1/\lambda] = 1$, and we can substitute for x in (8) by (4):

$$s = [a_0] + \sum [a_j](-x_j^t) - \{a_0 + \sum a_j(-x_j^t)\} = -f_0 - \sum f_j(-x_j^t). \tag{9}$$

This is the derived row used in Section 13.1. For $\lambda > 1$, $[1/\lambda] = 0$* and (8) becomes

$$s = \left[\frac{a_0}{\lambda}\right] + \sum_{j=1}^{n} \left[\frac{a_j}{\lambda}\right](-x_j^t). \tag{10}$$

Equation (10) then must be satisfied by any feasible integer solution to (1). Note that if $a_0 < 0$ in (4), $[a_0/\lambda] < 0$ in (10); therefore (10) can be used as a pivot row in the dual simplex method. In particular, for any $a_j < 0$ we can always choose λ large enough so that the pivot $[a_j/\lambda]$ in (10) is -1. This will maintain the tableau always in integers. The selection of an appropriate λ will speed up the convergence of the algorithm. Let us first review the algorithm. The algorithm needs a starting dual feasible solution which can be obtained by adding a constraint $x_{n+m+1} = M - x_1 - \cdots - x_n \geq 0$, where M is a large constant, and pivoting on this row with the lexicographically smallest column as the pivot column. The algorithm consists of the following steps:

STEP 0. Start with an all-integer matrix $\mathbf{A}^0$ in (2), which is dual feasible ($\mathbf{A}^0$ does not have to be an all-integer matrix, as will be discussed below).

STEP 1. Among $a_{i0} < 0$ $(i = 1, \ldots, n + m)$ select the row with the smallest i; this is the generating row. (If $a_{i0} \geq 0$ $(i = 1, \ldots, n + m)$, then the problem is solved.)

STEP 2. Choose $\lambda > 0$ (the rule will be described later) and add the derived row

$$s = \left[\frac{a_{i0}}{\lambda}\right] + \sum \left[\frac{a_{ij}}{\lambda}\right](-x_j)$$

to the bottom of the tableau. This is the pivot row.

STEP 3. Perform a dual simplex step, drop the pivot row, and return to step 1.

Finiteness Proof. This proof also depends on the assumption that there is a lower bound $\bar{x}_0$ for the objective function x_0. Since all the pivot steps are dual simplex steps,

$$\boldsymbol{\alpha}_0^t \succ \boldsymbol{\alpha}_0^{t+1}.$$

Since all numbers remain integers, if a_{00} decreases, it must decrease by an integer amount and will be below $\bar{x}_0$ after a finite number of steps. If the algorithm is not finite, then a_{00} must remain fixed for all $t > t_0$, say. Consider now the first component a_{10} of $\boldsymbol{\alpha}_0$; it must also decrease by an integer amount if it strictly decreases. If a_{10} decreases below zero, then it will be selected as the generating row. If $a_{1j} \geq 0$ for all j, then it shows that the

* This means that in deriving the cut (10) from (4), the left-hand side of (4) is required only to be nonnegative but not an integer if $\lambda > 1$. Hence any positive linear combination of existing rows may serve as a generating row.

program is not feasible. If $a_{1j} < 0$ for some j, then the derived row

$$s = \left[\frac{a_{10}}{\lambda}\right] + \sum_{j=1}^{n} \left[\frac{a_{1j}}{\lambda}\right](-x_j)$$

also has $[a_{10}/\lambda] < 0$ and $[a_{1j}/\lambda] = -1$ for at least one j. (The rule for selecting λ ensures this.) Pivoting on the row will strictly increase a_{10}. Since $\boldsymbol{\alpha}_0^t \succ \boldsymbol{\alpha}_0^{t+1}$, this implies that a_{00}^{t+1} must decrease, contradicting our assumption that a_{00} is fixed. Therefore, a_{10} must (if the algorithm is not finite) remain fixed for all cycles $t > t_1$, say, where $t_1 > t_0$. The same argument now can be applied to the second component, the third, and so forth. So after a finite number of steps, all a_{i0} $(i = 1, \ldots, n + m)$ are nonnegative integers. This completes the proof.

Now we shall describe the rule for choosing λ in step 2 of the all-integer algorithm. Let the generating row be

$$x = a_0 + \sum a_j(-x_j)$$

and the derived row be

$$s = [a_0/\lambda] + \sum [a_j/\lambda](-x_j).$$

For any $a_j < 0$, we can always select λ large enough that $[a_j/\lambda] = -1$. According to the lexicographic dual simplex method of choosing the pivot column, we want, if $\boldsymbol{\alpha}_s$ is the pivot column,

$$\left|\frac{-1}{[a_s/\lambda]}\boldsymbol{\alpha}_s\right| = \min_j \left|\frac{-1}{[a_j/\lambda]}\boldsymbol{\alpha}_j\right| \qquad (a_j < 0),$$

since $[a_s/\lambda] = -1$; $[a_j/\lambda]$ is a negative integer, $-1, -2, \ldots$, say, $-\mu_j$:

$$\frac{\boldsymbol{\alpha}_s}{1} \prec \frac{\boldsymbol{\alpha}_j}{\mu_j} \prec \frac{\boldsymbol{\alpha}_j}{1} \tag{11}$$

so that $\boldsymbol{\alpha}_s$ must be the smallest column lexicographically. This means that among all possible pivot columns (with $a_{vj} < 0$) the pivot column is always the lexicographically smallest column no matter what λ is used.

Now consider two values of λ which both produce $[a_s/\lambda_1] = -1$ and $[a_s/\lambda_2] = -1$. The amount by which $\boldsymbol{\alpha}_0$ will be decreased is

$$\boldsymbol{\alpha}_0^{t+1} = \boldsymbol{\alpha}_0^t + \left[\frac{a_{v0}}{\lambda_i}\right]\boldsymbol{\alpha}_s^t \qquad (\lambda_i = \lambda_1, \lambda_2).$$

Therefore the smaller the λ, the more the 0th column decreases lexicographically. We should select λ so that 1. it will be large enough to produce a pivot of -1 and 2. subject to 1, it gives the biggest decrease in $\boldsymbol{\alpha}_0$. So the rule is as follows:

STEP 0. Let the row v be the source row.

STEP 1. Let $\boldsymbol{\alpha}_s$ be the lexicographically smallest column among columns with $a_{vj} < 0$.

STEP 2. For each $a_{vj} < 0$, let μ_j be the largest integer such that $\boldsymbol{\alpha}_s \prec \boldsymbol{\alpha}_j/\mu_j$.

STEP 3. Let $[-a_{vj}/\lambda_j] = \mu_j$, or $\lambda_j = -a_{vj}/\mu_j$ (the row v is the source row). This is the λ_j that will make $\boldsymbol{\alpha}_s \prec \boldsymbol{\alpha}_j/[-a_{vj}/\lambda_j]$.

STEP 4. Let $\lambda = \max_j \lambda_j$ for $a_{vj} < 0$.

The selection of λ discussed above is to make the pivot -1, keep the tableau dual feasible, and at the same time cause the greatest decrease lexicographically in the 0th column. The Gomory cut does not represent an inequality which is as strong as possible, and it may be either stronger or weaker than the generating row. For example, let the generating row be

$$x = -4 - 3(-x_1) - 5(-x_2). \tag{12}$$

If we use $\lambda = 2$, we get

$$s = -2 - 2(-x_1) - 3(-x_2) \geq 0. \tag{13}$$

For $\lambda = 3$, we get

$$s = -2 - 1(-x_1) - 2(-x_2) \geq 0. \tag{14}$$

For $\lambda = 4$, we get

$$s = -1 - 1(-x_1) - 2(-x_2) \geq 0. \tag{15}$$

Thus (14) is stronger than (12), (12) is stronger than (13), and (13) is stronger than (15).

Another thing is that if the value of λ as obtained above can be increased such that the value of $[a_0/\lambda]$ and $[a_j/\lambda]$ $(a_j > 0)$, are unchanged, then the generated row will be stronger although the 0th column is decreased by the same amount.

From a given generated row

$$x_0 = a_0 + \sum_{a_j<0} a_j(-x_j) + \sum_{a_j'>0} a_j'(-x_j). \tag{16}$$

The larger the value of λ, the smaller the absolute values of the coefficients in the generated cut. Naturally, we would like to have the absolute value of $[a_0/\lambda]$ large and the absolute values of $[a_j/\lambda]$ small. If the value of λ (as calculated by the above rule) can be increased such that values of $[a_j'/\lambda]$ and $[a_0/\lambda]$ do not change, then use the larger λ. We could possibly reduce the absolute value of $[a_j/\lambda]$ for some j to make a stronger cut.

For example, let the objective function be

$$x_0 = 20 - x_1 - 2x_2 - 3x_3 - x_4$$

and the generating row be

$$x = -20 + (-7)(-x_1) + (-8)(-x_2) + (-15)(-x_3) + 18(-x_4).$$

Using the above procedure for selecting λ, we would get $\lambda = 7$, with the resulting cut

$$s = -3 + x_1 + 2x_2 + 3x_3 - 2x_4 \geq 0.$$

If we use $\lambda = 9$ instead of 7, we would get the cut

$$s^* = -3 + x_1 + x_2 + 2x_3 - 2x_4 \geq 0,$$

which is stronger (see Wilson [214]).

One interesting feature of the all-integer algorithm is that the validity of this algorithm does not depend on the coefficients a_{ij} being integers. Assume that we have an integer program

$$\max x_0 = a_{00} - \sum c_j x_j \qquad (j = 1, \ldots, n)$$

subject to

$$x_{n+i} = a_{i0} - \sum a_{ij} x_j \geq 0 \qquad (i = 1, \ldots, m),$$

$$x_j \geq 0.$$

Here a_{00} and c_j are integers and a_{i0} and a_{ij} can be real numbers. Then we have Tableau 14.1 in which the first $n + 1$ rows are all integers.

Tableau 14.1

		$-x_1$	$-x_2$	$\ldots$	$-x_n$
x_0	a_{00}	$c_1,$	$c_2,$	$\ldots,$	c_n
x_1	0	-1			
x_2	0		-1		
.	.			.	
.	.			.	
.	.			.	
x_n	0				-1
x_{n+1}	a_{10}				
.	.				
.	.			a_{ij}	
.	.				
x_{n+m}	a_{m0}				

Now for any source row (omitting the row subscript)

$$x = a_0 + \sum a_j(-x_j).$$

Whether a_0 and a_j are real numbers or integers, the cut derived from it

$$s = \left[\frac{a_0}{\lambda}\right] + \sum \left[\frac{a_j}{\lambda}\right](-x_j),$$

is always with integer coefficients and with the pivot -1. The result of such a pivot will keep the first $n+1$ rows all integers. Note that the s variable is a nonnegative integer variable. Therefore the finiteness proof goes through without much change. As soon as the a_{i0} $(i = 1, \ldots, n)$ in the 0th column become nonnegative integers and the rest of the numbers in the 0th column are nonnegative, the computation is stopped.

We have discussed two integer algorithms of which the first one is called the fractional algorithm (i.e., $\lambda = 1$) and the second one is called the all-integer algorithm (i.e., $\lambda > 1$). Table 14.1 lists their differences.

Table 14.1

Fractional Algorithm	All-Integer Algorithm
a_{ij} have to be integers in starting tableau	a_{ij} may be real in the starting tableau. (a_{0j} must be integers)
$a_{ij}^t \not\equiv 0 \pmod 1$ in the successive tableau	If a_{ij} are integers to start, then a_{ij} will remain integers
Either the primal or dual simplex method is used to obtain the *L.P.* optimum and then dual simplex method is used	Dual simplex method is used throughout computation
a_{i0} noninteger makes ith row a generating row	a_{i0} negative makes ith row a generating row ($i \neq 0$)
Pivot row is $$s = -f_0 - \sum f_j(-x_j^t),$$ $$0 < f_0 < 1,\ 0 \leq f_j < 1$$	Pivot row is $$s = \left[\frac{a_0}{\lambda}\right] + \sum\left[\frac{a_j}{\lambda}\right](-x_j^t),$$ $$a_0 < 0,\ a_j \lesseqgtr 0$$
Pivot column s is determined by $$\frac{1}{f_s}\boldsymbol{\alpha}_s \prec \frac{1}{f_j}\boldsymbol{\alpha}_j$$ for all j	Pivot column s is always lexicographically smallest column with $a_{vj} < 0$, and is determined before cut is generated
Many inequalities may be added at one time and then dual simplex method is used	One inequality is added at a time, if all-integer tableau is to be maintained.

14.2 EXAMPLE

Consider the integer program of

$$\max x_0 = -10x_1 - 14x_2 - 21x_3$$

subject to

$$2x_1 + 2x_2 + 7x_3 \geq 14,$$
$$8x_1 + 11x_2 + 9x_3 \geq 12,$$
$$9x_1 + 6x_2 + 3x_3 \geq 10,$$
$$x_1, x_2, x_3 \geq 0 \text{ integers.}$$

Then we have Tableau 14.2. Here all entries in the generating row are negative and the first column is the lexicographically smallest.

Tableau 14.2

	1	$-x_1$	$-x_2$	$-x_3$	
x_0	1	10	14	21	
x_1	0	−1	0	0	
x_2	0	0	−1	0	
x_3	0	0	0	−1	
x_4	−14	−2	−2	−7	←Generating row
x_5	−12	−8	−11	−9	
x_6	−10	−9	−6	−3	
s_1	−4	−1*	−1	−2	$\lambda = 7/2$

$$\mu_1 = 1, \quad 10 \leq \frac{14}{\mu_2}, \quad \mu_2 = \left[\frac{14}{10}\right] = 1, \quad 10 \leq \frac{21}{\mu_3}, \quad \mu_3 = \left[\frac{21}{10}\right] = 2,$$

$$\lambda_1 = \frac{2}{\mu_1} = 2, \quad \lambda_2 = \frac{2}{\mu_2} = 2, \quad \lambda_3 = \frac{7}{\mu_3} = \frac{7}{2},$$

$$\lambda = \max(2, 2, 7/2) = 7/2.$$

The cut is then

$$s = \left[\frac{-14}{\lambda}\right] - \left[\frac{-2}{\lambda}\right]x_1 - \left[\frac{-2}{\lambda}\right]x_2 - \left[\frac{-7}{\lambda}\right]x_3,$$

$$s_1 = -4 + x_1 + x_2 + 2x_3 \geq 0.$$

This is added to the bottom of Tableau 14.2. Pivot steps lead to Tableaux 14.3, 14.4, 14.5, and 14.6. The optimum solution from Tableau 14.6 is $x_0 = -52$, $x_1 = 1$, $x_2 = 0$, and $x_3 = 2$.

Tableau 14.3

	1	$-s_1$	$-x_2$	$-x_3$	
x_0	−40	10	4	1	
x_1	4	−1	1	2	
x_2	0	0	−1	0	
x_3	0	0	0	−1	
x_4	−6	−2	0	−3	←Generating row
x_5	20	−8	−3	7	
x_6	26	−9	3	15	
s_2	−2	−1	0	−1*	$\lambda = 3$

Tableau 14.4

	1	$-s_1$	$-x_2$	$-s_2$	
x_0	−42	9	4	1	
x_1	0	−3	1	2	
x_2	0	0	−1	0	
x_3	2	1	0	−1	
x_4	0	1	0	−3	
x_5	6	−15	−3	7	
x_6	−4	−24	3	15	←Generating row
s_3	−1	−1*	0	0	$\lambda = 24$

Tableau 14.5

	1	$-s_3$	$-x_2$	$-s_2$	
x_0	−51	9	4	1	
x_1	3	−3	1	2	
x_2	0	0	−1	0	
x_3	1	1	0	−1	
x_4	−1	1	0	−3	←Generating row
x_5	21	−15	−3	7	
x_6	20	−24	3	15	
s_4	−1	0	0	−1*	$\lambda = 3$

Tableau 14.6

	1	$-s_3$	$-x_2$	$-s_4$
x_0	−52	9	4	1
x_1	1	−3	1	2
x_2	0	0	−1	0
x_3	2	1	0	−1
x_4	2	1	0	−3
x_5	14	−15	−3	7
x_6	5	−24	3	15

MIXED INTEGER PROGRAMMING 15

15.1 INTRODUCTION (Gomory [81])

In this chapter we study the integer program in which *only a subset* of the variables is restricted to consist of integers. We shall discuss two types of methods for solving such problems; one is due to Gomory [81] and the other is due to Benders [18].

The first algorithm, due to Gomory [81], is basically the same as the algorithm developed in Chapter 13, namely:

STEP 1. Start with an optimum tableau of the linear program.

STEP 2. Select a row to be a generating row (also called a source row).

STEP 3. Derive from the source row a cut, which is added to the bottom of the tableau to be used as the pivot row.

STEP 4. Do a dual simplex step and return to step 2.

The only difference is in deriving the cut from the source row. Let the integer program be

$$\max x_0 = a_{00} - a_{01}x_1 - a_{02}x_2 - \cdots - a_{0n}x_n \tag{1}$$

subject to

$$\begin{aligned} x_{n+1} &= a_{n+1,0} - a_{n+1,1}x_1 - a_{n+1,2}x_2 - \cdots - a_{n+1,n}x_n \geq 0, \\ &\vdots \\ x_{n+m} &= a_{n+m,0} - a_{n+m,1}x_1 - a_{n+m,2}x_2 - \cdots - a_{n+m,n}x_n \geq 0, \\ & x_j \geq 0 \qquad (j = 1, \ldots, n), \end{aligned} \tag{2}$$

and some of the x_j are restricted to be integers. We shall solve this problem as if it were a linear program and use the dual simplex method. If in the tableau $a_{0j} \geq 0\ (j = 1, \ldots, n)$, $a_{i0} \geq 0\ (i = 1, \ldots, n + m)$, and all variables restricted to be integers are indeed integers, then this is clearly the optimum solution to the mixed integer problem. Therefore, let us assume that one $a_{i0} \geq 0$ is not an integer and x_i is restricted to be an integer. Rewriting this equation and omitting row subscripts, we have

$$x = a_0 + \sum a_j(-x_j). \tag{3}$$

Since x is to be an integer, $x \equiv 0 \pmod 1$, and a_0 by assumption is not an integer, $a_0 \equiv f_0 \pmod 1$. Hence any integer solution to (2) must satisfy

$$\sum_j a_j x_j \equiv f_0 \pmod 1. \tag{4}$$

Let the coefficients on the left-hand side of (4) be partitioned into two sets, $J^+ = \{j \mid a_j \geq 0\}$ and $J^- = \{j \mid a_j < 0\}$. Then

$$\sum_{j \in J+} a_j x_j + \sum_{j \in J-} a_j x_j \equiv f_0 \pmod 1, \tag{5}$$

where $0 < f_0 < 1$.

The left-hand side of (5) is either positive or negative. If it is positive, then it must be f_0, $1 + f_0$, ... etc., and we have

$$\sum_{j \in J+} a_j x_j \geq \sum_{j \in J+} a_j x_j + \sum_{j \in J-} a_j x_j \geq f_0. \tag{6}$$

If the left-hand side of (5) is negative, then it must be $-1 + f_0$, $-2 + f_0$, etc., and we have

$$\sum_{j \in J-} a_j x_j \leq \sum_{j \in J+} a_j x_j + \sum_{j \in J-} a_j x_j \leq -1 + f_0. \tag{7}$$

We multiply both sides of (7) by $f_0/(-1 + f_0) < 0$ to get

$$\sum_{j \in J-} \frac{f_0}{f_0 - 1} a_j x_j \geq f_0. \tag{8}$$

Now either (6) or (8) holds. Since the left-hand sides of (6) and (8) are both nonnegative, and one of them is greater than or equal to f_0, we have

$$\sum_{j \in J+} a_j x_j + \sum_{j \in J-} \frac{f_0}{f_0 - 1} a_j x_j \geq f_0. \tag{9}$$

The inequality (9) is then an inequality which must be satisfied by every integer solution but is not satisfied by the current solution, since substituting $x_j = 0$ for all j in (9) makes the left-hand side zero. Note that in deriving (9), we use only the fact that x in the left-hand side of (3) must be an integer and the x_j in the right-hand side of (3) must be nonnegative. Therefore, if some x_j are not restricted to be integers, (9) still represents a valid inequality that must be satisfied. Introducing a nonnegative slack variable s, we can rewrite (9) as an equation:

$$s = -f_0 + \sum_{j \in J+} a_j x_j + \sum_{j \in J-} \frac{f_0}{f_0 - 1} a_j x_j, \tag{10}$$

which can be put at the bottom of the tableau to make the tableau primal infeasible. We then do a dual simplex step and use (10) as the pivot row. If some x_j on the left-hand side of (9) are restricted to be integers, then we can use this fact to improve (9) to a stronger inequality, i.e., we want the coefficients a_j ($j \in J^+$) and $f_0 a_j/(f_0 - 1)$ ($j \in J^-$) to be as small as possible. Because (9) was derived from (4), let us consider a term $a_k x_k$ in (4) for which x_k is restricted to be an integer. Decreasing or increasing a_k by an integer amount clearly will not destroy the congruence relation (4). Among all $a_k \geq 0$, i.e. $k \in J^+$, the smallest coefficient that can be obtained is then f_k. Among all $a_k < 0$, setting $a_k = f_k - 1$ will give the smallest value to $(f_0/(f_0 - 1))a_k$. Therefore, we want to decrease or increase a_k by an integral amount in (5) so that it gives a term with the smallest coefficient in (9), i.e., the minimum of

$$\left(f_k, \frac{f_0}{1 - f_0}(1 - f_k)\right).$$

(Note that a function $g(y) = y/(1 - y)$ is increasing with y for $y < 1$.) Clearly

$$f_k(1 - f_0) \leq f_0(1 - f_k) \qquad \text{if } f_k \leq f_0,$$

or

$$f_k \leq \frac{f_0}{1 - f_0}(1 - f_k) \qquad \text{if } f_k \leq f_0,$$

and

$$f_k > \frac{f_0}{1 - f_0}(1 - f_k) \qquad \text{if } f_k > f_0.$$

Therefore, from an equation like (4) we get an equation

$$s = -f_0 - \sum_j f_j^* (-x_j), \tag{11}$$

where

$$f_j^* = \begin{cases} a_j & \text{if } a_j \geq 0 \quad \text{and} \quad x_j \text{ noninteger,} \\ \dfrac{f_0}{f_0 - 1} a_j & \text{if } a_j < 0 \quad \text{and} \quad x_j \text{ noninteger,} \\ f_j & \text{if } f_j \leq f_0 \quad \text{and} \quad x_j \text{ integer,} \\ \dfrac{f_0}{1 - f_0}(1 - f_j) & \text{if } f_j > f_0 \quad \text{and} \quad x_j \text{ integer.} \end{cases} \tag{12}$$

Equation (11) is then added to the bottom of the tableau and the problem is remaximized.

To prove finiteness of this algorithm, let us assume that the starting tableau is dual feasible and the lexicographic dual simplex method is applied. This means that the 0th column is decreased lexicographically at every step. Let a_{i0} denote an entry in the 0th column and the source row, and a'_{i0} denote its value after a pivot. Then

$$\begin{aligned} a'_{i0} &\leq [a_{i0}] && \text{if } a_{is} > 0, \\ a'_{i0} &\geq [a_{i0}] + 1 && \text{if } a_{is} < 0, \end{aligned} \tag{13}$$

where the sth column is the pivot column. This means that after a pivot step, the entry in the 0th column and in the source row is either decreased to the next smaller integer $[a_{i0}]$ or increased to the next larger integer $[a_{i0}] + 1$.

To show (13) let us examine the detail of the pivot step. If the ith row is chosen to be the source row and sth column is chosen to be the pivot column, we have

$$a'_{i0} = a_{i0} - \frac{f_{i0}}{f^*_{is}} a_{is}. \tag{14}$$

From formula (12), $f^*_{is} = a_{is}$ if $a_{is} > 0$ and x_s is not restricted to be an integer. This reduces (14) to

$$a'_{i0} = a_{i0} - \frac{f_{i0}}{a_{is}} \cdot a_{is} = [a_{i0}].$$

If $a_{is} < 0$ and x_s is not restricted to be an integer, (14) reduces to

$$a'_{i0} = a_{i0} - \frac{f_{i0} a_{is}}{a_{is} f_{i0}/(f_{i0} - 1)} = [a_{i0}] + 1.$$

If x_s is restricted to be an integer and $f_{is} \le f_{i0}$, (14) reduces to

$$a'_{i0} = a_{i0} - \frac{f_{i0}}{f_{is}} a_{is} \begin{cases} = [a_{i0}] & \text{if } a_{is} = f_{is}, \\ < [a_{i0}] & \text{if } a_{is} > f_{is}. \end{cases}$$

If x_s is restricted to be an integer and $f_{is} > f_{i0}$, (14) reduces to

$$a'_{i0} = a_{i0} - \frac{f_{i0}}{f_{i0}/(1 - f_{i0})} \frac{a_{is}}{1 - f_{is}} = a_{i0} - (1 - f_{i0}) \frac{a_{is}}{1 - f_{is}}. \tag{15}$$

If $0 < a_{is} < 1$, i.e., $a_{is} = f_{is}$, (15) becomes

$$a'_{i0} < a_{i0} - f_{i0} = [a_{i0}] \qquad \text{as } \frac{f_{i0}}{1 - f_{i0}} < \frac{f_{is}}{1 - f_{is}}.$$

If $-1 < a_{is} < 0$, i.e., $a_{is} = f_{is} - 1$, (15) becomes

$$a'_{i0} = a_{i0} - (1 - f_{i0}) \frac{f_{is} - 1}{1 - f_{is}} = [a_{i0}] + 1$$

If $1 < a_{is}$, (15) becomes

$$a'_{i0} = a_{i0} - f_{i0} \frac{1 - f_{i0}}{f_{i0}} \cdot \frac{a_{is}}{1 - f_{is}} < a_{i0} - f_{i0} = [a_{i0}].$$

If $a_{is} < -1$, (15) becomes

$$a'_{i0} > a_{i0} - (1 - f_{i0}) \left(\frac{-1 + f_{is}}{1 - f_{is}} \right) = a_{i0} + (1 - f_{i0}) = [a_{i0}] + 1.$$

We have just proved that the element a_{i0} in the source row is either increased to the next larger integer or decreased to the next smaller integer after a pivot. In order to prove finiteness we have to assume that the optimum value of z is an integer in addition to the usual assumption that there exists a lower bound to the optimum value of z. In the starting tableau we put all m' constraints where the left-hand sides represent integer-valued variables above those constraints which are only required to be nonnegative. Since z is required to be an integer, the a_{i0} $(i = 0, 1, \ldots, m')$ are all required to be integers and the first $m' + 1$ rows are possible source rows. Since $\boldsymbol{\alpha}_0^t$ decreases lexicographically in each step and the amount of decrease or increase of a_{i0} in the source row is to the next integer, a_{00} cannot decrease indefinitely and still be above the assumed lower bound. Therefore a_{00} has to remain fixed at an integer value for all cycles $t > t_0$. Therefore, the first row will be used as the source row if a_{10} is noninteger. Then a_{10} cannot increase to the next integer after cycles $t > t_0$, as that would contradict the fact that $\boldsymbol{\alpha}_0^t$ decreases lexicographically unless a_{00} decreases, but a_{00} is assumed to be fixed at an integer value after all cycles $t > t_0$. Therefore a_{10} must also remain fixed after a certain cycle. Thus, we can move to the second, third, and finally $(m' + 1)$th row until all a_{i0} $(i = 0, 1, \ldots, m')$ are integers.

15.2 PARTITIONING IN MIXED INTEGER PROGRAMMING (Benders [18])

Consider a mixed integer program

$$\min z = \mathbf{c}_1\mathbf{x} + \mathbf{c}_2\mathbf{y}$$

subject to (1)

$$\mathbf{A}_1\mathbf{x} + \mathbf{A}_2\mathbf{y} \geq \mathbf{b},$$
$$\mathbf{x}, \mathbf{y} \geq \mathbf{0}, \quad \mathbf{y} \equiv \mathbf{0} \pmod 1),$$

i.e., only $\mathbf{y}$ is restricted to be an integer vector.

For given values of $\mathbf{y}$, problem (1) becomes

$$\min \mathbf{c}_1\mathbf{x}$$

subject to

$$\mathbf{A}_1\mathbf{x} \geq \mathbf{b} - \mathbf{A}_2\mathbf{y}, \qquad \mathbf{x} \geq \mathbf{0}. \tag{2}$$

Then (2) is a standard linear program. The dual program of (2) is

$$\max \mathbf{u}(\mathbf{b} - \mathbf{A}_2\mathbf{y})$$

subject to (3)

$$\mathbf{u}\mathbf{A}_1 \leq \mathbf{c}_1, \qquad \mathbf{u} \geq \mathbf{0}.$$

We note two interesting features of (3). First, the feasible region of $\mathbf{u}$ defined by $\mathbf{u}\mathbf{A}_1 \leq \mathbf{c}_1$ is independent of $\mathbf{y}$. Second, no matter what values $\mathbf{y}$ may take, the maximum of $\mathbf{u}(\mathbf{b} - \mathbf{A}_2\mathbf{y})$ always occurs on a vertex of the convex polytope defined by $\mathbf{u}\mathbf{A}_1 \leq \mathbf{c}_1$, provided that the convex polytope is bounded from above. Let $\mathbf{u}^p$ $(p = 1, \ldots, P)$ denote a generic vertex of the convex polytope. Then we may write (3) as

$$\max \mathbf{u}^p (\mathbf{b} - \mathbf{A}_2\mathbf{y})$$

subject to

$$\mathbf{u}^p \geq \mathbf{0} \qquad (p = 1, \ldots, P). \tag{3'}$$

If (3) has no feasible solution, then from duality theory, (2) either has no finite optimum solution or also has no feasible solution. If (3) has no finite optimum solution, then (2) has no feasible solution. Either case would imply that (1) has no finite optimum solution. Therefore, we are interested only in the case that (3) has a finite optimum solution. Note that this means that the convex set $\mathbf{uA}_1 \leq \mathbf{c}_1$ is not empty, but it *does not imply* that the convex set $\mathbf{uA}_1 \leq \mathbf{c}_1$ is bounded. It is possible for the convex set $\mathbf{uA}_1 \leq \mathbf{c}_1$ to be unbounded and for $\mathbf{u}$ to go to infinity for certain values of $(\mathbf{b} - \mathbf{A}_2\mathbf{y})$ and yet for the optimum vertex associated with the optimum value of $\mathbf{y}$ to still have finite coordinates. This situation is shown in Fig. 15.1, where the ○ denotes the optimum vertex and the convex set is unbounded.

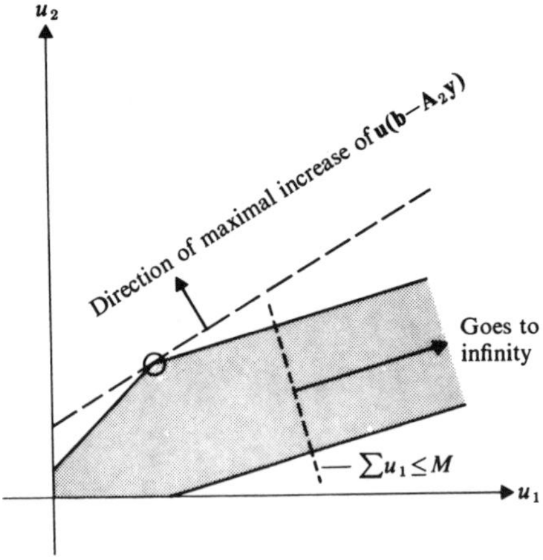

Fig. 15.1

In the case in which $\mathbf{u}$ goes to infinity for certain values of $(\mathbf{b} - \mathbf{A}_2\mathbf{y})$ we can add the constraint $\sum u_i \leq M$ (where M is a very large positive constant) to the constraint set $\mathbf{uA}_1 \leq \mathbf{c}_1$. This is shown by the long dashed line in Fig. 15.1.

If the convex set $\mathbf{uA}_1 \leq \mathbf{c}_1$ is bounded from above or if it becomes bounded from above after the constraint $\sum u_i \leq M$ is added, then (3) and (3′) are equivalent programs, and this is the case that we are interested in. Of course we do not know whether $\mathbf{uA}_1 \leq \mathbf{c}_1$ is bounded or not before solving the program (3). Let us substitute (3′) into (1) and we have

$$\min z$$

subject to

$$z \geq \mathbf{c}_2\mathbf{y} + \max_{\mathbf{u}^p} \mathbf{u}^p (\mathbf{b} - \mathbf{A}_2\mathbf{y}), \tag{1'}$$

$$\mathbf{u}^p \geq \mathbf{0} \qquad (p = 1, \ldots, P).$$

Each $\mathbf{u}^p$ gives one constraint and (1′) is a pure integer program for a fixed number of $\mathbf{u}^p$.

If we know the optimum vertex $\mathbf{u}^*$, we can solve (1′) as a pure integer program by any of the existing methods to obtain optimum values z^* and $\mathbf{y}^*$. Substituting the optimum $\mathbf{y}^*$ into (2), we solve the linear program min $\mathbf{c}_1\mathbf{x}$ subject to $\mathbf{A}_1\mathbf{x} \geq \mathbf{b} - \mathbf{A}_2\mathbf{y}^*$ and obtain the optimum value $\mathbf{x}^*$. Substituting $\mathbf{x}^*$ and $\mathbf{y}^*$ into (1), we have $z = \mathbf{c}_1\mathbf{x}^* + \mathbf{c}_2\mathbf{y}^*$. This value z should, of course, be the same as the z^* obtained from (1′). If we do not know the optimum vertex, we can list all vertices $\mathbf{u}^p$ and solve (1′). The trouble with this approach is that typically there are too many vertices $\mathbf{u}^p$, so we shall use the following iterative procedure to get the optimum vertex $\mathbf{u}^*$. Take any feasible $\bar{\mathbf{u}}$ (not necessarily a vertex) that satisfies $\bar{\mathbf{u}}\mathbf{A} \leq \mathbf{c}_1$, substitute it into (1′), and let the solution to (1′) for this value of $\bar{\mathbf{u}}$ be $\bar{z}$ and $\bar{\mathbf{y}}$. Use $\bar{\mathbf{y}}$ in (3) and solve for $\mathbf{u}$ that maximizes $\mathbf{u}(\mathbf{b} - \mathbf{A}_2\bar{\mathbf{y}})$. Let the solution be $\bar{\bar{\mathbf{u}}}$. Put $\bar{\bar{\mathbf{u}}}$ into (1′), i.e., add one more inequality and solve for $\mathbf{y}$ again; this is iterated until the optimum $\mathbf{u}^*$ is obtained.

For optimum $\mathbf{u}^*$, $\mathbf{y}^*$, and z^* we have from (1′)

$$z^* = \mathbf{c}_2\mathbf{y}^* + \mathbf{u}^*(\mathbf{b} - \mathbf{A}_2\mathbf{y}^*).$$

For a given $\bar{\mathbf{u}}$, we have from (1′)

$$\bar{z} = \mathbf{c}_2\bar{\mathbf{y}} + \bar{\mathbf{u}}(\mathbf{b} - \mathbf{A}_2\bar{\mathbf{y}}),$$

and $\bar{z} < z^*$ since $\bar{z} \geq \mathbf{c}_2\bar{\mathbf{y}} + \bar{\mathbf{u}}(\mathbf{b} - \mathbf{A}_2\bar{\mathbf{y}})$ is only a subset of all the constants in (1′). The true optimum z^* is obtained in (1′) only when all $\mathbf{u}^p$ are used or the optimum $\mathbf{u}^*$ is used. To check if a vertex $\bar{\mathbf{u}}$ is an optimum vertex, we first use $\bar{\mathbf{u}}$ to solve (1′) and get $\bar{\mathbf{y}}$ and $\bar{z}$ and then use $\bar{\mathbf{y}}$ in (3) to maximize $\mathbf{u}(\mathbf{b} - \mathbf{A}_2\bar{\mathbf{y}})$. If $\bar{z} - \mathbf{c}_2\bar{\mathbf{y}} = \max_{\mathbf{u}} \mathbf{u}(\mathbf{b} - \mathbf{A}_2\bar{\mathbf{y}})$, then $\bar{\mathbf{u}}$ is the optimum vertex.

Now we formally state the partitioning algorithm.

STEP 0. Start with a $\bar{\mathbf{u}} \geq \mathbf{0}$ that satisfies $\mathbf{u}\mathbf{A}_1 \leq \mathbf{c}_1$. This $\bar{\mathbf{u}}$ does not have to be a vertex. If none exists, then the original problem (1) has no feasible solution. Go to step 1.

STEP 1. Solve the pure integer program

$$\min z$$

subject to

$$z \geq \mathbf{c}_2\mathbf{y} + \bar{\mathbf{u}}(\mathbf{b} - \mathbf{A}_2\mathbf{y}),$$

$$\mathbf{y} \geq \mathbf{0}, \qquad \mathbf{y} \equiv \mathbf{0} \pmod 1.$$

If z is unbounded from below, take a z to be any small value $\bar{z}$.

STEP 2. Using $\bar{\mathbf{y}}$ obtained in step 1, we solve the linear program

$$\max_{\mathbf{u}} \mathbf{u}(\mathbf{b} - \mathbf{A}_2\bar{\mathbf{y}})$$

subject to

$$\mathbf{u}\mathbf{A}_1 \leq \mathbf{c}_1, \qquad \mathbf{u} \geq \mathbf{0}.$$

If $\mathbf{u}$ goes to infinity with $\mathbf{u}(\mathbf{b} - \mathbf{A}_2\bar{\mathbf{y}})$ finite, add the constraint $\sum u_i \leq M$, where M is a large positive constant, and resolve this problem.

Let the solution of this program be $\bar{\bar{\mathbf{u}}}$. Determine whether

$$\bar{z} - \mathbf{c}_2\bar{\mathbf{y}} \leq \bar{\bar{\mathbf{u}}}(\mathbf{b} - \mathbf{A}_2\bar{\mathbf{y}}).$$

If the equality is satisfied, go to step 3. If it is not satisfied, go to step 1, and add $z \geq \mathbf{c}_2\mathbf{y} + \bar{\bar{\mathbf{u}}}(\mathbf{b}_2 - \mathbf{A}_2\mathbf{y})$ to the existing set of constraints in (1′). An inequality in (1′) can be dropped if the corresponding slack variable becomes positive.

STEP 3. Use $\bar{\mathbf{y}}$ obtained in step 1. Solve the linear program

$$\min \acute{\mathbf{c}}_1\mathbf{x}$$

subject to

$$\mathbf{A}_1\mathbf{x} \geq \mathbf{b} - \mathbf{A}_2\bar{\mathbf{y}}, \qquad \mathbf{x} \geq \mathbf{0}.$$

Let the solution be $\bar{\mathbf{x}}$. We claim that $\bar{\mathbf{x}}$ and $\bar{\mathbf{y}}$ are then the optimum solution and $z^* = \mathbf{c}_1\bar{\mathbf{x}} + \mathbf{c}_2\bar{\mathbf{y}}$.

Now we shall prove that (a) this algorithm is finite, (b) it gives the optimum solution, and (c) at any time, an upper and a lower bound to the true optimum z^* can be obtained.

To prove that the algorithm is finite, we note that there are only a finite number of vertices in the convex set $\mathbf{u}\mathbf{A}_1 \leq \mathbf{c}_1$, if it is bounded. If it is not bounded, after adding $\sum u_i \leq M$, the convex set $\mathbf{u}\mathbf{A}_1 \leq \mathbf{c}_1$, $\sum u_i \leq M$ will be bounded. The only question is in the iteration process of steps 1 and 2, whether a new vertex $\mathbf{u}^p$ is always generated from (3). In problem (3) different values of $\mathbf{y}$ represent different objective functions. It seems plausible that two nonoptimum values $\mathbf{y}'$ and $\mathbf{y}''$ could give the same vertex $\bar{\mathbf{u}}$. This is shown in Fig. 15.2. Fortunately, this can never happen.

Let the solution of step 1 be $\bar{z}$ and $\bar{\mathbf{y}}$, i.e.,

$$\bar{z} = \mathbf{c}_2\bar{\mathbf{y}} + \bar{\mathbf{u}}(\mathbf{b} - \mathbf{A}_2\bar{\mathbf{y}}) \qquad \text{or} \qquad \bar{z} - \mathbf{c}_2\bar{\mathbf{y}} = \bar{\mathbf{u}}(\mathbf{b} - \mathbf{A}_2\bar{\mathbf{y}}). \tag{4}$$

Since $\bar{z}$ is obtained with a subset of the constraints in (1′)

$$\bar{z} \leq z^*, \tag{5}$$

where z^* is the true optimum value.

From the duality theory $\max \mathbf{u}(\mathbf{b} - \mathbf{A}_2\bar{\mathbf{y}}) = \min \mathbf{c}_1\mathbf{x}$, where $\mathbf{u}$ is constrained by $\mathbf{u}\mathbf{A}_1 \leq \mathbf{c}_1$ and $\mathbf{x}$ is constrained by $\mathbf{A}_1\mathbf{x} \geq \mathbf{b} - \mathbf{A}_2\bar{\mathbf{y}}$. Let the solution of step 2 be $\bar{\bar{\mathbf{u}}}$. Then

$$\bar{\bar{\mathbf{u}}}(\mathbf{b} - \mathbf{A}_2\bar{\mathbf{y}}) = \mathbf{c}_1\bar{\mathbf{x}}. \tag{6}$$

Note that $\bar{\mathbf{x}}$ and $\bar{\mathbf{y}}$ provide a feasible solution since

$$\mathbf{A}_1\bar{\mathbf{x}} + \mathbf{A}_2\bar{\mathbf{y}} \geq \mathbf{b}.$$

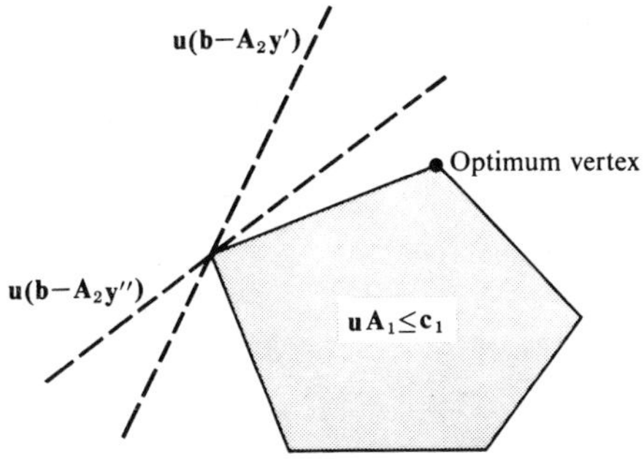

Fig. 15.2

It follows that $\mathbf{c}_1\bar{\mathbf{x}} + \mathbf{c}_2\bar{\mathbf{y}} \geq z^*$ or

$$\mathbf{c}_1\bar{\mathbf{x}} \geq z^* - \mathbf{c}_2\bar{\mathbf{y}}. \tag{7}$$

From (4), (5), (6), and (7) we have

$$\bar{\bar{\mathbf{u}}}(\mathbf{b} - \mathbf{A}_2\bar{\mathbf{y}}) = \mathbf{c}_1\bar{\mathbf{x}} \geq z^* - \mathbf{c}_2\bar{\mathbf{y}} \geq \bar{z} - \mathbf{c}_2\bar{\mathbf{y}} = \bar{\mathbf{u}}(\mathbf{b} - \mathbf{A}_2\bar{\mathbf{y}}),$$

where the equality holds only if $\bar{z}$ is the true optimum value. If

$$\bar{\bar{\mathbf{u}}}(\mathbf{b} - \mathbf{A}_2\bar{\mathbf{y}}) > \bar{\mathbf{u}}(\mathbf{b} - \mathbf{A}_2\bar{\mathbf{y}}),$$

then $\bar{\bar{\mathbf{u}}} \neq \bar{\mathbf{u}}$, and it means we always get a new vertex on each repetition of step 2 or the optimum vertex is obtained.

To prove that the algorithm will give the optimum solution, it is necessary to know that if all $\mathbf{u}^p$ are listed in (1′), the optimum solution will be obtained.

To see that upper and lower bounds can be obtained, consider z in (1′), which is a lower bound to the true optimum z^*. Since not all constraints in (1′) are listed, to set an upper bound on z^*, we supplement step 2 with the solution of

$$\min \mathbf{c}_1\mathbf{x}$$

subject to

$$\mathbf{A}_1\mathbf{x} \geq \mathbf{b} - \mathbf{A}_2\bar{\mathbf{y}}, \qquad \mathbf{x} \geq \mathbf{0},$$

where $\bar{\mathbf{y}}$ is the value used in step 2. This would then give a feasible solution $(\bar{\mathbf{x}}, \bar{\mathbf{y}})$ to (1), and $\mathbf{c}_1\bar{\mathbf{x}} + \mathbf{c}_2\bar{\mathbf{y}}$ is then the desired upper bound at every step.

Let us solve the following example by the partitioning algorithm:

$$\min 5x + 2y_1 + 2y_2$$

subject to

$$\begin{aligned} x + 3y_1 + 2y_2 &\geq 5, \\ 4x - y_1 + y_2 &\geq 7, \\ 2x + y_1 - y_2 &\geq 4, \end{aligned} \tag{8}$$

$$x \geq 0, \qquad y_1, y_2 \geq 0, \qquad y_1 \equiv y_2 \equiv 0 \pmod 1).$$

Rewriting (8), we have

$$\min 5x$$

subject to

$$\begin{bmatrix} 1 \\ 4 \\ 2 \end{bmatrix} x \geq \begin{bmatrix} 5 - 3y_1 - 2y_2 \\ 7 + y_1 - y_2 \\ 4 - y_1 + y_2 \end{bmatrix}, \qquad x \geq 0. \tag{9}$$

The dual program of (9) is

$$\max (u_1, u_2, u_3) \begin{bmatrix} 5 - 3y_1 - 2y_2 \\ 7 + y_1 - y_2 \\ 4 - y_1 + y_2 \end{bmatrix}$$

subject to

$$u_1 + 4u_2 + 2u_3 \leq 5,$$
$$u_1, u_2, u_3 \geq 0. \tag{10}$$

One feasible solution of (10) is $u_1 = 0$, $u_2 = 5/4$, $u_3 = 0$.

Rewriting (8), we have

$$\min z$$

subject to

$$z \geq 2y_1 + 2y_2 + \max \mathbf{u}^p \begin{bmatrix} 5 - 3y_1 - 2y_2 \\ 7 + y_1 - y_2 \\ 4 - y_1 + y_2 \end{bmatrix}, \tag{8'}$$
$$u_1, u_2, u_3 \geq 0.$$

Substituting (0, 5/4, 0) of (10) into (8′), we have

$$\min z$$

subject to

$$z \geq 2y_1 + 2y_2 + \tfrac{5}{4}(7 + y_1 - y_2), \tag{8''}$$
$$y_1, y_2 \geq 0.$$

The solution of (8″) is $\bar{z} = 35/4$, and $\bar{y}_1 = \bar{y}_2 = 0$.

Substituting $\bar{y}_1 = \bar{y}_2 = 0$ into (10), we have

$$\max 5u_1 + 7u_2 + 4u_3$$

subject to

$$u_1 + 4u_2 + 2u_3 \leq 5, \tag{10'}$$
$$u_1, u_2, u_3 \geq 0.$$

The solution is (5, 0, 0), with $5u_1 + 7u_2 + 4u_3 = 25$.

Since $35/4 - (2, 2)[0\ 0] < 25$, we add (5, 0, 0) into (8′):

$$\min z$$

subject to

$$z \geq 2y_1 + 2y_2 + (5/4)(7 + y_1 - y_2),$$
$$z \geq 2y_1 + 2y_2 + 5(5 - 3y_1 - 2y_2),$$
$$y_1, y_2 \geq 0.$$

The solution is $y_1 = 1$, $y_2 = 0$, and $z = 12$.

Substituting $y_1 = 1$ and $y_2 = 0$ into (10), we have

$$\max 2u_1 + 8u_2 + 3u_3$$

subject to

$$u_1 + 4u_2 + 2u_3 \leq 5,$$
$$u_1, u_2, u_3 \geq 0.$$

The solution is $u_1 = 5$, $u_2 = 0$, $u_3 = 0$, with $2u_1 + 8u_2 + 3u_3 = 10$. Since $10 = z - (2, 2)\mathbf{y} = 12 - 2 \times 1 - 2 \times 0 = 10$, the solution is optimum. Substituting $y_1 = 1$, $y_2 = 0$ into (9), we have

$$\min 5x$$

subject to

$$\begin{bmatrix} 1 \\ 4 \\ 2 \end{bmatrix} x \geq \begin{bmatrix} 2 \\ 8 \\ 3 \end{bmatrix}, \qquad x \geq 0.$$

The solution is $x = 2$ with $5x = 5 \times 2 = 10$ as expected. The optimum solution to (8) is $x = 2$, $y_1 = 1$, $y_2 = 0$, and $z^* = 12$.

15.3 APPLICATIONS

In this section we shall mention some problems which can be formulated as integer programs. These serve as examples to illustrate some of the standard techniques of converting problems into integer programs. More references and applications can be found in Balinski [6] and Dantzig [33] [34]. Many integer programs have special structures and should be treated by special methods. A typical class of problems is that of covering and matching (see Balinski [6], Edmonds [54] [55] [56], and Witzgall and Zahn [216]). Another class of problems is called the knapsack problem, which is treated in Chapter 18.

As we have seen in Part 1, the optimum solution of a linear program may not be an integer solution and yet there are many problems which naturally require integer solutions. Some of these problems do not appear as integer programs at first glance, but can be converted into integer programs. If only some variables are required to be integers, then the integer program is called a *mixed integer program* (see Sections 15.1, 15.2). Here we discuss just some classes of problems that can be converted into integer programs. In most of the following problems certain variables are required to be zero or one.

The first class of problems is that in which a variable can take only one of several values. For example the load-carrying capacity of trucks may vary only among certain standard capacities. Let $b_{11}, b_{12}, b_{13}, \ldots, b_{1k}$ be the values that x_j can take. Then

$$x_j = \delta_1 b_{11} + \delta_2 b_{12} + \cdots + \delta_k b_{1k},$$
$$\delta_1 + \cdots + \delta_k = 1,$$
$$\delta_i \geq 0, \text{ integers} \qquad (i = 1, \ldots, k).$$

This forces x_j to take only one of the values $b_{11}, \ldots, b_{1k}$. The same technique can be applied if a vector $\mathbf{x}$ can take only certain vectors as its solutions. If $\mathbf{b}_1, \ldots, \mathbf{b}_k$ are possible solutions, then

$$\mathbf{x} = \delta_1 \mathbf{b}_1 + \delta_2 \mathbf{b}_2 + \cdots + \delta_k \mathbf{b}_k,$$
$$\delta_1 + \cdots + \delta_k = 1,$$
$$\delta_i \geq 0, \text{ integers} \qquad (i = 1, \ldots, k).$$

The second class of problems is that in which the constraints do not have to be satisfied simultaneously. In a linear program all constraints have to hold. Each constraint defines a half-space which is convex. The solution space, being the intersection of all the half-spaces, is also convex. When not all constraints have to be satisfied, the solution space may be the union of only some convex sets and, hence, may not be convex or may even be disconnected. Consider the solution space of the following problem:

$$\max x_1 + x_2$$

subject to either

$$3x_1 + x_2 \leq 4, \quad \text{or}$$
$$2x_1 + 3x_2 \leq 5,$$
$$x_1, x_2 \geq 0.$$

The solution space is the nonconvex shaded area in Fig. 15.3.

To formulate this problem as an integer program, we need to know an upper bound of $3x_1 + x_2 - 4$ and $2x_1 + 3x_2 - 5$. Such an upper bound is not hard to obtain. It is sufficient to take a large positive number say 100 in this case. Then we can formulate the preceding program as an integer program:

$$\max x_1 + x_2$$

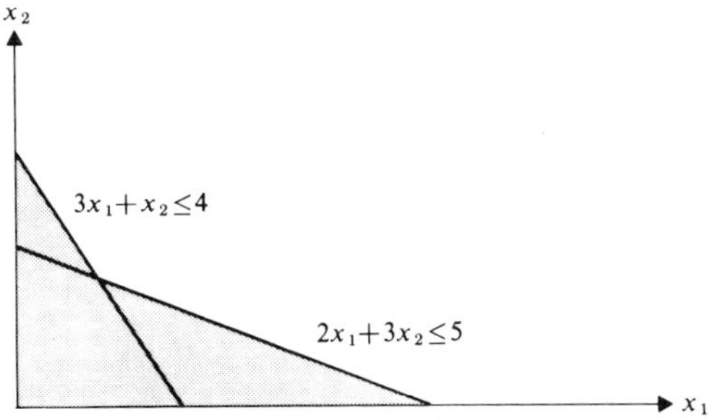

Fig. 15.3

subject to
$$3x_1 + x_2 - 4 - 100\delta \leq 0,$$
$$2x_1 + 3x_2 - 5 - 100(1 - \delta) \leq 0,$$
$$x_1, x_2 \geq 0, \qquad 1 \geq \delta \geq 0, \text{ integers.}$$

Note that when $\delta = 1$, the first constraint is satisfied automatically since $3x_1 + x_2 - 4 \leq 100$, and the second one reduces to $2x_1 + 3x_2 - 5 \leq 0$. When $\delta = 0$, the second constraint is satisfied automatically and the first constraint reduces to $3x_1 + x_2 - 4 \leq 0$. Note also that if δ is not restricted to be integer, the solution space in the variables x_1, x_2, and δ is convex.

If the constraint is either $g_1(\mathbf{x}) \geq 0$ or $g_2(\mathbf{x}) \geq 0$, then we need to know a lower bound of $g_1(\mathbf{x})$, say l_1, and a lower bound of $g_2(\mathbf{x})$, say l_2, and convert them into
$$g_1(\mathbf{x}) - l_1\delta \geq 0,$$
$$g_2(\mathbf{x}) - l_2(1 - \delta) \geq 0,$$
$$1 \geq \delta \geq 0, \text{ integers.}$$

The same idea can be generalized to treat problems where only k out of p constraints should be satisfied. Let the p constraints be $g_1(\mathbf{x}) \geq 0, \ldots,$ $g_m(\mathbf{x}) \geq 0$, $g_{m+1}(\mathbf{x}) \leq 0, \ldots, g_p(\mathbf{x}) \leq 0$, where $l_1, \ldots, l_m$ are the lower bounds of $g_1(\mathbf{x}), \ldots, g_m(\mathbf{x})$ and $u_{m+1}, \ldots, u_p$ are the upper bounds of $g_{m+1}(\mathbf{x})$, $\ldots, g_p(\mathbf{x})$. Then we can write the constraints as
$$\begin{aligned}
g_1(\mathbf{x}) - \delta_1 l_1 &\geq 0,\\
&\vdots\\
g_m(\mathbf{x}) - \delta_m l_m &\geq 0,\\
g_{m+1}(\mathbf{x}) - \delta_{m+1} u_{m+1} &\leq 0,\\
&\vdots\\
g_p(\mathbf{x}) - \delta_p u_p &\leq 0,
\end{aligned}$$
$$\sum_{i=1}^{p} \delta_i = p - k,$$
$$1 \geq \delta_i \geq 0, \text{ integers.}$$

Note that when $\delta_i = 1$ for a certain constraint, that constraint is satisfied automatically. When $\delta_i = 0$ for a constraint, that constraint reduces to $g_i(\mathbf{x}) \geq 0$ or $g_i(\mathbf{x}) \leq 0$.

The idea of letting δ equal one or zero can be used to force the solution $\mathbf{x}$ to satisfy one set of constraints among many sets of constraints. Take three sets of constraints for example (each set may define a convex set and the three convex sets may be disconnected):

$$\begin{array}{lll} f_1(\mathbf{x}) \leq 0, & g_1(\mathbf{x}) \leq 0, & h_1(\mathbf{x}) \geq 0, \\ f_2(\mathbf{x}) \leq 0, & g_2(\mathbf{x}) \leq 0, & h_2(\mathbf{x}) \geq 0, \\ \vdots & \vdots & \vdots \\ f_m(\mathbf{x}) \leq 0, & g_n(\mathbf{x}) \leq 0, & h_p(\mathbf{x}) \geq 0. \end{array}$$

These are equivalent to

$$\begin{array}{lll} f_1(\mathbf{x}) - \delta_1 u_1 \leq 0, & g_1(\mathbf{x}) - \delta_2 u_1' \leq 0, & h_1(\mathbf{x}) - \delta_3 l_1 \geq 0, \\ f_2(\mathbf{x}) - \delta_1 u_2 \leq 0, & g_2(\mathbf{x}) - \delta_2 u_2' \leq 0, & h_2(\mathbf{x}) - \delta_3 l_2 \geq 0, \\ \vdots & \vdots & \vdots \\ f_m(\mathbf{x}) - \delta_1 u_m \leq 0, & g_n(\mathbf{x}) - \delta_2 u_n' \leq 0, & h_p(\mathbf{x}) - \delta_3 l_p \geq 0, \end{array}$$

$$\delta_1 + \delta_2 + \delta_3 = 2,$$

$$1 \geq \delta_j \geq 0, \text{ integers.}$$

The third class of problems deals with the case in which the objective function can be written as the sum of many functions each being a nonlinear function of one variable x_j, i.e., $z = \sum_j z_j(x_j)$. A typical problem is one in transportation where the shipping cost along a route consists of two parts. The first part is a fixed charge for the route used, which is independent of the amount shipped. The second part is proportional to the amount shipped along that route. Thus the total shipping cost z_j along a route j is given by

$$z_j = \begin{cases} k_j + cx_j & \text{if } x_j > 0, \\ 0 & \text{if } x_j = 0, \end{cases}$$

where k_j is the fixed charge and x_j is the amount shipped along route j. This can be written as

$$z_j = \delta k_j + cx_j, \qquad x_j \leq \delta M,$$

$$1 \geq \delta \geq 0 \text{ integers,}$$

where M is an upper bound on x_j.

Let us approximate an arbitrary nonlinear objective function by piecewise linear functions, as shown in Fig. 15.4. In an interval where the function is linear, the value of the function is a linear convex combination of its

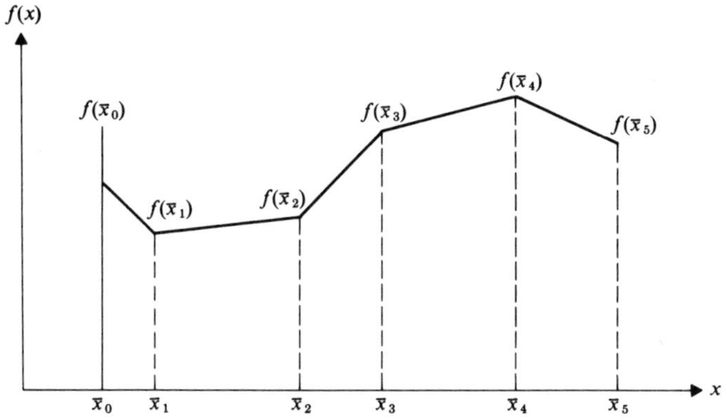

Figure 15.4

values at the two ends. Thus we let

$$
\begin{aligned}
x &= \lambda_0 \bar{x}_0 + \lambda_1 \bar{x}_1 + \cdots + \lambda_n \bar{x}_n,\\
f(x) &= \lambda_0 f(\bar{x}_0) + \lambda_1 f(\bar{x}_1) + \cdots + \lambda_n f(\bar{x}_n),\\
1 &= \lambda_0 + \lambda_1 + \cdots + \lambda_n,\\
&\lambda_i \geq 0 \qquad (i = 0, \ldots, n),\\
\lambda_0 &\leq \delta_0,\\
\lambda_1 &\leq \delta_0 + \delta_1,\\
\lambda_2 &\leq \delta_1 + \delta_2,\\
&\vdots\\
\lambda_{n-1} &\leq \delta_{n-2} + \delta_{n-1},\\
\lambda_n &\leq \delta_{n-1},\\
&\delta_0 + \delta_1 + \cdots + \delta_{n-1} = 1,\\
0 \leq \delta_i &\leq 1, \text{ integers} \qquad (i = 0, 1, \ldots, n-1).
\end{aligned}
$$

Note that when a $\delta_i = 1$, then λ_i and λ_{i+1} can be nonzero and have a sum equal to one, and the rest of the λ's are all zero.

The fourth class of problems may be called the miscellaneous class. There is no standard way of converting them into integer programs. One formulation may involve far fewer variables than another formulation. To cite a few of these problems, we have the orthogonal latin square problem, the traveling salesman problem, the minimum coloring of a map, certain problems in coding, and so on. We shall discuss only the traveling salesman problem and the coloring problem, because they are the more publicized problems. Formulation of a problem as an integer program does not mean that it is solved, because the formulation may involve too many variables, too many constraints, and so forth. They do show however, the great number of varieties of problems that can be formulated as integer programs.

One of the most famous unsolved problems in mathematics is to prove or disprove that any map in the plane can be colored using four colors or less. A map partitions the plane into many regions; the restriction is that two regions having a common boundary line should have different colors. If there is an algorithm that can give the minimum number of colors of any map, then that would serve to establish or destroy a counterexample.

Let us assume that the map can be colored in four colors and let 0,1,2, and 3 represent the four colors. Each region i is represented by an integer-valued variable x_i. For two regions i and j, which are adjacent, we want $x_i \neq x_j$. This is equivalent to either

$$x_i - x_j \geq 1 \qquad \text{or} \qquad x_j - x_i \geq 1.$$

Using the technique discussed earlier, we may write

$$x_i - x_j - 1 \geq -4\delta_{ij}, \qquad x_j - x_i - 1 \geq -4(1 - \delta_{ij}).$$

Furthermore, we want

$$3 \geq x_i \geq 0, \text{ integers,}$$
$$1 \geq \delta_{ij} \geq 0, \text{ integers.}$$

Since all the constraints are inequalities, we can introduce slack variables and artificial variables and let the objective function be the sum of the artificial variables. If the objective function becomes zero, then the map can be colored in four colors. If the minimal value of the objective function is greater than zero, then the map cannot be colored in four colors.

The traveling salesman problem may be stated as follows. Given n cities and distances d_{ij} from city i to city j. How should a traveling salesman travel starting from his home city, visiting every city exactly once, and returning to his home city so that the total distance traveled is minimum? We do not require $d_{ij} = d_{ji}$ but we require $d_{ij} \geq 0$ and $d_{ij} + d_{jk} \geq d_{ik}$ for all i, j, k. Assume that the traveling salesman starts from city 1. Then any permutation of 2, 3, . . ., n represents a possible tour. Thus there are $(n-1)!$ tours to be calculated if we enumerate them all.

If we do not require $d_{ij} + d_{jk} \geq d_{ik}$, then the problem is to visit each city at least once before going home. But this is actually the same as the first formulation, if we first find the shortest paths between every pair of cities and replace the original distances by the shortest distances found. Therefore, we shall restrict ourselves to the first formulation, which requires $d_{ij} + d_{jk} \geq d_{ik}$.

For our particular formulation, we shall assume that there are $n + 1$ cities and the salesman starts at city 0, visits every other city exactly once, ends his tour at city n, *does not* return home, and requires the total distance traveled to be minimum. This is called an open tour as a contrast to the closed tour mentioned above. To convert the closed tour version into the open tour version, we can artificially split the home city into two cities and let the two cities be city 0 and city n. So we shall work with the open tour version of starting at city 0 and ending at city n. Now we shall let $x_{ij} = 1$ if the salesman travels from city i to city j and $x_{ij} = 0$ if he does not. Since each city must be visited once, we have

$$\sum_{i=1}^{n-1} x_{ij} = 1 \qquad (j = 1, \ldots, n;\ i \neq j).$$

Since we must leave every city (except city n), we have

$$\sum_{j=1}^{n} x_{ij} = 1 \qquad (i = 0, 1, \ldots, n-1;\ i \neq j).$$

The two sets of constraints guarantee that in the graph of the traveling salesman's locus, city 0 and city n are of degree 1 and all other cities are of degree 2.

But it is possible to satisfy the above two sets of constraints by having the salesman travel only to some of the cities and then go to city n and connect the cities not visited by a loop or several loops. To make such subtours impossible, we require a third set of constraints. First, we associate with each city i, a real number y_i $(0 \leq y_i \leq n)$. Then we require

$$y_i - y_j + nx_{ij} \leq n - 1 \qquad (0 \leq i \leq n-1,\ 1 \leq j \leq n,\ i \neq j).$$

To see that this set of constraints will rule out any subtour, we consider a subtour that contains k cities for which $x_{ij} = 1$ in the tour. To each arc with $x_{ij} = 1$, we have an inequality. If we add all the inequalities corresponding to the k arcs of the subtour, then the differences $y_i - y_j$ will cancel each other and we have $nk \leq (n-1)k$, a contradiction. Thus, solution of subtours will not be accepted by the third set of constraints. On the other hand, to show that any open tour can meet our third set of constraints, let $y_i = t$ if city i is the tth city on the open tour. Thus $y_i - y_j \leq n - 1$ for all i and j and the third set of constraints is satisfied for $x_{ij} = 0$. For $x_{ij} = 1$, we have $y_i = t$ and $y_j = t + 1$. Thus $t - (t+1) + n = n - 1$. The objective function is then

$$\min z = \sum_{i=0}^{n-1} \sum_{j=1}^{n} d_{ij}x_{ij}.$$

INTEGER PROGRAMS WITH PARABOLIC CONSTRAINTS 16

16.1 INTRODUCTION (Witzgall [215])

In this chapter, we shall study integer programs with parabolic constraints. We first define a parabolic constraint.

Definition. A parabolic constraint of rank k is one which can be put into the form

$$a_{00} - L_0(\mathbf{x}) - b_1(L_1(\mathbf{x}))^2 - \cdots - b_k(L_k(\mathbf{x}))^2 \geq 0, \tag{1}$$

where

$$L_s(\mathbf{x}) = a_{s1}x_1 + \cdots + a_{sn}x_n \qquad (s = 0, 1, \ldots, k) \tag{2}$$

are a set of $k + 1$ linearly independent homogeneous linear forms of n variables and

$$b_i \geq 0 \qquad (i = 1, \ldots, k).$$

Note that (1) can be changed by a linear transformation into a constraint of the form

$$y_0 - y_1^2 - \cdots - y_k^2 \geq 0. \tag{3}$$

A parabolic constraint of rank zero is then a linear constraint, and a parabolic constraint of rank $n - 1$ characterizes a convex n-dimensional paraboloid.

Many integer programs can be put into this form. In particular a quadratic positive semidefinite objective function with linear constraints, say, can be put into a linear objective function with parabolic constraints. For example, let the objective function be

$$\min z = a + \sum_{i=1}^{n} a_i x_i + \sum_{i,j=1}^{n} a_{ij} x_i x_j. \tag{4}$$

We can introduce z as a new variable and transform the objective function into a parabolic constraint, i.e.,

$$\min z$$

subject to

$$z - a - \sum_{i=1}^{n} a_i x_i - \sum_{i,j=1}^{n} a_{ij} x_i x_j \geq 0. \tag{5}$$

In order to have a constraint belong to the parabolic type, we require that the quadratic part of (1), i.e., $b_1(L_1(\mathbf{x}))^2 + \cdots + b_k(L_k(\mathbf{x}))^2$ be positive definite or positive semidefinite, and that the $k + 1$ homogeneous linear forms in (2) be linearly independent.

To check whether a given quadratic constraint

$$a_0 + \sum_{i=1}^{n} a_i x_i + \sum_{i,j=1}^{n} a_{ij} x_i x_j \geq 0 \tag{6}$$

is parabolic or not, we proceed as follows. If all a_{ii} are nonpositive, then (6) is negative definite, negative semidefinite, or indefinite. If one a_{ii} is positive, say a_{11}, then the subform in (6),

$$a_{11}x_1^2 + (a_{12} + a_{21})x_1x_2 + \cdots + (a_{1n} + a_{n1})x_1x_n,$$

will give the following terms by completing the square:

$$\frac{1}{a_{11}}\left(a_{11}x_1 + \frac{a_{12} + a_{21}}{2} x_2 + \cdots + \frac{a_{1n} + a_{n1}}{2} x_n\right)^2.$$

If (6) is parabolic, the remaining quadratic form has to be positive semidefinite. Hence we may repeat the process of completing squares. In the case of a parabolic constraint, the quadratic part will become the sum of $n - 1$ or fewer squared linear forms.

Consider an integer program with a linear objective function and parabolic constraints (some of them may be linear constraints):

$$\max c_0 - \sum c_j x_j \tag{7}$$

subject to

$$a_{00} - L_0(\mathbf{x}) - b_1(L_1(\mathbf{x}))^2 - \cdots - b_k(L_k(\mathbf{x}))^2 \geq 0 \tag{8}$$

$$x_j \geq 0 \qquad (j = 1, \ldots, n).$$

For simplicity we have just one constraint in (8) and all the x_j in (7) and (8) are nonbasic variables. If $c_j \geq 0$ in (7), then the solution obtained by setting all nonbasic variables equal to zero is clearly a dual feasible solution. Any nonnegative $\mathbf{x}'$ would give an objective function $c_0 - \sum c_j x_j'$ less than c_0. Whether the solution is also primal feasible or not depends on $a_{00} \lesseqgtr 0$.

In order to have (8) satisfied, it is necessary (but not sufficient) to have

$$a_{00} - L_0(\mathbf{x}) \geq 0. \tag{9}$$

This is because the quadratic part of (8) is always nonnegative, i.e.,

$$b_1(L_1(\mathbf{x}))^2 + \cdots + b_k(L_k(\mathbf{x}))^2 \geq 0 \qquad (\text{for } b_i \geq 0;\ i = 1, \ldots, k).$$

Then (9) represents a linear constraint which must be satisfied by every feasible solution of the original problem. If $a_{00} < 0$ in (9), we can consider (9) as a source row and derive from it a Gomory cut just as we did before in Section 13.1. If we use the Gomory cut as the pivot row and do a pivot (a pivot step is a linear transformation of nonbasic variables), then we will obtain a new objective function (7) and new constraints derived from (8) by substitution into a new set of nonbasic variables. Consequently, we will have a new linear part (9) to be qualified as the source row if its a_{00} is negative. It will be shown that this process is a finite one.

Geometrically, the hyperplane $a_{00} - L_0(\mathbf{x}) = 0$ is a tangent plane to the constraint surface defined by (8). This is stated in the following lemma.

Lemma 16.1. The hyperplane $T = \{\mathbf{x} \mid a_{00} - L_0(\mathbf{x}) = 0\}$ is a tangent plane to the constraint surface defined by (8). It is uniquely determined as the tangent plane which is parallel to the polar of the origin with respect to the constraint surface.

Proof. Since (8) implies (9), the points satisfying (8) are on one side of the hyperplane defined by T. T is a tangent plane because the intersection of T and the zero space L of the quadratic part of (8), i.e.,

$$L = \{\mathbf{x} \mid L_1(\mathbf{x}) = 0, \ldots, L_k(\mathbf{x}) = 0\},$$

is nonempty. $L \cap T \neq 0$ because $L_0(\mathbf{x}), L_1(\mathbf{x}), \ldots, L_k(\mathbf{x})$ are linearly independent. There is no other tangent plane parallel to T. Otherwise there would be a plane with $a_{00} - L_0(\mathbf{x}) \leq \gamma$ for all values of $\mathbf{x}$ satisfying (8), which is a contradiction since $a_{00} - L_0(\mathbf{x}) \leq \gamma$ is on one side of T while the convex n-dimensional paraboloid is on the other side of T. Due to the fact that T represents a tangent plane to (8) we cut off some part of the convex region defined by (8) (but not integer point) when we get a Gomory cut from T. In order to prove finiteness, we assume that all coefficients appearing in (7) and (8) are integers and that there exists a lower bound to the feasible solution of (7) and (8). It is easier to talk about the algorithm and the finiteness proof when we have a definite tableau. This is discussed in the next section.

16.2 TABLEAU

As with Gomory's all-integer algorithm, we will have a starting tableau which is dual feasible and every constraint is expressed in terms of the negatives of nonbasic variables. We put the relations $x_j = -(-x_j) \geq 0$ as the first n rows under the objective row. These are called reference rows. (If some $c_j = 0$, then we have to introduce a dummy relation to make the starting tableau dual feasible; see Section 14.1.) Constraints like (8) are listed under these reference rows. A parabolic constraint,

$$a_{00} - (a_{01}x_1 + \cdots + a_{0n}x_n) - b_1(a_{11}x_1 + \cdots + a_{1n}x_n)^2 - \cdots - b_k(a_{k1}x_1 + \cdots + a_{kn}x_n)^2 \geq 0,$$

appears as in Tabeau 16.1.

Tableau 16.1

	1	$-x_1,$	$-x_2,$	$\ldots,$	$-x_n$	
z	c_0	$c_1,$	$c_2,$	$\ldots,$	c_n	
x_1	0	-1				
$\vdots$	$\vdots$		-1	$\ddots$		
x_n	0				-1	
s_1	a_{00}	$a_{01},$	$a_{02},$	$\ldots,$	a_{0n}	
	0	$a_{11},$	$a_{12},$	$\ldots,$	a_{1n}	b_1
	0					$\vdots$
	$\vdots$					
	0	$a_{k1},$	$a_{k2},$	$\ldots,$	a_{kn}	b_k
s_2						

Each parabolic constraint occupies $k + 1$ rows with a double line above them and a double line below them. A linear constraint occupies one row and they are likewise listed. More precisely, we should have a superscript on every coefficient of the parabolic constraint, since we may have many parabolic constraints. For example,

$$\max z = -3x_1 - x_2$$

Tableau 16.2

	1	$-x_1$	$-x_2$		
z	0	3	1		
x_1	0	−1	0		Reference rows
x_2	0	0	−1		
s_1	−3	−6	2		
	0	1	0	1	
s_2	−16	−5	−5		
	0	1	−1	1	
					←The bottom row is reserved for Gomory's cut, to be added later.

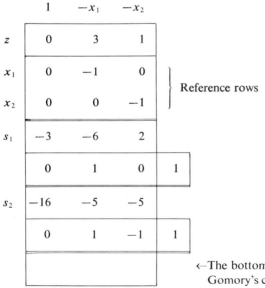

subject to

$$-3 + 6x_1 - 2x_2 - x_1^2 \geq 0,$$
$$-16 + 5x_1 + 5x_2 - (x_1 - x_2)^2 \geq 0,$$
$$x_1, x_2 \geq 0 \quad \text{integers.}$$

The tableau will appear as in Tableau 16.2. If all entries in the 0th column (the constant column) are nonnegative, then the tableau is primal feasible. Since we start with a dual feasible tableau, and will maintain dual feasibility in the subsequent tableau, we get the optimum solution when the tableau becomes also primal feasible.

16.3 TRANSFORMATION

Consider the nonsingular linear transformation between $\bar{x}_j$ and x_j defined by

$$\begin{aligned} \bar{x}_1 &= x_1, \\ &\vdots \\ \bar{x}_r &= p_0 - p_1 x_1 - p_2 x_2 - \cdots + x_r - \cdots - p_n x_n, \\ &\vdots \\ \bar{x}_n &= x_n. \end{aligned} \tag{1}$$

A linear expression such as $a_{00} - a_{01}x_1 - a_{02}x_2 - \cdots - a_{0n}x_n$ will become, under this transformation,

$$\bar{a}_{00} - \bar{a}_{01}\bar{x}_1 - \cdots - \bar{a}_{0r}\bar{x}_r - \cdots - \bar{a}_{0n}\bar{x}_n,$$

where

$$\begin{aligned} \bar{a}_{00} &= a_{00} + p_0 a_{0r}, \\ \bar{a}_{0j} &= a_{0j} + p_j a_{0r} \qquad (\text{for } j \neq r), \\ \bar{a}_{0r} &= a_{0r}. \end{aligned} \tag{2}$$

Note that if p_j and a_{0j} $(j = 0, 1, \ldots, n)$ are integers, then $\bar{a}_{0j}$ $(j = 0, 1, \ldots, n)$ are also integers.

The quadratic form $-b_s(a_{s1}x_1 + \cdots + a_{sn}x_n)^2$ will likewise transform under (1) into $-b_s(\bar{a}_{s1}\bar{x}_1 + \cdots + \bar{a}_{sn}\bar{x}_n + p_0\bar{a}_{sr})^2$, where

$$\begin{aligned} \bar{a}_{sj} &= a_{sj} + a_{sr}p_j \qquad (\text{for } j \neq r), \\ \bar{a}_{sr} &= a_{sr}. \end{aligned} \tag{3}$$

Writing in more detail, we have

$$\begin{aligned} -b_s(\bar{a}_{s1}\bar{x}_1 + \cdots + \bar{a}_{sn}\bar{x}_n + p_0\bar{a}_{sr})^2 &= -b_s(\bar{a}_{s1}\bar{x}_1 + \cdots + \bar{a}_{sn}\bar{x}_n)^2 \\ &\quad - 2b_s p_0 \bar{a}_{sr}(\bar{a}_{s1}\bar{x}_1 + \cdots + \bar{a}_{sn}\bar{x}_n) - b_s(p_0\bar{a}_{sr})^2. \end{aligned} \tag{4}$$

Equation (4) expresses the result of a transformation under (1) on one row, i.e., $-b_s(L_s(\mathbf{x}))^2$. To put a parabolic constraint like (8) of Section 16.1

Tableau 16.3

1	$-\bar{x}_1$	$-\bar{x}_2$	$\dots$	$\dots$	$-\bar{x}_n$	
a'_{00}	a'_{01}	a'_{02}	$\dots$	$\dots$	a'_{0n}	
0	a'_{11}	a_{12}	$\dots$	$\dots$	a'_{1n}	b_1
0						$\cdot$
0						$\cdot$
0						$\cdot$
0	a'_{k1}	a'_{k2}	$\dots$	$\dots$	a'_{kn}	b_k

in terms of new variables $\bar{x}_j$, we have Tableau 16.3, where

$$a'_{00} = \bar{a}_{00} - \sum_{s=1}^{k} b_s(p_0\bar{a}_{sr})^2,$$

$$a'_{0j} = \bar{a}_{0j} - 2\sum_{s=1}^{k} b_s p_0 \bar{a}_{sr}\bar{a}_{sj} \qquad (j = 1, \dots, n), \tag{5}$$

$$a'_{ij} = \bar{a}_{ij} \qquad (\text{for } i, j = 1, \dots, n).$$

Note that the $\bar{a}_{ij}$ given in (2) and (3) are obtained if we treat all the rows as linear constraints. Equations (5) then restore the tableau to the standard parabolic form (8) of Section 16.1.

16.4 THE ALGORITHM

The algorithm consists of the following steps:

STEP 0. Start with a dual feasible tableau like Tableau 16.1. Each parabolic constraint of rank k occupies $k + 1$ rows and the a_{i0} ($i = 1, \dots, k$) are zero. This is called the standard form.

STEP 1. If there is no negative entry in the 0th column, the current solution obtained by setting all nonbasic variables equal to zero is the optimum solution. Otherwise, choose the first negative entry in the 0th column and use it as the source row (because $a_{i0} = 0$ in a parabolic constraint, only the linear part $a_{00} - L_0(\mathbf{x}) \geq 0$ or a linear constraint will be chosen as the source row).

STEP 2. Let the source row be $a_{00} - a_{01}x_1 - a_{02}x_2 - \cdots - a_{0n}x_n \geq 0$. In the tableau, since everything is in terms of $-x_j$, we have

a_{00}	a_{01}	a_{02}	$\dots$	$\dots$	$\dots$	a_{0n}

.

We choose, among $a_{0j} < 0$, the lexicographically smallest column as the pivot column $\boldsymbol{\alpha}_r$. Let μ_j be the largest integer for which $(1/\mu_j)\boldsymbol{\alpha}_j \succ \boldsymbol{\alpha}_r$.

Then define

$$\lambda = \max_j \left(\frac{-a_{0j}}{\mu_j} \right) \qquad (a_{0j} < 0).$$

Note that $\mu_r = 1$ and the pivot will always be -1.

STEP 3. Obtain the Gomory cut

$$s = \left[\frac{a_{00}}{\lambda}\right] - \left[\frac{a_{01}}{\lambda}\right] x_1 - \cdots + x_r - \cdots - \left[\frac{a_{0n}}{\lambda}\right] x_n \geq 0.$$

This is put at the bottom of the tableau as

$\left[\frac{a_{00}}{\lambda}\right]$	$\left[\frac{a_{01}}{\lambda}\right]$	...	...	-1	...	...	$\left[\frac{a_{0n}}{\lambda}\right]$

.

STEP 4. Use the Gomory cut as the pivot row and -1 as the pivot and treat all rows in the tableau just as if they were all linear constraints. For a parabolic constraint we get

$\bar{a}_{00}$	$\bar{a}_{01}$,	...,	...,	$\bar{a}_{0n}$	
$\bar{a}_{10}$	$\bar{a}_{11}$,	...,	...,	$\bar{a}_{1n}$	b_1
⋮					⋮
⋮					⋮
⋮					⋮
$\bar{a}_{k0}$	$\bar{a}_{k1}$,	...,	...,	$\bar{a}_{kn}$	b_k

where $\bar{a}_{i0}$ $(i = 1, \ldots, k)$ may not be zero.

STEP 5. Restore the tableau to the standard form using (5) of Section 16.3. Return to step 1.

16.5 EXAMPLES

Let us do two numerical examples before giving the finiteness proof. Consider the program

$$\max z = -3x_1 - x_2$$

subject to

$$-3 - (-6x_1 + 2x_2) - x_1^2 \geq 0,$$

$$-16 - (-5x_1 - 5x_2) - (x_1 - x_2)^2 \geq 0,$$

$$x_1, x_2 \geq 0, \ \text{integers}.$$

We have Tableau 16.4 (← and ↑ indicate source row and pivot column respectively).

Tableau 16.4

	1	$-x_1$	$-x_2$		
z	0	3	1		
x_1	0	-1	0		
x_2	0	0	-1		
s_1	-3	-6	2		←Source row
	0	1	0	1	
s_2	-16	-5	-5		
	0	1	-1	1	
s_3	-1	-1	0		
		↑ Pivot column			

After the pivot we have Tableau 16.5. To restore the tableau to the standard form, we have

$$a'_{00} = \bar{a}_{00} - \sum b_s(p_0\bar{a}_{s1})^2 = 3 - 1 \cdot (-1 \cdot 1)^2 = 2,$$

$$a'_{01} = \bar{a}_{01} - 2\sum b_s p_0 \bar{a}_{s1} \cdot \bar{a}_{s1} = -6 - 2 \cdot 1 \cdot (-1)(1)(1) = -4,$$

$$a'_{02} = \bar{a}_{02} - 2\sum b_s p_0 \bar{a}_{s1}\bar{a}_{s2} = 2 - 2 \cdot 1 \cdot (-1) \cdot 1 \cdot 0 = 2.$$

Tableau 16.5

	1	$-s_3$	$-x_2$	
z	-3	3	1	
x_1	1	-1	0	
x_2	0	0	-1	
s_1	3	-6	2	
	-1	1	0	1
s_2	-11	-5	-5	
	-1	1	-1	1
s_3	0	-1	0	

Similarly we have

$$a'_{00} = -11 - 1 \cdot (-1 \cdot 1)^2 = -12,$$

$$a'_{01} = -5 - 2 \cdot 1 \cdot (-1) \cdot 1^2 = -3,$$

$$a'_{02} = -5 - 2 \cdot 1 \cdot (-1) \cdot 1 \cdot (-1) = -7.$$

We have then Tableau 16.6.

Tableau 16.6

	1	$-s_3$	$-x_2$		
z	-3	3	1		
x_1	1	-1	0		
x_2	0	0	-1		
s_1	2	-4	2		
	0	1	0	1	
s_2	-12	-3	-7		←
	0	1	-1	1	
s_4	-2	-1	-1		
			↑		

Tableau 16.7

	1	$-s_3$	$-s_4$		
z	-5	2	1		
x_1	1	-1	0		
x_2	2	1	-1		
s_1	-2	-6	2		←
	0	1	0	1	
s_2	-2	-4	-3		
	0	2	-1	1	
s_5	-1	-1	0		
		↑			

The successive standard tableaux are Tableaux 16.7, 16.8 and 16.9 with Tableau 16.9 being the optimum one.

Tableau 16.8

	1	$-s_5$	$-s_4$		
z	-7	2	1		
x_1	2	-1	0		
x_2	1	1	-1		
s_1	3	-4	2		
	0	1	0	1	
s_2	-2	4	-7		←
	0	2	-1	1	
s_6	-1	0	-1		
			↑		

Tableau 16.9

	1	$-s_5$	$-s_6$	
z	-8	2	1	
x_1	2	-1	0	
x_2	2	1	-1	
s_1	1	-4	2	
	0	1	0	1
s_2	4	0	-5	
	0	2	-1	1
s_6	0	0	-1	

Consider the integer programs

$$\min z = x_1^2 + 3x_2^2 + 2x_3^2$$

subject to

$$\begin{aligned} x_1 + 2x_2 - x_3 &\geq 5, \\ -3x_1 + x_2 + x_3 &\geq -2, \\ x_1, x_2, x_3 &\geq 0 \text{ integers.} \end{aligned}$$

To transform this problem into an integer program with parabolic constraint, let us introduce $x_4 = -w$ as another variable:

$$\max w = -x_4$$

subject to

$$\begin{aligned} -5 - (-x_1 - 2x_2 + x_3) &\geq 0, \\ 2 - (3x_1 - x_2 - x_3) &\geq 0, \\ x_4 - x_1^2 - 3x_2^2 - 2x_3^2 &\geq 0. \end{aligned}$$

To make the starting tableau dual feasible, let us introduce a dummy constraint $-x_1 - x_2 - x_3 + x_4 + M \geq 0$, where M is chosen so that it becomes a dummy constraint. (We could have introduced $-x_1 - x_2 - x_3 - x_4 + c \geq 0$.) Here we take M to be 2, and we have the starting Tableau 16.10.

Tableau 16.10

	1	$-x_1$	$-x_2$	$-x_3$	$-x_4$		
w	0	0	0	0	+1		
s_1	2	1	1	1	−1		
x_1	0	−1	0	0	0		
x_2	0	0	−1	0	0		
x_3	0	0	0	−1	0		
x_4	0	0	0	0	−1		
s_2	−5	−1	−2	+1	0		←
s_3	2	3	−1	−1	0		
s_4	0	0	0	0	−1		
	0	1	0	0	0	1	
	0	0	1	0	0	3	
	0	0	0	1	0	2	
s_5	−3	−1	−1	0	0		
		↑					

Tableau 16.11

	1	$-s_5$	$-x_2$	$-x_3$	$-x_4$	
w	0	0	0	0	+1	
s_1	−1	1	0	1	−1	
x_1	3	−1	1	0	0	
x_2	0	0	−1	0	0	
x_3	0	0	0	−1	0	
x_4	0	0	0	0	−1	
s_2	−2	−1	−1	1	0	←
s_3	−7	3	−4	−1	0	
s_4	0	0	0	0	−1	
	−3	1	−1	0	0	1
	0	0	1	0	0	3
	0	0	0	1	0	2
s_5	0	−1	0	0	0	
		↑				

Tableau 16.12

	1	$-s_5$	$-x_2$	$-x_3$	$-x_4$	
w	0	0	0	0	+1	
s_1	−1	1	0	1	−1	←
x_1	3	−1	1	0	0	
x_2	0	0	−1	0	0	
x_3	0	0	0	−1	0	
x_4	0	0	0	0	−1	
s_2	−2	−1	−1	1	0	
s_3	−7	3	−4	−1	0	
s_4	−9	6	−6	0	−1	
	0	1	−1	0	0	1
	0	0	1	0	0	3
	0	0	0	1	0	2
s_6	−1	1	0	1	−1	
					↑	

After the pivot we have Tableaux 16.11 and 16.12. To restore the tableau to standard form, we have

$$
\begin{aligned}
a'_{00} &= \bar{a}_{00} - \sum b_s(p_0 \cdot \bar{a}_{s1})^2 \\
&= 0 - 1 \cdot (-3 \cdot 1)^2 - 3 \cdot (-3 \cdot 0)^2 - 2 \cdot (-3 \cdot 0)^2 \\
&= -9, \\
a'_{01} &= \bar{a}_{01} - 2 \sum b_s p_o \bar{a}_{s1}^2 = 0 - 2 \cdot 1 \cdot (-3) \cdot 1^2 \\
&\quad - 2 \cdot 3 \cdot (-3) \cdot 0^2 - 2 \cdot 2 \cdot (-3) \cdot 0^2 = 6, \\
a'_{02} &= \bar{a}_{02} - 2 \sum b_s p_o \bar{a}_{s1} \cdot \bar{a}_{s2} = 0 - 2 \cdot 1 \cdot (-3)(1)(-1) = -6.
\end{aligned}
$$

Tableau 16.13

	1	$-s_5$	$-x_2$	$-x_3$	$-s_6$	
w	-1	1	0	1	1	
s_1	0	0	0	0	-1	
x_1	3	-1	1	0	0	
x_2	0	0	-1	0	0	
x_3	0	0	0	-1	0	
x_4	1	-1	0	-1	-1	
s_2	-2	-1	-1	1	0	←
s_3	-7	3	-4	-1	0	
s_4	-8	5	-6	-1	-1	
	0	1	-1	0	0	1
	0	0	1	0	0	3
	0	0	0	1	0	2
s_7	-2	-1	-1	1	0	
			↑			

The successive tableaux in standard form are shown in Tableaux 16.13 through 16.18. Corresponding to each tableau, there is a set of nonbasic variables. The linear transformation of nonbasic variables defined by (2) of Section 16.3 will generally not transform a parabolic constraint into the standard form, and a computation has to be done to restore the parabolic constraint to the standard form. In order to save space, we shall only exhibit the tableaux corresponding to the standard forms after every pivot.

Tableau 16.14

	1	$-s_5$	$-s_7$	$-x_3$	$-s_6$ ↓	
w	−1	1	0	1	1	
s_1	0	0	0	0	−1	
x_1	1	−2	1	1	0	
x_2	2	1	−1	−1	0	
x_3	0	0	0	−1	0	
x_4	1	−1	0	−1	−1	
s_2	0	0	−1	0	0	
s_3	1	7	−4	−5	0	
s_4	−12	−9	10	9	−1	←
	0	2	−1	−1	0	1
	0	−1	1	1	0	3
	0	0	0	1	0	2
s_8	−2	−1	1	1	−1*	

Tableau 16.15

	1	$-s_5$	$-s_7$	$-x_3$	$-s_8$	
w	−3	0	1	2	1	
s_1	2	1	−1	−1	−1	
x_1	1	−2	1	1	0	
x_2	2	1	−1	−1	0	
x_3	0	0	0	−1	0	
x_4	3	0	−1	−2	−1	
s_2	0	0	−1	0	0	
s_3	1	7	−4	−5	0	
s_4	−10	−8	+9	8	−1	←
	0	2	−1	−1	0	1
	0	−1	1	1	0	3
	0	0	0	1	0	2
s_9	−2	−1	1	1	−1	
		↑				

Tableau 16.16

	1	$-s_9$	$-s_7$	$-x_3$	$-s_8$		
w	-3	0	1	2	1		
s_1	0	1	0	0	-2		
x_1	5	-2	-1	-1	2		
x_2	0	1	0	0	-1		
x_3	0	0	0	-1	0		
x_4	3	0	-1	-2	-1		
s_2	0	0	-1	0	0		
s_3	-13	7	3	2	-7		←
s_4	-22	20	9	8	-21		
	0	2	1	1	-2	1	
	0	-1	0	0	1	3	
	0	0	0	1	0	2	
s_{10}	-2	1	0	0	-1		
					↑		

Tableau 16.17

	1	$-s_9$	$-s_7$	$-x_3$	$-s_{10}$		
w	-5	1	1	2	1		
s_1	4	-1	0	0	-2		
x_1	1	0	-1	-1	2		
x_2	2	0	0	0	-1		
x_3	0	0	0	-1	0		
x_4	5	-1	-1	-2	-1		
s_2	0	0	-1	0	0		
s_3	1	0	3	2	-7		
s_4	-8	-1	1	0	7		←
	0	0	1	1	-2	1	
	0	0	0	0	1	3	
	0	0	0	1	0	2	
s_{11}	-8	-1	1	0	7		
		↑					

Tableau 16.18

	1	$-s_{11}$	$-s_7$	$-x_3$	$-s_{10}$	
w	-13	1	2	2	8	
s_1	12	-1	-1	0	-9	
x_1	1	0	-1	-1	2	
x_2	2	0	0	0	-1	
x_3	0	0	0	-1	0	
x_4	13	-1	-2	-2	-8	
s_2	0	0	-1	0	0	
s_3	1	0	3	2	-7	
s_4	0	-1	0	0	0	
	0	0	1	1	-2	1
	0	0	0	0	1	3
	0	0	0	1	0	2

Tableau 16.18 is optimum with

$$x_1 = 1, \qquad x_2 = 2, \qquad x_3 = 0, \qquad x_4 = 13.$$

16.6 FINITENESS PROOF

There are two situations in which the algorithm will terminate:

1. All entries except a_{00} in the source row are nonnegative.
2. The tableau becomes primal feasible.

In the first case, we have a constraint like

$$a_{00} - a_{01}x_1 - a_{02}x_2 - \cdots - a_{0n}x_n - \sum_s b_s(L_s(\mathbf{x}))^2 \geq 0.$$

Since $a_{00} < 0$, $a_{0i} \geq 0\ (i = 1, \ldots, n)$ and $x_j \geq 0$, the lefthand side of the above inequality is negative, and the program is infeasible. To show that the algorithm will terminate excluding case 1, we use the same argument as in the all-integer algorithm. The 0th column will decrease lexicographically at each step, and we have assumed that there exists a lower bound to the integer feasible solution.

Just as in the all-integer algorithm, the coefficients in constraints need not be integers as long as the entries in the reference rows and the objective row are integers.

PRIMAL INTEGER PROGRAMMING* 17

by R. D. Young, Rice University

17.1 INTRODUCTION AND THE ALGORITHM

The term "primal," applied to an integer programming algorithm, denotes a method that proceeds to an optimal solution through a sequence of successively better solutions that are all feasible in the sense of satisfying both the integer and the linear restrictions on the variables.† One of the prospective advantages of a primal algorithm is the possibility of stopping calculation before an optimal solution has been obtained and using the best solution that has been generated. Additionally, it is possible to use a primal algorithm in conjunction with dual algorithms to generate a variety of composite algorithms that may alternate between primal feasible and dual feasible phases.

The natural precedent and model for a primal algorithm is the Gomory all-integer algorithm, since this algorithm generates a sequence of dual feasible, all-integer solutions and the primal algorithm must generate a sequence of primal feasible, all-integer solutions. It will be recalled that the Gomory all-integer algorithm is a modified version of the dual simplex method. The essential modification consists of generating a Gomory cut from one of the legitimate pivot rows in the tableau in a way that ensures the cut itself will be a legitimate pivot row with a pivot coefficient of -1. Using the cut as the pivot row then guarantees that a given dual feasible, all-integer tableau will be transformed into another dual feasible, all-integer tableau by the pivot operation.

Fortunately, it is possible to analogously modify the simplex method to obtain an algorithm that preserves primal feasible, all-integer tableaux. To provide a notational context for describing the procedure, we shall consider the following integer program:

$$\max x_0 = a_{00} - \sum_{j=m+1}^{n} a_{0j} x_j$$

---

* The primary sources for this chapter are Glover [76] and Young [225]. The procedures given in this chapter are most similar to those of Glover, while the proofs are closer to those given by Young.

† The algorithms discussed in Chapters 13 and 14 should be classified as dual algorithms since all preterminal solutions are not feasible for the original program.

subject to

$$x_i + \sum_{j=m+1}^{n} a_{ij}\, x_j = a_{i0} \quad (i = 1, 2, \ldots, m), \tag{1}$$

$$x_k \geq 0, \quad \text{integers} \quad (k = 1, 2, \ldots, n),$$

in which the constants a_{0j}, a_{ij}, and a_{i0} are all integers and $a_{i0} \geq 0$.

Suppose that $\mathbf{a}_s$ is chosen as the pivot column and row v is the natural pivot row, i.e., $a_{v0}/a_{vs} \leq a_{i0}/a_{is}$ for all rows i with $a_{is} > 0$. *Before* carrying out the Gaussian elimination of the simplex method, we adjoin to the tableau a Gomory cut generated from the row v:*

$$s_k = [a_{v0} / \lambda] + \sum_{j \in J} [a_{vj} / \lambda]\,(-x\,), \tag{2}$$

where J is the index set of the nonbasic variables in (1), s_k is a new (basic) slack variable, and λ is a (temporarily) undetermined positive constant.

Now note that if we set $\lambda = a_{vs}$, then (2) will have two important properties. First, the pivot ratio for the cut is

$$\frac{[a_{v0} / a_{vs}]}{[a_{vs} / a_{vs}]} = \left[\frac{a_{v0}}{a_{vs}}\right] \leq \frac{a_{v0}}{a_{vs}}.$$

This means that primal feasibility will be preserved if the cut (2) is used as the pivot row. The second property is

$$[a_{vs} / a_{vs}] = 1,$$

which means that the pivot is 1 (if the cut is used as the pivot row). It is well known, and easily verified by inspection of the simplex method change of basis formulas, that a unit pivot will convert an all-integer tableau into another all-integer tableau.

These ideas are the foundation of an intuitive primal integer programming algorithm (see Ben-Israel and Charnes [17]). To emphasize the elementary structure of primal cutting plane algorithms we state this algorithm and solve an example problem before introducing the modifications that are needed to get a finiteness proof:

STEP 0. Start with a column tableau having $a_{i0} \geq 0$ $(i \geq 1)$ and all coefficients a_{0j}, a_{ij}, and a_{i0} integers.

STEP 1. Check to determine whether $a_{0j} \geq 0$ $(j \geq 1)$; if so, stop; the current basis is optimal; otherwise go to step 2.

STEP 2. Select a column s with $a_{0s} < 0$ to be the pivot column. Select a row v, the natural pivot row that minimizes a_{i0}/a_{is} among all rows with $a_{is} > 0$, to serve as the source row for generating a Gomory cut.

---

* This is the formula used for cut generation in the Gomory all-integer algorithm. See Section 14.1.

STEP 3. Derive a Gomory cut from the source row and adjoin it to the bottom of the tableau, i.e., equation (2) where $\lambda = a_{vs}$.

STEP 4. Do a pivot step using the cut (2) as the pivot row. The slack variable s_k in (2) becomes a nonbasic variable. Return to step 1.

We illustrate this intuitive algorithm by solving the following problem:

$$\max x_0 = 3x_1 + x_2$$

subject to

$$2x_1 + 3x_2 \leq 6,$$

$$2x_1 - 3x_2 \leq 3,$$

$$x_1, x_2 \geq 0, \quad \text{integers}.$$

A graph of the problem and of the four cuts successively generated in the course of solving the problem appears in Fig. 17.1.

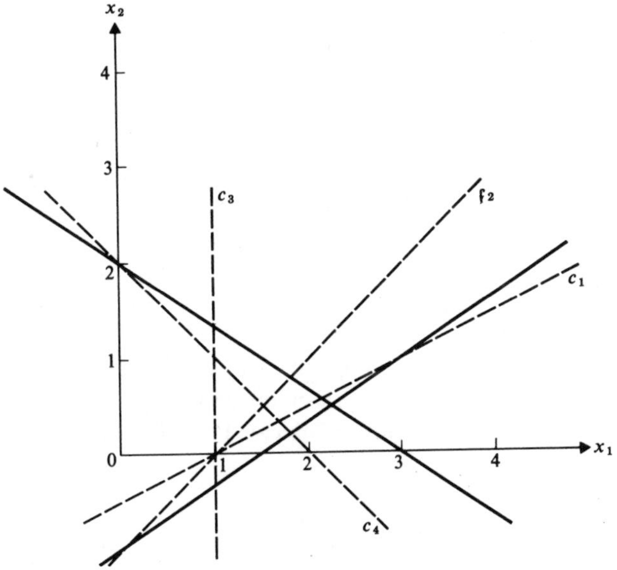

Fig. 17-1

After adding slack variables (x_3, x_4) the problem is expressed in Tableau 17.1. We choose x_1 as the incoming variable. The x_4 row is the natural pivot row and is chosen as the source row. We adjoin the cut, generated from the source row by (2), in the last row of the tableau. The new variable s_1 is the slack variable for the cut. The cut is generated by dividing each constant in the source row by $2 = a_{vs} = \lambda$ and writing the integer part of the quotient in the cut row. Next a pivot operation is performed using the x_1

Tableau 17.1

	1	$-x_1$ ↓	$-x_2$	
x_0	0	−3	−1	
x_1	0	−1	0	
x_2	0	0	−1	
x_3	6	2	3	
x_4	3	2	−3	←Source row
s_1	1	1*	−2	←Gomory cut

column as the pivot column and the s_1 row as the pivot row. The result is Tableau 17.2. The cut is graphed as c_1 on Fig. 17.1.

Tableau 17.2

	1	$-s_1$	$-x_2$ ↓	
x_0	3	3	−7	
x_1	1	1	−2	
x_2	0	0	−1	
x_3	4	−2	7	←Source row
x_4	1	−2	1	
s_2	0	−1	1*	←Gomory cut

We choose x_2 as the incoming variable. The x_3 row is the natural pivot row and source row. The cut is written in the bottom row. The pivot operation is performed and the result is Tableau 17.3. The cut is designated c_2 in Fig. 17.1.

Tableau 17.3

	1	$-s_1$ ↓	$-s_2$	
x_0	3	−4	7	
x_1	1	−1	2	
x_2	0	−1	1	
x_3	4	5	−7	←Source row
x_4	1	−1	−1	
s_3	0	1*	−2	←Gomory cut

We choose the s_1 column as the pivot column. The source row is the x_3 row. We generate the cut and conduct the pivot operation, which yields Tableau 17.4. As is usual with cutting plane algorithms we drop the pivot row and s_1 from the system after the pivot operation has been accomplished. The cut is designated c_3 on Fig. 17.1.

Tableau 17.4

	1	$-s_3$	$-s_2$ ↓	
x_0	3	4	-1	
x_1	1	1	0	
x_2	0	1	-1	
x_3	4	-5	3	←Source row
x_4	1	1	-3	
s_4	1	-2	1*	←Gomory cut

Carrying out the indicated pivot leads to Tableau 17.5, which is optimal. The cut is designated c_4 on Fig. 17.1. The optimum solution is $x_1 = 1$, $x_2 = 1$, $x_0 = 4$.

Tableau 17.5

	1	$-s_3$	$-s_4$
x_0	4	2	1
x_1	1	1	0
x_2	1	-1	1
x_3	1	1	-3
x_4	4	-5	3

The procedure we have described does not, unfortunately, support a proof of finiteness. To establish a basis for proving finiteness, we must place further restrictions on the procedure.

The essential difficulty with finiteness follows from the possibility that the cut (2) may have a zero in the constant column, i.e.,

$$[a_{v0} / \lambda] = [a_{v0} / a_{vs}] = 0.$$

This occurred in cycles 2 and 3 of the above example problem. When a zero occurs in the constant column of the cut, then the subsequent pivot operation, in which the cut serves as pivot row, leads to no change in the constant column $\mathbf{a}_0$ of the tableau. Thus the values of all variables are unchanged and in particular the objective function value of the solution does not change.

This phenomenon is similar to the degeneracy that can occur in linear programming problems. As in the case of the simplex method, a proof of finiteness must establish that degeneracy can persist for at most a finite sequence of cycles. The means of resolving degeneracy in linear programming are not available, unfortunately, in this integer programming situation. Degeneracy is handled in linear programming, ultimately, by an appeal to the finiteness of the set of all basic solutions—which follows from the fixed (and finite) number of variables and constraints in a linear programming problem. Cutting plane methods of integer programming systematically create new constraints and variables, and thereby nullify a straightforward application of the approach to degeneracy used in linear programming.

The problem of finiteness in primal methods is clarified by the distinction between *stationary cycles* (the degenerate cycles we have just described, i.e., $[a_{v0} / a_{vs}] = 0$) and *transition cycles* (cycles that lead to new solutions with positive improvement in the value of the objective function, i.e., $[a_{v0} / a_{vs}] \geq 1$). By virtue of the all-integer character of the primal algorithm, we have $a_{0s} \leq -1$ and $[a_{v0} / a_{vs}] \geq 1$ in a transition cycle. Therefore a transition cycle results in at least a unit improvement in the objective function value of the solution. Evidently, then, a finite number of transition cycles is sufficient to obtain an optimal solution for any bounded and solvable problem. The essential problem of finiteness is reduced to showing that every sequence of stationary cycles is finite.*

Three modifications of the procedure we have described are sufficient to yield a finite algorithm. First, a new equation must be adjoined to the initial tableau. Second, the pivot column $\mathbf{a}_s$ must be selected, consistent with $a_{0s} < 0$, so as to satisfy additional rules. Third, the row used as a source for the Gomory cut is not always the natural pivot row; instead, the source row is selected from a set of eligible rows in compliance with a rule chosen from a class of rules that will guarantee finiteness.

The new equation adjoined to the original tableau is a familiar device: a constraint expressing a limit on the sum of the (original) nonbasic variables. We shall index this row with the symbol L. The constraint is

$$t_L + \sum_{j \in J} x_j = a_{L0}. \tag{3}$$

The integer constant a_{L0} is chosen large enough so that every feasible in-

---

* To obtain a brief and relatively uncluttered exposition of a primal algorithm and its finiteness proof we shall generally suppress the distinction between stationary and transition cycles. (Glover [76] was the first to state an algorithm that did not make explicit use of this distinction.) It is possible to take account of this distinction in both the operation of the algorithm and the proof of finiteness (see Ben-Israel and Charnes [17], and Young [224] and [225]). In computation it may be worthwhile to exercise this option.

teger solution satisfies (3) with a nonnegative and integer value for the slack variable t_L. It is well known that adjoining the row (3) creates a feasible solution for the dual problem. Although we shall not explicitly emphasize this property of the L row here, it is this characteristic of the L row that is essential to its role in the primal algorithm*.

The purpose of introducing the L row is to help us choose the pivot column. Let a_{Lj} denote the coefficient in the jth column and the Lth row. Corresponding to each column $\mathbf{a}_j$, we define a new column vector† $\mathbf{r}_j$ as follows:

$$\mathbf{r}_j = [a_{0j} / a_{Lj}, a_{1j} / a_{Lj}, \ldots, a_{mj} / a_{Lj}]. \tag{4}$$

The pivot column selection rule is to select $\mathbf{a}_s$ to be the pivot column if $\mathbf{r}_s$ is the lexicographically smallest column among the columns $\mathbf{r}_j$ with $a_{Lj} > 0$.

The source row selection criterion does not lend itself to succinct expression. We shall give a brief statement of the essential requirement and then develop the significance of the statement.

We require that the source row selection rule have the following implication:

For any row index i, tableaux will occur at finite intervals in which $a_{is} \leq a_{i0}$. (5)

This should not be interpreted to require $a_{is} \leq a_{i0}$ for all i in some tableau (which is a necessary and sufficient condition for a transition cycle). Our requirement is consistent with $a_{is} > a_{i0}$ for all i in some tableaux.

Any source row selection rule that implies (5) will be termed an *acceptable* rule. The property (5) is sufficient‡ to support a proof of finiteness. The property (5) does not provide an immediate and positive means of generating acceptable source row selection rules. With the aid of Theorem 17.1 below, and some supplemental discussion, we shall develop operational means of detecting and generating acceptable rules.

If source row selection is to be a nontrivial problem, there must be several rows, typically, that could serve as the source row. Our initial discussion and example emphasized the use of the natural pivot row for a source row. This row will always generate a cut that has a 1 in the pivot column and is

---

* See Young [224] and [225] and Glover [76]; also see Section 17.4.

† In the definition (4) we have assumed that the column vector $\mathbf{a}_j$, from (1), has $m+1$ rows. The vector $\mathbf{r}_j$ will be used with reference to tableaux that are augmented by adjoining to the original system in the form (1): the L row and identity relations in the nonbasic variables. It will be assumed that the vector $\mathbf{r}_j$ always includes a component for each row of the augmented tableau. The only restriction on this augmentation is that the 0th row of the tableau retain its identity as the locus of the relative objective function coefficients.

‡ The property (5) is not the weakest restriction we could have used for defining acceptable source row selection rules, but weaker restrictions seem typically to require a more complex statement, and to avoid that disadvantage we use (5), for which we claim only simplicity and sufficiency. For alternatives, see Glover [76] and Young [225].

a legitimate pivot row. Typically it is possible to find other rows in the tableau from which cuts with these same properties may be generated. Assume that the cut is generated from the formula*

$$s_k = [a_{v0}/a_{vs}] + \sum_{j \in J} [a_{vj}/a_{vs}](-x_j). \tag{6}$$

Then v is a legitimate source row if and only if

$$0 \leq [a_{v0}/a_{vs}] \leq \theta_s, \tag{7}$$

where θ_s is the natural pivot ratio:

$$\theta_s = \min_{a_{is} > 0} (a_{i0}/a_{is}).$$

We define the set of legitimate source rows, $V(s)$, as the set of all rows that satisfy (7).

Now we consider the construction of rules for selection of $v \in V(s)$ that will imply (5). We note that in a transition cycle, $\theta_s \geq 1$, which implies $a_{i0} \geq a_{is}$ for all i; hence (5) is satisfied for each i independent of the choice of the source row. Accordingly, our attention can be confined to source row selection in stationary cycles.

In a stationary cycle we have $\theta_s < 1$ and therefore

$$V(s) = \{i \mid 0 \leq a_{i0} / a_{is} < 1\}.$$

Hence row i can be chosen as a source row if and only if

$$a_{i0} < a_{is}. \tag{8}$$

Now note that (8) is the complement of the requirement in (5). Thus if (5) fails, there is an unbounded sequence of tableaux in which row i is available for selection as the source row. This is significant because to force the occurrence of (5) we must be able to select row i as the source row when $a_{is} > a_{i0}$.

The procedure for forcing $a_{is} \leq a_{i0}$ to occur can be deduced as an easy corollary of the following theorem.

Theorem 17.1. Let a tableau be given; let row v be the source row, and let $\mathbf{a}_s$ be the pivot column. Let a_{vj} be a typical constant in row v, and let $\bar{a}_{vj}$ be the corresponding coefficient in the next tableau. If the cut

$$s_k = [a_{v0} / a_{vs}] + \sum_{j \in J} [a_{vj} / a_{vs}](-x_j) \tag{9}$$

is used as the pivot row, then $\bar{a}_{vj} \geq 0$ for all $j \in \bar{J}$ except the index k of the

* Setting $\lambda = a_{vs}$, as we do in (6), automatically gives us a 1 in the cut and the pivot column. It is possible in particular cases to set $\lambda < a_{vs}$ and retain the relation $1 = [a_{vs}/\lambda]$ (which still guarantees a unit pivot coefficient) and obtain in addition a stronger ("deeper") cut. This idea was suggested by Wilson [214]. We do not pursue this option here because it leads to more complex rules for source row selection, and hence to a more complicated exposition. Those interested in computation, however, should remain aware of this possibility.

slack variable in (9), and

$$\bar{a}_{vj} < a_{vs} \qquad \text{for all } j \in \bar{J}. \tag{10}$$

We omit proof of Theorem 17.1, which only requires substitution in the pivot formulas; see [225] or [76].

To connect Theorem 17.1 with our criterion for source row selection rules we begin by noting that in a stationary cycle $[a_{v0} / a_{vs}] = 0$, so that $\bar{a}_{v0} = a_{v0} = \underline{a}_{v0}$, where $\underline{a}_{v0}$ is the value (in row v and column 0) in the tableau that resulted from the most recent transition cycle. Now if $a_{vs} - a_{v0} = y > 0$, then as a consequence of (10) we must have (for any selection of $\bar{s}$) $\bar{a}_{v\bar{s}} - a_{v0} = \bar{y} < y$. Therefore if row v is repeatedly selected as the source row, so long as $a_{vs} > a_{v0} = \underline{a}_{v0}$, then a finite sequence of such selections must lead to a tableau in which $a_{vs} \leq a_{v0}$.

Thus we can implement our requirement for an acceptable source row selection rule with any rule that has the following property: if any row i in some tableau has $a_{is} > a_{i0} = \underline{a}_{i0}$, and this condition persists in subsequent tableaux, then eventually (within a finite interval) row i will be selected as the source row and will thereafter continue to be selected as the source row until $a_{is} \leq \underline{a}_{i0}$ (and i ceases to be a legitimate source row). The similarity between this rule and the source row selection rule of the Gomory all-integer algorithm is noteworthy.

The following two rules are examples of acceptable source row selection rules.

Rule 1.

a. Generate a sequential list of row indices that is finite and includes each row index at least once. Go to step (b).

b. If the list is empty or contains no indices in $V(s)$, return to (a); otherwise, find the first index, v, on the list that is a legitimate source row, i.e., $v \in V(s)$. Select v as the source row. Remove v and all preceding indices from the list. Go to step (c).

c. Repeatedly select the row v chosen in step (b) so long as $v \in V(s)$. In the first tableau for which $v \notin V(s)$, return to (b).

Rule 2.

a. Select as the source row the row $v \in V(s)$ which has been a member of $V(s)$ through the longest sequence of immediately preceding tableaux; break ties by an arbitrary selection. Go to step (b).

b. Repeatedly select the row v chosen in step (a) so long as $v \in V(s)$. In the first tableau for which $v \notin V(s)$ return to (a).

Before proceeding to a summary statement of the primal algorithm we shall, for purposes of formal convenience, elaborate the tableau format we have used in the foregoing discussion. Let the original problem be given in equation form as follows:

$$\max x_0 = a_{00} - \sum_{j=m+1}^{n} a_{0j} x_j$$

subject to

$$\begin{aligned} & x_i + \sum_{j=m+1}^{n} a_{ij}x_j = a_{i0} && (i = 1, \ldots, m), \\ & x_j - x_j = 0 && (j = m+1, \ldots, n), \\ & x_k \geq 0, \text{ integer} && (k = 1, 2, \ldots, n). \end{aligned} \tag{11}$$

This formulation differs from (1) only by the addition of the identity relations $x_j - x_j = 0$ $(j = m + 1, \ldots, n)$. It will be assumed hereafter that the matrix equation form of the tableau is $\mathbf{I}_{n+1}\mathbf{x}+\mathbf{A}\mathbf{x}_N = \mathbf{a}_0$, where

$$\mathbf{x} = [x_0, x_1, \ldots, x_n],\ \mathbf{x}_N = [x_{m+1}, \ldots, x_n],$$

and the matrix $\mathbf{A}$ includes identity relations in its last $n - m$ rows. For notational simplicity we shall let J symbolize the index set of nonbasic variables in any tableau. We shall use the tableau format (11) to describe both the original tableau and typical subsequent tableaux.

We now give a formal statement of the primal algorithm.

STEP 0. Adjoin a row (indexed by L) to the initial tableau expressing an upper bound on the sum of the nonbasic variables:

$$x_L + \sum_{j \in J} x_j = a_{L0},$$

where the positive integer a_{L0} is chosen so that $x_L \geq 0$ is compatible with every feasible integer solution to the remaining constraints. Go to step 1.

STEP 1. Check for optimality; if $a_{0j} \geq 0$ for all $j \in J$, then the current basic solution is optimal and computation may be stopped. Otherwise go to step 2.

STEP 2. Select the pivot column $\mathbf{a}_s$ satisfying

$$a_{Ls} > 0 \qquad \text{and} \qquad \mathbf{r}_s \prec \mathbf{r}_j \qquad \text{for all } j\,(\neq s) \in J$$

with $a_{Lj} > 0$. Go to step 3.

STEP 3. Select the source row v from the set

$$V(s) = \{i \mid 0 \leq [a_{i0}/\,a_{is}] \leq \theta_s\},$$

according to an acceptable source row selection rule. Go to step 4.

STEP 4. Adjoin the cut

$$s_k = [a_{v0}\,/\,a_{vs}] + \sum_{j \in J} [a_{v0}\,/\,a_{vs}]\,(-x_j) \tag{12}$$

to the tableau. Go to step 5.

STEP 5. Conduct the pivot operation with $\mathbf{a}_s$ serving as the pivot column and the cut (12) serving as the pivot row. Go to step 6.

STEP 6. Delete the cut (and pivot) row (12) from the system. Return to step 1.

Several comments are in order:

1) There is no need to check for an unbounded solution with this algorithm, since the L row, (3), makes this outcome impossible. This fact can be immediately confirmed by noting that we always have $a_{Ls} > 0$.

2) The discard of the pivot row after every cycle of the algorithm may give the misleading impression that essential information is lost. It has become standard practice to discard the slack variables from previous Gomory cuts that reenter the basis. When $\mathbf{a}_s$ corresponds to such a Gomory slack variable, dropping the pivot row amounts to discarding this slack variable. The only other possibility is that $\mathbf{a}_s$ corresponds to one of the original components of $\mathbf{x}_N$. In this case the system will contain two variables representing x_s, one basic and the other nonbasic. There will be an identity equation in the tableau linking the two variables, namely,

$$x_{s,\,\text{basic}} - x_{s,\,\text{nonbasic}} = 0. \tag{13}$$

After the pivot operation, the row (13) will have become identical with the pivot row. By dropping the pivot row at this juncture we merely eliminate the redundant representation of x_s and the pivot row. This practice preserves the property of (11) whereby only the nonbasic variables have redundant representation.

3) Since a new Gomory cut always serves as pivot row, the variable removed from the basis is always a Gomory slack variable. Accordingly, no variable of the original system (11) ever leaves the basis. The size of the system is obviously invariant from tableau to tableau.

4) After a cycle has been completed, the nonbasic column $\bar{\mathbf{a}}_k$ corresponding to the Gomory slack variable that has just been driven nonbasic is the negative of the pivot column $\mathbf{a}_s$ for the cycle, i.e., $\bar{\mathbf{a}}_k = -\mathbf{a}_s$.

5) Since the pivot row is adjoined before the pivot and discarded immediately thereafter, it is straightforward to represent the tableau to tableau transitions of the algorithm as elementary column operations in which integer multiples of the pivot column are added to each column—the integer multipliers being generated from the transitory all-integer pivot row. Elementary column operations cannot change the column rank of the tableau. From (11) it is evident that the columns of the first tableau are linearly independent, and therefore the columns of all subsequent tableaux must be linearly independent. Accordingly, it is not possible that $\mathbf{r}_k = \mathbf{r}_j$ for any pair of columns $\mathbf{a}_k$ and $\mathbf{a}_j$ in any tableau, since this would imply proportionality and linear dependence between $\mathbf{a}_k$ and $\mathbf{a}_j$. From this we may conclude that the pivot column selection rule must always yield a unique choice.

6) The primal algorithm requires that the initial tableau (11) embody a basic, feasible, integer solution. To be computationally effective it is probably necessary to start the primal algorithm at a "good" (i.e., optimal, or nearly optimal) basic integer solution. In many applied problems good solutions are frequently known or easily generated. It may be difficult, however, to express the good integer solution as a basic solution since, for example, such a solution may be in the interior of the solution set for (11). Fortunately, a systematic means of overcoming this problem is available.

Let

$$\max x_0 = \sum_{j \in J} d_{0j} x_j$$

subject to

$$\mathbf{I}\mathbf{x}_B + \mathbf{D}\mathbf{x}_N = \mathbf{d}_0, \tag{14}$$

$$\mathbf{x}_B,\ \mathbf{x}_N \geq \mathbf{0},\ \text{integers},$$

represent an original formulation of the problem in which $\mathbf{D}$ and $\mathbf{d}_0$ contain all-integer constants and $\mathbf{d}_0 \geq \mathbf{0}$. Let $\mathbf{x}_B = \boldsymbol{\xi}_B$ and $\mathbf{x}_N = \boldsymbol{\xi}_N$ be a good integer solution. To convert $\mathbf{x}_B = \boldsymbol{\xi}_B$ and $\mathbf{x}_N = \boldsymbol{\xi}_N$ into a basic, feasible, integer solution we proceed as follows:

Calculate a new integer column vector $\mathbf{d}_\xi$ by

$$\mathbf{d}_\xi = \mathbf{D}\,\boldsymbol{\xi}_N = \sum_j \mathbf{d}_j \xi_j,$$

where $\mathbf{d}_j$ is a column vector of $\boldsymbol{D}$. Since $\boldsymbol{\xi} = (\boldsymbol{\xi}_B, \boldsymbol{\xi}_N)$ is a feasible integer solution, we must have

$$\mathbf{0} \leq \boldsymbol{\xi}_B = \mathbf{d}_0 - \mathbf{D}\,\boldsymbol{\xi}_N = \mathbf{d}_0 - \mathbf{d}_\xi.$$

Hence $\mathbf{d}_\xi \leq \mathbf{d}_0$.

Adjoin $\mathbf{d}_\xi$ to (14) and adjoin a corresponding new nonbasic variable x_ξ. The augmented tableau may then be expressed as

$$\mathbf{x}_B + \sum_j \mathbf{d}_j x_j + \mathbf{d}_\xi x_\xi = \mathbf{d}_0, \tag{15}$$

where j varies over the indices of $\mathbf{x}_N$.

Since $\mathbf{d}_\xi \leq \mathbf{d}_0$, a transition cycle is possible if $\mathbf{d}_\xi$ is designated the pivot column.

Conduct one (transition) cycle with $\mathbf{d}_\xi$ as pivot column.

Use the resulting tableau as the starting point for application of the primal algorithm.

When an optimal solution, $\hat{\mathbf{x}}_B$, $\hat{\mathbf{x}}_N$, $\hat{\mathbf{x}}_\xi$ to (15) has been obtained, this solution can be transformed into the optimal solution $\mathbf{x}_B^*$, $\mathbf{x}_N^*$ to (14) by substitution into (15) as follows:

$$\hat{\mathbf{x}}_B + \sum_j \mathbf{d}_j \hat{x}_j + \mathbf{d}_\xi \hat{x}_\xi = \mathbf{d}$$

$$\hat{\mathbf{x}}_B + \sum_j \mathbf{d}_j \hat{x}_j + \Big(\sum_j \mathbf{d}_j \xi_j\Big) \hat{x}_\xi = \mathbf{d}_0,$$

$$\hat{\mathbf{x}}_B + \sum_j \mathbf{d}_j (\hat{x}_j + \xi_j \hat{x}_\xi) = \mathbf{d}_0.$$

Thus we have

$$\mathbf{x}_B^* = \hat{\mathbf{x}}_B, \qquad \mathbf{x}_N^* = \hat{\mathbf{x}}_N + \boldsymbol{\xi}_N \hat{x}_\xi.$$

This procedure is a direct application of concepts developed by Ben-Israel and Charnes [17].

17.2 EXAMPLE

We shall illustrate this algorithm by a numerical example. The source row selection rule used here is Rule 2 discussed in Section 17.1.

Consider an integer program

$$\max x_0 = x_1 + x_2 + x_3$$

subject to

$$\begin{aligned} -4x_1 + 5x_2 + 2x_3 &\leq 4, \\ -2x_1 + 5x_2 \qquad &\leq 5, \\ -3x_1 - 2x_2 + 2x_3 &\leq 6, \\ 2x_1 - 5x_2 \qquad &\leq 1, \\ x_j \geq 0, \quad \text{integers.} \end{aligned}$$

Introducing slack variables x_4, x_5, x_6, and x_7 and the L row, we have Tableau 17.6. The constant 10 in the L row was determined by very casual inspection of the problem. In Tableau 17.6 we have $\mathbf{r}_{x_1} \prec \mathbf{r}_{x_j}$ $(j = 2, 3)$, so the pivot column is the x_1 column. The natural pivot ratio for x_1 is $\frac{1}{2}$ determined from the x_7 row. This is the only row i where $[a_{i0}/a_{is}] \leq \frac{1}{2}$; hence $V(x_1) = \{x_7 \text{ row}\}$, and the choice of the source row is unique. Now the cut (and pivot) row

Tableau 17.6

	1	↓ $-x_1$	$-x_2$	$-x_3$	
x_0	0	−1	−1	−1	$V(x_1) = \{x_7 \text{ row}\}$
x_4	4	−4	5	2	
x_5	5	−2	5	0	
x_6	6	3	−2	2	
x_7	1	2	−5	0	← Source row
x_1	0	−1	0	0	
x_2	0	0	−1	0	
x_3	0	0	0	−1	
x_L	10	1	1	1	
s_1	0	1	−3	0	← Cut and pivot row

is generated from the x_7 row by dividing the row by $a_{vs} = 2$ and writing the integer parts of the quotients as the cut row. The new basic variable s_1 in the cut row is the slack variable for the cut. The pivot step produces Tableau 17.7. The problem is solved after 7 cycles, which we display in Tableaux 17.8 through 17.13 below, along with the sets $V(s)$.

Tableau 17.7

	1	$-s_1$	$-x_2$ ↓	$-x_3$	
x_0	0	1	−4	−1	$V(x_2) = \{x_6 \text{ row}\}$
x_4	4	4	−7	2	
x_5	5	2	−1	0	
x_6	6	−3	7	2	← Source row
x_7	1	−2	1	0	
x_1	0	1	−3	0	
x_2	0	0	−1	0	
x_3	0	0	0	−1	
x_L	10	−1	4	1	
s_2	0	−1	1	0	← Cut and pivot row

Tableau 17.8

	1	$-s_1$ ↓	$-s_2$	$-x_3$	
x_0	0	−3	4	−1	$V(s_1) = \{x_6 \text{ row}\}$
x_4	4	−3	7	2	
x_5	5	1	1	0	
x_6	6	4	−7	2	← Source row
x_7	1	−1	−1	0	
x_1	0	−2	3	0	
x_2	0	−1	1	0	
x_3	0	0	0	−1	
x_L	10	3	−4	1	
s_3	1	1	−2	0	← Cut and pivot row

Tableau 17.9

	1	$-s_3$	$-s_2$ ↓	$-x_3$	
x_0	3	3	−2	−1	$V(s_2) = \{x_5 \text{ row}\}$
x_4	7	3	1	2	
x_5	4	−1	3	0	← Source row
x_6	2	−4	1	2	
x_7	2	1	−3	0	
x_1	2	2	−1	0	
x_2	1	1	−1	0	
x_3	0	0	0	−1	
x_L	7	−3	2	1	
s_4	1	−1	1	0	← Cut and pivot row

Tableau 17.10

	1	$-s_3$	$-s_4$	$-x_3$ ↓	
x_0	5	1	2	−1	$V(x_3) = \{x_6 \text{ row}\}$
x_4	6	4	−1	2	
x_5	1	2	−3	0	
x_6	1	−3	−1	2	← Source row
x_7	5	−2	3	0	
x_1	3	1	1	0	
x_2	2	0	1	0	
x_3	0	0	0	−1	
x_L	5	−1	−2	1	
s_5	0	−2	−1	1	← Cut and pivot row

Note in Tableau 17.11 that using the x_4 row as source row would lead to an optimal tableau. We select the other option to provide a better example of operation of the source row selection rule.

Tableau 17.11

	1	$-s_3$ ↓	$-s_4$	$-s_5$	
x_0	5	−1	1	1	$V(s_3)=\{x_4$ row, x_5 row$\}$
x_4	6	8	1	−2	
x_5	1	2	−3	0	← Source row
x_6	1	1	1	−2	
x_7	5	−2	3	0	
x_1	3	1	1	0	
x_2	2	0	1	0	
x_3	0	−2	−1	1	
x_L	5	1	−1	−1	
s_6	0	1	−2	0	← Cut and pivot row

Tableau 17.12

	1	$-s_6$	$-s_4$ ↓	$-s_5$	
x_0	5	1	−1	1	$V(s_4)=\{x_4$ row, x_6 row$\}$
x_4	6	−8	17	−2	← Source row
x_5	1	−2	1	0	
x_6	1	−1	3	−2	
x_7	5	+2	−1	0	
x_1	3	−1	3	0	
x_2	2	0	1	0	
x_3	0	+2	−5	1	
x_L	5	−1	1	−1	
s_7	0	−1	1	−1	← Cut and pivot row

Note in Tableau 17.12 that the x_4 row must be selected because it was in $V(s_3)$ for the previous tableau and the x_6 row was not.

Tableau 17.13 is optimal. To provide a more complete example of the source row selection rule, we note, hypothetically, that if this tableau were *not* optimal and s_6 were the incoming variable, then the source row selection rule would require the x_4 row to be selected again as the source row.

Tableau 17.13

	1	$-s_6$	$-s_7$	$-s_5$
x_0	5	0	1	0
x_4	6	9	-17	15
x_5	1	-1	-1	1
x_6	1	2	-3	1
x_7	5	1	1	-1
x_1	3	2	-3	3
x_2	2	1	-1	1
x_3	0	-3	5	-4
x_L	5	0	-1	0

The optimal solution is $x_1 = 3, x_2 = 2, x_3 = 0, x_0 = 5$.

17.3 PROOF OF FINITENESS

The proof that this primal algorithm is finite has two parts that have a necessary sequence. First we use the pivot column selection procedure to prove that $\mathbf{r}_s$ increases lexicographically from tableau to tableau. Then we use this result and the properties of acceptable source row selection rules to show that $\mathbf{r}_s \succ 0$ (which implies optimality) must occur after a finite sequence of tableaux or cycles.

To develop our proof it will be convenient to use the following definitions. Let

$$\mathbf{Ix} + \mathbf{Ax}_N = \mathbf{a}_0 \qquad \text{or} \qquad \mathbf{Ix} + \sum_{j \in J} \mathbf{a}_j \mathbf{x}_j = \mathbf{a}_0 \tag{16}^*$$

represent a typical tableau. Let

$$\mathbf{Ix} + \bar{\mathbf{A}}\mathbf{x}_N = \bar{\mathbf{a}}_0 \tag{17}$$

represent the tableau that results from applying a cycle of the algorithm to (16). All data present and determined in (17) are signified by the superior bar, e.g., $\bar{\mathbf{a}}_{\bar{s}}$ is the pivot column chosen from (17), while $\mathbf{a}_{\bar{s}}$ is the column in (16) that corresponds to the incoming variable $\bar{s}$ chosen from (17). We let $\mathscr{I}$ represent an index set of the rows in (16) and (17); $\mathscr{I}$ will contain in total $n + 2$ indices. We shall occasionally, in contexts where no misunderstanding can result, use $\mathbf{A}$ as a shorthand designation for (16) and $\bar{\mathbf{A}}$ as a designation of (17). We define†

$$\rho_i = a_{is} / a_{Ls}, \qquad i \in \mathscr{I}. \tag{18}$$

* In this chapter, owing to the extensive cross referencing between sections, we shall number the equations consecutively through the chapter rather than through section, as has been our previous practice.

†The definitions ρ_i and Δ will be the subject of an interpretative discussion in Section 17.4.

Then

$$\mathbf{r}_s = \begin{bmatrix} \rho_0 \\ \rho_1 \\ \vdots \\ \rho_n \\ \rho_L \end{bmatrix}. \tag{19}$$

We define, further,

$$\delta_{ij} \equiv -\rho_i a_{Lj} + a_{ij}, \qquad i \in \mathscr{I}, \tag{20}$$

and

$$\mathbf{\Delta}_j \equiv \begin{bmatrix} \delta_{0j} \\ \delta_{1j} \\ \vdots \\ \delta_{nj} \\ \delta_{Lj} \end{bmatrix}. \tag{21}$$

These definitions and the change of basis formulas of the primal algorithm together imply the following relations for all $j \in J$:

$$a_{Lj}\,\mathbf{r}_s = \mathbf{a}_j - \mathbf{\Delta}_j, \tag{22}$$

$$\bar{a}_{Lj}\,\mathbf{r}_s = \bar{\mathbf{a}}_j - \mathbf{\Delta}_j, \tag{23}$$

$$\bar{\mathbf{r}}_{\bar{s}} = \mathbf{r}_s + (1 / \bar{a}_{L\bar{s}})\,\mathbf{\Delta}_{\bar{s}}, \tag{24}$$

$$\bar{\mathbf{\Delta}}_j = \mathbf{\Delta}_j - (\bar{a}_{Lj} / \bar{a}_{L\bar{s}})\,\mathbf{\Delta}_{\bar{s}}, \tag{25}$$

$$\bar{\mathbf{\Delta}}_j = \bar{a}_{Lj}\,(\bar{\mathbf{r}}_j - \bar{\mathbf{r}}_{\bar{s}}) \text{ if } \bar{a}_{Lj} \neq 0. \tag{26}$$

The derivation of (22), (23), (24), (25), and (26) is straightforward and is given below in Section 17.4. These relations support the following three theorems:

Theorem 17.2.

$$\left.\begin{array}{l} \mathbf{r}_s \prec \mathbf{0} \\ \mathbf{\Delta}_j \succ \mathbf{0} \text{ for all } j\,(\neq s) \in J \\ \bar{\mathbf{A}} \text{ is not optimal} \end{array}\right\} \Rightarrow \begin{array}{l}\text{There exists a } j \in \bar{J} \text{ such that } \bar{a}_{Lj} > 0 \text{ and} \\ \bar{\mathbf{r}}_{\bar{s}} \prec \mathbf{0}.\end{array}$$

Theorem 17.3.

$$\left.\begin{array}{l} \mathbf{r}_s \prec \mathbf{0} \\ \mathbf{\Delta}_j \succ \mathbf{0} \text{ for all } j\,(\neq s) \in J \\ \bar{\mathbf{A}} \text{ is not optimal} \end{array}\right\} \Rightarrow \bar{\mathbf{\Delta}}_j \succ \mathbf{0} \text{ for all } j\,(\neq \bar{s}) \in \bar{J}.$$

Theorem 17.4.

$$\left.\begin{array}{l} \mathbf{r}_s \prec \mathbf{0} \\ \mathbf{\Delta}_j \succ \mathbf{0} \text{ for all } j\,(\neq s) \in J \\ \bar{\mathbf{A}} \text{ is not optimal} \end{array}\right\} \Rightarrow \bar{\mathbf{r}}_{\bar{s}} \succ \mathbf{r}_s.$$

The main result we seek is the conclusion of Theorem 17.4. To establish the hypothesis of this theorem we proceed inductively. We show that in the first tableau $\mathbf{r}_s \prec \mathbf{0}$ and $\mathbf{\Delta}_j \succ \mathbf{0}$ for all $j\ (\neq s) \in J$. Then the hypothesis of Theorem 17.4 always follows for subsequent tableaux from Theorems 1.72 and 17.3. In the first tableau $a_{Lj} = 1$ for all $j \in J$. Therefore $\mathbf{r}_j = \mathbf{a}_j$ for all $j \in J$, and $\mathbf{a}_j = \mathbf{r}_j \succ \mathbf{r}_s = \mathbf{a}_s$. Substituting into (22) we have $\mathbf{\Delta}_j = \mathbf{a}_j - \mathbf{a}_s \succ \mathbf{0}$. Since $\mathbf{r}_s = \mathbf{a}_s \prec \mathbf{a}_j = \mathbf{r}_j$ for all $j\ (\neq s) \in J$, if $\mathbf{r}_s \succ \mathbf{0}$, then $\mathbf{a}_j \succ \mathbf{0}$ for all $j \in J$, which implies that the initial tableau is optimal. Thus if the initial tableau is not optimal, then $\mathbf{r}_s \prec \mathbf{0}$ and $\mathbf{\Delta}_j \succ \mathbf{0}$ for all $j\ (\neq s) \in J$.

Proof of Theorem 17.2. Theorem 17.2 follows from (23). Assume that the theorem is false because $\bar{a}_{Lj} \leq 0$ for all $j\ (\neq s) \in J$ ($\bar{a}_{Ls} < 0$ is certainly true). Then the left-hand side of (23) is lexicographically nonnegative for every j. Since $\mathbf{\Delta}_j \succ \mathbf{0}$ for $j\ (\neq s) \in J$ (and $\mathbf{\Delta}_s = \mathbf{0}$, while $\bar{a}_{Ls} < 0$), it follows that $\mathbf{r}_s \prec \mathbf{0}$ implies $\bar{\mathbf{a}}_j \succ \mathbf{0}$ for all $j \in J$. But $\bar{\mathbf{a}}_j \succ \mathbf{0}$ for all j implies that $\bar{\mathbf{A}}$ is optimal, which contradicts our assumption that Theorem 17.2 is false. Hence we must have $\bar{a}_{Lj} > 0$ for some j, and it is possible to define $\bar{\mathbf{a}}_{\bar{s}}$ and $\bar{\mathbf{r}}_{\bar{s}}$. Now assume that Theorem 17.2 is false because $\bar{\mathbf{r}}_{\bar{s}} \succ \mathbf{0}$. The first part of this proof showed that $\bar{a}_{Lj} \leq 0$ implies $\bar{\mathbf{a}}_j \succ \mathbf{0}$. If $\bar{\mathbf{r}}_{\bar{s}} \succ \mathbf{0}$, then for all j with $\bar{a}_{Lj} > 0$, we have $(1/\bar{a}_{Lj})\bar{\mathbf{a}}_j = \bar{\mathbf{r}}_j \succ \bar{\mathbf{r}}_{\bar{s}} \succ \mathbf{0}$. Hence $\bar{a}_{Lj} > 0$ implies $\bar{\mathbf{a}}_j \succ \mathbf{0}$. This implies that $\bar{\mathbf{A}}$ is optimal, which again contradicts our assumption that Theorem 17.2 is false.

Proof of Theorem 17.3. Theorem 17.3 follows directly from (25) and (26). If $\bar{a}_{Lj} \leq 0$, we can conclude $\bar{\mathbf{\Delta}}_j \succ \mathbf{0}$ from (25), since $\mathbf{\Delta}_j \succeq \mathbf{0}$, $\mathbf{\Delta}_{\bar{s}} \succ \mathbf{0}$ and $\bar{a}_{L\bar{s}} > 0$. If $\bar{a}_{Lj} > 0$, then, from (26), $\bar{\mathbf{\Delta}}_j \succ \mathbf{0}$, since if $\bar{a}_{Lj} > 0$, then $\bar{\mathbf{r}}_{\bar{s}} \prec \bar{\mathbf{r}}_j$, as a result of the rule by which $\bar{\mathbf{r}}_{\bar{s}}$ is selected.

Proof of Theorem 17.4. The theorem follows directly from (24); $\bar{\mathbf{r}}_{\bar{s}} \succ \mathbf{r}_s$, since $\bar{a}_{L\bar{s}} > 0$ and $\mathbf{\Delta}_{\bar{s}} \succ \mathbf{0}$.

It is a corollary of Theorem 17.2 that the first tableau in which $\mathbf{r}_s$ cannot be defined or $\mathbf{r}_s \succ \mathbf{0}$ is optimal. To show that this condition must eventually occur we shall prove the following two theorems:

Theorem 17.5. If an acceptable source row selection rule is used, then at finite intervals adjacent pairs of tableaux must occur for which

$$\frac{a_{0s}}{a_{Ls}} < \frac{\bar{a}_{0\bar{s}}}{\bar{a}_{L\bar{s}}}.$$

Theorem 17.6. If an acceptable source row selection rule is used, then after a finite sequence of cycles (or tableaux), an optimal condition must occur.

It will be useful as a preliminary to the proof of these two theorems to develop a simple definition and some elementary conclusions based on the definition.

Let $\underline{a}_{i0}$ be the constant in row i and column 0 in the first tableau of a sequence of stationary cycles. Then for every tableau in the sequence of stationary cycles, $a_{i0} = \underline{a}_{i0}$ for all $i \in \mathscr{I}$. For any component i of $\mathbf{r}_s$, in any tableau, we define a_{is} / a_{Ls} to be *within bounds* if

$$a_{is} \leq a_{i0} = \underline{a}_{i0} \qquad \text{and} \qquad a_{Ls} \leq a_{L0} = \underline{a}_{L0}.$$

Now we note that if $a_{is} / a_{Ls} \leq \underline{a}_{i0} / \underline{a}_{L0}$, then $a_{Ls} \leq \underline{a}_{L0} \Rightarrow a_{is} / a_{Ls}$ is within bounds, and if $a_{is} / a_{Ls} \geq \underline{a}_{i0} / \underline{a}_{L0}$, then $a_{is} \leq \underline{a}_{i0} \Rightarrow a_{is} / a_{Ls}$ is within bounds.

Finally, we observe that if a_{is} and a_{Ls} are always integers, if $a_{Ls} > 0$ (as required by the pivot column selection rule), if $a_{is} / a_{Ls} \geq r$ (a constant), and if a_{is} / a_{Ls} is within bounds, then there is only a finite number of possible values for the ratio a_{is} / a_{Ls}.

Proof of Theorem 17.5. Since $\mathbf{r}_s \prec \bar{\mathbf{r}}_{\bar{s}}$, we know that all components of $\mathbf{r}_s$ cannot remain fixed. Suppose, however, that the first component a_{0s} / a_{Ls} remains constant for an unbounded sequence S of stationary cycles, while a_{1s} / a_{Ls} increases at finite intervals.* Then an unbounded number of increases in a_{1s} / a_{Ls} must occur. Let r be the value of a_{1s} / a_{Ls} in the first tableau. Then $r \leq a_{1s} / a_{Ls}$ for all succeeding tableaux. Let S_1 consist of the tableaux in S for which $r \leq a_{1s}/a_{Ls} \leq \underline{a}_{10}/\underline{a}_{L0}$, and let S_2 consist of the tableaux in which $a_{1s} / a_{Ls} > \underline{a}_{10} / \underline{a}_{L0}$. Hence $S = S_1 \cup S_2$.

The source row selection rule requires that $a_{Ls} \leq \underline{a}_{L0}$ at finite intervals. Hence in S_1, a_{1s} / a_{Ls} must be within bounds at finite intervals whenever $a_{Ls} \leq \underline{a}_{L0}$, and the subsequence of S_1 during which a_{1s} / a_{Ls} is within bounds must be unbounded if S_1 is unbounded. But this unbounded subsequence of S_1 (during which a_{1s} / a_{Ls} is within bounds) must contain an unbounded number of increases in a_{1s} / a_{Ls}, since a_{1s} / a_{Ls} increases at finite intervals. This is impossible because there is only a finite number of within bounds values for a_{1s} / a_{Ls}. Hence S_1 must be finite. An analogous argument shows that S_2 must be finite. Thus S must be finite, contradicting the assumption that the first component of $\mathbf{r}_s$ remains fixed for an unbounded sequence of stationary cycles.

Proof of Theorem 17.6. Let r be the value for a_{0s} / a_{Ls} in the first tableau in a sequence of stationary cycles. Define a_{0s} / a_{Ls} to be *within bounds* whenever $a_{Ls} \leq \underline{a}_{L0}$. Then there is only a finite number of within-bounds and negative values for $\underline{a}_{0s} / a_{Ls}$ if $a_{Ls} > 0$ and $a_{0s} / a_{Ls} \geq r$. The source row selection rule implies that a_{0s} / a_{Ls} will be within bounds at finite intervals. Since a_{0s}/a_{Ls} must also increase at finite intervals, a finite sequence of cycles is sufficient to exhaust the finite number of negative within-bounds values for the ratio a_{0s} / a_{Ls}. This implies, via Theorem 17.2, an optimal tableau. The remaining possibility is that $a_{Lj} \leq 0$ for all $j \in J$ in some tableau. This also, by Theorem 17.2, implies optimality.

---

* This assumption entails no loss in generality, since we shall show that no component of $\mathbf{r}_s$ can undergo an unbounded number of increases while all preceding components of $\mathbf{r}_s$ remain fixed, and it is immaterial whether we call the first changing component the second or the ith.

17.4 INTERPRETATIONS AND DERIVATIONS

In this section there are two topics: first we discuss some interpretation of the concepts we used in the finiteness proofs of the preceding section; second we derive the relations used in the finiteness proofs.

There are two main interpretive contexts for the system of notation we have used in developing the proof: one emphasizes duality, the other geometry. We shall first develop an interpretation in terms of duality.

Consider the sequence of tableaux generated by a sequence of (stationary) cycles of the primal algorithm. Let the kth tableau be stated as a linear programming problem:

$$\min \mathbf{a}_k^0 \mathbf{x}_{N_k}$$

subject to

$$\mathbf{I}\mathbf{x}_{B_k} + \mathbf{A}^k \mathbf{x}_{N_k} = \mathbf{a}_{0_k}, \tag{27}$$

$$\mathbf{x}_{B_k}, \mathbf{x}_{N_k} \geq \mathbf{0}.$$

In (27) $\mathbf{a}_k^0$ is the row vector of relative objective function values (i.e., $z_j - c_j$ values), $\mathbf{a}_{0_k}$ is the column vector of constants (except the current value of the objective function), and $\mathbf{A}^k$ is the matrix of nonbasic tableau coefficients *except the objective function coefficients* $\mathbf{a}_k^0$. The dual problem to (27) is

$$\max \mathbf{w}_k' \mathbf{a}_{0_k}$$

subject to

$$\mathbf{w}_k' \mathbf{A}^k \leq \mathbf{a}_k^0; \qquad \mathbf{w}_k' \leq \mathbf{0}. \tag{28}$$

The sequence of tableaux of the primal algorithm generates a sequence of dual problems (28). Now we shall state a generalized, lexicographic version of (28):

$$\max \mathbf{P}\, \mathbf{a}_0$$

subject to

$$\mathbf{P}\mathbf{A} \leq \begin{bmatrix} \mathbf{a}^0 \\ \mathbf{A} \end{bmatrix}, \tag{29}$$

where $\mathbf{P}$ is a matrix with lexicographically nonpositive columns. The vector $\mathbf{P}\mathbf{a}_0$ is to be maximized in the lexicographic sense and the inequality

$$\mathbf{P}\mathbf{A} \leq \begin{bmatrix} \mathbf{a}^0 \\ \mathbf{A} \end{bmatrix}$$

is to be understood in the following sense: each column of the matrix $\mathbf{PA}$ is lexicographically less than or equal to the corresponding column of

$$\begin{bmatrix} \mathbf{a}^0 \\ \mathbf{A} \end{bmatrix}.$$

A feasible solution to (29) contains, in the first row of $\mathbf{P}$, a feasible solution to (28). Similarly an optimal solution to (29) contains an optimal solution to

(28). We have dropped the subscript k in (29), but it is obvious that a sequence of (stationary) cycles generates a sequence of problems (29).

The constructs $\mathbf{r}_j$, ρ_i, $\mathbf{\Delta}_j$ and δ_{ij} used in the finiteness proofs of Section 17.3 have a special relation to the problems (29). Consider a solution $\hat{\mathbf{P}}$ to (29) constructed as follows. All components of $\hat{\mathbf{P}}$ are zeros except in the column of $\hat{\mathbf{P}}$ that corresponds to the L row of $\mathbf{A}$; let this single nonzero column of $\hat{\mathbf{P}}$ be given by

$$\mathbf{r}_s = \begin{pmatrix} \rho_0 \\ \rho_1 \\ \vdots \\ \rho_n \\ \rho_L \end{pmatrix}.$$

We shall show that this solution is feasible for (29). Since $\mathbf{r}_s \prec 0$ (Theorem 17.2), we have all columns of $\hat{\mathbf{P}}$ lexicographically nonpositive. The jth column of the matrix product $\hat{\mathbf{P}}\mathbf{A} = [\mathbf{0}, \mathbf{r}_s]\cdot\mathbf{A}$ is $a_{Lj}\,\mathbf{r}_s$, which, from (22), is equal to

$$\begin{pmatrix} a_{0j} \\ a_{1j} \\ \vdots \\ a_{Lj} \end{pmatrix} - \begin{pmatrix} \delta_{0j} \\ \delta_{1j} \\ \vdots \\ \delta_{Lj} \end{pmatrix}.$$

Since $\mathbf{\Delta}_j \succ \mathbf{0}$ (Theorem 17.3), we may conclude that for all columns $\mathbf{a}_j$ of $\mathbf{A}$ in (29),

$$a_{Lj}\,\mathbf{r}_s \preceq \begin{pmatrix} \mathbf{a}_{0j} \\ \mathbf{a}_j \end{pmatrix},$$

and our solution $\hat{\mathbf{P}} = [\mathbf{0}, \mathbf{r}_s]$ is feasible for (29). Thus we see that the δ_{ij}'s of (21) are the slack variables for (29) and that the ρ's of (18) are the essential constituents of a feasible solution to (29).

With our definition of $\hat{\mathbf{P}}$, the objective function $\hat{\mathbf{P}}\mathbf{a}_0$ reduces to $\mathbf{r}_s\, a_{L0}$. Since a_{L0} is constant during a sequence of stationary cycles, while $\mathbf{r}_s$ increases lexicographically, we get a sequence of improving solutions to the problems (29). When a tableau is finally reached in which the first component of $\mathbf{r}_s$ is nonnegative, then (28) has a feasible solution with a value of zero in the objective function. This sets a lower limit of zero on an optimal solution to (27), which can be achieved by setting $\mathbf{x}_N = \mathbf{0}$. Hence in this tableau we have optimal solutions to (27) and (28).

The general primal-dual character of the primal algorithm is suggested by the following observations: the pivot column always corresponds to an exactly satisfied constraint of (29), that is, $\mathbf{\Delta}_s = \mathbf{0}$ is always satisfied; and we generate a monotonically improving sequence of solutions to the dual problems (28) and (29). Hopefully this brief discussion has suggested some of the significance of the notational constructs used in Section 17.3.

The definitions (18), (19), (20), and (21) are also useful in developing a comparatively simple geometric portrayal of the evolution of the tableau through the sequence of cycles of the primal algorithm.

The data of the tableau may be regarded as a set of column vectors $\{\mathbf{a}_j \mid j \in J\}$ which corresponds to a set of points in an $(n+2)$-dimensional Euclidian space. The definition (20) that implies the vector equation (22) may be interpreted as a change of origin, i.e., we write (22) as

$$\mathbf{a}_j = \mathbf{a}_{Lj}\,\mathbf{r}_s + \boldsymbol{\Delta}_j,$$

and interpret this as expressing the vector $\mathbf{a}_j$ as a deviation $\boldsymbol{\Delta}_j$ from the point $a_{Lj}\,\mathbf{r}_s$ on the ray generated by the vector $\mathbf{r}_s$. One advantage of algebraically "seeing" $\mathbf{a}_j$ in terms of its deviation $\boldsymbol{\Delta}_j$ from $a_{Lj}\,\mathbf{r}_s$ is that this representation emphasizes certain geometric relationships in the tableau structures and the transitions of the primal algorithm.

First we note that the set of points $\{\mathbf{a}_j \mid j \in J\}$ in any tableau generated in the course of a solution by the primal algorithm is contained in a half-space that has the origin and the vector $\mathbf{r}_s$ in its boundary.

To establish our assertion we construct a nonnull row vector $\mathbf{u}'$ such that $\mathbf{u}'\mathbf{r}_s = 0$ and $\mathbf{u}'\mathbf{a}_j \geq 0$, for all $j \in J$. We have

$$\mathbf{a}_j = a_{Lj}\,\mathbf{r}_s + \boldsymbol{\Delta}_j.$$

Therefore

$$\mathbf{u}'\mathbf{a}_j = a_{Lj}\,\mathbf{u}'\mathbf{r}_s + \mathbf{u}'\boldsymbol{\Delta}_j.$$

To construct $\mathbf{u}'$, suppose that we let $u_0 = 1$ and $u_1 = u_2 = \cdots u_n = 0$, and determine u_L so that $\mathbf{u}'\mathbf{r}_s = 0$. Since $\boldsymbol{\Delta}_j \succ \mathbf{0}$ for all $j \in J$, we have $\delta_{0j} \geq 0$ and by definition [see (18) and (20)] we have $\delta_{Lj} = 0$ for all $j \in J$. Hence $\mathbf{u}'\boldsymbol{\Delta}_j \geq 0$ as desired.*

Next we note that the movement of each $\mathbf{a}_j$ to the position $\bar{\mathbf{a}}_j$ that occurs as a result of a cycle of the algorithm exhibits a certain geometric regularity. Specifically (22) and (23) show that the movement from $\mathbf{a}_j$ to $\bar{\mathbf{a}}_j$ is parallel to $\mathbf{r}_s$ and therefore is parallel to the hyperplane defined by $\mathbf{u}'$. This parallel movement is obvious, since $\bar{\mathbf{a}}_j$ has the same displacement $\boldsymbol{\Delta}_j$ from $\bar{a}_{Lj}\,\mathbf{r}_s$ as $\mathbf{a}_j$ has from $a_{Lj}\,\mathbf{r}_s$. Direct algebraic verification is also possible by subtracting (22) from (23). This yields

$$\bar{\mathbf{a}}_j - \mathbf{a}_j = (\bar{a}_{Lj} - a_{Lj})\,\mathbf{r}_s,$$

which shows that the vector connecting $\bar{\mathbf{a}}_j$ and $\mathbf{a}_j$ is a scalar multiple of $\mathbf{r}_s$.

The finiteness proof for the primal algorithm indicates that the half-space containing the set $\{\mathbf{a}_j \mid j \in J\}$ eventually coincides with the half-space defined by $a_{0j} \geq 0$ for all j.

---

* If we define $u_i = \epsilon^i$ for $i = 0, 1, \cdots, n$ and continue to define u_L so that $\mathbf{u}'\mathbf{r}_s = 0$, we can make the stronger assertion that $\mathbf{u}'\mathbf{a}_j = \mathbf{u}'\boldsymbol{\Delta}_j > 0$ for all $j \neq s$ for some positive and sufficiently small ϵ.

Thus we can depict the process of the algorithm as accomplishing a sequence of shifts in a half-space containing all the points $\{\mathbf{a}_j \mid j \in J\}$ which finally terminates in a half-space containing only vectors $\mathbf{a}_j$ with $a_{0j} \geq 0$. A more detailed picture of the tableau to tableau shift in the half-space (which we shall not pursue here) may be developed by analysis of (24), (25), and (26).

We shall terminate this section with the derivations for (22) through (26). The source of (22) is (19), (20), and (21); (22) is merely a vector form of the scalar equations given in (20).

The derivation of (23) is from the pivot operation of the primal algorithm. The change of basis formula for the primal algorithm is

$$\bar{a}_{ij} = a_{ij} - a_{pj}a_{is}, \qquad (i \in \mathscr{I}), \tag{30}$$

$$\bar{a}_{Lj} = a_{Lj} - a_{pj}a_{Ls}, \tag{31}$$

where p denotes the pivot row.

We multiply (31) by ρ_i and obtain

$$\rho_i\,\bar{a}_{Lj} = \rho_i a_{Lj} - a_{pj}\rho_i a_{Ls}.$$

Substitution, based on (18) and (20), yields.

$$\rho_i\,\bar{a}_{Lj} = a_{ij} - \delta_{ij} - a_{pj}a_{is}.$$

Then, substitution from (30) gives

$$\rho_i\,\bar{a}_{Lj} = \bar{a}_{ij} - \delta_{ij}. \tag{32}$$

The vector form of (32) is (23).

We derive (24), (25), and (26) as follows. By analogy to (22) we write

$$\bar{a}_{Lj}\,\bar{\mathbf{r}}_{\bar{s}} = \bar{\mathbf{a}}_j - \bar{\mathbf{\Delta}}_j. \tag{33}$$

Subtracting (33) from (23), we have

$$\bar{a}_{Lj}(\mathbf{r}_s - \bar{\mathbf{r}}_{\bar{s}}) = \bar{\mathbf{\Delta}}_j - \mathbf{\Delta}_j. \tag{34}$$

When $j = \bar{s}$, (23) becomes

$$\bar{a}_{L\bar{s}} \cdot \mathbf{r}_s = \bar{\mathbf{a}}_{\bar{s}} - \mathbf{\Delta}_{\bar{s}}. \tag{35}$$

Since $\bar{a}_{L\bar{s}} > 0$ we can divide (35) by this quantity and obtain

$$\mathbf{r}_s = \bar{\mathbf{r}}_{\bar{s}} - \left(\frac{1}{\bar{a}_{L\bar{s}}}\right)\mathbf{\Delta}_{\bar{s}}. \tag{24}$$

Now we can use (24) to eliminate $\mathbf{r}_s$ and $\bar{\mathbf{r}}_{\bar{s}}$ from (34), which yields

$$\bar{\mathbf{\Delta}}_j = \mathbf{\Delta}_j - (\bar{a}_{Lj}/\bar{a}_{L\bar{s}})\,\mathbf{\Delta}_{\bar{s}}. \tag{25}$$

Finally we can use the relation $\bar{\mathbf{a}}_j = \bar{a}_{Lj}\,\bar{\mathbf{r}}_j$ (which is valid if $\bar{a}_{Lj} \neq 0$) to eliminate $\bar{\mathbf{a}}_j$ from (33). The result is

$$\bar{\mathbf{\Delta}}_j = \bar{a}_{Lj}\,(\bar{\mathbf{r}}_j - \bar{\mathbf{r}}_{\bar{s}}). \tag{26}$$

KNAPSACK PROBLEM 18

18.1 KNAPSACK PROBLEM (Gilmore and Gomory [75], Gomory [84])

We shall now consider the simplest integer program, i.e., an integer program with only one constraint. This problem, like the shortest path problem, is of interest on its own merits and also often occurs as a subproblem in a problem of optimization. Due to its simple structure, it can be solved by a dynamic programming technique. (See [15], [16], or [74] for example.) We shall discuss this technique and generalize it to the general integer program in the next chapter.

The name "knapsack problem" arises from the following hypothetical situation. Consider a hiker who is going to carry a knapsack with him on his trip. To fill the knapsack he must choose among many things, each of which has a weight and a value to him. Certainly, he would like to carry with him the maximum amount of value with the total weight less than a prescribed amount.

Let a_j be the weight of the jth item, c_j be the value of the jth item, x_j be the number of items of type j that the hiker carries with him, and let b denote the total weight limitation. Then the problem becomes

$$\max \sum c_j x_j \qquad (c_j \geq 0, \text{ integers}; j = 1, \ldots, n)$$

subject to

$$\sum a_j x_j \leq b \qquad (a_j \text{ and } b \text{ positive integers}),$$

$$x_j \geq 0, \text{ integers}.$$

In order to solve this problem, we have to introduce a new function $\psi_k(y)$. Define

$$\psi_k(y) = \max \sum_{j=1}^{k} c_j x_j \qquad (0 \leq k \leq n),$$

with

$$\sum_{j=1}^{k} a_j x_j \leq y \qquad (0 \leq y \leq b),$$

i.e., $\psi_k(y)$ is the maximum value obtained by using the first k items only when the total weight limitation is y. Then $\psi_0(y) = 0$ for all y $(0 \le y \le b)$, since no items are chosen and $\psi_k(0) = 0$ for all k $(0 \le k \le n)$, since the total weight limitation is zero. Then $\psi_1(y) = [y/a_1]\, c_1$, since we want to put in as many of the first item as possible. For a general $\psi_k(y)$ we have the following recursive relation:

$$\psi_k(y) = \max\,\{\psi_{k-1}(y),\ \psi_k(y - a_k) + c_k\}. \tag{1}$$

The reason is simply this: when the first k items are chosen to obtain $\psi_k(y)$, either the kth item is used at least *once* or not at all. If it is not used, then $\psi_k(y)$ is the same as $\psi_{k-1}(y)$. If it is used at least once, then the total weight limitation is reduced to $y - a_k$. Obviously we must make the best use of the weight limitation $y - a_k$, and the optimum value when the first k items are allowed is, by definition, $\psi_k(y - a_k)$. Note that we use $\psi_k(y - a_k)$ instead of $\psi_{k-1}(y - a_k)$ because the kth item may be used more than once. We can prepare a table with n by b entries; each entry is the value $\psi_k(y)$ $(k = 1, \ldots, n;$ $y = 1, \ldots, b)$. Using the recursive relation (1), we can calculate $\psi_k(y)$ in the order of $\psi_1(1), \psi_1(2), \ldots, \psi_1(b); \psi_2(1), \ldots, \psi_2(b); \ldots; \psi_n(1), \ldots, \psi_n(b)$. In the recursive relation (1) we define ψ_k (negative number) $= -\infty$.

After $\psi_k(y)$ $(k = 1, \ldots, n; y = 1, \ldots, b)$ are computed, there is still the job of finding for any $\psi_k(y)$ the optimal x_j's that yield this value. For this we need a second table of n by b entries. In getting $\psi_k(y)$ in the first table, we need to record an index in the corresponding entry in the second table. If $i(k, y) = j$, this means that the jth item is used in $\psi_k(y)$ at least once. We first let $i(1, y) = 0$ for $\psi_1(y) = 0$ and $i(1, y) = 1$ for $\psi_1(y) \neq 0$. Then set

$$i(k, y) = \begin{cases} i(k-1, y) & \text{if } \psi_{k-1}(y) > \psi_k(y - a_k) + c_k, \\ k & \text{if } \psi_{k-1}(y) \le \psi_k(y - a_k) + c_k. \end{cases} \tag{1'}$$

Note that $i(1, y) = 1$ means that the first item is used in $\psi_1(y)$. Assume now that we know how to yield $\psi_{k-1}(y)$; then these indices are shown in the $k - 1$ row. If $i(k - 1, y) = j$, then it implies that $x_j \ge 1$ in $\psi_{k-1}(y)$. Now we want to find out the optimal x_j's that yield $\psi_{k-1}(y - a_j)$. This is shown in the entry $i(k - 1, y - a_j)$. If $i(k - 1, y - a_j) = j$ again, it implies that $x_j \ge 1$ in $\psi_{k-1}(y - a_j)$ or $x_j \ge 2$ in $\psi_{k-1}(y)$. If $i(k - 1, y - a_j) = q$, it implies that $x_q \ge 1$ in $\psi_{k-1}(y - a_j)$. To see whether it is advantageous to use the kth item when the weight limitation is y, we shall compare the value of $\psi_{k-1}(y)$ and $\psi_k(y)$. [At the moment $\psi_k(y)$ is unknown.] If in $\psi_k(y)$ we use the kth item at least once, then $\psi_k(y) = \psi_k(y - a_k) + c_k$. Thus if $\psi_{k-1}(y) \le \psi_k(y) = \psi_k(y - a_k) + c_k$, then we set $i(k, y) = k$. If $\psi_{k-1}(y) > \psi_k(y) = \psi_k(y - a_k) + c_k$, it does not pay to use the kth item at all, so we set $i(k, y) = i(k - 1, y)$. Note that we know $\psi_{k-1}(0) = 0$ and $\psi_k(0) = 0$, so the indices in the kth row as well as the values of $\psi_k(y)$ can be calculated from left to right using (1) and (1′).

Table 18.1. Values of $\psi_k(y)$

k \ y	1	2	3	4	5	6	7	8	9	10
1	0	1	1	2	2	3	3	4	4	5
2	0	1	3	3	4	6	6	7	9	9
3	0	1	3	5	5	6	8	10	10	11
4	0	1	3	5	5	6	9	10	10	12

Table 18.2. Values of $i(k, y)$

k \ y	1	2	3	4	5	6	7	8	9	10
1	0	1	1	1	1	1	1	1	1	1
2	0	1	2	2	2	2	2	2	2	2
3	0	1	2	3	3	3	3	3	3	3
4	0	1	2	3	3	3	4	3	4	4

Before making any comments, let us do a numerical example. Assume that we have four items, the total weight limitation is 10, and $c_1 = 1$, $c_2 = 3$, $c_3 = 5$, $c_4 = 9$, $a_1 = 2$, $a_2 = 3$, $a_3 = 4$, and $a_4 = 7$. Start with the first row from left to right and then the second row from left to right, etc. We obtain the two Tables 18.1 and 18.2. Note that in computing $\psi_4(10)$ we have actually computed all values $\psi_k(y)$ for $1 \leq k \leq 4$ and $0 \leq y \leq 10$. From Table 18.1, we see that $\psi_4(10) = 12$. From Table 18.2, the corresponding value is 4, that is, the fourth item is used at least once. Therefore we look for

$$i(4, 10 - a_4) = i(4, 10 - 7) = i(4, 3) = 2,$$

which means that the second item is used at least once. Then we have

$$i(4, 3 - a_3) = i(4, 0) = 0,$$

which means that we have all the x_j we needed in making up $\psi_4(10) = 12$. One important feature of this computation is that when we are computing $\psi_k(y)$ $(0 \leq y \leq b)$ we need only $\psi_{k-1}(y)$ $(0 \leq y \leq b)$. Hence we need not keep the entire table and can erase an entry in a row as soon as the entry beneath it is computed. This saves tremendous memory capacity in a computer. The same is true in computing the second table, and we need only the last row to determine the values of the x_j's.

Another thing that should be noted is the value of $i(4,8) = 3$, i.e., when the total weight limitation is 8, we do not use the fourth item, which has the greatest value per pound.

If x_j are not restricted to integers, then the problem can be easily solved by first selecting

$$\max_j \frac{c_j}{a_j} = \frac{c_r}{a_r},$$

i.e., the rth item is the item with maximum value per pound. The knapsack is then filled with the rth item with $x_r = b/a_r$. The trouble with this approach is that the x_r may not be integers. Let $\rho_j = c_j/a_j$ and reorder the subscripts of the items so that

$$\rho_1 \geq \rho_2 \geq \rho_3 \cdots \geq \rho_n,$$

where ρ_j denotes the value per pound of the item j. Intuitively we would fill the knapsack with the first item and then with whatever the weight allowance left, fill it with the second item, etc. This intuitive approach usually gives very good results but it does not always give the optimum solution due to integer restrictions. One thing is intuitively clear, i.e., if b is large compared to a_1, then $x_1 > 0$ in the optimum solution. To see this, let us assume that $x_1 = 0$ in the optimum solution. Then the maximum value will certainly not exceed $\rho_2 b$. However, if we try to fill the knapsack with only the first item, we can get a value

$$c_1\left[\frac{b}{a_1}\right] > c_1\left(\frac{b}{a_1} - \frac{a_1}{a_1}\right) = c_1 \cdot \frac{b - a_1}{a_1} = \rho_1 a_1 \frac{b - a_1}{a_1} = \rho_1(b - a_1). \tag{2}$$

To find the value b which yields

$$c_1\left[\frac{b}{a_1}\right] > \rho_1(b - a_1) \geq \rho_2\, b,$$

we solve the equation

$$\rho_1(b - a_1) = \rho_2 b \qquad \text{or} \qquad b = \frac{\rho_1}{\rho_1 - \rho_2}\, a_1,$$

i.e., for

$$b \geq \frac{\rho_1}{\rho_1 - \rho_2}\, a_1, \qquad \rho_1(b - a_1) \geq \rho_2 b.$$

In other words, for b sufficiently large, $x_1 > 0$ in the optimum solution. This means that

$$\psi_n(b) = c_1 + \psi_n(b - a_1) \qquad \text{for } b > \rho_1 a_1/(\rho_1 - \rho_2). \tag{3}$$

Define $\theta(b) = \rho_1 b - \psi_n(b)$; here $\theta(b)$ represents the difference in the optimum value of the objective functions without and with the integer restrictions. Then

$$\begin{aligned}
\theta(b - a_1) &= \rho_1(b - a_1) - \psi_n(b - a_1) \\
&= \rho_1 b - \rho_1 a_1 - (\psi_n(b) - c_1) \quad \text{from (3) and for sufficiently large } b \\
&= \rho_1 b - \psi_n(b) \\
&= \theta(b).
\end{aligned}$$

This shows that the function $\theta(b)$ is periodic in nature with period a_1 for b sufficiently large. The difference function $\theta(b)$ is well defined whether $b \gtrless \rho_1 a_1/(\rho_1 - \rho_2)$. We can get a recursive relation between the functions $\theta(b)$ as follows. Assume that in the optimum solution $x_j > 0$; then $\theta(b) = \theta(b - a_j)$ plus the loss from not fulfilling the weight a_j with the first item. The loss is $(\rho_1 - \rho_j)a_j$. Since in the optimum solution there must be some $x_j > 0, \theta(b)$ is obtained by minimizing with respect to j:

$$\theta(b) = \min_j \{\theta(b - a_j) + (\rho_1 - \rho_j)a_j\}. \tag{4}$$

Expression (4) then gives a recursive formulation in which $\theta(b)$ can be calculated for all b.

Let us consider a numerical example where

$$\begin{array}{lllll} c_1 = 18, & c_2 = 14, & c_3 = 8, & c_4 = 4, & c_5 = 0, \\ a_1 = 15, & a_2 = 12, & a_3 = 7, & a_4 = 4, & a_5 = 1, \\ \rho_1 = 1.2, & \rho_2 = 1.166, & \rho_3 = 1.142, & \rho_4 = 1, & \rho_5 = 0. \end{array}$$

Now

$$\frac{\rho_1}{\rho_1 - \rho_2} a_1 = \frac{(18/15)}{(18/15) - (14/12)} 15 = 540.$$

This estimate 540 is *sufficient* but not *necessary*. This means that for two weight limitations b and b' with $b \geq b' \geq 540$ and $b = b' \pmod{a_1}$, the optimum solutions to both problems are almost the same except that we will fulfill

Table 18.3

Values of b	Solutions	$\sum_j a_j x_j$	$\theta(b)$
0			
1			
⋮			
25			
26			1.2
⋮			⋮
40			2.0
41			1.2
⋮			⋮
55			2.0

θ(b) are the same for the two intervals

Table 18.4

b (mod a_1)	(x_j's) Periodic Solution	$\sum_{j=2}^{n} a_j x_j$	θ value
0	0	0	0
1	1	1	1.2
2	1,1	2	2.4
3	4,7,7	18	1.6
4	4	4	0.8
5	1,4	5	2.0
6	7,7,7	21	1.2
7	7	7	0.4
8	1,7	8	1.6
9	12,12	24	0.8
10	1,12,12	25	2.0
11	4,7	11	1.2
12	12	12	0.4
13	1,12	13	1.6
14	7,7	14	0.8

the part of the weight limitation $b - b'$ by the first item. Assume that we calculate $\theta(b)$ for all values of b starting with $b = 0, 1, \ldots$. Then it will be seen that $\theta(b)$ is periodic, i.e., $\theta(b) = \theta(b + 15)$ for $b \geq 26$.

Now print row 15 to row 30 of Table 18.3 with the value of b (mod a_1) in the first column. The value of x_1 in the second column is not shown, and the value of $\sum_{j=2}^{n} a_j x_j$ is shown in the third column.

To see how Table 18.4 can be used to find $\psi_n(b)$ for all b take $b = 43$, e.g.,

$$43 \equiv 13 \pmod{15}.$$

In the 13th row we have periodic solution 1, 12, which means that we shall fill the knapsack with weight limitation $b = 43$ by $x_1 = 2$, $x_2 = 1$, and $x_5 = 1$, which gives total weight $2 \times 15 + 1 \times 12 + 1 \times 1 = 43$. If $b = 25$, say, then $25 \equiv 10 \pmod{15}$. In the 10th row we have the periodic solution 1, 12, 12 with total weight 25. This means that for $b = 25$ x_1 should be zero, or in other words, the periodic solution does not apply. But for $b = 40$, where $40 - 15 \equiv 25$, we have $x_1 = 1$, $x_2 = 2$, and $x_5 = 1$. We can list all the places where the periodic solution applies as well as where it does not apply (0 means that the periodic solution does not apply):

b (mod a_1)	0	1	2	3	4	5	6	7	8	9	10	11	12	13	14
	×	×	×	0	×	×	0	×	×	0	0	×	×	×	×

ON RELATIONS BETWEEN LINEAR PROGRAMS AND INTEGER PROGRAMS* 19

19.1 INTRODUCTION (Gomory [84], Kortanek and Jeroslow [133])

In Section 13.1, we used an equation, Eq. (4), to generate a cut, Eq. (9). In generating the cut, we require the left-hand side of Eq. (4) to be an integer only (not necessarily nonnegative) and the x_j on the right-hand side to be nonnegative integers. Therefore any integer combination of equations like Eb. (4) of Section 13.1 can be used as a source row and a Gomory cut may be derived from that. Since there are infinitely many ways to get integer combinations, infinitely many source rows may be produced from a given tableau. It seems that infinitely many cuts may be added. However, it will be shown that only a finite number of cuts need be added. Any other cut generated from the tableau would be implied by one of the finite number of cuts.

Let us use a row vector $\mathbf{R}_i = (r_0, r_1, \ldots, r_n)$ to represent a source row and a row vector $\bar{\mathbf{F}}_i = (f_0, f_1, \ldots, f_n)$ to represent the Gomory cut, and let ϕ be the mapping which maps a source row $\mathbf{R}_i$ to a Gomory cut $\bar{\mathbf{F}}_i$. Then the mapping maps the row vector $\mathbf{R}_i$ into its fractional part and

$$\phi(\mathbf{R}_i) = \phi(\mathbf{R}_j),$$

if $\mathbf{R}_i$ and $\mathbf{R}_j$ differ by a vector with all integer components. Furthermore, let $\mathbf{R}_1$ and $\mathbf{R}_2$ be any two source rows and n be an arbitrary integer. Then

$$\phi(\mathbf{R}_1 + \mathbf{R}_2) \equiv \phi(\mathbf{R}_1) + \phi(\mathbf{R}_2) = \bar{\mathbf{F}}_1 + \bar{\mathbf{F}}_2,$$

and

$$\phi(n\mathbf{R}_1) \equiv n\phi(\mathbf{R}_1) = n\bar{\mathbf{F}}_1.$$

Thus the row vectors of fractional parts representing Gomory's cuts form an abelian group under the operation of addition (mod 1).

* Many results in Chapters 19 and 20 are rephrases or direct quotations from a paper by Dr. R. E. Gomory [86]. The reader is strongly urged to read the original paper since many theorems and proofs are not given here. The author wishes to thank American Elsevier Publishing Co., IBM Corporation, for permission to use the materials in the paper.

Let us study in detail how the successive tableaux of an integer program are generated. The starting tableau has an all-integer matrix $\mathbf{A}_0$; the next matrix $\mathbf{A}_1$ is obtained from $\mathbf{A}_0$ by a pivot operation. The pivot operation is equivalent to multiplying $\mathbf{A}_0$ on the right by $\mathbf{B}_0^{-1}$, i.e.,

$$\mathbf{A}_0\mathbf{B}_0^{-1} = \mathbf{A}_1,$$

where $\mathbf{B}_0$ is a submatrix of $\mathbf{A}_0$.

In Example 1 of Section 13.2,

$$\mathbf{A}_0 = \begin{bmatrix} 0 & -4 & -5 & -1 \\ 0 & -1 & 0 & 0 \\ 0 & 0 & -1 & 0 \\ 0 & 0 & 0 & -1 \\ 10 & 3 & 2 & 0 \\ 11 & 1 & 4^* & 0 \\ 13 & 3 & 3 & 1 \end{bmatrix},$$

$$\mathbf{B}_0 = \begin{bmatrix} +1 & 0 & 0 & 0 \\ 0 & +1 & 0 & 0 \\ -11 & -1 & -4 & 0 \\ 0 & 0 & 0 & +1 \end{bmatrix}, \qquad \mathbf{B}_0^{-1} = \begin{bmatrix} +1 & 0 & 0 & 0 \\ 0 & +1 & 0 & 0 \\ -11/4 & -1/4 & -1/4 & 0 \\ 0 & 0 & 0 & +1 \end{bmatrix}.$$

In general,

$$\mathbf{B}_0^{-1} = \begin{bmatrix} +1 & & & & & & \\ & +1 & & & & & \\ & & +1 & & & & \\ & & & \ddots & & & \\ \dfrac{-a_{r0}}{a_{rs}} & \cdots & & \dfrac{-1}{a_{rs}} & \cdots & \dfrac{-a_{rn}}{a_{rs}} & \\ & & & & \ddots & & \\ & & & & & +1 & \\ & & & & & & +1 \end{bmatrix},$$

where a_{rs} is the pivot. This means $|\det \mathbf{B}_0| = a_{rs}$.

Let $\mathbf{a}_i^0$ be a row of $\mathbf{A}_0$ and $\mathbf{a}_i'$ be a row of $\mathbf{A}_1$. Then

$$\mathbf{a}_i^0\mathbf{B}_0^{-1} = \mathbf{a}_i'$$

or, alternatively,

$$\mathbf{a}_i^0 = \mathbf{a}_i'\mathbf{B}_0. \tag{1}$$

Equation (1) can be considered as a system of equations with $\mathbf{a}_i'$ as the unknowns. From Cramer's rule every component of $\mathbf{a}_i'$ is the ratio of two determinants; the denominator is the determinant of $\mathbf{B}_0$. Let $|\det \mathbf{B}_0| = D$. Then D is equal to the absolute value of the pivot element. Then every component of $\mathbf{a}_i'$ is of the form h/D, where h is an integer.

Consider the relation between the original matrix $\mathbf{A}_0$ and the current matrix $\mathbf{A}_t$. We have

$$\mathbf{A}_0\mathbf{B}_0^{-1}\mathbf{B}_1^{-1} \cdots \mathbf{B}_{t-1}^{-1} = \mathbf{A}_t$$

or

$$\mathbf{A}_0 = \mathbf{A}_t\mathbf{B}_{t-1}\mathbf{B}_{t-2} \cdots \mathbf{B}_0 = \mathbf{A}_t\mathbf{B}.$$

Since $\det \mathbf{B} = \det \mathbf{B}_{t-1} \det \mathbf{B}_{t-2} \cdots \det \mathbf{B}_0$, then every entry in $\mathbf{A}_t$ is of the form h/D, where D now stands for the absolute value of the product of the successive pivots and h is an integer.

In the fractional algorithm of integer programming, if we keep all the Gomory cuts, the number of rows is increased. These Gomory cuts are all-integer inequalities if expressed in terms of the original nonbasic variables. Thus we can imagine them as part of the original all-integer matrix $\mathbf{A}_0$, and the above reasoning can be applied to produce the following theorem.

Theorem 19.1. Every entry occurring in the tableau using the fractional algorithm is of the form h/D, where h is an integer and D is the product of the successive pivots transforming the original tableau to the given tableau.

What we have been doing is multiplying an all-integer matrix $\mathbf{A}$ by an inverse matrix $\mathbf{B}^{-1}$ and then taking the fractional parts of the row vectors of $\mathbf{AB}^{-1}$. Now we shall consider the same process, except we shall deal with the fractional parts of the column vectors of $\mathbf{B}^{-1}\mathbf{A}$. This is because we shall use the column vectors of $\phi\mathbf{B}^{-1}\mathbf{A}$ instead of the row vectors of $\phi\,(\mathbf{AB}^{-1})$ in our next algorithm. However, whatever results are obtained in one formulation are also true in the other formulation.

Let us consider column vectors with m components. These column vectors under the usual operation of addition form an abelian group. We shall use $\mathbf{R}$ to denote m-vectors with real entries and $\mathbf{Z}$ to denote m-vectors with integer entries. Let $\{\mathbf{R}\}$ denote the abelian group whose elements are real m-vectors and $\{\mathbf{Z}\}$ the abelian group whose elements are integer m-vectors. Clearly $\{\mathbf{Z}\}$ is a subgroup of $\{\mathbf{R}\}$, and any m-vector with real entries will belong to $\{\mathbf{R}\}$ and any m-vector with integer entries will belong to $\{\mathbf{Z}\}$.

Let $\mathbf{A}$ be an $m \times n$ matrix with integer components, i.e., $\mathbf{A} = [\mathbf{a}_1, \ldots, \mathbf{a}_n]$. Then $\{\mathbf{A}\}$ denotes the abelian group generated by the column vectors of $\mathbf{A}$. Any vector which can be written as $\sum_{j=1}^{n} n_j\mathbf{a}_j$ with n_j integers will belong to

$\{\mathbf{A}\}$. If the matrix $\mathbf{A}$ contains an $m \times m$ identity matrix, then $\{\mathbf{A}\} = \{\mathbf{Z}\}$; in general $\{\mathbf{A}\}$ will be a subgroup of $\{\mathbf{Z}\}$.

Assume that $\mathbf{A}$ is of rank m and $\mathbf{B} = [\mathbf{b}_1, \ldots, \mathbf{b}_m]$ is an $m \times m$ submatrix of $\mathbf{A}$, also of rank m. We can also consider the abelian group $\{\mathbf{B}\}$ generated by the column vectors of $\mathbf{B}$. Thus an element of $\{\mathbf{B}\}$ is of the form $\sum_{j=1}^{m} n_j \mathbf{b}_j$ with n_j integers. Since $\mathbf{A}$ and $\mathbf{B}$ are of the same rank, any column vector $\mathbf{a}_j$ of $\mathbf{A}$ can be written as a linear combination of vectors $\mathbf{b}_i$ $(i = 1, \ldots, m)$ with the coefficients of combination being *real numbers* but not necessarily *integers*. Thus $\{\mathbf{B}\}$ is a subgroup of $\{\mathbf{A}\}$ in general. The product $\mathbf{B}^{-1}\mathbf{A}$, which will be another $m \times n$ matrix, is denoted by $\boldsymbol{\alpha}$, and we shall use $\{\boldsymbol{\alpha}\}$ to denote the abelian group generated by the column vectors of $\boldsymbol{\alpha}$.

Let $\bar{\mathbf{R}}$ and $\bar{\boldsymbol{\alpha}}$ be the fractional part of $\mathbf{R}$ and $\boldsymbol{\alpha}$, respectively, so that

$$\mathbf{R} = \bar{\mathbf{R}} + \mathbf{Z}, \qquad \boldsymbol{\alpha} = \bar{\boldsymbol{\alpha}} + \mathbf{Z}.$$

Then $\{\bar{\boldsymbol{\alpha}}\}$ is the abelian group generated by the fractional parts of the column vectors of $\boldsymbol{\alpha}$ under addition (mod 1).

Thus from a given group $\{\mathbf{A}\}$ we use $\mathbf{B}^{-1}$ to map $\{\mathbf{A}\}$ into $\{\boldsymbol{\alpha}\}$, and we use the mapping ϕ from $\{\boldsymbol{\alpha}\}$ to $\{\bar{\boldsymbol{\alpha}}\}$. This is indicated symbolically as

$$\{\mathbf{A}\} \xrightarrow{\mathbf{B}^{-1}} \{\boldsymbol{\alpha}\} \xrightarrow{\phi} \{\bar{\boldsymbol{\alpha}}\}.$$

It is easy to check that the composite mapping $\phi\mathbf{B}^{-1}$, which maps $\{\mathbf{A}\}$ to $\{\bar{\boldsymbol{\alpha}}\}$, is a homomorphism.

Lemma 19.1. $\{\mathbf{A}\}/[\text{kernel of } \phi\mathbf{B}^{-1}]$ and $\{\bar{\boldsymbol{\alpha}}\}$ are isomorphic. This lemma stated more generally is as follows: let f be a homomorphism between a module $\{\mathbf{A}\}$ and $\{\mathbf{A}'\}$. Then the kernel of f forms a normal submodule $\{\mathbf{H}\}$ of $\{\mathbf{A}\}$, and the mapping f^*: $\{\mathbf{A}\}/\{\mathbf{H}\} \to \{\mathbf{A}'\}$ defined by $f^*(a_1 + \mathbf{H}) = f(a_1)$ is an isomorphism between $\{\mathbf{A}\}/\{\mathbf{H}\}$ and $\{\mathbf{A}'\}$.

Proof. Let x be any element in the kernel of f, i.e., $f(x) = 0'$, where $0'$ is the neutral or zero element of $\{\mathbf{A}'\}$. Let a_1 be any element of $\{\mathbf{A}\}$. Then

$$\begin{aligned} f(-a_1 + x + a_1) &= f(-a_1) + f(x) + f(a_1) = f(-a_1) + 0' + f(a_1) \\ &= -f(a_1) + f(a_1) = 0'. \end{aligned}$$

This means that $-a_1 + x + a_1$ belongs to $\mathbf{H}$ or $-a_1 + \mathbf{H} + a_1$ is contained in $\mathbf{H}$. Interchanging a_1 and $-a_1$ in the above argument, we can show that $(a_1 + x - a_1)$ also belongs to $\mathbf{H}$, or $a_1 + \mathbf{H} - a_1$ is contained in $\mathbf{H}$.

Replacing x by $a_1 + \mathbf{H} - a_1$, we see that $-a_1 + (a_1 + \mathbf{H} - a_1) + a_1$ is contained in $-a_1 + \mathbf{H} + a_1$, or $\mathbf{H}$ is contained in $-a_1 + \mathbf{H} + a_1$. Therefore, $\mathbf{H} = -a_1 + \mathbf{H} + a_1$ for any element $a_1 \in \{\mathbf{A}\}$, or $\mathbf{H}$ is a normal submodule.

To prove the second assertion, let a_1 and a_2 be in the same coset of $\mathbf{H}$. Since $\mathbf{H}$ is a submodule, $-a_1 + a_2$ is also in $\mathbf{H}$ and $f(-a_1 + a_2) = 0'$.

Using this result, we have

$$f(a_2) = f(a_1 - a_1 + a_2) = f(a_1) + f(-a_1 + a_2)$$
$$= f(a_1) + 0' = f(a_1).$$

Therefore f^* maps all the elements in any coset of **H** into the same element of $\{\mathbf{A}'\}$; that is to say, if $a_1 + \mathbf{H} = a_2 + \mathbf{H}$, then $f(a_1) = f(a_2)$.

Let $f = \phi\mathbf{B}^{-1}$. Then the lemma is proved.

Lemma 19.2. The kernel of $\phi\mathbf{B}^{-1} = \{\mathbf{B}\}$.

Proof.

$$\sum_{j=1}^{n} \lambda_j \mathbf{a}_j \in \text{kernel of } (\phi\mathbf{B}^{-1})$$

$$\Longleftrightarrow \phi\left(\mathbf{B}^{-1}\left(\sum_{j=1}^{n} \lambda_j \mathbf{a}_j\right)\right) = \mathbf{0}$$

$$\Longleftrightarrow \mathbf{B}^{-1}\left(\sum_{j=1}^{n} \lambda_j \mathbf{a}_j\right) = \boldsymbol{\mu} \qquad (\boldsymbol{\mu} \text{ is some integer vector})$$

$$\Longleftrightarrow \sum_{j=1}^{n} \lambda_j \mathbf{a}_j = \mathbf{B}\boldsymbol{\mu} = \sum_{i=1}^{m} \mu_i \mathbf{b}_i$$

$$\Longleftrightarrow \sum_{j=1}^{n} \lambda_j \mathbf{a}_j \in \{\mathbf{B}\}.$$

Theorem 19.2. $\{\mathbf{A}\}/\{\mathbf{B}\} \cong \{\bar{\boldsymbol{\alpha}}\}$.

This theorem follows directly from Lemmas 19.1 and 19.2.

We have said that **B** is a basis in **R**, so every vector can be expressed by vectors in **B** if real coefficients are allowed. If **B** spanned **A** with integer coefficients, then $\{\mathbf{A}\}/\{\mathbf{B}\}$ would only have the neutral element $\bar{0} + \{\mathbf{B}\}$ and $\{\bar{\boldsymbol{\alpha}}\}$ would also consist of one element, the zero. *Therefore, the size of* $\{\bar{\boldsymbol{\alpha}}\}$ *is in some sense a measure of the degree to which* **B** *fails to span* **A** *with integer coefficients.*

Let us now study the structure of $\{\mathbf{Z}\}/\{\mathbf{B}\}$. Since $\{\mathbf{Z}\}$ is m-dimensional, the unit vectors $\mathbf{e}_i$ $(i = 1, \ldots, m)$

$$\mathbf{e}_i = \begin{bmatrix} 0 \\ 0 \\ 0 \\ 1 \\ 0 \\ 0 \\ 0 \\ 0 \end{bmatrix} \leftarrow i\text{th component}$$

serve as a basis for $\{\mathbf{Z}\}$ and certainly also for $\{\mathbf{B}\}$, where

$$\mathbf{b}_j = \sum_{i=1}^{m} b_{ij}\mathbf{e}_i \qquad (j = 1, \ldots, m).$$

Therefore, the matrix $\mathbf{B}$,

$$\begin{array}{c} \\ \mathbf{e}_1 \\ \mathbf{e}_2 \\ \vdots \\ \\ \mathbf{e}_m \end{array} \begin{array}{c} \mathbf{b}_1, \quad \mathbf{b}_2, \quad \ldots, \quad \mathbf{b}_m \\ \begin{bmatrix} b_{11} & & b_{1m} \\ b_{21} & & \\ b_{31} & & \vdots \\ \vdots & & \\ b_{m1} & & b_{mm} \end{bmatrix} \end{array},$$

expresses every $\mathbf{b}_i$ in terms of $\mathbf{e}_j$.

By changing the basis vectors $\mathbf{b}_i$ and the unit vector $\mathbf{e}_j$, we can diagonalize the matrix so that it is of the form

$$\begin{array}{c} \\ \mathbf{e}'_1 \\ \mathbf{e}'_2 \\ \vdots \\ \mathbf{e}'_m \end{array} \begin{array}{c} \mathbf{b}'_1, \quad \mathbf{b}'_2, \quad \ldots, \quad \mathbf{b}'_m \\ \begin{bmatrix} \epsilon_1 & & & \\ & \epsilon_2 & & \\ & & \ddots & \\ & & & \epsilon_m \end{bmatrix} \end{array} = \mathbf{B}',$$

where ϵ_i is a divisor of ϵ_{i+1} $(i = 1, \ldots, m-1)$. (The process of transforming into Smith's normal form is written in detail in the Appendix A.) Since the process does not change the determinant, $D = |\det \mathbf{B}| = \det \mathbf{B}' = \epsilon_1 \cdot \epsilon_2 \cdots \epsilon_m$, and $\mathbf{b}'_i = \epsilon_{(i)} \cdot \mathbf{e}'_{(i)}$ $(i = 1, \ldots, m)$. Since $\mathbf{e}'_i$ $(i = 1, \ldots, m)$ are basis for $\{\mathbf{Z}\}$,

$$\{\mathbf{Z}\} = z\mathbf{e}'_1 \oplus z\mathbf{e}'_2 \oplus \cdots \oplus z\mathbf{e}'_m \qquad (z \text{ are any integers}), \tag{2}$$

and $\mathbf{b}'_i$ $(i = 1, \ldots, m)$ are a basis for $\{\mathbf{B}\}$,

$$\{\mathbf{B}\} = z\mathbf{b}'_1 \oplus z\mathbf{b}'_2 \oplus \cdots \oplus z\mathbf{b}'_m = z\epsilon_1\mathbf{e}'_1 \oplus z\epsilon_2\mathbf{e}'_2 \oplus \cdots \oplus z\epsilon_m\mathbf{e}'_m. \tag{3}$$

From (2) and (3) we have

$$\begin{aligned} \frac{\{\mathbf{Z}\}}{\{\mathbf{B}\}} &= \frac{z\mathbf{e}'_1 \oplus z\mathbf{e}'_2 \oplus \cdots \oplus z\mathbf{e}'_m}{z\epsilon_1\mathbf{e}'_1 \oplus z\epsilon_2\mathbf{e}'_2 \oplus \cdots \oplus z\epsilon_m\mathbf{e}'_m} \\ &\cong \frac{z\mathbf{e}'_1}{z\epsilon_1\mathbf{e}'_1} \oplus \frac{z\mathbf{e}'_2}{z\epsilon_2\mathbf{e}'_2} \oplus \cdots \oplus \frac{z\mathbf{e}'_m}{z\epsilon_m\mathbf{e}'_m} \\ &\cong \frac{z}{z\epsilon_1} \oplus \frac{z}{z\epsilon_2} \oplus \cdots \oplus \frac{z}{z\epsilon_m}. \end{aligned}$$

Note that $\mathbf{b}'_i = \epsilon_{(i)}\mathbf{e}'_{(i)}$, so that there are at most ϵ_i elements in that group, i.e., $\bar{0}$, $\mathbf{e}'_i$, $2\mathbf{e}'_i$, ... $(\epsilon_i - 1)\mathbf{e}'_i$, so the order of the cyclic group is ϵ_i.

Therefore, $\{\mathbf{Z}\}/\{\mathbf{B}\}$ is the direct sum of m cyclic groups; the ith cyclic group is of order ϵ_i ($i = 1, \ldots, m$), where ϵ_i divides ϵ_{i+1}. In particular, the size of the group is $\epsilon_1 \cdot \epsilon_2 \ldots \epsilon_m = D$.

Let $[\{\mathbf{Z}\} : \{\mathbf{A}\}]$ be the number of cosets of $\{\mathbf{A}\}$ in $\{\mathbf{Z}\}$, and $[\{\mathbf{A}\} : \{\mathbf{B}\}]$ be the number of cosets of $\{\mathbf{B}\}$ in $\{\mathbf{A}\}$. Then

$$D = [\{\mathbf{Z}\} : \{\mathbf{B}\}] = [\{\mathbf{Z}\} : \{\mathbf{A}\}] \cdot [\{\mathbf{A}\} : \{\mathbf{B}\}]$$

as $\{\mathbf{A}\} \supset \{\mathbf{B}\}$. This means that $[\{\mathbf{A}\} : \{\mathbf{B}\}]$ always divides D. If $\mathbf{A}$ should contain an identity matrix of $m \times m$, then $\{\mathbf{Z}\} = \{\mathbf{A}\}$ and $[\{\mathbf{Z}\} : \{\mathbf{A}\}] = 1$, so that

$$\mathrm{D} = [\{\mathbf{A}\} : \{\mathbf{B}\}] = \text{order of } \{\bar{\boldsymbol{\alpha}}\}.$$

Since $\{\bar{\boldsymbol{\alpha}}\}$ is isomorphic to $\{\mathbf{A}\}/\{\mathbf{B}\}$, we have the following theorem.

Theorem 19.3. For any given integer matrices $\mathbf{A}$ and their submatrices $\mathbf{B}$ and $\boldsymbol{\alpha} = \mathbf{B}^{-1}\mathbf{A}$, there exist positive integers ϵ_i ($i = 1, \ldots, m$) such that $\epsilon_1 \cdot \epsilon_2 \cdots \epsilon_m = D = |\det \mathbf{B}|$, ϵ_i divides ϵ_{i+1} ($i = 1, \ldots, m - 1$), and

$$\{\bar{\boldsymbol{\alpha}}\} \cong \frac{z}{\epsilon_1 z} \oplus \frac{z}{\epsilon_2 z} \oplus \cdots \oplus \frac{z}{\epsilon_m z},$$

or $\{\bar{\boldsymbol{\alpha}}\}$ is isomorphic with one of its submodules. Therefore, the size of $\{\bar{\boldsymbol{\alpha}}\}$ can never exceed D and it always divides D. If $\mathbf{A}$ contains the identity matrix, then $\{\mathbf{A}\}/\{\mathbf{B}\}$ is of order D.

We have shown that the row of fractions $(f_0, f_1, \ldots, f_n)$ forms an abelian group under addition (mod 1) and, furthermore, the abelian group is the direct sum of several cyclic groups each of order ϵ_i with $\epsilon_1 \cdot \epsilon_2 \cdots \epsilon_m = D$. Now consider a row of fractions

$$\bar{\mathbf{F}}_i = \left(\frac{p_0}{D}, \frac{p_1}{D}, \frac{p_2}{D}, \ldots, \frac{p_j}{D}, \ldots, \frac{p_n}{D}\right).$$

This row then represents an element in one of the cyclic groups.

If there is no common factor between p_j ($j = 0, 1, \ldots, n$) and D, then the row is of order D and hence generates the whole group. In other words, the whole group is a cyclic group.

If there is a common factor c between p_j ($j = 0, 1, \ldots, n$) and D, then the row is of order D/c. That is to say, the row is of the order of the denominator of the reduced fractions

We have shown that $\{\bar{\boldsymbol{\alpha}}\}$ is isomorphic to the direct sum of many cyclic groups each of order ϵ_i. Now we will show that if the matrix $\mathbf{B}$ is diagonalized such that $\mathbf{b}'_i = \epsilon_{(i)}\mathbf{e}'_{(i)}$, then we have the next theorem.

Theorem 19.4. $\{\bar{\boldsymbol{\alpha}}\} = \{\phi\mathbf{B}^{-1}(\mathbf{e}'_1)\} \oplus \{\phi\mathbf{B}^{-1}(\mathbf{e}'_2)\} \oplus \cdots \oplus \{\phi\mathbf{B}^{-1}(\mathbf{e}'_m)\}$.

Proof. Let $\phi\mathbf{B}^{-1}(\mathbf{e}_1') = h_1$. We shall prove that h_1 is a generator of $\{\bar{\boldsymbol{\alpha}}\}$ or h_1 is of order ϵ_1.

Since $\{\bar{\boldsymbol{\alpha}}\} \cong \{\mathbf{A}\}/\{\mathbf{B}\}$, the least positive multiple of $\mathbf{e}_1'$ that will be mapped into zero under $\phi\mathbf{B}^{-1}$ is $\epsilon_1\mathbf{e}_1' = \mathbf{b}_1'$. Then $\phi\mathbf{B}^{-1}(\epsilon_1\mathbf{e}_1') = \epsilon_1\phi\mathbf{B}^{-1}(\mathbf{e}_1') = \epsilon_1 h_1 = 0$ or h_1 is of order ϵ_1. The same reasoning can be used in $\phi\mathbf{B}^{-1}(\mathbf{e}_i')$ $(i = 1, \ldots, m)$. Thus

$$\{\bar{\boldsymbol{\alpha}}\} = \{\phi\mathbf{B}^{-1}(\mathbf{e}_1')\} \oplus \cdots \oplus \{\phi\mathbf{B}^{-1}(\mathbf{e}_m')\} = \{h_1\} \oplus \{h_2\} \oplus \cdots \oplus \{h_m\}.$$

Example. Let

$$\mathbf{A} = \begin{bmatrix} -1 & 2 & 0 & 1 & 0 & 0 \\ 2 & 0 & 0 & 0 & 1 & 0 \\ 1 & -2 & 2 & 0 & 0 & 1 \end{bmatrix},$$

and

$$\mathbf{B} = \begin{bmatrix} -1 & 2 & 0 \\ 2 & 0 & 0 \\ 1 & -2 & 2 \end{bmatrix}, \qquad \mathbf{B}^{-1} = \begin{bmatrix} 0 & 4/8 & 0 \\ 4/8 & 2/8 & 0 \\ 4/8 & 0 & 4/8 \end{bmatrix}. \tag{4}$$

If we use

$$\begin{aligned} \mathbf{e}_1' &= -\mathbf{e}_1 + \mathbf{e}_3 + 2\mathbf{e}_2, & \mathbf{b}_1' &= \mathbf{b}_1, \\ \mathbf{e}_2' &= \mathbf{e}_3\ , & \mathbf{b}_2' &= \mathbf{b}_3, \\ \mathbf{e}_3' &= \mathbf{e}_2, & \mathbf{b}_3' &= 2\mathbf{b}_1 + \mathbf{b}_2, \end{aligned}$$

then the matrix $\mathbf{B}$ is diagonalized to

$$\mathbf{B}' = \begin{bmatrix} 1 & 0 & 0 \\ 0 & 2 & 0 \\ 0 & 0 & 4 \end{bmatrix}$$

Then

$$\mathbf{e}_1' = -\begin{bmatrix} 1 \\ 0 \\ 0 \end{bmatrix} + \begin{bmatrix} 0 \\ 0 \\ 1 \end{bmatrix} + 2\begin{bmatrix} 0 \\ 1 \\ 0 \end{bmatrix} = \begin{bmatrix} -1 \\ 2 \\ 1 \end{bmatrix}, \qquad \mathbf{e}_2' = \begin{bmatrix} 0 \\ 0 \\ 1 \end{bmatrix}, \qquad \mathbf{e}_3' = \begin{bmatrix} 0 \\ 1 \\ 0 \end{bmatrix},$$

$$\mathbf{B}^{-1}\begin{bmatrix} -1 \\ 2 \\ 1 \end{bmatrix} = \begin{bmatrix} 1 \\ 0 \\ 0 \end{bmatrix}, \qquad \mathbf{B}^{-1}\begin{bmatrix} 0 \\ 0 \\ 1 \end{bmatrix} = \begin{bmatrix} 0 \\ 0 \\ 4/8 \end{bmatrix}, \qquad \mathbf{B}^{-1}\begin{bmatrix} 0 \\ 1 \\ 0 \end{bmatrix} = \begin{bmatrix} 4/8 \\ 2/8 \\ 0 \end{bmatrix},$$

$$\phi\begin{bmatrix} 1 \\ 0 \\ 0 \end{bmatrix} = \begin{bmatrix} 0 \\ 0 \\ 0 \end{bmatrix}, \qquad \phi\begin{bmatrix} 0 \\ 0 \\ 4/8 \end{bmatrix} = \begin{bmatrix} 0 \\ 0 \\ 4/8 \end{bmatrix}, \qquad \phi\begin{bmatrix} 4/8 \\ 2/8 \\ 0 \end{bmatrix} = \begin{bmatrix} 4/8 \\ 2/8 \\ 0 \end{bmatrix}.$$

Thus it follows that

$$\{\bar{\alpha}\} = \begin{bmatrix} 0 \\ 0 \\ 4/8 \end{bmatrix} \oplus \begin{bmatrix} 4/8 \\ 2/8 \\ 0 \end{bmatrix}.$$

19.2 THE ASYMPTOTIC ALGORITHM (Gomory [84], [85], [86])

Consider an integer program

$$\max \mathbf{c}'\mathbf{x}'$$

subject to

$$\mathbf{A}'\mathbf{x}' \leq \mathbf{b}, \tag{1}$$
$$\mathbf{x}' \geq \mathbf{0}, \quad \text{integers,}$$

where $\mathbf{A}'$ is an $m \times n$ integer matrix, $\mathbf{b}$ an integer m-vector, and $\mathbf{c}'$ an integer n-vector. Alternatively, the integer program (1) can be written as

$$\max \mathbf{cx}$$

subject to

$$\mathbf{Ax} = \mathbf{b}, \tag{2a}$$
$$\mathbf{x} \geq \mathbf{0} \quad \text{integers,}$$

where $\mathbf{A}$ is an $m \times (m + n)$ integer matrix, $\mathbf{c}$ an $(m + n)$ vector, and $\mathbf{x}$ is an $(m + n)$ vector which includes the slack variables introduced to convert the inequalities of (1) to the equalities of (2a). For simplicity we shall assume that $\mathbf{A}$ contains an $m \times m$ identity matrix $\mathbf{I}$. Partitioning $\mathbf{A}$ as $[\mathbf{B}, \mathbf{N}]$, we can write (2a) as

$$\max \mathbf{c}_B\mathbf{x}_B + \mathbf{c}_N\mathbf{x}_N$$

subject to

$$\mathbf{Bx}_B + \mathbf{Nx}_N = \mathbf{b}, \tag{2b}$$
$$\mathbf{x}_B, \mathbf{x}_N \geq \mathbf{0} \quad \text{integers,}$$

where $\mathbf{B}$ is an $m \times m$ nonsingular matrix. Expressing $\mathbf{x}_B$ in terms of $\mathbf{x}_N$, i.e., $\mathbf{x}_B = \mathbf{B}^{-1}\mathbf{b} - \mathbf{B}^{-1}\mathbf{N}\mathbf{x}_N$, we can write (2b) as

$$\max \mathbf{c}_B\mathbf{B}^{-1}\mathbf{b} - (\mathbf{c}_B\mathbf{B}^{-1}\mathbf{N} - \mathbf{c}_N)\mathbf{x}_N$$

subject to

$$\mathbf{x}_B + \mathbf{B}^{-1}\mathbf{N}\mathbf{x}_N = \mathbf{B}^{-1}\mathbf{b}, \tag{2c}$$
$$\mathbf{x}_B, \mathbf{x}_N \geq \mathbf{0} \quad \text{integers.}$$

If we consider (2c) as a linear program, i.e., drop the integer restriction on $\mathbf{x}_B$ and $\mathbf{x}_N$, and $\mathbf{B}$ is the optimum basis of the linear program, then the optimum solution to the linear program is

$$\mathbf{x}_B = \mathbf{B}^{-1}\mathbf{b}, \ \mathbf{x}_N = \mathbf{0},$$

where $\mathbf{c}_B\mathbf{B}^{-1}\mathbf{N} - \mathbf{c}_N \geq \mathbf{0}$. If $\mathbf{B}^{-1}\mathbf{b}$ happens to be an integer vector, then

$$\mathbf{x}_B = \mathbf{B}^{-1}\mathbf{b}, \ \mathbf{x}_N = \mathbf{0},$$

is, of course, also the optimum solution to the integer program (2c). When $\mathbf{B}^{-1}\mathbf{b}$ is not an integer vector, then we must increase $\mathbf{x}_N$ from zero to some nonnegative integer vector such that

$$\mathbf{x}_B = \mathbf{B}^{-1}\mathbf{b} - \mathbf{B}^{-1}\mathbf{N}\mathbf{x}_N \geq \mathbf{0}, \quad \text{integers.}$$

This raises two questions: (1) When is $\mathbf{B}^{-1}\mathbf{b} - \mathbf{B}^{-1}\mathbf{N}\mathbf{x}_N \geq \mathbf{0}$? (2) When is $\mathbf{B}^{-1}\mathbf{b} - \mathbf{B}^{-1}\mathbf{N}\mathbf{x}_N$ an integer vector? Let us consider the second question first. Denote $\mathbf{B}^{-1}\mathbf{N}$ as $[\boldsymbol{\alpha}_1, \boldsymbol{\alpha}_2, \ldots, \boldsymbol{\alpha}_n]$ and $\mathbf{B}^{-1}\mathbf{b}$ as $\boldsymbol{\beta}_0$. Then we can express the second question as a problem to find x_j such that

$$\sum_j \boldsymbol{\alpha}_j x_j \equiv \boldsymbol{\beta}_0 \pmod 1, \tag{3}$$

$$x_j \equiv 0 \pmod 1, \qquad x_j \geq 0 \qquad (j = 1, \ldots, n).$$

Since any integer components of $\boldsymbol{\alpha}_j$ multiplied by an integer x_j will be zero (mod 1), we are only interested in the fractional parts of the components of the vectors $\boldsymbol{\alpha}_j$ and $\boldsymbol{\beta}_0$. Let $\phi(\boldsymbol{\alpha}_j) = \bar{\boldsymbol{\alpha}}_j$, and $\phi(\boldsymbol{\beta}_0) = \bar{\boldsymbol{\beta}}_0$. Then (3) is equivalent to

$$\sum_j \bar{\boldsymbol{\alpha}}_j x_j \equiv \bar{\boldsymbol{\beta}}_0 \pmod 1, \tag{4}$$

$$x_j \equiv 0 \pmod 1, \qquad x_j \geq 0 \qquad (j = 1, \ldots, n).$$

Note that (4) could have been obtained by applying the mapping $f = \phi\mathbf{B}^{-1}$ to the constraints of (2b).

Since in (2c) $\mathbf{c}_N^* = \mathbf{c}_B\mathbf{B}^{-1}\mathbf{N} - \mathbf{c}_N \geq \mathbf{0}$, we want to increase $\mathbf{x}_N$ as little as possible. Thus when the restriction $\mathbf{x}_B \geq \mathbf{0}$ is dropped, the integer program (2c) becomes

$$\max \mathbf{c}_B\mathbf{B}^{-1}\mathbf{b} - \mathbf{c}_N^*\mathbf{x}_N$$

subject to

$$\sum_j \bar{\boldsymbol{\alpha}}_j x_j \equiv \bar{\boldsymbol{\beta}}_0, \tag{5}$$

$$x_j \equiv 0 \pmod 1, \quad x_j \geq 0 \quad (j = 1, \ldots, n).$$

For each integer program (2b), there is an associated linear program by dropping the integer constraints on $\mathbf{x}$. The feasible points of the linear program associated with (2b) are a convex polyhedron which will be denoted by P'. The convex hull of all integer points within P' is denoted by P. It is well known that the optimum solution to (2b) is a vertex of P. In Fig. 19.1(a), P' is the bounded quadrangle drawn in solid lines and P is the hexagon within P'.

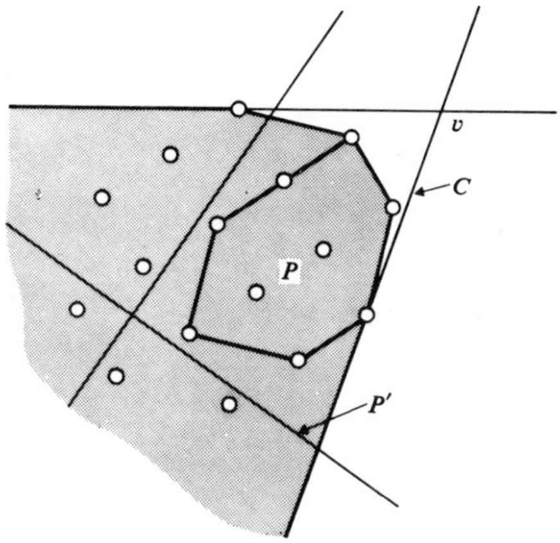

Fig. 19-1(a)

The integer program (5) is obtained from (2b) by dropping the requirement $\mathbf{x}_B \geq \mathbf{0}$. The feasible points of the linear program associated with (5) is a cone which is denoted by C. The convex hull of all integer points within C is denoted by $P_{x'}(\mathbf{B}, \mathbf{N}, \mathbf{b})$, which is called the corner polyhedron. In Fig. 19.1(a), C is the unbounded region with the vertex v, and $P_{x'}(\mathbf{B}, \mathbf{N}, \mathbf{b})$ is the unbounded shaded area.

The corner polyhedron is very important and will be studied in detail in Chapter 20. To facilitate the study of the corner polyhedron, we shall introduce another space. As we have shown in Section 19.1, the column vectors $\bar{\boldsymbol{\alpha}}_j$ of (5) are elements of an abelian group G. Let the images of all nonbasic column vectors $\mathbf{a}_j$ in (2b) be the set η, i.e., η be the set of nonzero group elements $f(\mathbf{a}_j)$ $(j = 1, \ldots, n)$. Let $n' = |\eta| \leq n$, because two vectors $\mathbf{a}_j$ may be mapped into a single group element g. We introduce n' variables $t(g)$, one for each $g \in \eta$; and let $\mathbf{t}$ be the n'-vector with components $t(g)$. If all the vectors $\mathbf{a}_j$ are mapped into different nonzero elements g, then the $\mathbf{t}$-space is exactly the same as the $\mathbf{x}_N$-space. If the $\mathbf{x}_N$ satisfy the constraints (5), then the variables $t(g)$ satisfy the group relation

$$\sum_{g \in \eta} t(g) \cdot g = g_0, \qquad (6)$$
$$t(g) \geq 0 \quad \text{integers},$$

where $\bar{\boldsymbol{\beta}}_0$ of (5) is replaced by the group element g_0. Since the cardinal number of the group G is $|G| = |\det \mathbf{B}| = D$, we have $n' \leq D$, since there may be some elements of G which are not images of any nonbasic columns $\mathbf{a}_j$ under f.

Let

$$c^*(g) = \min_{j \in J} c_j^* \qquad (J = \{j \mid f(\mathbf{a}_j) = g\}),$$

i.e., if more than one column is mapped into a single g, we have associated

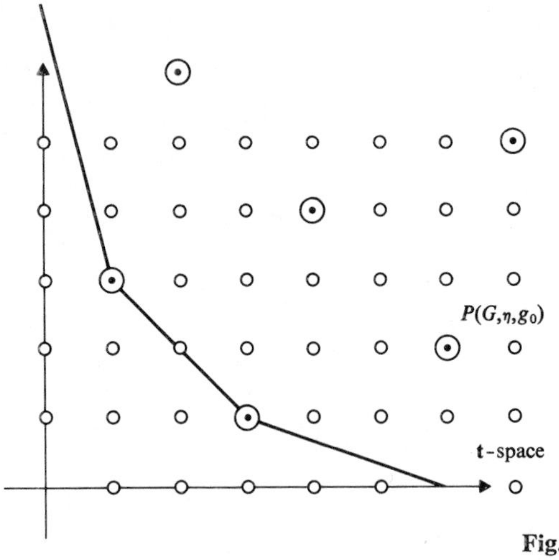

Fig. 19-1(b)

the minimum cost of the columns to the group element g. Then we have a minimization problem in the t-space corresponding to (5):

$$\min \sum_{g \in \eta} c^*(g)t(g) \qquad (c^*(g) \geq 0)$$

subject to

$$\sum_{g \in \eta} t(g) \cdot g = g_0, \tag{7}$$

$$t(g) \geq 0, \quad \text{integers.}$$

The correspondence between the $\mathbf{x}$-space of (2a) and the $\mathbf{t}$-space of (7) is a natural one. Given any integer program, there is an optimum basis $\mathbf{B}$ for the associated linear program. This partitions the vector $\mathbf{x}$ into $\mathbf{x} = [\mathbf{x}_B, \mathbf{x}_N]$. Once $\mathbf{x}_N$ is assigned, the value of $\mathbf{x}_B$ is uniquely determined by $\mathbf{x}_B = \mathbf{B}^{-1}(\mathbf{b} - \mathbf{N}\mathbf{x}_N)$. The relation between the $\mathbf{x}_N$ which satisfies the constraint of (5) and the $\mathbf{t}$ which solves the constraints of (7) is

$$t(g) = x_i \qquad (i \in \{i \mid f(\mathbf{a}_i) = g\}). \tag{8a}$$

Since we are interested in the optimum solution to (5), if $f(\mathbf{a}_i) = f(\mathbf{a}_j) = g$ and $c_j > c_i$, then we let $x_j = 0$. In this way, there is a one to one correspondence between $t(g)$ of (7) and x of (5). We shall write this correspondence as

$$t(g) = x_i \qquad (f(\mathbf{a}_i) = g). \tag{8b}$$

The point $\mathbf{x} = [\mathbf{x}_B, \mathbf{x}_N]$, with $\mathbf{x}_B = \mathbf{B}^{-1}\mathbf{b}$, $\mathbf{x}_N = \mathbf{0}$, corresponds to the origin in $\mathbf{x}_N$-space and also corresponds to the origin in n'-dimensional $\mathbf{t}$-space. The portion of the $\mathbf{x}$-space in which $\mathbf{x}_N \geq \mathbf{0}$ corresponds to the first (or nonnegative) orthant in $\mathbf{t}$-space (Fig. 19.1b).

In terms of the original $\mathbf{x}'$-space of (1), the nonnegative orthant of $\mathbf{t}$-space corresponds to the cone C in Fig. 19.1(a). If a point in $\mathbf{t}$-space satisfies the group relation (6), it is shown as a circled point in Fig. 19.1(b). A point $\mathbf{x}'$ of C will give a point $(\mathbf{x}_B, \mathbf{x}_N)$; the point $\mathbf{x}'$ is an integer point if and only if the $\mathbf{x}_N$ corresponds to one of these circled points in $\mathbf{t}$-space.

As we have mentioned before, the corner polyhedron in $\mathbf{x}'$-space is denoted by $P_{x'}(\mathbf{B}, \mathbf{N}, \mathbf{b})$. In $\mathbf{x}$-space, the corner polyhedron is denoted by

$$P_x(\mathbf{B}, \mathbf{N}, \mathbf{b}).$$

The corresponding polyhedron in $\mathbf{t}$-space is denoted by

$$P(G, \eta, g_0).$$

We have shown $P_{x'}(\mathbf{B}, \mathbf{N}, \mathbf{b})$ and $P(G, \eta, g_0)$ in Fig. 19.1(a) and (b). These polyhedra are essentially the same and we shall work with $P(G, \eta, g_0)$ most of the time. Since $\mathbf{t}$-space is n'-dimensional, we shall refer to an $(n'-1)$-dimensional hyperplane defining the $P(G, \eta, g_0)$ as a face of $P(G, \eta, g_0)$. A face of a polyhedron is denoted by an inequality. It is understood that the face is defined by the equality and all the points of the polyhedron satisfy the inequality. The correspondence between the vertices and faces of $P_x(\mathbf{B}, \mathbf{N}, \mathbf{b})$ and $P(G, \eta, g_0)$ is straightforward. A point $(\mathbf{x}_B, \mathbf{x}_N)$ is a vertex of $P_x(\mathbf{B}, \mathbf{N}, \mathbf{b})$ if and only if $\mathbf{t} = F(\mathbf{x}_B, \mathbf{x}_N)$ is a vertex of $P(G, \eta, g_0)$, and if $f(\mathbf{a}_i) = f(\mathbf{a}_j) = g$ $(i \neq j)$, then either $x_i = 0$ or $x_j = 0$. From a vertex in $\mathbf{t}$-space, we can produce the corresponding vertex in $\mathbf{x}$-space using $t(g)$ as the numerical value for the nonbasic variable x_j, where $f(\mathbf{a}_j) = g$, and 0 for all other nonbasic variables x_i with $f(\mathbf{a}_i) = f(\mathbf{a}_j) = g$. This sets up the correspondence between $t(g)$ and $\mathbf{x}_N$, and $\mathbf{x}_B$ is then uniquely determined by $\mathbf{x}_B = \mathbf{B}^{-1}(\mathbf{b} - \mathbf{N}\mathbf{x}_N)$.

For a face of $P(G, \eta, g_0)$, we represent it by an inequality $\sum \gamma(g)t(g) \geq \gamma_0$ or more briefly by $(\boldsymbol{\gamma}, \gamma_0)$, where $\boldsymbol{\gamma}$ is an n'-vector and γ_0 a scalar. In $\mathbf{x}$-space, we use $(\boldsymbol{\gamma}'_B, \boldsymbol{\gamma}'_N, \gamma'_0)$ to represent a face. Because $\mathbf{x}_B = \mathbf{B}^{-1}(\mathbf{b} - \mathbf{N}\mathbf{x}_N)$, the inequality can also be represented in $\mathbf{x}_N$-space by $(\mathbf{0}, \bar{\boldsymbol{\gamma}}_N, \bar{\gamma}_0)$. Then $(\mathbf{0}, \bar{\boldsymbol{\gamma}}_N, \bar{\gamma}_0)$ is a face of $P(G, \eta, g_0)$, where $\gamma(g) = \gamma(f(\mathbf{a}_i)) = \bar{\gamma}_i$. Thus, we can obtain a face of $P_x(\mathbf{B}, \mathbf{N}, \mathbf{b})$ by simply writing the coefficients $\gamma(g)$ of the corresponding face in $\mathbf{t}$-space.

We are interested in solving (7) and the structure of the convex hull of all integer vectors $\mathbf{t}$ that solve (6) for three reasons. First, the problem (7), having only one congruence constraint, can be solved using a technique similar to the one used in solving the knapsack problem. The solution obtained will, in most cases, give the optimum solution to the original integer program (2a). Second, when the righthand $\mathbf{b}$ in (2a) is sufficiently large and does not lie in the boundary of the cone spanned by columns of $\mathbf{B}$, then the solution of (7) always gives a solution of (2a). Thus, the solution of (7) may be considered as solving an integer program with the right-hand side $\mathbf{b}$ asymptotically large. Third, the faces of the convex hull of all integer points $\mathbf{t}$ satisfying (7) gives the strongest cuts that can be generated at the point ($\mathbf{x}_B = \mathbf{B}^{-1}\mathbf{b}$, $\mathbf{x}_N = \mathbf{0}$). That is to say, any Gomory cut introduced without using the condition $\mathbf{x}_B \geq \mathbf{0}$ will be a linear convex combination of the faces of this convex hull. We have denoted the convex hull of all integer points $\mathbf{t}$ satisfying (6) by $P(G, \eta, g_0)$. We are interested in finding the vertex of $P(G, \eta, g_0)$ which is the optimum solution to (7).

There are many integer points within the convex hull $P(G, \eta, g_0)$. We say that an integer point $\mathbf{t}$ of $P(G, \eta, g_0)$ is irreducible if there exists no other integer point $\mathbf{t}'$ with components all less than or equal to the components of $\mathbf{t}$ and such that $\sum t'(g) \cdot g = g_0$. For example, a component $t(g)$ of an irreducible point $\mathbf{t}$ cannot be greater than the order of g. In other words, an integer point $\mathbf{t} = (t(g))$ of $P(G, \eta, g_0)$ is irreducible if for any set of integers $r(g)$ and $r'(g)$ the conditions,

$$0 \leq r(g) \leq t(g), \qquad 0 \leq r'(g) \leq t(g), \qquad \text{and} \qquad \sum_{g \in \eta} r(g) \cdot g = \sum_{g \in \eta} r'(g) \cdot g$$

imply that $r(g) = r'(g)$ for all $g \in \eta$.

Theorem 19.5. Every vertex of $P(G, \eta, g_0)$ is irreducible.

Proof. We shall prove this theorem by contradiction. Let $\mathbf{v}$ be a vertex of $P(G, \eta, g_0)$ and let us assume that $\mathbf{v} = (t(g))$, $g \in \eta$, is reducible, i.e., there are integers $r(g)$ and $r'(g)$,

$$0 \leq r(g) \leq t(g), \qquad 0 \leq r'(g) \leq t(g),$$

and

$$r(g) \neq r'(g) \text{ for some } g \qquad \text{and} \qquad \sum_{g \in \eta} r(g) \cdot g = \sum_{g \in \eta} r'(g) \cdot g.$$

Since $\mathbf{v}$ is a point of $P(G, \eta, g_0)$, we have

$$\begin{aligned} g_0 &= \sum_{g \in \eta} t(g) \cdot g - \sum_{g \in \eta} r(g) \cdot g + \sum_{g \in \eta} r'(g) \cdot g \\ &= \sum_{g \in \eta} (t(g) - r(g) + r'(g)) \cdot g \end{aligned}$$

and

$$\begin{aligned} g_0 &= \sum_{g \in \eta} t(g) \cdot g + \sum_{g \in \eta} r(g) \cdot g - \sum_{g \in \eta} r'(g) \cdot g \\ &= \sum_{g \in \eta} (t(g) - r'(g) + r(g)) \cdot g. \end{aligned}$$

By assumption $t(g) - r(g) \geq 0$ and $t(g) - r'(g) \geq 0$. Therefore the vectors $\mathbf{v}_1 = (t(g) - r(g) + r'(g))$, $g \in \eta$, and $\mathbf{v}_2 = (t(g) - r'(g) + r(g))$, $g \in \eta$, both have nonnegative integer components and sum to g_0. Hence both $\mathbf{v}_1$ and $\mathbf{v}_2$ belong to $P(G, \eta, g_0)$. But $\mathbf{v} = (\mathbf{v}_1 + \mathbf{v}_2)/2$. This contradicts the assumption that $\mathbf{v}$ is a vertex. Thus every vertex of $P(G, \eta, g)$ is irreducible.

In general, it is not true that the vertices of $P(G, \eta, g_0)$ are the only irreducible points. But if G is the direct sum of cyclic groups of order 2 or of groups of order 3, the only irreducible points of $P(G, \eta, g_0)$ are indeed the vertices. See Gomory [86].

Theorem 19.6. If $\mathbf{t} = (t(g))$ is an irreducible point of $P(G, \eta, g_0)$, then the components $t(g)$ satisfy

$$\prod_{g \in \eta} (1 + t(g)) \leq |G| = D, \tag{9}$$

where $|G|$ is the cardinal number of the group G.

Proof. Let $\mathbf{t}' = (t'(g))$ be any point with $0 \leq t'(g) \leq t(g)$and $t'(g)$ integers. Such vector $\mathbf{t}'$ has $|\eta|$ components and each component can take any of the values $0, 1, \ldots, t(g)$. Therefore, there are at most $\Pi_{g \in \eta}(1 + t(g))$ possible different vectors $\mathbf{t}'$ with $(t'(g)) \leq (t(g))$. If $\mathbf{t}$ is irreducible, the sum

$$\sum_{g \in \eta} t'(g) \cdot g = g\ (t')$$

must be a different group element for each $\mathbf{t}'$. However, there are only $|G|$ different group elements; hence the inequality. [Note that the bound on $t(g)$ applies equally well to $\mathbf{x}_N$.]

Corollary 19.1: If $\mathbf{t} = (t(g))$ is an irreducible point of $P(G, \eta, g_0)$, then

$$\sum_{g \in \eta} t(g) \leq D - 1. \tag{10a}$$

Proof. If the product of several positive integer variables is fixed, then the maximum sum of these integer variables is achieved by all variables (except one) being equal to one. In the Theorem 19.6, we have

$$\prod_{g \in \eta} (1 + t(g)) \leq |G| = D.$$

Thus the greatest sum $\sum_{g \in \eta} t(g)$ is achieved by letting $t(g) = 0$ for all $g \neq h$. Letting $t(g) = 0$ for all $g \neq h$, we have

$$(1 + 0) \cdots (1 + t(h)) \cdots (1 + 0) \leq |G| = D,$$

or

$$1 + t(h) \leq D,$$

or

$$t(h) \leq D - 1,$$

or

$$\sum_{g \in \eta} t(g) = (0 + \cdots + t(h) + \cdots + 0) \leq D - 1.$$

Now we shall connect the solution $\mathbf{t}$ of (7) to the solution $\mathbf{x}$ of (2a). As

$$c^*(g) = \min_{j \in J} c_j^* \quad (J = \{j \mid f(\mathbf{a}_j) = g\}),$$

if $\bar{\mathbf{t}}$ is any solution to (7) and $\bar{\mathbf{x}}$ is any solution to (5), we have

$$\sum_{j \in J} c_j^* \bar{x}_j \geq \sum_{g \in \eta} c^*(g) \bar{t}(g),$$

or, alternatively,

$$\mathbf{c}_N^*\bar{\mathbf{x}}_N \geq \mathbf{c}^*\bar{\mathbf{t}}. \tag{10b}$$

Let $\mathbf{t}^*$ be an optimum solution to (7) and $\mathbf{x}_N^*$ be the corresponding solution to (5). [The correspondence is by the relation (8b).] Then

$$\mathbf{c}_N^*\mathbf{x}_N^* = \mathbf{c}^*\mathbf{t}^*, \tag{11}$$

where $x_j^* = 0$ if $f(\mathbf{a}_j) = f(\mathbf{a}_i) = g$ and $c_j^* > c_i^*$. Because $\mathbf{t}^*$ is the optimum solution to (7), we have, from (10b),

$$\mathbf{c}^*\mathbf{t}^* \leq \mathbf{c}^*\bar{\mathbf{t}} \leq \mathbf{c}_N^*\bar{\mathbf{x}}_N. \tag{12}$$

Denote the value of the objective function of (2b) by $z_I(\mathbf{b})$ and $\mathbf{c}_B\mathbf{B}^{-1}\mathbf{b}$ by $z_L(\mathbf{b})$. Then

$$z_I(\mathbf{b}) = z_L(\mathbf{b}) - \mathbf{c}_N^*\bar{\mathbf{x}}_N, \tag{13}$$

where $\bar{\mathbf{x}}_N$ is any feasible solution to (2b).

Let $\mathbf{x}_N^*$ be the optimum solution to (5). Then it follows from (11), (12), and (13) that

$$\mathbf{c}_B\mathbf{B}^{-1}\mathbf{b} - \mathbf{c}_N^*\mathbf{x}_N^* = \mathbf{c}_B\mathbf{B}^{-1}\mathbf{b} - \mathbf{c}^*\mathbf{t}^* \geq z_L(\mathbf{b}) - \mathbf{c}_N^*\bar{\mathbf{x}}_N = z_I(\mathbf{b}). \tag{14}$$

Therefore, if the solution $\mathbf{x}_N^*$ gives a feasible solution to (2b), i.e., $\mathbf{x}_B^* = \mathbf{B}^{-1}(\mathbf{b} - \mathbf{N}\mathbf{x}_N^*) \geq \mathbf{0}$, then by (14), $(\mathbf{x}_B^*, \mathbf{x}_N^*)$ is also an optimum solution to (2b). The preceding result can be summarized as a theorem.

Theorem 19.7. If $\mathbf{t}^*$ is an optimum solution to (7), then the corresponding solution $\mathbf{x}^* = (\mathbf{B}^{-1}(\mathbf{b} - \mathbf{N}\mathbf{x}_N^*), \mathbf{x}_N^*)$ is an optimum solution to (2b) provided that $\mathbf{B}^{-1}(\mathbf{b} - \mathbf{N}\mathbf{x}_N^*) \geq \mathbf{0}$.

Now, we shall study the question: when is

$$\mathbf{x}_B = \mathbf{B}^{-1}\mathbf{b} - \mathbf{B}^{-1}\mathbf{N}\mathbf{x}_N \geq \mathbf{0}?$$

We see that $\mathbf{x}_B = \mathbf{B}^{-1}\mathbf{b}$ is the solution of the linear program. The vector $\mathbf{B}^{-1}\mathbf{b}$ is nonnegative if $\mathbf{b}$ is in the cone generated by the columns of $\mathbf{B}$. We will denote this cone by K_B. Now if $(\mathbf{b} - \mathbf{N}\mathbf{x}_N)$ is also in the cone K_B, then $\mathbf{B}^{-1}(\mathbf{b} - \mathbf{N}\mathbf{x}_N) \geq \mathbf{0}$. Geometrically, if point $\mathbf{b}$ is far away from any boundary points of the cone K_B and if the length of the vector $\mathbf{N}\mathbf{x}_N$ is small, then the difference $\mathbf{b} - \mathbf{N}\mathbf{x}_N$ is also inside the cone K_B. If we use $K_B(d)$ to denote the subset of points in K_B at a Euclidean distance d or more from any boundary point of K_B, then in this notation $K_B = K_B(0)$ and the condition $\mathbf{b} \in K_B(d)\ \|\mathbf{N}\mathbf{x}_N\| \leq d$ ensures that $\mathbf{B}^{-1}(\mathbf{b} - \mathbf{N}\mathbf{x}_N) \geq \mathbf{0}$. Now let $l_{\max}$ denote the length of the longest nonbasic column, i.e., $\max_j(\sum_i a_{ij}^2)^{1/2}\ (j = 1, \ldots, n)$:

$$\|\mathbf{N}\mathbf{x}_N\| = \|\sum_{j=1}^{n} \mathbf{a}_j x_j\| \leq l_{\max} \sum_{j=1}^{n} x_j = l_{\max} \sum_{g \in \eta} t(g) \leq l_{\max}(D - 1).$$

Thus the following theorem gives a sufficient condition for $\mathbf{x}_B \geq \mathbf{0}$.

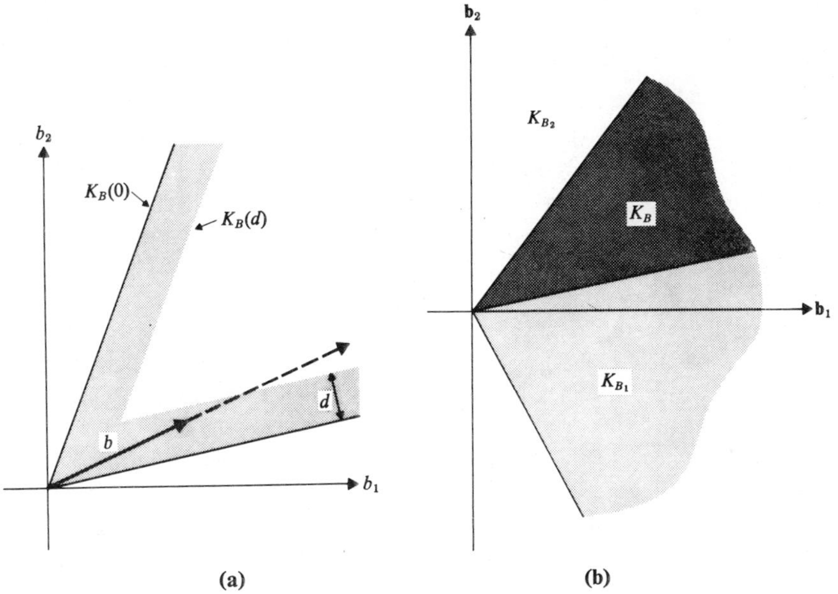

Fig. 19.2

Theorem 19.8. If $\mathbf{b} \in K_B(l_{\max}(D-1))$, where $D = |\det \mathbf{B}|$ and $l_{\max}$ is the length of the longest nonbasic column, then $(\mathbf{x}_B^*, \mathbf{x}_N^*)$ is the optimum integer solution to (2b), where $\mathbf{x}_B^* = \mathbf{B}^{-1}(\mathbf{b} - \mathbf{N}\mathbf{x}_N^*)$, $\mathbf{x}_N^*$ corresponds to $\mathbf{t}^*$ by (8b), and $\mathbf{t}^*$ is the optimum solution of (7).

Let us draw the cone K_B. In Fig. 19.2(a) there is a band of points which are of distance d or less from the boundary points of K_B. Note that a given $\mathbf{b}$ may be in the band, but $\lambda\mathbf{b}$ when $\lambda \geq 1$ may not be in the band.

Another sufficient condition similar to Theorem 19.8 can be obtained. Let l_i be the maximum element in the row i of the matrix $\mathbf{B}^{-1}\mathbf{N}$. Construct the column vector $\mathbf{l} = [l_1, \ldots, l_i, \ldots, l_m]$. Then if $\mathbf{B}^{-1}\mathbf{b} - (D-1)\,\mathbf{l} \geq \mathbf{0}$, then the optimum solution $\mathbf{t}^*$ of (7) can be used to solve the integer program (2a).

Given an integer program (2a), we consider the matrix $\mathbf{A}$ and the vector $\mathbf{c}$ as fixed and the right-hand side as a vector which may assume any one of several values $\mathbf{b}^1, \mathbf{b}^2, \ldots, \mathbf{b}^k$. For any given right-hand side $\mathbf{b}^i$ there is an optimum basis $\mathbf{B}^i$ of the associated linear program. In the m-dimensional requirement space, the space can be partitioned into several cones corresponding to different optimum bases $\mathbf{B}^i$. This is shown in Fig. 19.2(b).

If a basis $\mathbf{B}$ is optimum for a right-hand side $\mathbf{b}$ and $\mathbf{b}'$ is another right-hand side for which $\mathbf{B}^{-1}\mathbf{b}' \geq \mathbf{0}$, then $\mathbf{B}$ is also an optimum basis for $\mathbf{b}'$. Theorem 19.8 shows that the cone K_B has a band of fixed width $l_{\max}(|\det \mathbf{B}| - 1)$. If both $\mathbf{b}$ and $\mathbf{b}'$ are points not lying in the band, then the optimum solution to (7) can be used. Let us write the optimum solution for the two right-hand sides **b** and **b**′ as $\mathbf{x}^*(\mathbf{b})$ and $\mathbf{x}^*(\mathbf{b}')$. Then

$$\begin{aligned} \mathbf{x}^*(\mathbf{b}) &= (\mathbf{x}_B^*(\mathbf{b}), \mathbf{x}_N^*) = (\mathbf{B}^{-1}\mathbf{b}, \mathbf{0}) + (-\mathbf{B}^{-1}\mathbf{N}\mathbf{x}_N^*, \mathbf{x}_N^*), \\ \mathbf{x}^*(\mathbf{b}') &= (\mathbf{x}_B^*(\mathbf{b}'), \mathbf{x}_N^*) = (\mathbf{B}^{-1}\mathbf{b}', \mathbf{0}) + (-\mathbf{B}^{-1}\mathbf{N}\mathbf{x}_N^*, \mathbf{x}_N^*). \end{aligned} \tag{15}$$

Note that we have written the solutions in two parts; the first part corresponds to the linear programming solution, the second part is the correction needed to make $\mathbf{x}_B^*$ integral. It should be emphasized here that $\mathbf{x}_N^*$ is obtained from $\mathbf{t}^*$ of (7), which is the optimum vertex of $P(G, \eta, g_0)$. Once the optimum basis **B** is determined, G and η are also determined. But $\mathbf{t}^*$ is the same for two right-hand sides if they are mapped into the same element g_0. That is to say, if two right-hand sides differ by an integer combination of columns of **B**, i.e., $\mathbf{b} \equiv \mathbf{b}' \pmod{\mathbf{B}}$, then their images are the same, and the second parts of (15) are the same. The difference between $\mathbf{x}^*(\mathbf{b})$ and $\mathbf{x}^*(\mathbf{b}')$ is in the first part, i.e., $\mathbf{B}^{-1}(\mathbf{b} - \mathbf{b}')$.

As there are exactly $|G|$ possible group elements for the optimum basis **B**, there are $|G|$ possible g_0, and (15) can have at most $|G|$ different second parts. We can calculate the second part of (15) for each $g_0 \in G$. When this is done, the solution to the integer programming problem has been obtained for *all* right-hand sides **b** lying in $K_B(d)$, where $d = l_{\max}(D - 1)$. Note that the integer optimum solution is periodic in nature, with the periodicity the columns of the optimum basis **B** of the associated linear program.

Every **b** for which the associated linear program can be solved belongs to some K_B. This cone may be one of the cones shown in Fig. 19.2(b) for example. This means that **b** can be expressed as columns of **B** or $\mathbf{b} = \sum_i \lambda_i \mathbf{a}_i$, where $\lambda_i \geq 0$. This **b** may or may not lie in $K_B(l_{\max}(D - 1))$. But if $\lambda_i > 0$ for all i, then $k\mathbf{b}$ for sufficiently large k will always lie in $K_B(l_{\max}(D - 1))$. In Fig. 19.2(a) we show the case for $k = 2$. This means that the integer program $\mathbf{Ax} = k\mathbf{b}$ can always be solved for sufficiently large k, unless the associated linear program solution is degenerate. This is why we use the name "asymptotic integer algorithm" in the beginning of this section. We remark here that the width of the band $d = l_{\max}(D - 1)$ usually gives a sufficient condition which is too conservative.

When **b** does lie in the domain of applicability, we have from (9)

$$\prod_{g \in \eta} (1 + t(g)) \leq D.$$

The solution x_j ($j \in J$) of (2a) is numerically equal to some $t(g)$. See (8a) and (8b). Hence, we have

$$\prod_{j=1}^{n} (1 + x_j) \leq D. \tag{16}$$

When $D = |\det \mathbf{B}| = 1$(this is the case when the matrix **A** is unimodular), we have from (16) $x_j = 0$ for all j. Then $d = l_{\max}(D - 1) = 0$, and the form of the optimum integer solution is like the usual linear programming solution with at most m nonzero components. As D increases from 1, the band will no longer be of zero width and the form of the optimum solution will also change. If $\mathbf{b}$ lies in the domain of applicability, there are at most $m + p$ nonzero components in the optimum solution. To get an upper bound of p, assume that we have p components in $\mathbf{x}_N^*$ nonzero, or $x_j \geq 1$ for p of the components. Then from (9), we have

$$D \geq \prod_j (1 + x_j) \geq 2^p,$$

or

$$p \leq \log_2 D.$$

Thus, the case $D = 1$ can be considered as the integer program where the optimum solution becomes integers automatically. As D increases, the solution gradually moves away from the form of the linear program solution to the general integer program solution. But at all times the number of nonzero, nonbasic variables is bounded from above by $\log_2 D$.

Starting with any integer program (2a), we can get the optimum basis $\mathbf{B}$ for the associated linear program. Using the mapping $\phi\mathbf{B}^{-1}$ to the constraints of (2a), we can transform the constraints into a single congruent relation (6). If we solve the group minimization problem (7), we can get $\mathbf{x}_N^*$ by (8b) and $\mathbf{x}_B^*$ by $\mathbf{x}_B^* = \mathbf{B}^{-1}(\mathbf{b} - \mathbf{N}\mathbf{x}_N^*)$. If $\mathbf{x}_B^* \geq \mathbf{0}$, then $(\mathbf{x}_B^*, \mathbf{x}_N^*)$ is the optimum integer solution to our original integer program (2a). Now let us discuss in detail how to solve the group minimization problem (7). The problem (7) is very much like the knapsack problem except that a congruent relation has replaced the single inequality constraint. For any set $S \subset \eta$ and element $h \in G$ we define

$$\psi(S, h) = \min \sum_{g \in S} c^*(g)t(g)$$

subject to

$$\sum_{g \in S} t(g) \cdot g = h, \qquad (17)$$

$$t(g) \geq 0, \quad \text{integers}.$$

If S is the empty set 0, then we define $\psi(0, h) = \infty$. If h is the zero element of the group, $\psi(S, 0) = 0$. For any other S and h either a group element $g' \in S$ is used *at least* once or it is not used at all in making up $\psi(S, h)$. In the former case,

$$t(g') \geq 1 \quad \text{and} \quad \psi(S, h) = c^*(g') + \psi(S, h - g'), \qquad (18)$$

and in the latter case,

$$t(g') = 0 \quad \text{and} \quad \psi(S, h) = \psi(S - g', h). \qquad (19)$$

Therefore, combining (18) and (19), we have the recursive relation

$$\psi(S, h) = \min_{g'} \{\psi(S - g', h), c^*(g') + \psi(S, h - g')\}. \qquad (20)$$

This recursive relation enables us to calculate $\psi(S, h)$ for all $S \subseteq \eta$ and every $h \in G$. For ease of computation we shall do the numerical examples *entirely in terms of the variables* x_j. In Chapter 20 we will study the faces of $P(G, \eta, g_0)$ and then we shall discuss them in terms of the **t**-space.

Define

$$\psi_s(\bar{\mathbf{y}}) = \min \sum_j c_j^* x_j$$

subject to

$$\sum_j \bar{\boldsymbol{\alpha}}_j x_j \equiv \bar{\mathbf{y}},$$

$$x_j \equiv 0 \pmod 1), \qquad x_j \geq 0 \qquad (j = 1, \ldots, s).$$

In other words, $\psi_s(\bar{\mathbf{y}})$ is the optimum value when only the first s columns $\bar{\boldsymbol{\alpha}}_j$ are allowed to make up the required column $\bar{\mathbf{y}}$. Since in $\psi_s(\bar{\mathbf{y}})$, either $\bar{\boldsymbol{\alpha}}_s$ is not used or used at least once. We have the recursive relation similar to (20):

$$\psi_s(\bar{\mathbf{y}}) = \min \{\psi_{s-1}(\bar{\mathbf{y}}), \psi_s(\bar{\mathbf{y}} - \bar{\boldsymbol{\alpha}}_s) + c_s^*\}. \tag{21}$$

This recursive relation then enables us to calculate $\psi_s(\bar{\mathbf{y}})$ for all s, $1 \leq s \leq n'$, and $\bar{\mathbf{y}}$ starting from $\psi_s(\bar{\mathbf{0}}) = 0$, $\psi_0(\bar{\mathbf{y}}) = +\infty$, provided that the whole group can be generated by $\bar{\boldsymbol{\alpha}}_s$. If $\bar{\boldsymbol{\alpha}}_s$ generates the whole group, for any $\bar{\mathbf{y}}$ we have $\bar{\mathbf{y}} \equiv r\bar{\boldsymbol{\alpha}}_s$, $1 \leq r \leq n'$, so that we can form the difference $\bar{\mathbf{y}} - \bar{\boldsymbol{\alpha}}_s$ as required in (21).

Consider the numerical example (Balinski [6])

$$\max z = -4x_3 - 5x_4$$

subject to

$$\begin{aligned} -3x_3 - x_4 + x_5 \qquad\qquad &= -2, \\ -x_3 - 4x_4 \qquad + x_1 \qquad &= -5, \\ -3x_3 - 2x_4 \qquad\qquad + x_2 &= -7, \\ x_j \geq 0, \quad \text{integers} \quad (j = 1, \ldots, 5). \end{aligned} \tag{22}$$

The linear program will give the optimum basis

$$\mathbf{B} = \begin{bmatrix} -3 & -1 & 1 \\ -1 & -4 & 0 \\ -3 & -2 & 0 \end{bmatrix}$$

with $|\det \mathbf{B}| = +10$. Applying

$$\mathbf{B}^{-1} = \begin{bmatrix} 0 & 2/10 & -4/10 \\ 0 & -3/10 & 1/10 \\ 1 & 3/10 & -11/10 \end{bmatrix}$$

to the constraints in (22), we have

$$\max z = -(7/10)x_1 - (11/10)x_2 - (112/10)$$

subject to

$$\begin{pmatrix}1\\0\\0\end{pmatrix}x_3 + \begin{pmatrix}0\\1\\0\end{pmatrix}x_4 + \begin{pmatrix}0\\0\\1\end{pmatrix}x_5 + \begin{pmatrix}2/10\\-3/10\\3/10\end{pmatrix}x_1 + \begin{pmatrix}-4/10\\1/10\\-11/10\end{pmatrix}x_2 = \begin{pmatrix}18/10\\8/10\\42/10\end{pmatrix}.$$

Therefore we want

$$\min + (7/10)x_1 + (11/10)x_2$$

subject to

$$\begin{pmatrix}2/10\\7/10\\3/10\end{pmatrix}x_1 + \begin{pmatrix}6/10\\1/10\\9/10\end{pmatrix}x_2 \equiv \begin{pmatrix}8/10\\8/10\\2/10\end{pmatrix}. \tag{23}$$

Since $\psi_s(\bar{\mathbf{0}}) = 0$, we have

$$\psi_1(\bar{\boldsymbol{\alpha}}_1) = c_1^*, \qquad \psi_1(2\bar{\boldsymbol{\alpha}}_1) = 2c_1^*, \ldots, \psi_1(9\bar{\boldsymbol{\alpha}}_1) = 9c_1^*,$$

and for each $r\bar{\boldsymbol{\alpha}}_1$ $(r = 1, \ldots, D-1)$, we now have $r\bar{\boldsymbol{\alpha}}_1 \equiv t\bar{\boldsymbol{\alpha}}_2$. For example, $\bar{\boldsymbol{\alpha}}_1 \equiv 7\bar{\boldsymbol{\alpha}}_2$, $2\bar{\boldsymbol{\alpha}}_1 \equiv 4\bar{\boldsymbol{\alpha}}_2$, etc.

In order to use

$$\psi_2(\bar{\mathbf{y}}) = \min\,\{\psi_1(\bar{\mathbf{y}}), \psi_2(\bar{\mathbf{y}} - \bar{\boldsymbol{\alpha}}_2) + c_2^*\}, \tag{24}$$

we have to know $\psi_2(\bar{\mathbf{y}} - \bar{\boldsymbol{\alpha}}_2)$. The only $\psi_2(\bar{\mathbf{y}})$ that is known at the moment is $\psi_2(\bar{\mathbf{0}}) = 0$. Therefore, we start with

$$\begin{aligned}\psi_2(\bar{\boldsymbol{\alpha}}_2) &= \min\,\{\psi_1(\bar{\boldsymbol{\alpha}}_2), \psi_2(\bar{\boldsymbol{\alpha}}_2 - \bar{\boldsymbol{\alpha}}_2) + c_2^*\}\\ &= \min\,\{\psi_1(3\bar{\boldsymbol{\alpha}}_1), \psi_2(\bar{\mathbf{0}}) + c_2^*\}\\ &= \min\,\{+21/10, 0 + 11/10\} = +11/10.\end{aligned}$$

Having computed $\psi_2(\bar{\boldsymbol{\alpha}}_2)$, we then get

$$\begin{aligned}\psi_2(2\bar{\boldsymbol{\alpha}}_2) &= \min\,\{\psi_1(2\bar{\boldsymbol{\alpha}}_2), \psi_2(2\bar{\boldsymbol{\alpha}}_2 - \bar{\boldsymbol{\alpha}}_2) + c_2^*\}\\ &= \min\,\{\psi_1(6\bar{\boldsymbol{\alpha}}_1), \psi_2(\bar{\boldsymbol{\alpha}}_2) + c_2^*\}\\ &= \min\,\{+42/10, +11/10 + 11/10\}\\ &= +22/10.\end{aligned}$$

This can be continued until $\psi_2((D-1)\bar{\boldsymbol{\alpha}}_2)$ is reached. To keep track of the values of x_j that make up the current $\psi_s(\bar{\mathbf{y}})$, we need the index i which reveals the last variable made equal to one:

$$i(s, \bar{\mathbf{y}}) = \begin{cases} i(s-1, \bar{\mathbf{y}}) & \text{if } \psi_{s-1}(\bar{\mathbf{y}}) < \psi_s(\bar{\mathbf{y}} - \bar{\boldsymbol{\alpha}}_s) + c_s^*,\\ s & \text{if } \psi_{s-1}(\bar{\mathbf{y}}) \geq \psi_s(\bar{\mathbf{y}} - \bar{\boldsymbol{\alpha}}_s) + c_s^*.\end{cases} \tag{25}$$

Table 19.1

zeroth column ↓ (column $\bar{\mathbf{0}}$); ↓ third column (column $3\bar{\boldsymbol{\alpha}}_1=\bar{\boldsymbol{\alpha}}_2$)

s \ $\bar{\mathbf{y}}$	$\bar{\mathbf{0}}$	$\bar{\boldsymbol{\alpha}}_1=7\bar{\boldsymbol{\alpha}}_2$	$2\bar{\boldsymbol{\alpha}}_1=4\bar{\boldsymbol{\alpha}}_2$	$3\bar{\boldsymbol{\alpha}}_1=\bar{\boldsymbol{\alpha}}_2$	$4\bar{\boldsymbol{\alpha}}_1=8\bar{\boldsymbol{\alpha}}_2$
$\psi_1(\bar{\mathbf{y}})$	0	+7/10	+14/10	+21/10	+28/10
i	—	1	1	1	1
$\psi_2(\bar{\mathbf{y}})$	0	+7/10	+14/10	+11/10	+18/10
i	—	1	1	2	2

s \ $\bar{\mathbf{y}}$	$5\bar{\boldsymbol{\alpha}}_1=5\bar{\boldsymbol{\alpha}}_2$	$6\bar{\boldsymbol{\alpha}}_1=2\bar{\boldsymbol{\alpha}}_2$	$7\bar{\boldsymbol{\alpha}}_1=9\bar{\boldsymbol{\alpha}}_2$	$8\bar{\boldsymbol{\alpha}}_1=6\bar{\boldsymbol{\alpha}}_2$	$9\bar{\boldsymbol{\alpha}}_1=3\bar{\boldsymbol{\alpha}}_2$
$\psi_1(\bar{\mathbf{y}})$	+35/10	+42/10	+49/10	+56/10	+63/10
i	1	1	1	1	1
$\psi_2(\bar{\mathbf{y}})$	+25/10	+22/10	+29/10	+36/10	+33/10
i	2	2	2	2	2

↑ sixth column (column $6\bar{\boldsymbol{\alpha}}_1=2\bar{\boldsymbol{\alpha}}_2$)

The computation can be summarized in Table 19.1, where $\psi_s(\bar{\mathbf{y}})$ for all $1 \leq s \leq 2$ and $\bar{\mathbf{y}} \in \{\bar{\boldsymbol{\alpha}}\}$ are listed. Note that in Table 19.1, we compute from left to right in the $\psi_1(\bar{\mathbf{y}})$ row, but in the $\psi_2(\bar{\mathbf{y}})$ row the first entry computed is in the third column and the second entry computed is in the sixth column. Note that after the last two rows are calculated, the first two rows can be erased. This saves a lot of memory capacity in a computer.

One advantage of this algorithm is that once a table like Table 19.1 is constructed, we can solve the integer program (22) with any right-hand side $\mathbf{b}$. For example, if the right-hand side is $[-6, -7, -8]$, then $\mathbf{B}^{-1}[-6, -7, -8] = [18/10, 13/10, 7/10]$:

$$[18/10, 13/10, 7/10] \equiv [8/10, 3/10, 7/10] \equiv 3\bar{\boldsymbol{\alpha}}_2 \equiv 9\bar{\boldsymbol{\alpha}}_1 \pmod 1.$$

This means that $x_1 = 0$ and $x_2 = 3$ and the optimum solution is $x_3 = 3$, $x_4 = 1$, $x_5 = 4$, $x_1 = 0$, $x_2 = 3$.

Now we shall discuss the case in which an $\bar{\boldsymbol{\alpha}}_s$ is of order d, which divides D $(d \neq D)$ In this case $d\bar{\boldsymbol{\alpha}}_s = \bar{\mathbf{0}}$ and not all elements of $\{\bar{\boldsymbol{\alpha}}\}$ are reached.

Let $\bar{\mathbf{y}}$ be an element not reached in the computation. Then $\psi_s(\bar{\mathbf{y}})$ is unknown, so we tentatively assume that $\psi'_s(\bar{\mathbf{y}}) = \psi_{s-1}(\bar{\mathbf{y}})$. Then we get $\psi'_s(\bar{\mathbf{y}})$ as the tentative value of $\psi_s(\bar{\mathbf{y}})$:

$$\psi'_s(\bar{\mathbf{y}} + r\bar{\boldsymbol{\alpha}}_s) = \min\{\psi'_s(\bar{\mathbf{y}} + r\bar{\boldsymbol{\alpha}}_s - \bar{\boldsymbol{\alpha}}_s) + c^*_s,\ \psi_{s-1}(\bar{\mathbf{y}} + r\bar{\boldsymbol{\alpha}}_s)\},$$
$$(r = 1, \ldots, d). \tag{26}$$

After d steps, $d\bar{\boldsymbol{\alpha}}_s = \bar{\mathbf{0}}$, so we get $\psi'_s(\bar{\mathbf{y}} + d\bar{\boldsymbol{\alpha}}_s) = \psi'_s(\bar{\mathbf{y}})$, which may be different from $\psi_{s-1}(\bar{\mathbf{y}})$, We use it to calculate $\psi''_s(\bar{\mathbf{y}} + r\bar{\boldsymbol{\alpha}}_s)$ the second time. As soon as one of these $\psi''_s(\bar{\mathbf{y}} + r\bar{\boldsymbol{\alpha}}_s)$ values agrees with the old, the calculation is stopped. This procedure is repeated for $(D/d) - 1$ starting points $\bar{\mathbf{y}}$ to get all $\psi_s(\bar{\mathbf{y}})$, $\bar{\mathbf{y}} \in \{\bar{\boldsymbol{\alpha}}\}$.

We shall show that (1) the calculation will stop after q steps where $d \leq q \leq 2d$, (2) the $\psi_s''(\bar{\mathbf{y}} + r\bar{\boldsymbol{\alpha}}_s)$ values are the correct values $\psi_s(\bar{\mathbf{y}} + r\bar{\boldsymbol{\alpha}}_s)$.

Proof. By assuming that $\psi_s'(\bar{\mathbf{y}}) = \psi_{s-1}(\bar{\mathbf{y}})$, we can only overestimate $\psi_s(\bar{\mathbf{y}})$. There are two cases:

1. If $\psi_s(\bar{\mathbf{y}} + r\bar{\boldsymbol{\alpha}}_s) = \psi_{s-1}(\bar{\mathbf{y}} + r\bar{\boldsymbol{\alpha}}_s)$ for some r, $1 \leq r \leq d$, then

$$\psi_s'(\bar{\mathbf{y}} + q\bar{\boldsymbol{\alpha}}_s) = \psi_s(\bar{\mathbf{y}} + q\bar{\boldsymbol{\alpha}}_s) \qquad (d \geq q > r)$$

and in the second time

$$\psi_s''(\bar{\mathbf{y}} + q\bar{\boldsymbol{\alpha}}_s) = \psi_s(\bar{\mathbf{y}} + q\bar{\boldsymbol{\alpha}}_s) \quad (q = 1, \ldots, r).$$

2. If $\psi_s(\bar{\mathbf{y}} + r\bar{\boldsymbol{\alpha}}_s) \neq \psi_{s-1}(\bar{\mathbf{y}} + r\bar{\boldsymbol{\alpha}}_s)$ for all $r = 1, \ldots, d$, this implies that for all r,

$$\psi_s(\bar{\mathbf{y}} + r\bar{\boldsymbol{\alpha}}_s) = \psi_s(\bar{\mathbf{y}} + \mathrm{r}\bar{\boldsymbol{\alpha}}_s - \bar{\boldsymbol{\alpha}}_s) + c_s^*.$$

But

$$\begin{aligned}\psi_s(\bar{\mathbf{y}}) &= \psi_s(\bar{\mathbf{y}} + d\bar{\boldsymbol{\alpha}}_s)\\ &= \psi_s(\bar{\mathbf{y}} + (d-1)\bar{\boldsymbol{\alpha}}_s) + c_s^*\\ &= \psi_s(\bar{\mathbf{y}} + (d-2)\bar{\boldsymbol{\alpha}}_s) + 2c_s^*\\ &= \cdots = \psi_s(\bar{\mathbf{y}}) + dc_s^*.\end{aligned}$$

This is a contradiction if $c_s^* \neq 0$.

If $c_s^* = 0$, then let $\bar{\mathbf{y}}$ be an element not reachable by using $\bar{\boldsymbol{\alpha}}_s$ alone. Take $\bar{\mathbf{y}}_1 + r\bar{\boldsymbol{\alpha}}_s = \bar{\mathbf{y}}$, where

$$\bar{\mathbf{y}}_1 = \sum_{j=1}^{s-1} \bar{\boldsymbol{\alpha}}_j x_j \qquad \text{and} \qquad 1 \leq r \leq d.$$

Then, as $c_s^* = 0$,

$$\psi_{s-1}(\bar{\mathbf{y}}_1) = \psi_s(\bar{\mathbf{y}}_1 + r\bar{\boldsymbol{\alpha}}_s),$$

or $\psi_{s-1}(\bar{\mathbf{y}}_1) = \psi_s(\bar{\mathbf{y}}_1)$ for some $\bar{\mathbf{y}}_1$ in the group, or $\psi_{s-1}(\bar{\mathbf{y}} + r\bar{\boldsymbol{\alpha}}_s) = \psi_s(\bar{\mathbf{y}} + r\bar{\boldsymbol{\alpha}}_s)$ for some $1 \leq r \leq d$, and this reduces to the first case.

Let us identify the group-element which is the image of a given nonbasic column under the mapping $\phi\mathbf{B}^{-1}$. There are two methods of obtaining this identification. The first method starts with the matrix $\mathbf{A} = [\mathbf{B}, \mathbf{N}]$. We want to obtain the group $\{\mathbf{A}\}/\{\mathbf{B}\}$ by reducing $\mathbf{B}$ to the Smith normal form. We know that there exist nonsingular unimodular matrices $\mathbf{P}$ and $\mathbf{Q}$ such that

$$\mathbf{PBQ} = \mathbf{S},$$

where $\mathbf{S}$ is in the Smith normal form. The matrices $\mathbf{P}$ and $\mathbf{Q}$ correspond to row and column operations respectively. If the group G is the direct sum of k cyclic groups, then the Smith normal form will be

$$\begin{bmatrix} 1 & & & & & \\ & \ddots & & & \text{\Large 0} & \\ & & 1 & & & \\ & & & \epsilon_1 & & \\ & \text{\Large 0} & & & \ddots & \\ & & & & & \epsilon_k \end{bmatrix}$$

where $\epsilon_1, \epsilon_2, \ldots, \epsilon_k = D$.

Note that the row operations affect **B** and **N** and the column operations affect **B** only. Thus when **B** is reduced to **S**, **N** becomes **PN**. The quotient group $\{\mathbf{A}\}/\{\mathbf{B}\}$ is obtained by subtracting columns of **S** from **PN**. Thus the first m–k components of every nonbasic column will be zero (mod 1) and the ith component ($i > m$–k) may have any one of the following values:

$$0, 1, \ldots, \epsilon_{i-m+k} - 1 \quad (\text{mod } \epsilon_{i-m+k}).$$

Thus every nonbasic column vector is identified.

The second method is to find the group $\{\mathbf{B}^{-1}\}/\{\mathbf{I}\}$. Since the first part of the asymptotic integer algorithm is to solve the integer program as a linear program, we have $\mathbf{B}^{-1}\mathbf{A} = [\mathbf{I}, \mathbf{B}^{-1}\mathbf{N}]$ at the completion of the simplex computation. If we take the fractional parts of $\mathbf{B}^{-1}\mathbf{N}$, then these represent the group elements where addition is modular one (if every entry of $\mathbf{B}^{-1}\mathbf{N}$ is written as h/D, then we can take the numerators h and add them to modular D). Let us denote the inverse of **S** by $\mathbf{S}^{-1}$; then

$$\mathbf{S}^{-1} = \begin{bmatrix} 1 & & & & & \\ & \ddots & & & \text{\Large 0} & \\ & & 1 & & & \\ & & & \left(\frac{1}{\epsilon_1}\right) & & \\ & & & & \ddots & \\ & \text{\Large 0} & & & & \left(\frac{1}{\epsilon_k}\right) \end{bmatrix}$$

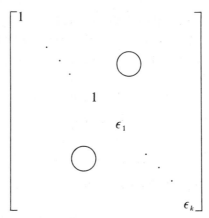

This implies that there exist nonsingular unimodular matrices $\mathbf{Q}^{-1}$ and $\mathbf{P}^{-1}$ such that $\mathbf{Q}^{-1}\mathbf{B}^{-1}\mathbf{P}^{-1} = \mathbf{S}^{-1}$, where $\mathbf{Q}^{-1}$ represents row operations and $\mathbf{P}^{-1}$ represents column operations. In the second method of identifying the nonbasic columns, we start from $[\mathbf{B}^{-1}, \mathbf{B}^{-1}\mathbf{N}]$. After we have applied $\mathbf{Q}^{-1}$ and $\mathbf{P}^{-1}$, we have

$$[\mathbf{Q}^{-1}\mathbf{B}^{-1}\mathbf{P}^{-1}, \mathbf{Q}^{-1}\mathbf{B}^{-1}\mathbf{N}] = [\mathbf{S}^{-1}, \mathbf{Q}^{-1}\mathbf{B}^{-1}\mathbf{N}].$$

If we take the fractional part of $\mathbf{Q}^{-1}\mathbf{B}^{-1}\mathbf{N}$, then the entries of the first $m-k$ rows of $\mathbf{Q}^{-1}\mathbf{B}^{-1}\mathbf{N}$ should all be zero. The ith components $(i > m-k)$ of a column of $\mathbf{Q}^{-1}\mathbf{B}^{-1}\mathbf{N}$ will have one of the following values:

$$0, 1/\epsilon_{i-m+k}, 2/\epsilon_{i-m+k}, \ldots, (\epsilon_{i-m+k} - 1)/\epsilon_{i-m+k}.$$

Thus every nonbasic column is identified.

Consider the numerical example

$$\max z = x_1 + 2x_2 + 3x_3 + x_4 + x_5 + (1/6)\, x_7$$

subject to

$$\begin{aligned} x_1 + 4x_3 + 2x_4 + x_5 + x_6 &= 41, \\ 4x_1 + 3x_2 + x_3 - 4x_4 - x_5 + x_7 &= 47, \\ x_j \geq 0, \quad \text{integers} \quad (j = 1, \ldots, 7). \end{aligned} \tag{27}$$

The optimum basis of the linear program is

$$\begin{bmatrix} 0 & 2 \\ 3 & -4 \end{bmatrix}$$

with $|\det \mathbf{B}| = 6$:

$$\mathbf{B}^{-1} = \begin{bmatrix} 2/3 & 1/3 \\ 1/2 & 0 \end{bmatrix}, \qquad \mathbf{c}_B\mathbf{B}^{-1} = (2, 1)\begin{bmatrix} 2/3 & 1/3 \\ 1/2 & 0 \end{bmatrix} = (11/6, 2/3),$$

$$z_1 = (11/6, 2/3)\begin{pmatrix} 1 \\ 4 \end{pmatrix} = 27/6, \qquad z_3 = (11/6, 2/3)\begin{pmatrix} 4 \\ 1 \end{pmatrix} = 8,$$

$$z_5 = (11/6, 2/3)\begin{pmatrix} 1 \\ -1 \end{pmatrix} = 7/6, \qquad z_6 = (11/6, 2/3)\begin{pmatrix} 1 \\ 0 \end{pmatrix} = 11/6,$$

$$z_7 = (11/6, 2/3)\begin{pmatrix} 0 \\ 1 \end{pmatrix} = 2/3.$$

Therefore, the objective function of $\min c_j^* x_j$ in (7) becomes

$$\min z = +(21/6)\, x_1 + (30/6)\, x_3 + (1/6)\, x_5 + (11/6) x_6 + (3/6)\, x_7. \tag{28}$$

There are two ways to obtain the congruent relation $\sum \bar{\boldsymbol{\alpha}}_j x_j \equiv \bar{\boldsymbol{\beta}}_0 \pmod 1$ in decomposition form. Let us write the matrix $[\mathbf{B}, \mathbf{N}, \mathbf{b}, \mathbf{I}]$ of (27), where the identity matrix on the right is for checking purposes only:

$$\left[\begin{array}{cc|ccccc|c} 0 & 2 & 1 & 4 & 1 & 1 & 0 & 41 \\ 3 & -4 & 4 & 1 & -1 & 0 & 1 & 47 \end{array}\right] \begin{bmatrix} 1 & 0 \\ 0 & 1 \end{bmatrix}.$$

Let $\mathbf{b}_1' = \mathbf{b}_1$, $\mathbf{b}_2' = \mathbf{b}_1 + \mathbf{b}_2$. We have

$$\left[\begin{array}{cc|cccccc|c} 0 & 2 & 1 & 4 & 1 & 1 & 0 & 41 \\ 3 & -1 & 4 & 1 & -1 & 0 & 1 & 47 \end{array}\right] \quad \begin{bmatrix} 1 & 0 \\ 0 & 1 \end{bmatrix}.$$

Let $\mathbf{b}_1'' = \mathbf{b}_1' + 3\mathbf{b}_2'$, $\mathbf{b}_2'' = \mathbf{b}_2'$. We have

$$\left[\begin{array}{cc|ccccc|c} 6 & 2 & 1 & 4 & 1 & 1 & 0 & 41 \\ 0 & -1 & 4 & 1 & -1 & 0 & 1 & 47 \end{array}\right] \quad \begin{bmatrix} 1 & 0 \\ 0 & 1 \end{bmatrix}.$$

Let $\mathbf{e}_1' = \mathbf{e}_1$, $\mathbf{e}_2' = -2\mathbf{e}_1 + \mathbf{e}_2$, i.e., add two times row 2 to row 1 and let $\mathbf{b}_2''' = -\mathbf{b}_2''$. Then we have

$$\left[\begin{array}{cc|ccccc|c} 6 & 0 & 9 & 6 & -1 & 1 & 2 & 135 \\ 0 & 1 & 4 & 1 & -1 & 0 & 1 & 47 \end{array}\right] \quad \begin{bmatrix} 1 & 2 \\ 0 & 1 \end{bmatrix}.$$

Now we have a basis $\mathbf{B}'$ in diagonal form, and all vectors $\bar{\mathbf{a}}_j'$ should be mod $\binom{6}{1}$. For example, $\binom{9}{4} \equiv \binom{3}{0}$ mod $\binom{6}{1}$. Therefore we have to solve

$$\begin{pmatrix} 3 \\ 0 \end{pmatrix} x_1 + \begin{pmatrix} 0 \\ 0 \end{pmatrix} x_3 + \begin{pmatrix} 5 \\ 0 \end{pmatrix} x_5 + \begin{pmatrix} 1 \\ 0 \end{pmatrix} x_6 + \begin{pmatrix} 2 \\ 0 \end{pmatrix} x_7 \equiv \begin{pmatrix} 3 \\ 0 \end{pmatrix}. \tag{29}$$

Note that for checking

$$\begin{pmatrix} 1 & 2 \\ 0 & 1 \end{pmatrix} \begin{pmatrix} 1 \\ 4 \end{pmatrix} = \begin{pmatrix} 9 \\ 4 \end{pmatrix} \equiv \begin{pmatrix} 3 \\ 0 \end{pmatrix} \bmod \begin{pmatrix} 6 \\ 1 \end{pmatrix},$$

$$\begin{pmatrix} 1 & 2 \\ 0 & 1 \end{pmatrix} \begin{pmatrix} 4 \\ 1 \end{pmatrix} = \begin{pmatrix} 6 \\ 1 \end{pmatrix} \equiv \begin{pmatrix} 0 \\ 0 \end{pmatrix} \bmod \begin{pmatrix} 6 \\ 1 \end{pmatrix}, \quad \text{etc.}$$

Now (28) and (29) are the integer program that we have to solve.

Note that the row operations correspond to changes of basis in the space of all column vectors, and the column operations correspond to changes in the basis generated by the integer combinations of the columns of $\mathbf{B}$.

The second way is to start from the optimum tableau of the linear program. At the end of the simplex computation, we have

$$\left[\begin{array}{cc|ccccc|c} 1 & 0 & 2 & 3 & 2/6 & 4/6 & 2/6 & 43 \\ 0 & 1 & 3/6 & 2 & 3/6 & 3/6 & 0 & 123/6 \end{array}\right] = \begin{bmatrix} 4/6 & 2/6 \\ 3/6 & 0 \end{bmatrix} \left[\begin{array}{cc|ccccc|c} 0 & 2 & 1 & 4 & 1 & 1 & 0 & 41 \\ 3 & -4 & 4 & 1 & -1 & 0 & 1 & 47 \end{array}\right].$$

The tableau after subtracting the integer part and omitting the 6 in the denominator becomes (the identity on the left is added)

$$\left[\begin{array}{cc|ccccc|c} 1 & 0 & 0 & 0 & 2 & 4 & 2 & 0 \\ 0 & 1 & 3 & 0 & 3 & 3 & 0 & 3 \end{array}\right].$$

Let $\mathbf{e}_1' = \mathbf{e}_1$ and $\mathbf{e}_2' = -\mathbf{e}_1 + \mathbf{e}_2$, i.e., add row 2 to row 1. We have

$$\left[\begin{array}{cc|ccccc|c} 1 & 1 & 3 & 0 & 5 & 1 & 2 & 3 \\ 0 & 1 & 3 & 0 & 3 & 3 & 0 & 3 \end{array}\right].$$

Note that all numbers are mod 6. Let $\mathbf{e}_1'' = -3\mathbf{e}_2' + \mathbf{e}_1'$ and $\mathbf{e}_2'' = \mathbf{e}_2'$, i.e., add three times row 1 to row 2. We have

$$\left[\begin{array}{cc|ccccc|c} 1 & 1 & 3 & 0 & 5 & 1 & 2 & 3 \\ 3 & 4 & 0 & 0 & 0 & 0 & 0 & 0 \end{array}\right].$$

Note that the group $\{\mathbf{B}^{-1}\}/\{\mathbf{I}\}$ is of rank one; hence the second row consists of zeros. Since

$$\begin{bmatrix} 1 & 1 \\ 3 & 4 \end{bmatrix}$$

is the transformation, as a check we have

$$\begin{bmatrix} 1 & 1 \\ 3 & 4 \end{bmatrix} \mathbf{B}^{-1} = \begin{bmatrix} 1 & 1 \\ 3 & 4 \end{bmatrix} \begin{bmatrix} 4 & 2 \\ 3 & 0 \end{bmatrix} = \begin{bmatrix} 1 & 2 \\ 0 & 0 \end{bmatrix},$$

$$\bar{\boldsymbol{\alpha}}_1 = \begin{bmatrix} 1 & 1 \\ 3 & 4 \end{bmatrix} \begin{bmatrix} 0 \\ 3 \end{bmatrix} = \begin{bmatrix} 3 \\ 0 \end{bmatrix}, \qquad \bar{\boldsymbol{\alpha}}_3 = \begin{bmatrix} 1 & 1 \\ 3 & 4 \end{bmatrix} \begin{bmatrix} 0 \\ 0 \end{bmatrix} = \begin{bmatrix} 0 \\ 0 \end{bmatrix},$$

$$\bar{\boldsymbol{\alpha}}_5 = \begin{bmatrix} 1 & 1 \\ 3 & 4 \end{bmatrix} \begin{bmatrix} 2 \\ 3 \end{bmatrix} = \begin{bmatrix} 5 \\ 0 \end{bmatrix}, \qquad \bar{\boldsymbol{\alpha}}_6 = \begin{bmatrix} 1 & 1 \\ 3 & 4 \end{bmatrix} \begin{bmatrix} 4 \\ 3 \end{bmatrix} = \begin{bmatrix} 1 \\ 0 \end{bmatrix},$$

$$\bar{\boldsymbol{\alpha}}_7 = \begin{bmatrix} 1 & 1 \\ 3 & 4 \end{bmatrix} \begin{bmatrix} 2 \\ 0 \end{bmatrix} = \begin{bmatrix} 2 \\ 0 \end{bmatrix}, \qquad \bar{\boldsymbol{\beta}}_0 = \begin{bmatrix} 1 & 1 \\ 3 & 4 \end{bmatrix} \begin{bmatrix} 0 \\ 3 \end{bmatrix} = \begin{bmatrix} 3 \\ 0 \end{bmatrix},$$

and we have (29) again. Therefore the elements of the group are clearly

$$\begin{array}{cccccc} g_0 & g_1 & g_2 & g_3 & g_4 & g_5, \\ \begin{pmatrix} 0 \\ 0 \end{pmatrix} & \begin{pmatrix} 1 \\ 0 \end{pmatrix} & \begin{pmatrix} 2 \\ 0 \end{pmatrix} & \begin{pmatrix} 3 \\ 0 \end{pmatrix} & \begin{pmatrix} 4 \\ 0 \end{pmatrix} & \begin{pmatrix} 5 \\ 0 \end{pmatrix} \\ \bar{\boldsymbol{\alpha}}_3 & \bar{\boldsymbol{\alpha}}_6 & \bar{\boldsymbol{\alpha}}_7 & \bar{\boldsymbol{\alpha}}_1 & & \bar{\boldsymbol{\alpha}}_5 \end{array}$$

The relative costs of $\bar{\boldsymbol{\alpha}}_j$ are

$$c_1^* = 21, \qquad c_3^* = 30, \qquad c_5^* = 1, \qquad c_6^* = 11, \qquad c_7^* = 3.$$

We want to min $\sum c_j^* x_j$ $(j = 1, 3, 5, 6, 7)$. Subject to (29)

$$\begin{pmatrix} 3 \\ 0 \end{pmatrix} x_1 + \begin{pmatrix} 0 \\ 0 \end{pmatrix} x_3 + \begin{pmatrix} 5 \\ 0 \end{pmatrix} x_5 + \begin{pmatrix} 1 \\ 0 \end{pmatrix} x_6 + \begin{pmatrix} 2 \\ 0 \end{pmatrix} x_7 \equiv \begin{pmatrix} 3 \\ 0 \end{pmatrix} \bmod \begin{pmatrix} 6 \\ 1 \end{pmatrix}.$$

Let us use the recursive relation

$$\psi_s(\bar{\mathbf{y}}) = \min\{\psi_{s-1}(\bar{\mathbf{y}}), \psi_s(\bar{\mathbf{y}} - \bar{\boldsymbol{\alpha}}_s) + c_s^*\}.$$

We start with $\bar{\boldsymbol{\alpha}}_5$ as its cost is 1, the smallest, and is of order 6:

$$\psi_1(\bar{\mathbf{0}}) = 0,$$

$$\begin{aligned}
\psi_1(\bar{\boldsymbol{\alpha}}_5) &= \psi_1(g_5) = \min\{\infty, \psi_1(\bar{\mathbf{0}}) + 1\} = 1,\\
\psi_1(2\bar{\boldsymbol{\alpha}}_5) &= \psi_1(g_4) = \min\{\infty, \psi_1(g_5) + 1\} = 2,\\
\psi_1(3\bar{\boldsymbol{\alpha}}_5) &= \psi_1(g_3) = \min\{\infty, \psi_1(g_4) + 1\} = 3,\\
\psi_1(4\bar{\boldsymbol{\alpha}}_5) &= \psi_1(g_2) = \min\{\infty, \psi_1(g_3) + 1\} = 4,\\
\psi_1(5\bar{\boldsymbol{\alpha}}_5) &= \psi_1(g_1) = \min\{\infty, \psi_1(g_2) + 1\} = 5.
\end{aligned}$$

Next we start with $\bar{\boldsymbol{\alpha}}_7$ as its cost is 3, the second smallest,

$$\begin{aligned}
\psi_2(\bar{\boldsymbol{\alpha}}_7) &= \psi_2(g_2) = \min\{\psi_1(g_2), \psi_2(\bar{\mathbf{0}}) + 3\} = \min\{4, 3\} = 3,\\
\psi_2(2\bar{\boldsymbol{\alpha}}_7) &= \psi_2(g_4) = \min\{\psi_1(g_4), \psi_2(g_2) + 3\} = \min\{2, 3 + 3\} = 2,\\
\psi_2(3\bar{\boldsymbol{\alpha}}_7) &= \psi_2(\bar{\mathbf{0}}) = \min\{\psi_1(\bar{\mathbf{0}}), \psi_2(g_4) + 3\} = \min\{0, 2 + 3\} = 0.
\end{aligned}$$

Since $\bar{\boldsymbol{\alpha}}_7$ or g_2 is of order 3 which divides 6, we must have some other starting point in order to get $\psi_2'(g)$ for all g. Start at g_1:

$$\begin{aligned}
\psi_2'(g_1) &= \psi_1(g_1) = 5,\\
\psi_2'(g_1 + g_2) &= \psi_2'(g_3) = \min\{\psi_1(g_3), \psi_2'(g_1) + 3\} = \min\{3, 5 + 3\} = 3,\\
\psi_2'(g_3 + g_2) &= \psi_2'(g_5) = \min\{\psi_1(g_5), \psi_2'(g_3) + 3\} = \min\{1, 3 + 3\} = 1,\\
\psi_2'(g_5 + g_2) &= \psi_2''(g_1) = \min\{\psi_1(g_1), \psi_2'(g_5) + 3\} = \min\{5, 1 + 3\} = 4.
\end{aligned}$$

Note that $\psi_2'(g_5)$ does not use g_2. Note also that this is the second time we calculate $\psi_2''(g_1)$ and it does not agree with $\psi_2'(g_1)$, which is 5. Thus

$$\psi_2''(g_1 + g_2) = \psi_2''(g_3) = \min\{\psi_1(g_3), \psi_2''(g_1) + 3\} = \min\{3, 4 + 3\} = 3.$$

Note now that $\psi_2''(g_3) = \psi_2'(g_3)$, and we can stop the calculation.

The following table indicates the result of calculation:

	g_0	g_1	g_2	g_3	g_4	g_5
ψ_2'	0	5	3	3	2	1
ψ_2''	0	4	3	3	2	1
		$\bar{\boldsymbol{\alpha}}_7$	$\bar{\boldsymbol{\alpha}}_7$	$\bar{\boldsymbol{\alpha}}_5$	$\bar{\boldsymbol{\alpha}}_5$	$\bar{\boldsymbol{\alpha}}_5$

Due to the relatively high costs of $\bar{\boldsymbol{\alpha}}_1$, $\bar{\boldsymbol{\alpha}}_3$, and $\bar{\boldsymbol{\alpha}}_6$, we have $\psi_5(g) = \psi_2(g)$. Since

$$\bar{\boldsymbol{\beta}}_0 = \begin{bmatrix} 3 \\ 0 \end{bmatrix},$$

which is g_3, we should use $\bar{\boldsymbol{\alpha}}_5$ at least once. Backtracking, we get $x_5 = 3$

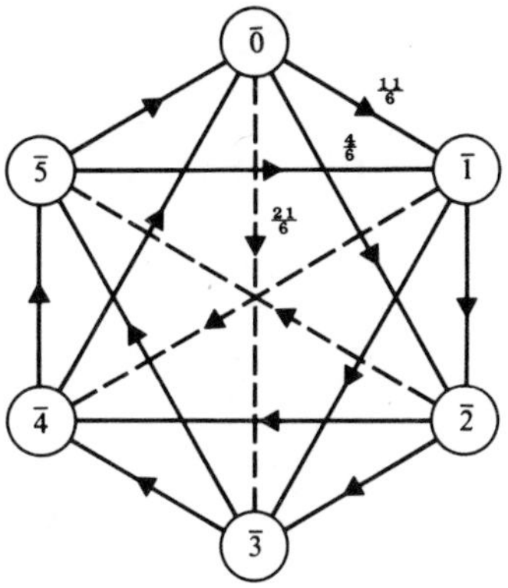

Fig. 19.3

and all other nonbasic variables equal to zero,

$$\mathbf{x}_B = \mathbf{B}^{-1}(\mathbf{b} - \mathbf{N}\mathbf{x}_N)$$

$$= \begin{bmatrix} 4/6 & 2/6 \\ 3/6 & 0 \end{bmatrix} \left(\begin{bmatrix} 41 \\ 47 \end{bmatrix} - 3 \begin{bmatrix} 1 \\ -1 \end{bmatrix} \right) = \begin{bmatrix} 4/6 & 2/6 \\ 3/6 & 0 \end{bmatrix} \begin{bmatrix} 38 \\ 50 \end{bmatrix} = \begin{bmatrix} 42 \\ 19 \end{bmatrix}.$$

Therefore the optimum integer solution is

$$x_2 = 42, \qquad x_4 = 19, \qquad x_5 = 3,$$

and all other variables equal zero.

In dealing with the group minimization problem, it is very useful to consider the graph $H(G, \eta, \mathbf{c})$. The graph has $|G|$ nodes, one node $N(g)$ for each $g \in G$. If a $g' \in \eta$, then there exists a directed arc from $N(g)$ to $N(g+g')$. The cost associated with this directed arc is $c(g')$. In Fig. 19.3 we have shown a graph $H(G, \eta, \mathbf{c})$ when G is a cyclic group of order 6, $\eta = (g_1, g_2, g_3)$, $\mathbf{c} = (11/6, 4/6, 21/6)$. Some of the arcs corresponding to g_3 are not drawn.

The group minimization problem (7) can be interpreted as finding the minimum cost chain or the shortest chain from $\bar{\mathbf{0}}$ to $N(g_0)$ in the graph $H(G, \eta, \mathbf{c})$. Let us consider the following numerical example:

$$\max z = 2x_1 + x_2 + x_3 + 3x_4 + x_5$$

subject to

$$\begin{aligned} 2x_2 + x_3 + 4x_4 + 2x_5 + x_6 \qquad &= 41, \\ 3x_1 - 4x_2 + 4x_3 + x_4 - x_5 \qquad + x_7 &= 47, \\ x_j \geq 0, \quad \text{integers} \qquad (j = 1, \ldots, 7). \end{aligned} \tag{30}$$

Note that this problem is almost the same as (27).

The optimum basis for the associated linear program is

$$\begin{bmatrix} 0 & 2 \\ 3 & -4 \end{bmatrix},$$

Tableau 19.1

	1	x_1	x_2	x_3	x_4	x_5	x_6	x_7	constant
z	1	0	0	21/6	5	2	11/6	4/6	639/6
x_1	0	1	0	2	3	1	4/6	2/6	43
x_2	0	0	1	3/6	2	1	3/6	0	123/6

Table 19.2

From $\bar{0}$ to g_0	Cost of path	Solution **t**
$\bar{0}$	0	0
$\bar{1}$	11/6	$t_1 = 1$
$\bar{2}$	4/6	$t_2 = 1$
$\bar{3}$	15/6	$t_1 = 1, \ t_2 = 1$
$\bar{4}$	8/6	$t_2 = 2$
$\bar{5}$	19/6	$t_1 = 1, \ t_2 = 2$

and the optimum tableau of the associated linear program would appear as Tableau 19.1.

It is clear that $f(\mathbf{a}_4) = f(\mathbf{a}_5) = \mathbf{0}$, since they are all with integer entries. A calculation the same as those done in connection with (27) will reveal that

$$f(\mathbf{a}_3) = g_3, \qquad f(\mathbf{a}_6) = g_1, \qquad \text{and} \qquad f(\mathbf{a}_7) = g_2.$$

Thus we would construct the graph as shown in Fig. 19.3.

The result of a shortest path calculation would give Table 19.2. The solution to an integer program is $(\mathbf{x}_B, \mathbf{x}_N)$ with $\mathbf{x}_B = \mathbf{B}^{-1}\mathbf{b} - \mathbf{B}^{-1}\mathbf{N}\mathbf{x}_N$. We have shown that the solution consists of two parts and the second part is a periodic correction. From the correspondence $t_1 = x_6$ and $t_2 = x_7$, we have the periodic corrections for all possible $\mathbf{b}$.

Thus

$$\mathbf{x}_N = (x_3, x_4, x_5, x_6, x_7) = \begin{cases} (0, 0, 0, 0, 0) & \text{if } f(\mathbf{b}) = \bar{0}, \\ (0, 0, 0, 1, 0) & \text{if } f(\mathbf{b}) = g_1, \\ (0, 0, 0, 0, 1) & \text{if } f(\mathbf{b}) = g_2, \\ (0, 0, 0, 1, 1) & \text{if } f(\mathbf{b}) = g_3, \\ (0, 0, 0, 0, 2) & \text{if } f(\mathbf{b}) = g_4, \\ (0, 0, 0, 1, 2) & \text{if } f(\mathbf{b}) = g_5. \end{cases}$$

We remark here that the solutions obtained using these periodic corrections are optimum integer solutions to (30) if and only if

$$\mathbf{x}_B = \mathbf{B}^{-1}\mathbf{b} - \mathbf{B}^{-1}\,\mathbf{N}\mathbf{x}_N \geq \mathbf{0}.$$

In the present case, $f[41,\ 47] = g_3$, so that

$$\mathbf{x}_N = (0,\ 0,\ 0,\ 1,\ 1).$$

Using $\mathbf{B}^{-1}\mathbf{b}$ and $\mathbf{B}^{-1}\mathbf{N}$ in the optimum tableau of the linear program, we have

$$\mathbf{x}_B = \begin{bmatrix} 43 \\ 123/6 \end{bmatrix} - \begin{bmatrix} 4/6 \\ 3/6 \end{bmatrix} 1 - \begin{bmatrix} 2/6 \\ 0 \end{bmatrix} 1 = \begin{bmatrix} 42 \\ 20 \end{bmatrix}.$$

Since both the components of $\mathbf{x}_B$ are nonnegative, the solution

$$(x_1, x_2, x_3, x_4, x_5, x_6, x_7) = (42, 20, 0, 0, 0, 1,1)$$

is the optimum solution.

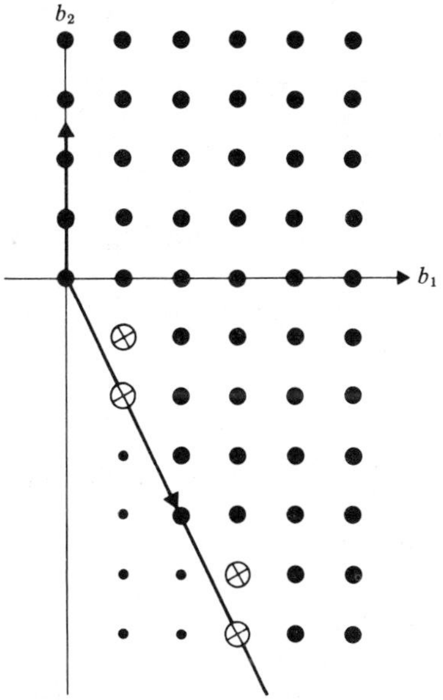

Fig. 19.4

Although we have given a sufficient condition (Theorem 19.8) that tells when the asymptotic algorithm works, actual computation will reveal that the algorithm works most of the time even if the sufficient condition is not satisfied. In Fig. 19.4, the black dot denotes the right-hand side **b** for which the asymptotic algorithm succeeds and white circles denote the right-hand side where the algorithm fails.

19.3 GROUP MINIMIZATION ALGORITHM (Hu [112])

In this section we present a new algorithm for solving the group minimization problem

$$\min \sum c^*(g) \cdot t(g)$$

subject to

$$\sum_{g \in G - \bar{0}} g \cdot t(g) = g_0, \tag{1}$$

$$t(g) \geq 0, \quad \text{integers.}$$

It is easy to see that problem (1) covers the case where $g \in \eta \subset G - \bar{0}$. For a group element $g' \notin \eta$, we can assume the cost $c^*(g')$ to be arbitrarily large so that g' will not be used in the optimum solution. Note that $c^*(g) \geq 0$ for all $g \in G$ because **B** is the optimum basis of the associated linear program. For convenience, we shall replace $c^*(g_i) = 0$ with a positive ϵ_i where

$$D\epsilon_i < \min c^*(g) \; (c^*(g) \neq 0).†$$

We shall assume that the group G is cyclic of order D.

Note that g_0 is one of the group element in G. So (1) really expresses a group element g_0 in terms of the other group elements in the cheapest way; $g_0 = g_0$ with cost $c^*(g_0)$ is another possibility. Instead of solving problem (1) for a particular g_0, we shall solve this problem for all possible right-hand sides $g_0 = g_1, g_2, \ldots, g_{D-1}$. Thus, for each group element, we want the cheapest cost of expressing that group element and the actual combination of group elements achieving that cost. To start the calculation, we have a row of $D - 1$ squares corresponding to the $D - 1$ nonzero group elements of G. Each square contains two entries; the first entry is the cost $c^*(g_p)$, the second entry is a number which reveals the combination expressing that group element g_p. In the beginning, we set $[c^*(g_p), p]$ to be the entries of the pth square. That is to say, we tentatively assume that $g_p = g_p$ is the cheapest way of expressing g_p for all $p = 1, \ldots, D - 1$. When we say the label of a square or a group, we mean the two entries associated with that square or group. A label is called a *temporary* label if it may be changed in a later calculation. A label is called a *permanent* label if it will not be changed in a later calculation. In the beginning, all labels are temporary labels because we are not sure that $g_p = g_p$ is the cheapest way of expressing g_p. We define the cost of a label to be its first entry. We say a label of g_a is less than another label of g_b if the cost of the label of g_a is less than the cost of the label of g_b.

---

† The reason for replacing zero costs by different costs ϵ_i is for the convenience of the proof. It is not necessary to do it in computation.

The algorithm (Hu[112]) can be stated as follows:

1. Compare the costs of all temporary labels and mark the label with the minimum cost to be the permanent label. In the case of a tie, mark any minimal label as the permanent label.

2. Let $g_{i_1}, g_{i_2}, \ldots, g_{i_r}$ be the group elements with permanent labels, and let g_{i_r} be the last group element to receive a permanent label. We then form the additions

$$c^*(g_{i_1}) + c^*(g_{i_r}),\ c^*(g_{i_2}) + c^*(g_{i_r}),\ \ldots,\ c^*(g_{i_r}) + c^*(g_{i_r})$$

and compare with

$$c^*(g_{i_1} + g_{i_r}),\ c^*(g_{i_2} + g_{i_r}),\ \ldots,\ c^*(g_{i_r} + g_{i_r}),$$

respectively. If $c^*(g_{i_j}) + c^*(g_{i_r}) \geq c^*(g_{i_j} + g_{i_r})$, no changes are made. If $c^*(g_{i_j}) + c^*(g_{i_r}) < c^*(g_{i_j} + g_{i_r})$, replace the label of $(g_{i_j} + g_{i_r})$ by that of $[c^*(g_{i_j}) + c^*(g_{i_r}), q]$ where q is the second entry of the label of g_{i_j}. (We can also replace the second entry of $(g_{i_j} + g_{i_r})$ by the second entry of g_{i_r}.) Go back to step 1. The algorithm is completed when all labels are marked as permanent labels.

Before we give a proof and count the number of operations in this algorithm, let us first do a numerical example. Assume that the group G is a cyclic group of order 10 and the corresponding costs are listed below:

$$c(g_i) = 10,\ 3,\ 2,\ 7,\ 8,\ 5,\ 4,\ 9,\ 7,$$

$$g_1,\ g_2,\ g_3,\ g_4,\ g_5,\ g_6,\ g_7,\ g_8,\ g_9.$$

We first fill a row of $D - 1$ squares which correspond to the $D-1$ group elements. All the labels are temporary labels:

g_1	g_2	g_3	g_4	g_5	g_6	g_7	g_8	g_9
10	3	2	7	8	5	4	9	7
1	2	3	4	5	6	7	8	9

1. Compare the costs of all temporary labels and mark [2, 3] to be the permanent label. This is indicated by putting an $*$ in the lower right-hand corner of the square.

2. Since [2, 3] is the only permanent label, we compare $c(g_3) + c(g_3)$ with $c(g_6)$ as $g_3 + g_3 = g_6$. Then $c(g_3) + c(g_3) = 2 + 2 = 4 < 5 = c(g_6)$. Replace [5, 6] of g_6 by [4, 3]. (Note that the second entry of g_6 is replaced by

the second entry of g_3.) This is shown below:

g_1	g_2	g_3	g_4	g_5	g_6	g_7	g_8	g_9
10	3	2	7	8	4	4	9	7
1	2	3 *	4	5	3	7	8	9

1. Compare the costs of all temporary labels and mark [3, 2] as a permanent label.

2. Since g_2 was the last group element to receive a permanent label, we compare

$$c(g_3) + c(g_2) = 2 + 3 = 5 < 8 = c(g_5) \qquad \text{replace [8, 5] by [5, 3],}$$
$$c(g_2) + c(g_2) = 3 + 3 = 6 < 7 = c(g_4) \qquad \text{replace [7, 4] by [6, 2].}$$

The result is shown below:

g_1	g_2	g_3	g_4	g_5	g_6	g_7	g_8	g_9
10	3	2	6	5	4	4	9	7
1	2 *	3 *	2	3	3	7	8	9

1. Compare the costs of all temporary labels and mark either [4, 3] or [4, 7] as the permanent label. Here we select [4, 3].

2. Since g_6 was the last group element to receive a permanent label, we compare

$$c(g_3) + c(g_6) = 2 + 4 = 6 < 7 = c(g_9) \qquad \text{replace [7, 9] by [6, 3],}$$
$$c(g_2) + c(g_6) = 3 + 4 = 7 < 9 = c(g_8) \qquad \text{replace [9, 8] by [7, 2],}$$
$$c(g_6) + c(g_6) = 4 + 4 = 8 > 3 = c(g_2) \qquad \text{no replacement.}$$

Then we have

g_1	g_2	g_3	g_4	g_5	g_6	g_7	g_8	g_9
10	3	2	6	5	4	4	7	6
1	2 *	3 *	2	3	3 *	7	2	3

1. Mark [4, 7] to be a permanent label.

2. We compare

$$c(g_3) + c(g_7) = 2 + 4 = 6 > 0 = c(\bar{0}) \qquad \text{no replacement,}$$
$$c(g_2) + c(g_7) = 3 + 4 = 7 > 6 = c(g_9) \qquad \text{no replacement,}$$
$$c(g_6) + c(g_7) = 4 + 4 = 8 > 2 = c(g_3) \qquad \text{no replacement,}$$
$$c(g_7) + c(g_7) = 4 + 4 = 8 > 6 = c(g_4) \qquad \text{no replacement.}$$

1. Mark [5, 3] as the permanent label.
2. Compare

$$c(g_3) + c(g_5) = 2 + 5 = 7 = 7 = c(g_8) \qquad \text{no replacement,}$$

$$c(g_2) + c(g_5) = 3 + 5 = 8 > 4 = c(g_7) \qquad \text{no replacement,}$$

$$c(g_6) + c(g_5) = 4 + 5 = 9 < 10 = c(g_1) \qquad \text{replace [10, 1] by [9, 3].}$$

Note here that the second entry of the current label of g_6 is 3:

$$c(g_7) + c(g_5) = 4 + 5 = 9 > 3 = c(g_2) \qquad \text{no replacement,}$$

$$c(g_5) + c(g_5) = 5 + 5 = 10 > 0 = c(\bar{0}) \qquad \text{no replacement.}$$

We continue, and mark [6, 2] as the permanent label and iterate between step 1 and step 2. But no further replacement can be made, so we will finally get

g_1	g_2	g_3	g_4	g_5	g_6	g_7	g_8	g_9
9	3	2	6	5	4	4	7	6
3 *	2 *	3 *	2 *	3 *	3 *	7 *	2 *	3 *

Suppose that we want to find the cheapest expression of g_1. The second entry of the label of g_1 is 3. Thus we know $g_1 = \sum t(g)\cdot g$ contains $t(g_3) \geq 1$. Tracing back, $g_1 - g_3 = g_8$, and we see that the second entry of g_8 is 2 which indicates $t(g_2) \geq 1$. Tracing back $g_8 - g_2 = g_6$, we see that the second entry of g_6 is 3 again, which indicates $t(g_3) \geq 2$. Tracing back, $g_6 - g_3 = g_3$, we see the second entry of g_3 is 3, which indicates $t(g_3) \geq 3$. Tracing back, $g_3 - g_3 = \bar{0}$, we know $g_1 = 3g_3 + g_2$ and the cost is 9, which is the first entry of g_1.

We shall denote the set of group elements with permanent labels by P, and the set of group elements with temporary labels by the set T. We shall use the phrase "combining group elements to create a group element g_0" to mean "finding different expressions $\sum g \cdot t(g) = g_0$ such that cost is $\sum c(g) \cdot t(g)$."

Lemma 19.3. A combination of group elements in T or a combination of group elements in P with one or more group elements in T cannot create a group element g_r such that

$$c(g_r) < \min_{g \in T} c(g) = c(g_s).$$

Proof. The combination of elements in T or the combination of elements in P with one or more elements in T contains at least one element, say g_t, in T. By assumption

$$c(g_t) \geq \min_{g \in T} c(g) = c(g_s).$$

Since costs of all elements are positive, the cost of the combination will not be less than $c(g_t)$, hence not less than $c(g_s)$.

In the algorithm, we specify that elements in P be added pairwise to check if the sum is a group element with less cost than the original element. In the algorithm, whenever a permanent label is marked, we add the new permanently labeled group element to itself and with every other element already in the set P. Thus, we have tried the sum of any two elements in P once.

We would never try the sum of three elements in P or any other expression $\sum_{g \in P} g \cdot t(g)$ with the cost $\sum_{g \in P} c(g) \cdot t(g)$. The next lemma says that so far as creating the element in T with minimum cost is concerned, pairwise combination of elements in P is just as good as all possible combinations of elements in P.

Lemma 19.4. If there exists a group element $g_m \in T$, $g_m = \sum_{g \in P} g \cdot t(g)$ with $\sum_{g \in P} c(g) \cdot t(g) < c(g_s)$, where g_s is any other element in T, then

$$g_m = \sum_{g \in P} g \cdot t(g) = g_a + g_b \qquad (g_a, g_b \in P)$$

and

$$\sum_{g \in P} c(g) \cdot t(g) = c(g_a) + c(g_b).$$

In other words, if a group element $g_m \in T$ exists which can be expressed in terms of elements in P with its cost less than the cost of any other element in T, then g_m can be obtained by pairwise addition of elements in P. (Note that this lemma does not imply that the group element with minimum cost in T is always the sum of two elements in P. For example $g_m = g_m$ may be the best combination for g_m.)

Proof. Assume that g_m in T can be expressed as the sum of elements in P. We can partition any sum into two terms. For example, let $g_m = 2g_d + g_e + g_f$ (g_d, g_e, g_f in P); then we can partition the sum into two terms, say

$$g_m = (2g_d) + (g_e + g_f) = g_a + g_b,$$

where $g_a = 2g_d$ is some element in G and $g_b = g_e + g_f$ is some other element in G ($2g_d \neq \bar{0}$ and $g_e + g_f \neq \bar{0}$). Otherwise the expression can be reduced with lower cost. (Remember that we replace zero costs by ϵ_i.) Neither g_a nor g_b can belong to T, since both $c(g_a)$ and $c(g_b)$ are less than $c(g_m)$, which is assumed to be the minimum cost in T. If g_a and g_b both belong to P, then the lemma is proved.

Now we shall prove that all permanent labels obtained in the algorithm are actually permanent, i.e., all permanent labels represent the minimum costs and the corresponding combinations of group elements which give these minimum costs.

Theorem 19.9. If a group element is given a permanent label by our algorithm, then this label represents the actual minimum cost of this group element and reveals the actual minimal expression for this group element.

Proof. Use induction on the cardinality of the set P.

By Lemma 19.3, the first permanent label represents the minimum cost of this element and the minimum expression, which in this case is just $g_{i_1} = g_{i_1}$. Now assume that for $|P| = n$, all permanent labels represent the minimum costs and the minimum expressions for all group elements in P. First, we will consider the *first entry* of the next permanent label.

Let $g_{i_1}, g_{i_2}, \ldots, g_{in}$ be the elements in P. By the induction hypothesis, we cannot replace any element in P by a combination of elements in G with lower costs. By Lemma 19.3, we cannot combine elements in P and T or just elements in T to create an element with cost less than the current minimum cost in T. Thus the only possibility left is to try a combination of elements in P. By Lemma 19.4, if such a combination exists, we will obtain the combination after completion of step 2 of the algorithm. Hence after the completion of step 2 of the algorithm, the minimum cost in T is the true minimum cost, which is the first entry of the new permanent label. Now, consider the second entry of the new permanent label. Let g_r be the $(n + 1)$th group element to receive a permanent label and let $g_r = g_a + g_b$ $(g_a, g_b \in P)$. If the label of g_a, $l(g_a) = \{c(a), a\}$, then the algorithm will replace $l(g_r)$ by $\{c(a) + c(b), a\}$. This then gives the correct indication that $t(g_a) \geq 1$ in the expression for g_r. Tracing back we have $g_r - g_a = g_b$, and the second entry of $l(g_b)$ is correct by the inductive assumption. (The case $g_r = g_r$ is trivial.)

If $g_r = g_a + g_b$ and $l(g_a) = \{c(g_a), j\}$, then the algorithm will replace $l(g_r)$ by $\{c(a) + c(b), j\}$ which indicates $t(g_j) \geq 1$ in the expression for g_r. But $l(g_a) = \{c(g_a), j\}$ implies that $g_a = g_j + g_k$, since we assume that $l(g_a)$ is correct.

Thus $g_r = g_a + g_b = g_j + (g_k + g_b)$. But we have just proved that the first entries of all permanent labels are correct. This implies that

$$c(g_r) = c(g_j) + c(g_k + g_b) > c(g_k + g_b).$$

If $(g_k + g_b) \in T$, then it will contradict the fact that g_r was the element in T that has just become an element in P. If $(g_k + g_b) \in P$, then the expression $l(g_r) = \{c(a) + c(b), j\}$ implies $t(g_j) \geq 1$ in the expression for g_r. Tracing back, $g_r - g_j = (g_k + g_b) \in P$. Because $(g_k + g_b) \in P$, it is one of the first n permanent group elements, and it, by assumption, has a correct permanent label. Therefore $l(g_r)$ is also correct.

Now let us count the number of operations in this algorithm and compare it with the number of operations in Gomory's algorithm in Section 19.2. In Gomory's algorithm, if the group is of order D, and D is a prime number, then D^2 additions and D^2 comparisons are needed. If D is not a prime number, then q additions and q comparisons are needed, where $D^2 < q < 2D^2$. Thus at most $4D^2$ operations are needed if D is not a prime number and at most $2D^2$ operations are needed if D is a prime number.

In step 1 of our algorithm, we have to select the minimum of $D - 1$ temporary labels. Thus $D - 1$ comparisons are needed the first time. In step 1, the second time, $D - 2$ comparisons are needed. Thus, the total needed is $(D - 1) + (D - 2) + \cdots + 1 = D(D - 1)/2 \doteq D^2/2$ comparisons in step 1.

In step 2, the number of additions and the number of comparisons is proportional to the cardinality of P. Thus we need $1 + 2 + \cdots + D - 2 = (D - 1)(D - 2)/2 \doteq D^2/2$ additions and the same number of comparisons. Therefore, a total of D^2 comparisons and $D^2/2$ additions is needed in our algorithm. If in step 1, we count D comparisons each time, then a total of $1.5D^2$ comparisons and $0.5D^2$ additions is needed. Thus, in the worst case, we need $2D^2$ operations independent of whether D is a prime or not. In summary the algorithm has the following advantages:

1. The number of operations is less than the number of operations in Gomory's algorithm ($2D^2$ instead of $2D^2$ to $4D^2$).
2. The steps are the same for selecting permanent group elements. They are independent of the order of the group G or the order of the element g.
3. When the particular g_0 in (1) belongs to P, then the computation can be stopped if desired.
4. Fewer memory locations are needed.

FACES OF AN INTEGER POLYHEDRON 20

20.1 INTRODUCTION (Gomory [86])

In Chapter 19 we were concerned with the solutions of three problems. The first problem was

$$\max \mathbf{c}_B \mathbf{x}_B + \mathbf{c}_N \mathbf{x}_N$$

subject to

$$\mathbf{B}\mathbf{x}_B + \mathbf{N}\mathbf{x}_N = \mathbf{b}, \tag{1}$$

$$\mathbf{x}_B, \mathbf{x}_N \geq \mathbf{0}, \qquad \text{integers.}$$

The convex hull of nonnegative integer points which satisfy the constraints of (1) is denoted by P. The second problem was

$$\max \mathbf{c}_B \mathbf{B}^{-1} \mathbf{b} - \mathbf{c}_N^* \mathbf{x}_N$$

subject to

$$\mathbf{x}_B + \mathbf{B}^{-1} \mathbf{N}\mathbf{x}_N = \mathbf{B}^{-1} \mathbf{b}, \tag{2}$$

$$\mathbf{x}_N \geq \mathbf{0}, \qquad \mathbf{x}_B, \qquad \mathbf{x}_N, \qquad \text{integers,}$$

where $\mathbf{c}_N^* = \mathbf{c}_B \mathbf{B}^{-1} \mathbf{N} - \mathbf{c}_N \geq \mathbf{0}$ and $\mathbf{B}$ is the optimum basis of the associated linear program of (1). The convex hull of nonnegative integer solutions which satisfy the constraints of (2) is denoted by $P_x(\mathbf{B}, \mathbf{N}, \mathbf{b})$. The third problem was

$$\min \sum_{g \in \eta} c^*(g)\, t(g)$$

subject to

$$\sum_{g \in \eta} t(g) \cdot g = g_0, \tag{3}$$

$$t(g) \geq 0, \qquad \text{integers.}$$

The convex hull of nonnegative integer solutions satisfying the constraints of (3) is denoted by $P(G, \eta, g_0)$.

We have shown that an optimum solution of (3) corresponds naturally to an optimum solution of (2). The optimum solution of (2) may also be the optimum solution of (1) provided that $\mathbf{x}_B \geq \mathbf{0}$. The polyhedra $P_x(\mathbf{B}, \mathbf{N}, \mathbf{b})$ and $P(G, \eta, g_0)$ are essentially alike. Point $(\mathbf{x}_B, \mathbf{x}_N)$ is a vertex of $P_x(\mathbf{B}, \mathbf{N}, \mathbf{b})$ if and only if $\mathbf{t} = F(\mathbf{x}_B, \mathbf{x}_N)$ is a vertex of $P(G, \eta, g_0)$. Whenever $f(\mathbf{a}_i) = f(\mathbf{a}_j)$, $i \neq j$, then either $x_i = 0$ or $x_j = 0$.

In this chapter we shall study $P(G, \eta, g_0)$ independent of the minimization of the objective function $\sum c^*(g)t(g)$. The convex hull $P(G, \eta, g_0)$ is important because its vertices are all optimum solutions of (1) with some right-hand side $\mathbf{b}$ asymptotically large. To state this property more precisely, if $\mathbf{c} = (\mathbf{c}_B, \mathbf{c}_N)$ is some vector such that $\mathbf{B}$ is the optimum nondegenerate basis of the linear program associated with (1), i.e., $\mathbf{c}_B\mathbf{B}^{-1}\mathbf{N} - \mathbf{c}_N = \mathbf{c}_N^* \geq \mathbf{0}$ and $\mathbf{B}^{-1}\mathbf{b} > \mathbf{0}$, then the optimum solution $\mathbf{x}$ of (1) is the same as the optimum solution of (2), which is a vertex of $P_x(\mathbf{B}, \mathbf{N}, \mathbf{b})$ provided that $\mathbf{b}$ is asymptotically large. This vertex of $P_x(\mathbf{B}, \mathbf{N}, \mathbf{b})$ can be obtained from the corresponding vertex of $P(G, \eta, g_0)$. Also, if $\mathbf{v}$ is any vertex of $P(G, \eta, g_0)$, then there exists a vector $\mathbf{c}$, the optimum basis $\mathbf{B}$, and $\mathbf{b}$ of (1) such that the optimum solution of (1) is obtained from the vertex $\mathbf{v}$.

Another important property of $P(G, \eta, g_0)$ is that the faces of $P(G, \eta, g_0)$ are in a sense the strongest cutting planes for the problem (1). In Chapter 13 we generate a Gomory cut after the optimum solution to the linear program is obtained. Any cutting plane generated without using the conditions $\mathbf{x}_B \geq \mathbf{0}$ is simply a nonnegative weighted combination of the faces.

We first note that $P(G, \eta, g_0)$ is either empty or n'-dimensional. If g_0 does not lie in the subgroup generated by the elements in η, then $P(G, \eta, g_0)$ is empty or there is no feasible solution to problem (3). This implies that $P_x(\mathbf{B}, \mathbf{N}, \mathbf{b})$ is also empty and the original integer program (1) has no solution. If $P(G, \eta, g_0)$ is not empty, let $\mathbf{t} = [t(g_1), \ldots, t(g_k), \ldots, t(g_{n'})]$ be a point of $P(G, \eta, g_0)$, let $s(h)$ be the order of the group element h, and let $\mathbf{u}(h)$ be the n'-dimensional vector with $t(h) = 1$, and all other components zero. Then the vector $\mathbf{t} + s(h)\,\mathbf{u}(h)$ is also a point of $P(G, \eta, g_0)$. For each $h \in \eta$, we have a feasible point $\mathbf{t} + s(h)\,\mathbf{u}(h)$. Clearly these $n' = |\eta|$ points are all independent; hence $P(G, \eta, g_0)$ is n'-dimensional.

Because $P(G, \eta, g_0)$ is n'-dimensional, we shall use the word "face" to mean an $(n' - 1)$-dimensional hyperplane with (i) all points of $P(G, \eta, g_0)$ on one side of this hyperplane and (ii) each point on the hyperplane written as a weighted sum of n' points of $P(G, \eta, g_0)$.

Each face of $P(G, \eta, g_0)$ can be represented by an inequality in the form [the points on the face satisfy the equality and all the points of $P(G, \eta, g_0)$ satisfy the inequality]

$$\sum_{g \in \eta} \gamma(g)\, t(g) \geq \gamma_0. \tag{4}$$

Now we shall prove (i) $\gamma(g) \geq 0$ and (ii) $\gamma_0 \geq 0$. Assume that there is a coefficient $\gamma(h) < 0$ in (4). Let $s(h)$ be the order of the group element h. Then $\mathbf{t} + ks(h)\,\mathbf{u}(h)$ is also a solution to (3) and, hence, also belongs to $P(G, \eta, g_0)$.

Because all points in $P(G, \eta, g_0)$ must be on one side of the face, we should have

$$\sum_{\substack{g \in \eta, \\ g \neq h}} \gamma(g)\, t(g) + \gamma(h)\,[t(h) + ks(h)] \geq \gamma_0, \tag{5}$$

for any positive integer k. But (5) cannot be true for sufficiently large k. Thus there does not exist any negative $\gamma(g)$ in (4). Because $\gamma(g) \geq 0$ and $t(g) \geq 0$, we conclude that $\gamma_0 \geq 0$ in (4).

We shall denote a face of $P(G, \eta, g_0)$ by $(\boldsymbol{\gamma}, \gamma_0)$, where $\boldsymbol{\gamma}$ is an n'-vector and γ_0 a scalar. In the $\mathbf{x}$-space we shall denote a face of $P_x(\mathbf{B}, \mathbf{N}, \mathbf{b})$ by $(\boldsymbol{\gamma}''_B, \boldsymbol{\gamma}''_N, \gamma''_0)$. As $\mathbf{x}_B = \mathbf{B}^{-1}(\mathbf{b} - \mathbf{N}\mathbf{x}_N)$, an inequality in the $\mathbf{x}$-space is equivalent to an inequality in the nonbasic variables $\mathbf{x}_N$. We shall use $(\mathbf{0}, \bar{\boldsymbol{\gamma}}_N, \bar{\gamma}_0)$ to denote the corresponding inequality in $\mathbf{x}_N$. Note that $(\mathbf{0}, \bar{\boldsymbol{\gamma}}_N, \bar{\gamma}_0)$ is a $(n-1)$-dimensional face of $P_x(\mathbf{B}, \mathbf{N}, \mathbf{b})$ if and only if $(\boldsymbol{\gamma}, \gamma_0)$ is an $(n' - 1)$-dimensional face of $P(G, \eta, g_0)$, where $\gamma[f(\mathbf{a}_i)] = \bar{\gamma}_i$. Thus to obtain a face of $P_x(\mathbf{B}, \mathbf{N}, \mathbf{b})$, we merely write the component values $\gamma(g)$ in all the corresponding places in $\bar{\boldsymbol{\gamma}}_N$.

We have used the inequality

$$\sum_{g \in \eta} \gamma(g)\, t(g) \geq \gamma_0 \tag{6}$$

to represent the half-space containing a face of $P(G, \eta, g_0)$, where $\gamma(g) \geq 0$ for all $g \in \eta$ and $\gamma_0 \geq 0$. The face has the properties that (i) all points of $P(G, \eta, g_0)$ are on one side of this face and (ii) all points on the face can be written as a weighted sum of vertices of $P(G, \eta, g_0)$. Let us denote the set of nonnegative integer solutions to (3) by T. Then we can easily prove that (6) provides a face of $P(G, \eta, g_0)$ if and only if (i)′ for every $\mathbf{t} \in T$, $\boldsymbol{\gamma} \cdot \mathbf{t} \geq \gamma_0$ and (ii)′ there are n' $\mathbf{t}^i \in T$ which generate the hyperplane $\boldsymbol{\gamma} \cdot \mathbf{t} = \gamma_0$.

Theorem 20.1. The inequaltiy $\boldsymbol{\gamma}\mathbf{t} \geq \gamma_0 > 0$ provides a face of $P(G, \eta, g_0)$ if and only if $\boldsymbol{\gamma}$ is a basic feasible solution of the system of inequalities

$$\boldsymbol{\gamma}\mathbf{t} \geq \gamma_0, \qquad \text{all } \mathbf{t} \in T. \tag{7}$$

This system involves one inequality for each $\mathbf{t} \in T$. (Recall that a basic feasible solution is one which satisfies all the inequalities and produces equality on a set of rows of rank n'.)

Proof. We first prove that if $(\boldsymbol{\gamma}, \gamma_0)$ is a face, then $(\boldsymbol{\gamma}, \gamma_0)$ is a basic feasible solution of (7). If $(\boldsymbol{\gamma}, \gamma_0)$ is a face, then by (i)′ $\boldsymbol{\gamma} \cdot \mathbf{t} \geq \gamma_0$ for all $\mathbf{t} \in T$ and by (ii)′ there are n' different vectors $\mathbf{t}^i \in T$ which satisfy $\boldsymbol{\gamma}\mathbf{t}^i = \gamma_0$ and generate the hyperplane $\boldsymbol{\gamma} \cdot \mathbf{t} = \gamma_0$. Since we have $\gamma_0 > 0$, the face does not pass through the origin. This implies that the n' vectors $\mathbf{t}^i$ are linearly independent. Therefore, $\boldsymbol{\gamma}$ is a basic solution to (7).

Now if $\boldsymbol{\gamma}$ is a basic feasible solution to the system of inequalities (7), we have $\boldsymbol{\gamma} \cdot \mathbf{t} \geq \gamma_0$ for all $\mathbf{t} \in T$, and hence (i)′ is satisfied. Because $\boldsymbol{\gamma}$ is a basic feasible solution, there are n' independent rows in (7) which are satisfied as equalities. We may then take these rows as the vectors $\mathbf{t}^i$. Since the $\mathbf{t}^i$ are linearly independent, they must generate the entire hyperplane $\boldsymbol{\gamma} \cdot \mathbf{t} = \gamma_0$; so (ii)′ is also satisfied. Therefore $(\boldsymbol{\gamma}, \gamma_0)$ is a face.

There are a number of remarks that can be made about Theorem 20.1.

1. We may as well fix γ_0 at 1 in the above theorem, since positive multiples of $(\boldsymbol{\gamma}, \gamma_0)$ yield the same face.
2. Although there are infinitely many vectors $\mathbf{t}$ in T, all $\mathbf{t}$ with $t(g) \geq s(g)$ are superfluous. Hence the total number of inequalities in (7) can be taken as $\Pi_{g \in \eta}\, s(g)$.
3. The large finite number of inequalities in (7) could be dealt with in a computation by using row-generating methods like those of references [82] and [91]. Basically we use either the primal or the dual simplex method but produce rows only when needed. (A computation for getting one face of the polyhedron is described in Section 20.2.)

For example, let us assume that we want to get a cutting plane for the integer program (2), and we would like to have a cutting plane which is as nearly parallel to the hyperplane defined by the objective function as possible. That is to say, we want a cutting plane where the angle between $\boldsymbol{\gamma}$ and $\mathbf{c}$ is minimized. In other words, we want

$$\min \frac{\mathbf{c} \cdot \boldsymbol{\gamma}}{\|\mathbf{c}\| \;\; \|\boldsymbol{\gamma}\|}$$

subject to

$$\boldsymbol{\gamma}\mathbf{t} \geq \gamma_0 \qquad \text{all } \mathbf{t} \in T.$$

Assume that we have all the $\mathbf{t} \in T$. Then this is a linear program with many rows, one row for each $\mathbf{t}$ in T. If we use the dual simplex method, we have a dual feasible $\bar{\boldsymbol{\gamma}}$ and the problem is to generate the inequality not satisfied by the current $\bar{\boldsymbol{\gamma}}$. Thus the computation consists of two parts. The first part is a regular dual simplex tableau with objective function $(\mathbf{c} \cdot \boldsymbol{\gamma}) / (\|\mathbf{c}\| \;\; \|\boldsymbol{\gamma}\|)$ and constrained by a subset of inequalities from (7). The second part is an auxiliary computation generating inequalities to be used by the first part. If using the current $\bar{\boldsymbol{\gamma}}$ in the graph $H(G, \eta, \bar{\boldsymbol{\gamma}})$, we find a shortest path from $\bar{0}$ to g_0 with length $\bar{\boldsymbol{\gamma}}\mathbf{t} < \gamma_0$. Then $\bar{\boldsymbol{\gamma}} \cdot \mathbf{t} \geq \gamma_0$ is an unsatisfied inequality. This inequality is then added to the first part. (The inequality should be updated before adding to the bottom of the dual simplex tableau.) Then we perform a dual simplex pivot step in the first part and obtain a new $\bar{\bar{\boldsymbol{\gamma}}}$. This new $\bar{\bar{\boldsymbol{\gamma}}}$ is used as lengths of arcs in the auxiliary computation. If, using $\bar{\bar{\boldsymbol{\gamma}}}$ as length of arcs, we cannot find a shortest path from $\bar{0}$ to g_0 with total length $\bar{\bar{\boldsymbol{\gamma}}} \cdot \mathbf{t} < \gamma_0$, then this $\bar{\bar{\boldsymbol{\gamma}}}$ is also primal feasible and hence optimum.

Because we restrict $\gamma_0 > 0$ in discussing the inequality in Theorem 20.1, there still remains the possibility $\gamma_0 = 0$. We now turn to the case $\gamma_0 = 0$.

Theorem 20.2. The only possible faces $(\boldsymbol{\gamma}, \gamma_0)$ of $P(G, \eta, g_0)$ with $\gamma_0 = 0$ are the n' hyperplanes $\boldsymbol{\gamma} = \mathbf{u}(h)$ or, equivalently, $t(h) = 0$ (i.e., those hyperplanes that contain the coordinate axes).

Proof. Suppose that $(\boldsymbol{\gamma}, 0)$ is a face of $P(G, \eta, g_0)$. Since this hyperplane is an $(n' - 1)$-dimensional subspace and it is generated by elements $\mathbf{t} \in T$, there must be a set of $n' - 1$ linearly independent $\mathbf{t} \in T$ on the hyperplane. For each of these vectors $\mathbf{t}^i$ $(i = 1, \ldots, n' - 1)$ we have $\boldsymbol{\gamma} \cdot \mathbf{t}^i = 0$, where $\mathbf{t}^i = [t^i(g_1), t^i(g_2), \ldots, t^i(g_{n'})]$. Because $\gamma(g) \geq 0$ and $t(g) \geq 0$, $\sum \gamma(g)t(g) = 0$ unless $\gamma(g) > 0$ implies $t(g) = 0$ and $t(g) > 0$ implies $\gamma(g) = 0$. This must be true for each of the vectors $\mathbf{t}^i$. If $t^i(g) = 0$, all i $(i = 1, \ldots, n' - 1)$, for more than one element g, then it will contradict that these $n' - 1$ $\mathbf{t}^i$ are of rank $n' - 1$. But if a vector

$$\mathbf{t} = [t(g_1), t(g_2), \ldots, t(g_{n'})]$$

has all positive components, then the $\gamma(g)$ must be all equal to zero for all $g \in \eta$ in order that $\sum \gamma(g) \cdot t(g) = 0$. Thus aside from the case $\gamma(g) = 0$ for all $g \in \eta$, the only possibility is $\gamma(h) > 0$ and $\gamma(g) = 0$ for all $g \in \eta$, $g \neq h$. This gives

$$\gamma(h)\, t(h) + \sum_{\substack{g \in \eta, \\ g \neq h}} \gamma(g)\, t(g) = 0 \qquad \text{or} \qquad \gamma(h)\, t(h) = 0.$$

This implies that $t(h) = 0$ is the face mentioned in the theorem.

We have shown that the condition $t(h) \geq 0$ gives the only possible faces with the right-hand side $\gamma_0 = 0$. It is easy to decide when this condition actually gives faces.

Theorem 20.3. The condition $t(h) \geq 0$ yields a face of $P(G, \eta, g_0)$ if and only if the element g_0 lies in the subgroups $G'_{\eta-h}$ generated by the elements of $\eta - h$. If $g_0 \notin G'_{\eta-h}$, then $t(h) \geq p > 0$ is a face. Here p is the smallest positive integer defining the coset $ph + G'_{\eta-h}$ in which g_0 lies. Furthermore p is the smallest positive integer giving the coset.

Proof. If $g_0 \notin G'_{\eta-h}$, then there exists no solution to the group relation

$$\sum_{g \in \eta} t(g) \cdot g = g_0$$

with $t(h) = 0$; hence, $t(h) \geq 0$ is not a face. If $g_0 \in G'_{\eta-h}$, then we have a representation

$$\sum_{g \in \eta - h} t(g) \cdot g = g_0, \qquad 0 \leq t(g) < s(g). \tag{8}$$

For a vector $\mathbf{t}$ which satisfies (8), we can add the $n' - 1$ unit vectors $s(g)\mathbf{u}(g)$ to $\mathbf{t}$ for all $g \in \eta - h$ to form $n' - 1$ independent solutions all with $t(h) = 0$. Hence $t(h) \geq 0$ is a face.

Now if $g_0 \notin G'_{\eta-h}$, since $G'_{\eta-h}$ splits G into cosets, if $P(G, \eta, g_0)$ is not empty, g_0 is in one of these cosets. These cosets must be of the form $ph + G'_{\eta-h}$, and we can choose for each coset the smallest possible p. This then gives one solution to the equality $t(h) = p$, and we can get $n' - 1$ other solutions by simply adding unit vectors $\mathbf{u}(g)$, $g \in \eta - h$. Since there is no representation for g_0 with $t(h) < p$, the inequality $t(h) \geq p$ is satisfied for all $\mathbf{t} \in T$. Q.E.D.

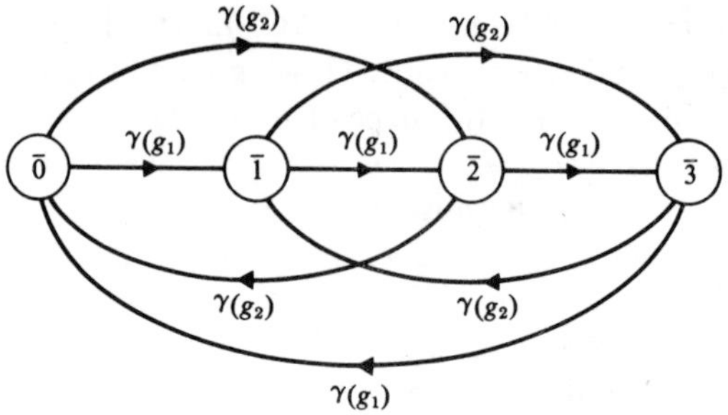

Fig. 20.1

In Chapter 19, we have introudced the graph $H(G, \eta, \mathbf{c})$, where **c** are the costs associated with the arcs, and we were interested in finding the shortest path from $\bar{0}$ to g_0. Now we can construct the graph $H(G, \eta, \boldsymbol{\gamma})$, where $\boldsymbol{\gamma}$ are the lengths associated with the arcs of the graph. A shortest path from $\bar{0}$ to g_0 is a solution to the group minimization problem (3) with total length $\gamma(g)\, t(g) = \gamma_0$. If the $\gamma(g)$ are selected in such a way that there are n' linearly independent shortest paths from $\bar{0}$ to g_0, then $(\boldsymbol{\gamma}, \gamma_0)$ is a face of $P(G, \eta, g_0)$.

The graph $H(G, \eta, g_0)$ for a cyclic group of four elements, $\bar{0}, g_1, g_2, g_3$ and $\eta = \{g_1, g_2\}$ is shown in Fig. 20.1.

Any of the standard shortest chain algorithms or the algorithm in Section 19.3 can be used to find the shortest chain from $\bar{0}$ to g_0 or to find the shortest chains from $\bar{0}$ to all N_g, $g \in G$. If a shortest chain P^* from $\bar{0}$ to g_0 contains $t(g)$ arcs corresponding to g, then we have a solution $\mathbf{t} = [t(g)]$ $(g \in \eta)$ to the group minimization problem with the objective function $\sum_{g \in \eta} \gamma(g)\, t(g)$. There are, of course, many different shortest chains corresponding to the same solution $t(g)$ but with corresponding arcs taken in different order. As we mentioned in Chapter 10, any subpath of a shortest path must itself be a shortest path. This is certainly true in the graph $H(G, \eta, \boldsymbol{\gamma})$, and we shall state it as a lemma.

Lemma 20.1. Let P^* be a shortest path from $\bar{0}$ to g_0 and **t** be the corresponding solution. If $\mathbf{t}'$ is any nonnegative integer vector with $t'(g) \leq t(g)$ and $\sum_{g \in \eta} t'(g) \cdot g = h$, then any path starting at N_g and ending at N_{g+h} with the corresponding solution to $t'(g)$ is a shortest path from N_g to N_{g+h}.

Proof. Since $t'(g) \leq t(g)$, the path corresponding to $[t'(g)]$ is a subpath of the shortest path corresponding to $[t(g)]$. If there exists a path from N_g to N_{g+h} corresponding to $[t''(g)]$ which is shorter than $[t'(g)]$, then the path corresponding to $[t''(g) + t(g) - t'(g)]$ would be a path from $\bar{0}$ to g_0 with distance shorter than $[t(g)]$. This is a contradiction. Q.E.D.

When we consider the faces of $P(G, \eta, g_0)$ which can be represented by $\sum_{g \in \eta} \gamma(g)\, t(g) \geq \gamma_0$ or $(\boldsymbol{\gamma}, \gamma_0)$, it is very convenient to think in terms of the graph $H(G, \eta, \boldsymbol{\gamma})$. We associate $\gamma(g)$ as the length of the arc corresponding to g. In this way, we can characterize a face of $P(G, \eta, g_0)$ in the graph $H(G, \eta, \boldsymbol{\gamma})$.

Lemma 20.2. If $(\boldsymbol{\gamma}, \gamma_0)$, $\gamma_0 > 0$, is a face of $P(G, \eta, g_0)$ and $g \in \eta$, then there is a shortest path from $N_{\bar{0}}$ to N_{g_0} with $t(g) > 0$. This implies that there is a shortest path from $N_{\bar{0}}$ to N_{g_0} passing through N_g. (There are many shortest paths from $N_{\bar{0}}$ to N_{g_0}. This lemma shows that every node N_g, $g \in \eta$, must be in at least one of the shortest paths.)

Proof. Because $(\boldsymbol{\gamma}, \gamma_0)$ is a face with $\gamma_0 > 0$, there exist n' linearly independent $\mathbf{t}^i$ with $\boldsymbol{\gamma}\mathbf{t}^i = \gamma_0$. For all other $\mathbf{t}$ satisfying $\sum_{g \in \eta} t(g) \cdot g = g_0$, we have $\boldsymbol{\gamma}\mathbf{t} \geq \gamma_0$. Thus each of the $\mathbf{t}^i$ represent a shortest path from $\bar{0}$ to g_0. If all $\mathbf{t}^i$ $(i = 1, \ldots, n')$ have $t^i(g) = 0$ for some g, the $\mathbf{t}^i$ will not be of rank n'. Therefore, at least one $\mathbf{t}^i$ has $t^i(g) \geq 1$.

Theorem 20.4. If $(\boldsymbol{\gamma}, \gamma_0)$, $\gamma_0 > 0$ is a face, $\gamma(g)$ is the length of the shortest path from $\bar{0}$ to g.

Proof. By Lemma 20.2, there is a shortest path from $\bar{0}$ to g_0 with $t(g) \geq 1$. Let $\mathbf{t}$ be the solution corresponding to the shortest path from $\bar{0}$ to g_0 and let $\mathbf{u}(g)$ be $\mathbf{t}'$ in Lemma 20.1. Then this one-arc path corresponding to $\mathbf{u}(g)$ is a subpath of the shortest path $\mathbf{t}$; hence $\mathbf{u}(g)$ itself must be a shortest path. The length of this one-arc path is $\gamma(g)$.

Corollary 20.1. If g_1 and g_2 both belong to η and $g = g_1 + g_2$ with $g \in \eta$, then $\gamma(g) \leq \gamma(g_1) + \gamma(g_2)$.

Proof. The solutions $t(g_1) = 1$ and $t(g_2) = 1$ provide a path to g of length $\gamma(g_1) + \gamma(g_2)$. But $\gamma(g)$ is the length of the shortest path to g; hence $\gamma(g) \leq \gamma(g_1) + \gamma(g_2)$.

Corollary 20.2. If g_1 and g_2 both belong to η and $g_1 + g_2 = g_0$, then $\gamma(g_1) + \gamma(g_2) = \gamma_0$.

Proof. By Lemma 20.2, there is a shortest path from $\bar{0}$ to g_0 with $t(g_1) > 0$. Let this solution be $\mathbf{t}$. Then $t(g_1) = 1$ is a subpath (of the shortest path) from $\bar{0}$ to g_0. If $g_1 + g_2 = g_0$, then $g_2 = g_0 - g_1$. But we know

$$\boldsymbol{\gamma} \cdot \mathbf{t} = \gamma_0,$$

or

$$\boldsymbol{\gamma}[\mathbf{u}(g_1)] + \boldsymbol{\gamma}[\mathbf{t} - \mathbf{u}(g_1)] = \gamma_0,$$

or

$$\gamma(g_1) + \gamma(g_2) = \gamma_0.$$

20.2. A FACE CALCULATION

In this section we shall describe a computation to get the coefficients of an inequality $\sum \gamma(g)\, t(g) \geq \gamma_0$ which represents a face of $P(G, \eta, g_0)$. Similar to Chapter 19, we define, for any $S \subset \eta$, and any $h \in G$,

$$\psi_S(h) = \min \sum \gamma(g)\, t(g)$$

subject to

$$\sum_{g \in S} g \cdot t(g) = h. \tag{1}$$

Then $\psi_S(h)$ satisfy the recursive relation

$$\psi_S(h) = \min \{\psi_{S-g}(h), \psi_S(h - g) + \gamma(g)\}. \tag{2}$$

At the start, all $\gamma(g)$ are unknown. We shall use the following recursive computation to find $\gamma(g)$ for all $g \in \eta$. As before, we define $\psi_0(g) = \infty > 1 = \gamma_0$ and $\psi_0(\bar{0}) = 0$. Assume that we know $\gamma(g)$ for all $g \in S$. Then the following three steps will give $\gamma(\bar{g})$ for $\bar{g} \in \eta$ and $\bar{g} \notin S$.

(i) Find the values of m_i for which $\psi_S(g_0 - m_i\bar{g}) < 1$. If there are none, set $\gamma(\bar{g}) = 0$, and proceed to find $\gamma(\bar{\bar{g}})$ where $\bar{\bar{g}} \notin S \cup \bar{g}$. If there are values $m_i (i = 1, \ldots, q)$ for which $\psi_S(g_0 - m_i\bar{g}) < 1$, then set

$$\gamma(\bar{g}) = \max_i \, [1 - \psi_S(g_0 - \mathrm{m}_i\bar{g})] \, / \, m_i. \tag{3}$$

(ii) Use this value of $\gamma(\bar{g})$ together with $\gamma(g)$, $g \in S$, to compute $\psi_{S \cup \bar{g}}(h)$ for all $h \in G$ as done in Chapter 19. When $S = \eta$ go to step (iii); otherwise return to step (i) where the membership of S is increased by 1.

(iii) When all $\gamma(g)$ have been obtained for all $g \in \eta$, the inequality $\sum \gamma(g)t(g) \geq 1$ represents a face of $P(G, \eta, g_0)$.

To prove that this computation works, we have to show that it will provide n' linearly independent shortest paths in the graph $H(G, \eta, \gamma)$. Without loss of generality, we can assume that all $\gamma(g) = 0$ for $g \in S$ and we want to calculate $\gamma(\bar{g})$.

Assume

$$\gamma(\bar{g}) = [1 - \psi_S(g_0 - m\bar{g})] \, / \, m > 0. \tag{4}$$

Then the shortest path using only arcs $g \in S \cup \bar{g}$ will consist of arcs of length $\psi_S(g_0 - m\bar{g}) = 0$ from $\bar{0}$ to $g_0 - m\bar{g}$ and followed by m arcs $\bar{g}$ of length $m\gamma(\bar{g})$. The total length will be $\psi_S(g_0 - m\bar{g}) + m\gamma(\bar{g}) = 0 + m\gamma(\bar{g}) = 1$. It follows from (3) that any other path from $\bar{0}$ to g_0 will be of length greater than or equal to 1. We can form $|S| + 1$ independent paths by adding loops each using $s(g)$ arcs where $g \in S$ and $\gamma(g) = 0$.

Now, consider the element $\bar{\bar{g}} \notin S \cup \bar{g}$. If the computation gives $\gamma(\bar{\bar{g}}) = 0$, then we can use $\bar{\bar{g}}$ to form a loop and add it to the previous shortest paths to get $|S| + 2$ independent shortest paths. If the computation (3) gives $\gamma(\bar{\bar{g}}) > 0$, then the path from $\bar{0}$ to $g_0 - m\bar{\bar{g}}$ will be of length $\psi_{S \cup \bar{g}}(g_0 - m\bar{\bar{g}})$ and the total length from $\bar{0}$ to g_0 is of length

$$\psi_{S \cup \bar{g}}(g_0 - m\bar{\bar{g}}) + m\gamma(\bar{\bar{g}}) = 1.$$

Because of the way m_i is selected in (3), any other paths from $\bar{0}$ to g_0 using $\bar{\bar{g}}$ will be of length greater than 1. All other paths not using $\bar{\bar{g}}$ have been shown to be of length greater than 1. So this is a shortest path, and since it uses $\bar{\bar{g}}$, it is independent of the previous paths.

Consider the numerical example where we want to find a face of $P(G,\eta,g_0)$, where G is a cyclic group of order 6, $\eta = \{g_1, g_2, g_3, g_5\}$ and $g_0 = g_3$. Then

$$\gamma(g_1) = \max_i \frac{1 - \psi'_0(g_3 - m_i g_1)}{m_i} = \frac{1 - \psi_0(\bar{0})}{3} = \frac{1}{3},$$

$$\gamma(g_2) = \max_i \frac{1 - \psi_{g_1}(g_3 - m_i g_2)}{m_i} = \frac{1 - \psi_{g_1}(g_1)}{1} = \frac{2}{3},$$

$$\gamma(g_3) = \max_i \frac{1 - \psi_{g_1 \cup g_2}(g_3 - m_i g_3)}{m_i} = \frac{1 - \psi_{g_1 \cup g_2}(\bar{0})}{1} = 1,$$

$$\gamma(g_5) = \max_i \frac{1 - \psi_{g_1 \cup g_2 \cup g_3}(g_3 - m_i g_5)}{m_i} = \frac{1 - \psi_{g_1 \cup g_2 \cup g_3}(\bar{0})}{3} = \frac{1}{3}.$$

Thus

$$\frac{1}{3} t_1 + \frac{2}{3} t_2 + t_3 + \frac{1}{3} t_5 \geq 1$$

is a face of $P(G, \eta, g_0)$.

20.3 THE POLYHEDRA $P(G, g_0)$

In the last section, we have shown how to get a face of $P(G, \eta, g_0)$. Now if $(\boldsymbol{\gamma}, \gamma_0)$ is a face of $P(G, \eta, g_0)$, we shall see that $[\boldsymbol{\gamma}, \gamma'_0(h)]$ will be a face of $P(G, \eta, h)$ for an appropriate choice of h and $\gamma'_0(h)$. This means the class of polyhedra $P(G, \eta, g_0)$ with different g_0 will have faces parallel to each other. In terms of the graph $H(G, \eta, \boldsymbol{\gamma})$, we can state it as a theorem.

Lemma 20.3 Let $(\boldsymbol{\gamma}, \gamma_0)$ provide a face of $P(G, \eta, g_0)$, with $\gamma_0 > 0$, i.e., there are n' independent shortest paths from $\bar{0}$ to g_0 in the graph $H(G,\eta,\boldsymbol{\gamma})$. If there is a shortest path from $\bar{0}$ to h passing the node g_0, then there is a constant $\gamma'_0(h)$ such that $[\boldsymbol{\gamma}, \gamma'_0(h)]$ provides a face of $P(G, \eta, h)$.

Proof. By the assumption that $(\boldsymbol{\gamma}, \gamma_0)$ is a face, there are solutions $\mathbf{t}^i$ ($i = 1, \ldots, n'$) which form n' linearly independent shortest paths from $\bar{0}$ to g_0. Let $\mathbf{t}^h$ correspond to the subpath from g_0 to h. Then the solution $\mathbf{t}^i + \mathbf{t}^h$ provides n' shortest paths from $\bar{0}$ to h. Now we want to show that these shortest paths are independent. This is proved by contradiction.

Assume that these solutions are dependent; then we can find coefficient w_i such that $w_i (\mathbf{t}^i + \mathbf{t}^h) = \mathbf{0}$ and $\sum w_i = 1$. Or we can have

$$\boldsymbol{\gamma}[\sum w_i(\mathbf{t}^i + \mathbf{t}^h)] = 0.$$

Since $\sum w_i = 1$ and $\boldsymbol{\gamma}\mathbf{t}^i = \gamma_0$ for all i, we have

$$\boldsymbol{\gamma} \cdot \mathbf{t}^i + \boldsymbol{\gamma}\mathbf{t}^h = 0 \qquad \text{or} \qquad \gamma_0 + \boldsymbol{\gamma}\mathbf{t}^h = 0.$$

But $\gamma_0 > 0$ and $\boldsymbol{\gamma}$ and $\mathbf{t}^h$ are all nonnegative, so this is a contradiction. Thus these solutions $\mathbf{t}^i + \mathbf{t}^h$ are independent and $[\boldsymbol{\gamma}, \gamma'_0(h)]$ is a face of $P(G, \eta, h)$.

Instead of considering the polyhedra $P(G, \eta, g_0)$ with different g_0, let us consider the polyhedra $P(G, \eta, g_0)$ with a fixed g_0 but different possible subsets $\eta \subset G$. It is understood that the subset η does not contain $\bar{0}$. It will be shown that all these polyhedra $P(G, \eta, g_0)$ with different η are intersections of a master polyhedron with appropriate choices of subspaces.

First let us define the polyhedra $P(G, G, g_0)$. This polyhedron is the convex hull of nonnegative integer vectors t satisfying

$$\sum_{g \in G-\bar{0}} g \cdot t(g) = g_0. \tag{1}$$

For $g_0 = \bar{0}$, we define $P(G, G, \bar{0})$ as the convex hull of nonzero, nonnegative integer vectors $\mathbf{t}$ satisfying (1). We shall call the polyhedra $P(G, G, g_0)$, *the master polyhedra*, and for simplicity, we shall denote it by $P(G, g_0)$ from now on.

Let $E(\eta)$ be the n'-dimensional subspace in $(D-1)$-dimensional space in which $t(g) = 0$ for $g \notin \eta$. We can consider $P(G, \eta, g_0)$ as lying in this space. All the solution vectors $\mathbf{t}^i$ are extended by adding components $t(g) = 0$ for all $g \notin \eta$. The following theorem then asserts that all the polyhedra $P(G, \eta, g_0)$ with different η can be obtained by intersecting the master polyhedron $P(G, g_0)$ with $E(\eta)$. In other words, we can obtain any $P(G, \eta, g_0)$ from $P(G, g_0)$ by simply setting some variables to zero.

Theorem 20.5. $P(G, \eta, g_0) = P(G, g_0) \cap E(\eta)$.

Proof. Let $\mathbf{t}$ be any integer vector in $P(G, \eta, g_0)$. Then $\mathbf{t}$ clearly is in $E(\eta)$. Since $\mathbf{t}$ also satisfies (1), $\mathbf{t}$ is also in $P(G, g_0)$. Thus $P(G, \eta, g_0) \subset P(G, g_0) \cap E(\eta)$.

Now consider a point t in $P(G, g_0) \cap E(\eta)$. Since $\mathbf{t} \in P(G, g_0)$, $\mathbf{t}$ can be expressed as a convex combination of integer points $\mathbf{t}^i \in P(G, g_0)$, where all $\mathbf{t}^i$ satisfy (1). Let $\mathbf{t} = \sum \lambda_i \mathbf{t}^i$ with $\lambda_i > 0$. Since $\mathbf{t} \in E(\eta)$, all the components $t(g)$ of $\mathbf{t}$ must be zero for $g \notin \eta$. This means that all $\mathbf{t}^i$ must have components $t^i(g) = 0$ for $g \notin \eta$. In other words all $\mathbf{t}^i$ are in $E(\eta)$. In addition, all $\mathbf{t}^i$ satisfy (1) and hence $\mathbf{t}^i$ satisfies the group equation defining $P(G, \eta, g_0)$ and all $\mathbf{t}^i$ belong to $P(G, \eta, g_0)$. Since $\mathbf{t}$ is a convex combination of points $\mathbf{t}^i$ in $P(G, \eta, g_0)$, $\mathbf{t}$ itself must be in $P(G, \eta, g_0)$. This shows that

$$P(G, g_0) \cap E(\eta) \subset P(G, \eta, g_0)$$

and completes the proof.

From the connection between $P(G, g_0)$ and various $P(G, \eta, g_0)$ as stated in the above theorem, there are also connections between faces and vertices of $P(G, g_0)$ with the faces and vertices of $P(G, \eta, g_0)$. The following theorem summarizes these connections.

Theorem 20.6.

(i) An inequality $(\boldsymbol{\gamma}, \gamma_0)$ is an $(n'-1)$-dimensional face of $P(G, \eta, g_0)$ if and only if there exists an inequality $(\boldsymbol{\gamma}', \gamma_0)$ which is a $(D-1)$-dimensional face of $P(G, g_0)$ with $\gamma'(g) = \gamma(g)$ for all $g \in \eta$.

(ii) Every vertex of $P(G, \eta, g_0)$ is a vertex of $P(G, g_0)$. A vertex $\mathbf{t} = [t(g)]$ of $P(G, g_0)$ is a vertex of $P(G, \eta, g_0)$ if and only if $\mathbf{t} \in E(\eta)$.

Before we give a proof of this theorem, let us see how it can be used to obtain faces and vertices of $P(G, \eta, g_0)$ once the faces and vertices of $P(G, g_0)$ are known. In Table 20.1, we list the faces of $P(G, g_0)$, where G is a cyclic group of order 6 and $g_0 = g_3$. In Table 20.2, we list the faces of $P(G, \eta, g_0)$, $\eta = [g_1, g_2, g_3, g_5]$. Table 20.2 is obtained from Table 20.1 by simply striking out the γ_4 column of Table 20.1. The fourth row of Table 20.2 is omitted because it is already implied by some other inequalities.

We list the vertices of $P(G_6, g_3)$ in Table 20.3 and the vertices of $P(G_6, \{g_1, g_2, g_3, g_5\}, g_3)$ in Table 20.4. Note that there is a vertex of $P(G_6, \eta, g_3)$ corresponding to a vertex of $P(G_6, g_3)$ if and only if the component $t(g_4) = t_4 = 0$ in Table 20.3.

Table 20.1. Faces of $P(G_6, g_3)$

γ_1	γ_2	γ_3	γ_4	γ_5	γ_0
1	0	1	0	1	1
2	1	3	2	1	3
1	2	3	2	1	3
1	2	3	1	2	3
1	0	0	0	0	0
0	1	0	0	0	0
0	0	1	0	0	1
0	0	0	1	0	0
0	0	0	0	1	0

Table 20.2. Faces of $P(G_6, \{g_1, g_2, g_3, g_5\}, g_3)$

γ_1	γ_2	γ_3	γ_5	γ_0
1	0	1	1	1
2	1	3	1	3
1	2	3	1	3
x	x	x	x	x
1	0	0	0	0
0	1	0	0	0
0	0	1	0	1
x	x	x	x	x
0	0	0	1	0

Table 20.3. Vertices of $P(G_6, g_3)$

t_1	t_2	t_3	t_4	t_5
3	0	0	0	0
1	1	0	0	0
0	0	1	0	0
1	0	0	2	0
0	2	0	0	1
0	0	0	1	1
0	0	0	0	3

Table 20.4. Vertices of $P(G_6, \eta, g_3)$

t_1	t_2	t_3	t_5
3	0	0	0
1	1	0	0
0	0	1	0
0	2	0	1
0	0	0	3

Proof of Theorem 20.6.
(i) From Theorem 20.5 we know that $P(G, \eta, g_0) = P(G, g_0) \cap E(\eta)$. Since the effect of intersection with $E(\eta)$ is just to strike out the variables $t(g), g \notin \eta$, and the $P(G, \eta, g_0)$ are determined by the inequalities $\boldsymbol{\gamma}\mathbf{t} \geq \gamma_0$, there must exist the corresponding inequality $\boldsymbol{\gamma}'\mathbf{t} \geq \gamma_0$ for which $\gamma'(g) = \gamma(g)$ for $g \in \eta$.
(ii) It also follows from Theorem 20.5 that if $\mathbf{t}$ is a vertex of $P(G, g_0)$ with $t(g) = 0, g \notin \eta$, then $\mathbf{t}$ is in $E(\eta)$ and it is automatically a vertex of $P(G, \eta, g_0)$. Now if $\mathbf{t}'$ is a vertex of $P(G, \eta, g_0)$ but not a vertex of $P(G, g_0)$, then $\mathbf{t}'$ must be a convex combination of nonnegative points $\mathbf{t}^i$ in $P(G, g_0)$. But all these points $\mathbf{t}^i$ must have $t^i(g) = 0$ for $g \notin \eta$. Otherwise it will contradict that $\mathbf{t}' = \sum \lambda_i \mathbf{t}^i$, $\lambda_i > 0$. This means that $\mathbf{t}^i$ are in $E(\eta)$ as well as in $P(G, g_0)$; or $\mathbf{t}^i$ are in $P(G, \eta, g_0)$, contradicting the assumption that $\mathbf{t}'$ is a vertex of $P(G, \eta, g_0)$.

Because of the importance of $P(G, g_0)$, we shall devote the remainder of this chapter to the study of $P(G, g_0)$.

20.4 AUTOMORPHISMS OF THE MASTER POLYHEDRA

In the study of the master polyhedron $P(G, g_0)$, we shall see that $P(G, g_0)$ is highly structured, we can get one face of $P(G, g_0)$ from another face of $P(G, g_0)$, and similarly with vertices. Also knowledge of $P(G, g_0)$ leads to knowledge about other master polyhedra $P(G, h)$. Just as we have used $H(G, \eta, \boldsymbol{\gamma})$ for the faces of $P(G, \eta, g_0)$, we shall use $H(G, \boldsymbol{\gamma})$ for the faces of $P(G, g_0)$.

First, let us consider the effect of automorphism of the group G.

Theorem 20.7. If $(\boldsymbol{\gamma}, \gamma_0)$ is a face of $P(G, g_0)$ with $\boldsymbol{\gamma} = [\gamma(g)]$, and $\bar{\phi} : G \rightarrow G$ is any automorphism of G, then $(\bar{\boldsymbol{\gamma}}, \gamma_0)$ with $\bar{\boldsymbol{\gamma}} = [\bar{\gamma}(g)] = [\gamma(\bar{\phi}^{-1} g)]$ is a face of $P(G, \bar{\phi}\, g_0)$.

Before we give a proof of this theorem, let us state it in terms of a numerical example.

Let G_4 be a cyclic group of order 4, $g_0 = g_3$, and

$$\bar{\phi} : (\bar{0}, g_1, g_2, g_3) \rightarrow (\bar{0}, g_3, g_2, g_1).$$

If $[\gamma(g_1), \gamma(g_2), \gamma(g_3), \gamma_0]$ is a face of $P(G_4, g_3)$, then $[\gamma(g_3), \gamma(g_2), \gamma(g_1), \gamma_0]$ is a face of $P(G_4, g_1)$.

Proof. We shall think in terms of the graph $H(G, \boldsymbol{\gamma})$ and show that the effect of automorphism of G will carry n' independent shortest paths into n' independent shortest paths. In $H(G, \boldsymbol{\gamma})$, let p^* be a path from $\bar{0}$ to g_0, i.e., a vector $\mathbf{t} = [t(g)]$ such that

$$\sum_{g \in G} t(g) \cdot g = g_0.$$

Applying the automorphism $\bar{\phi}$ to the above equation, we have

$$\sum_{g \in G} t(g)\, \bar{\phi}\,(g) = \bar{\phi}(g_0) = \sum_{g \in G} t(\bar{\phi}^{-1} g) \cdot g.$$

Thus the vector $\bar{\mathbf{t}} = [\bar{t}(g)] = [t(\bar{\phi}^{-1} g)]$ gives a path $\bar{p}^*$ from $\bar{0}$ to $\bar{\phi}^{-1} g_0$. Now if we let $\bar{\gamma}(g) = \gamma(\bar{\phi}^{-1}g)$, then the length of $\bar{p}^*$ in terms of $\bar{\gamma}(g)$ is

$$\sum_{g \in G} \bar{\gamma}(g)\, \bar{t}(g) = \sum_{g \in G} \gamma(\bar{\phi}^{-1} g)\, t(\bar{\phi}^{-1}g) = \sum_{g \in G} \gamma(g)\, t(g) = l(p^*).$$

Thus, under the automorphism $\bar{\phi}$, a path in $H(G,\boldsymbol{\gamma})$ goes to a path in $H(G,\bar{\boldsymbol{\gamma}})$ of equal length. Since $\bar{\phi}^{-1}$ exists, this sets up a one-to-one length-preserving correspondence between paths of $H(G,\boldsymbol{\gamma})$ and paths in $H(G,\bar{\boldsymbol{\gamma}})$. The shortest paths in $H(G,\boldsymbol{\gamma})$ then go to the shortest paths in $H(G,\bar{\boldsymbol{\gamma}})$. The shortest paths in $H(G, \bar{\boldsymbol{\gamma}})$ are independent because $\bar{\mathbf{t}}$ is simply a rearrangement of the component of $\mathbf{t}$ where $\mathbf{t}$ are assumed to be independent. Therefore $(\bar{\boldsymbol{\gamma}},\gamma_0)$ is a face of $P[G, \bar{\phi}(g_0)]$.

Because a polyhedron is completely determined by its faces, this theorem asserts that there is really only one polyhedron $P(G, g_0)$ for each automorphism class in G. If the mapping $\bar{\phi}$ leaves g_0 fixed, then there is a great deal of symmetry of $P(G, g_0)$. If $\bar{\phi}(g_0) = h \neq g_0$, then the polyhedron $P(G, h)$ can be obtained by rearranging the coordinates of $P(G, g_0)$. If G is a cyclic group of prime order, then there exists a $\bar{\phi}$ mapping g_0 onto every nonzero h, so all the various $P(G, h)$ have the same number of faces, vertices, etc. The effect of $\bar{\phi}$ on vertices can be stated in the following automorphism.

Corollary 20.3. If $\mathbf{t} = [t(g)]$ is a vertex of $P(G, g_0)$, then $\bar{\mathbf{t}} = [\bar{t}(g)] = [t(\bar{\phi}^{-1} g)]$ is a vertex of $P[G, \bar{\phi}(g_0)]$.

This is because a vertex is determined by faces, and a face is determined by $D-1$ independent shortest paths, and we have just proved that independent shortest paths will be mapped into independent shortest paths under the automorphism.

Theorem 20.8. Let $\mathbf{t} = [t(g)]$ be a vertex of $P(G, g_0)$. Also let $\mathbf{t}' = [t'(g)]$ with $0 \leq t'(g) \leq t(g)$ for all $g \in G$, and $h = \sum_{g \in G} t'(g) \cdot g$. Then $\mathbf{t}' = [t'(g)]$ is a vertex of $P(G, h.)$

This theorem then gives us vertices of $P(G, h)$ from the knowledge of the vertices of $P(G, g_0)$.

Proof. From Lemma 20.1, if $\mathbf{t}$ is a shortest path from $\bar{0}$ to g_0, then $\mathbf{t}'$ is a shortest path from $\bar{0}$ to h, using $\boldsymbol{\gamma}$ as the lengths associated with the arcs. If $\mathbf{t}$ is a vertex, then there are $D - 1$ independent vectors $\boldsymbol{\gamma}$ for which $\mathbf{t}$ is the minimizing vertex using $\boldsymbol{\gamma}$ as the objective function. For each vector $\boldsymbol{\gamma}$, $\mathbf{t}'$ is a shortest path in $H(G,\gamma)$; thus $\mathbf{t}'$ is a vertex.

Corollary 20.4. Let $\mathbf{t}$ be a vertex of $P(G, g_0)$, and let $\mathbf{t}'$ be a point such that $0 \leq t'(g) \leq t(g)$ for all $g \in G$, and $h = \sum t'(g) \cdot g$. If there is an automorphism $\bar{\phi}$ such that $\bar{\phi}h = g_0$, then $\mathbf{t}' = [t'(g)] = [t(\bar{\phi}^{-1} g)]$ is a vertex of $P(G, g_0)$.

Proof. This follows from Theorem 20.8 and Corollary 20.3.

Using Corollary 20.4 and Theorem 20.8, we can get many vertices of a given $P(G,g_0)$ from the knowledge of one vertex of $P(G, g_0)$. For example, consider the polyhedron $P(G_{11}, g_{10})$. If we know that $t_1 = 3$, $t_7 = 1$, and $t_j = 0\,(j \neq 1,7)$ is a vertex of $P(G_{11}, g_{10})$, then using Theorem 20.8, we get various $\mathbf{t}' \leq \mathbf{t}$ and $h = \sum t'(g) \cdot g$. The following are vertices of various $P(G_{11}, h)$, where h appears in the last column ($2g_1 + g_7 = g_9 = h$, etc.):

t_1	t_7	$t_m\ (m \neq 1, 7)$	h
3	0	0	g_3
2	1	0	g_9
2	0	0	g_2
1	1	0	g_8
1	0	0	g_1
0	1	0	g_7

Using Corollary 20.4, we can find $\bar{\phi}$ which will map h onto g_{10}. For example, in the first row $7 \times h = 7 \times g_3 = g_{21} = g_{10}$. The effect of multiplying 7 is to send g_1 into $\bar{g}_7$; thus $\bar{t}_7 = 3$, $\bar{t}_m = 0\ (m \neq 7)$ is a vertex of (G_{11}, g_{10}). Similarly, in the second row, we have $6 \times h = 6 \times g_9 = g_{10}$. The effect of multiplying 6 is to send g_1 into $\bar{g}_6$ and g_7 into $\bar{g}_9$. Thus $\bar{t}_6 = 2$, $\bar{t}_9 = 1$, $\bar{t}_m = 0$ ($m \neq 6, 9$) is a vertex of (G_{11}, g_{10}). If we continue to multiply the third row by 5, the fourth row by 4, the fifth row by 10, the last row by 3, we would get the following vertices for $P(G_{11}, g_{10})$

$$
\begin{array}{lll}
\bar{t}_7 = 3, & \bar{t}_5 = 0, & \text{all other components } 0,\\
\bar{t}_6 = 2, & \bar{t}_9 = 1, & \text{all other components } 0,\\
\bar{t}_5 = 2, & \bar{t}_2 = 0, & \text{all other components } 0,\\
\bar{t}_4 = 1, & \bar{t}_6 = 1, & \text{all other components } 0,\\
\bar{t}_{10} = 1, & \bar{t}_4 = 0, & \text{all other components } 0,\\
\bar{t}_3 = 0, & \bar{t}_{10} = 1, & \text{all other components } 0.
\end{array}
$$

Theorem 20.9. If $(\boldsymbol{\gamma}, \gamma_0)$ is a face of $P(G, g_0)$, $g_0 \neq \bar{0}$, then
(i) $\gamma(g) + \gamma(g_0 - g) = \gamma_0$ for all $g \in G$.
(ii) $\gamma(g) + \gamma(g') \geq \gamma(g + g')$ for all $g, g' \in G$.
(iii) $\gamma(g_0) = \gamma_0$ for $g_0 \neq \bar{0}$.

Proof.
(i) follows from Corollary 20.2 by taking $\eta = G$. But now (i) implies that the coefficient $\boldsymbol{\gamma}$ of group elements are related in pairwise fashion, since γ_0 is usually normalized to be 1. Knowledge of $\gamma(g)$ immediately gives $\gamma(g_0 - g) = 1 - \gamma(g)$.
(ii) follows from Corollary 20.1 by taking $\eta = G$.
(iii) follows from Theorem 20.4 by taking g to be g_0.

With the aid of Theorem 20.9, we can replace Theorem 20.1 which deals with $P(G, \eta, g_0)$ by the following theorem.

Theorem 20.10. $(\gamma, \gamma_0), \gamma_0 > 0$ is a face of the polyhedron $P(G, g_0), g_0 \neq \bar{0}$, if and only if it is a basic feasible solution to the following system of equations and inequalities:

$$\begin{aligned} &\gamma(g) + \gamma(g_0 - g) = \gamma_0, && g \in G, \quad g \neq g_0, \quad g \neq \bar{0}, \\ &\gamma(g) + \gamma(g') \geq \gamma(g + g'), && g, g' \in G, \quad g, g' \neq \bar{0}, \qquad (1) \\ &\gamma(g) \geq 0, && g \in G, \quad g \neq \bar{0}, \\ &\gamma(g_0) = \gamma_0 && (\text{if } g_0 = \bar{0}, \text{ this condition is dropped}). \end{aligned}$$

In contrast with Theorem 20.1, we can write down the condition (1) explicitly. A computer code has been developed to calculate faces of 36 polyhedra using this theorem. See Appendix D and Gomory [86]. The proof is given in Gomory [86].

20.5 SOME FACES FOR CYCLIC GROUPS

In this section, we shall describe a way to get a family of faces of $P(G, g_0)$, where G is a cyclic group. We shall first consider the case $g_0 \neq \bar{0}$. In terms of the graph $H(G, \gamma)$, we try to get D − 1 independent shortest paths. Assume that $g_0 = g_m$. We shall construct the independent shortest paths as follows. The first shortest path consists of m arcs g_1. The second shortest path consists of the arc g_2 once and $(m - 2)$ arcs g_1. In general, the pth shortest path consists of the arc g_p once followed by $(m - p)$ arcs g_1 if $p \leq m$; the pth shortest path consists of the arcs g_p once followed by $(p - m)$ arcs $g_{(D-1)}$ if $p > m$. Clearly, all these paths $(p = 1, \ldots, D-1)$ are independent. Now we shall assign the coefficients γ in a way such that all these paths will have total length 1 and other paths are longer. Let

$$\gamma(g_p) = \begin{cases} p/m & \text{if } p \leq m, \\ \dfrac{D - p}{D - m} & \text{if } p > m. \end{cases} \qquad (1)$$

Since $g_{D-1} = -g_1$, we can see that any path in the graph $H(G,\gamma)$ can be replaced by a set of g_1 or $-g_1$ without changing the total length of the path. It follows from (1) that these $D-1$ independent paths are shortest paths. Thus, we have a way to produce a face of $P(G, g_0)$ for $g_0 = g_m$ for any m. For example, consider $P(G_7, g_0) = P(G_7, g_6)$. Then according to (1),

$$\frac{1}{6}(t_1 + 2t_2 + 3t_3 + 4t_4 + 5t_5 + 6t_6) \geq 1 \text{ is a face.}$$

Similarly, we can get a face of $P(G_7, g_5)$ by using (1):

$$\frac{1}{5}(t_1 + 2t_2 + 3t_3 + 4t_4 + 5t_5 + 5 \times \frac{7 - 6}{7 - 5} t_6) \geq 1.$$

We shall now list faces of $P(G_7, g_0)$ for all possible g_0:

	$\gamma(g_1)$	$\gamma(g_2)$	$\gamma(g_3)$	$\gamma(g_4)$	$\gamma(g_5)$	$\gamma(g_6)$	γ_0
$P(G_7, g_5)$	2	4	6	8	10	5	10
$P(G_7, g_4)$	3	6	9	12	8	4	12
$P(G_7, g_3)$	4	8	12	9	6	3	12
$P(G_7, g_2)$	5	10	8	6	4	2	10
$P(G_7, g_1)$	6	5	4	3	2	1	6

We can use the above table to get other faces of $P(G_7, g_6)$ by mapping respectively $g_5, g_4, \ldots, g_1$ into g_6. We can map g_5 into g_6 by multiplying by 4. This automorphism ϕ will send g_1 to $\bar{4}$ ($4g_1 = \bar{4}$), g_2 to $\bar{1}$ ($4 \times g_2 = \bar{1}$), etc. Thus we get

$$2\bar{t}_4 + 4\bar{t}_1 + 6\bar{t}_5 + 8\bar{t}_2 + 10\bar{t}_6 + 5\bar{t}_3 \geq 10,$$

or

$$4\bar{t}_1 + 8\bar{t}_2 + 5\bar{t}_3 + 2\bar{t}_4 + 6\bar{t}_5 + 10\bar{t}_6 \geq 10$$

as a face of $P(G_7, g_6)$. Similarly,

$$5 \times g_4 = 20g_1 = 6g_1 = g_6, \text{ and we get}$$

$$9t_1 + 4t_2 + 6t_3 + 8t_4 + 3t_5 + 12t_6 \geq 12$$

as a face of $P(G_7, g_6)$.

Now, let us consider the case of $P(G, \bar{0})$. We want to get $D-1$ independent nontrivial shortest cycles from $\bar{0}$ to 0. This could be done by letting $\gamma(g_p) = p/D$ and construct the $D-1$ shortest cycles just as we did for the shortest paths. Thus

$$\frac{1}{7}(t_1 + 2t_2 + 3t_3 + 4t_4 + 5t_5 + 6t_6) \geq 1 \tag{2}$$

is a face of $P(G_7, g_0) = P(G_7, \bar{0})$.

Since every automorphism will map $\bar{0}$ to $\bar{0}$, every automorphism will send a face of $P(G, \bar{0})$ into another face of $P(G, \bar{0})$. If we consider the automorphism of multiplying by 2, 3, 4, 5, and 6, we get from (2) the following faces of $P(G_7, \bar{0})$:

$$4t_1 + t_2 + 5t_3 + 2t_4 + 6t_5 + 3t_6 \geq 7,$$

$$5t_1 + 3t_2 + t_3 + 6t_4 + 4t_5 + 2t_6 \geq 7,$$

$$2t_1 + 4t_2 + 6t_3 + t_4 + 3t_5 + 5t_6 \geq 7,$$

$$3t_1 + 6t_2 + 2t_3 + 5t_4 + t_5 + 4t_6 \geq 7,$$

$$6t_1 + 5t_2 + 4t_3 + 3t_4 + 2t_5 + t_6 \geq 7.$$

20.6 LIFTING UP FACES

In this section, we shall describe a way to get a face of $P(G, g_0)$ from a known face of $P(\bar{H}, h_0)$ where the mapping from G to $\bar{H}$ is a homomorphism. The exact condition is given in Theorem 20.11.

Theorem 20.11. Let ψ' be a homomorphism of G onto $\bar{H}$ with kernel K and with $g_0 \notin K$. If $(\boldsymbol{\gamma}', \gamma_0)$ is a face of $P(\bar{H}, \psi' g_0)$, then $(\boldsymbol{\gamma}, \gamma_0)$ is a face of $P(G, g_0)$ when $\gamma(g)$ is set to be $\gamma'(\psi' g)$. [We take $\gamma'(\bar{0}) = 0$, so that $\gamma(g) = 0$ for all $g \in K$.]

We shall not give a proof here; the interested reader is referred to Gomory [86]. We shall illustrate this theorem by two examples. Assume that we know $t_1 \geq 1$ is a face of $P(G_2, \bar{1})$; in other words, $(\gamma'(\bar{0}), \gamma'(\bar{1}); \gamma_0) = (0, 1; 1)$ is a face of $P(G_2, \bar{1})$. Consider now the homomorphism ψ' of mapping G_6 to G_2 by taking $\{\bar{0}, g_2, g_4\}$ to be the kernel K. Now since $\psi' g_5 = 1$, we get a face of $P(G_6, g_5)$

$$t_1 + 0 \cdot t_2 + 1 \cdot t_3 + 0 \cdot t_4 + 1 \cdot t_5 \geq 1.$$

Similarly, we can consider the homomorphism ψ' of mapping G_6 to G_3 by taking $\{\bar{0}, g_3\}$ as the kernel. If $\gamma(\bar{1}) = 1, \gamma(\bar{2}) = 2, \gamma_0 = 2$ is a face of $P(G_3, \bar{2})$, then

$$t_1 + 2t_2 + 0 \cdot t_3 + t_4 + 2t_5 \geq 2$$

is a face of $P(G_6, g_5)$ since $\psi' g_5 = \bar{2}$.

Theorem 20.11 has a converse as follows.

Theorem 20.12. Let $(\boldsymbol{\gamma}, \gamma_0)$ be a nontrivial face of $P(G, g_0)$. If $\gamma(g) = 0$ for some $g \neq \bar{0} \in G$, then there exists a group $\bar{H}$, homomorphism ψ', and face $(\boldsymbol{\gamma}', \gamma_0)$ of $P(\bar{H}, h_0)$ such that $H = \psi G$, and $\gamma(g) = \gamma'(\psi' g)$ $(h_0 = \psi' g_0)$.

The proof of this theorem and the proof of the next theorem are given in Gomory [86].

Before we state the next theorem, we shall introduce the term "special face" of $P(\bar{H}, \bar{0})$, where $\bar{H}$ is a cyclic group. By a special face, we mean either the face

$$\gamma(h_p) = \frac{p}{|\bar{H}|}, \qquad \gamma_0 = 1,$$

or one of the faces obtained from it by an automorphism. In Theorem 20.11 and Theorem 20.12, we deal with the case that $g_0 \notin K$. The next theorem gives a face of $P(G, g_0)$, where $g_0 \in K$, the kernel.

Theorem 20.13. Let $(\boldsymbol{\gamma}_1, 1)$ be a face of $P(\bar{H}, g_0)$ and $(\boldsymbol{\gamma}_2, 1)$ be a special face of $P(\bar{H}, \bar{0})$, where $\bar{H}$ is a cyclic group of order greater than two. If ψ' is a homomorphism mapping G onto $\bar{H}$, where $g_0 \in K$, the kernel, then the

Table 20.5

	$n_1 = 0$	$n_1 = 1$	$n_1 = 2$
$n_2 = 0$	0	1/3	2/3
$n_2 = 1$	1/2	1/3	2/3
$n_2 = 2$	1	1/3	2/3

inequality $(\boldsymbol{\gamma}, 1)$ defined by

$$\gamma(g) = \gamma_1(g), \qquad g \in K,$$

$$\gamma(g) = \gamma_2(\psi' g), \qquad g \notin K,$$

is a face of $P(G, g_0)$.

For example, consider the group consisting of pairs of integers $[n_1, n_2]$ added modular [3, 3] and let $g_0 = [0, 2]$. Then the group is $G_{3,3}$ and the mapping $\psi' : [n_1, n_2] \longrightarrow [n_1, 0]$ is a homomorphism. The kernel K is the subgroup of elements of the form $[0, n_2]$. From Appendix D, we know that $(1/2, 1; 1)$ is a face of $P(G_3, \bar{2})$ and $(1/3, 2/3; 1)$ is a special face of $P(G_3, \bar{0})$. Then we know that $\gamma[n_1, n_2]$ as given by Table 20.5 will form a face of $P(G_{3,3}, [0, 2])$.

20.7 CHARACTERS AND INCQUALITIES

In the previous sections, we have methods for producing some faces of $P(G, g_0)$ without using Theorem 20.1. If we want to use these methods to generate inequalities or cutting planes for the fractional integer algorithm, then we have to perform the following steps.

1. Use the simplex method to find the optimum basis $\mathbf{B}$ for the associated linear program. Assume the coefficient matrix $\mathbf{A} = [\mathbf{B}, \mathbf{N}]$. Then the simplex computation would transform the matrix $\mathbf{A}$ into $[\mathbf{I}, \mathbf{B}^{-1}\mathbf{N}]$.
2. Find the quotient group $\{\mathbf{I}\}/\{\mathbf{B}\}$ or $\{\mathbf{B}^{-1}\mathbf{N}\}/\{\mathbf{I}\}$ for the basis $\mathbf{B}$ in step 1 and see which group element corresponds to which nonbasic column $\mathbf{a}_j$ and to the right-hand side $\mathbf{b}$.
3. Create a face of $P(G, g_0)$ and then delete the variables corresponding to group elements not in η. This is then a face of $P(G, \eta, g_0)$ or a cutting plane for our problem.

In steps 2 and 3, we need to know about the group G, while in the fractional integer programming algorithm [79], we produce cutting planes immediately after step 1 without examining the group structure. In this section, we shall show how to produce cutting planes without knowing which nonbasic column corresponds to which group element. First let us exhibit the relations between different groups:

$$\begin{array}{ccc} \{\mathbf{B}, \mathbf{N}\} & \xrightarrow{\mathbf{B}^{-1}} & \{\mathbf{I}, \mathbf{B}^{-1}\mathbf{N}\} \\ \downarrow k_1 & & \downarrow k_2 \\ \{\mathbf{B}, \mathbf{N}\}/\{\mathbf{B}\} & \xrightarrow{\bar{\mathbf{B}}^{-1}} & \{\mathbf{I}, \mathbf{B}^{-1}\mathbf{N}\}/\{\mathbf{I}\} \end{array} \tag{1}$$

where $\mathbf{B}^{-1}$ sends $\{\mathbf{B}, \mathbf{N}\}$ onto $\{\mathbf{I}, \mathbf{B}^{-1}\mathbf{N}\}$, k_1 maps $\{\mathbf{B}, \mathbf{N}\}$ onto the quotient group $\{\mathbf{B}, \mathbf{N}\}/\{\mathbf{B}\}$, k_2 maps $\{\mathbf{I}, \mathbf{B}^{-1}\mathbf{N}\}$ onto the quotient group $\{\mathbf{I}, \mathbf{B}^{-1}\mathbf{N}\}/\{\mathbf{I}\}$. It is easy to see that $\{\mathbf{B}, \mathbf{N}\}/\{\mathbf{B}\}$ and $\{\mathbf{I}, \mathbf{B}^{-1}\mathbf{N}\}/\{\mathbf{I}\}$ are isomorphic. The isomorphism between the two quotient groups is denoted by $\bar{\mathbf{B}}^{-1}$. It should be emphasized here that the correspondence between a group element g and a nonbasic column $\mathbf{a}_j$ is determined by the fractional parts of $\mathbf{B}^{-1}\,\mathbf{a}_j$ alone. The order of the group G is equal to $|\det \mathbf{B}|$, which equals the product of the successive pivots.

Now we introduce the term "character of a group" or a "group character." A character of a group is a mapping ξ such that $\xi(g_1 + g_2) = \xi(g_1) + \xi(g_2)$, $(\xi_1 + \xi_2)(g) = \xi_1(g) + \xi_2(g)$. Usually, we think of the character of a group as the mapping which maps the group elements into the unit circle in the complex plane so that

$$\xi(g_1) = e^{i\theta_1}, \qquad \xi(g_2) = e^{i\theta_2}, \qquad \xi(g_1 + g_2) = e^{i(\theta_1+\theta_2)},$$

and so forth. Thus a group of order D is mapped into the Dth roots of unity in the complex plane. It is clear that the character itself forms a group called the character group, and the character group is isomorphic to the original group G. In our case, we shall deal with the additive group of the fractions n/D (mod 1, n integers) or the additive group of integers n (mod D). Thus we shall think of the character of a group G as the mapping which maps G into n/D (mod 1) or into integers n (mod D).

We define $\phi(n/D)$, where n is any integer, as the group element $g_p \in G_D$, where $n/D = p/D$ (mod 1), and G_D is the cyclic group of order D. In Chapter 19, we have shown that any entry of $\mathbf{B}^{-1}$ is of the form n/D, where n is an integer. It follows immediately that any integer combination of the entries of $\mathbf{B}^{-1}$ is also of the form n/D. Consider the scalar product of row $\mathbf{r}_i$ (of $\mathbf{B}^{-1}$) with an integer column vector $\mathbf{c}$. The scalar $(\mathbf{r}_i \cdot \mathbf{c})$ is of the form n/D, and we can map it into g_p, where $n/D = p/D$ (mod 1). For a fixed $\mathbf{r}_i$, we can consider this as mapping an integer column $\mathbf{c}$ into a group element $g \in G$.

Now we define the function $\xi_i(g)$, $g \in G$, by

$$\xi_i(g) = \phi(\mathbf{r}_i \cdot \mathbf{c}) \qquad \text{where} \qquad k_1\mathbf{c} \longrightarrow g. \tag{2}$$

This means that for any column vector $\mathbf{c}$ which is mapped into g by k_1 of (1), the function $\xi_i(g)$ is given by (2). First we have to justify the notation $\xi_i(g)$ and show that $\xi_i(g)$ is a function of g and $\xi_i(g)$ is independent of the particular choice of the column vector $\mathbf{c}$. Let $\mathbf{c}$ and $\mathbf{c}'$ be two column vectors such that $k_1\mathbf{c} = k_1\mathbf{c}' = g$. Then we have $k_1(\mathbf{c} - \mathbf{c}') = \bar{0} \in G$ and $k_2\mathbf{B}^{-1}(\mathbf{c} - \mathbf{c}') = \bar{0} \in \{\mathbf{I}, \mathbf{B}^{-1}\mathbf{N}\}/\{\mathbf{I}\}$. This implies that $\mathbf{B}^{-1}(\mathbf{c} - \mathbf{c}')$ must be an all-integer vector or $\mathbf{r}_i(\mathbf{c} - \mathbf{c}') \equiv 0 \pmod 1$. Hence $\phi(\mathbf{r}_i \cdot \mathbf{c}) = \phi(\mathbf{r}_i \cdot \mathbf{c}')$ for any $\mathbf{c}'$ with $k_1\mathbf{c}' = g$. It can be verified that $\xi_i(g_1 + g_2) = \xi_i(g_1) + \xi_i(g_2)$ and that ξ_i is a group character.

Once we have verified that ξ_i is a character, then an integer combination of ξ_i, $\xi = \sum_{i=1}^{m} n_i\xi_i$ is also a group character. It is easy to see that the columns of $\mathbf{B}^{-1}$ added modular 1 generate the group G, while the fractional part of the rows of $\mathbf{B}^{-1}$ used to define ξ_i generate the isomorphic character group.

Let us consider how to produce cutting planes for a given problem from the faces of $P(\bar{H}, g_0)$, where $\bar{H}$ is a cyclic group of order $D = |\det \mathbf{B}|$. For a given integer program, there is an optimum basis $\mathbf{B}$ of the associated linear program. This $\mathbf{B}$ then determines G. If ξ is a character which maps G into $n/D \pmod 1$, which is a cyclic group $\bar{H}$ of order D, then we can get cutting planes for our integer program from the faces of $P(\bar{H}, h_0)$. Let $(\boldsymbol{\gamma}, \gamma_0)$ be a face of $P(\bar{H}, h_0)$, where $\bar{H}$ is a cyclic group of order D. For a fixed character ξ of G, define

$$\gamma_\xi(g) = \gamma[\xi(g)].$$

If $t(g)$ gives a path in $H(G, \gamma_\xi)$ from $\bar{0}$ to g_0, i.e.,

$$\sum_{g \in G} g \cdot t(g) = g_0,$$

then

$$\sum_{g \in G} \xi(g) \cdot t(g) = \xi(g_0).$$

In other words, the mapping ξ maps a path in $H(G, \boldsymbol{\gamma}_\xi)$ to a path $H(\bar{H}, \boldsymbol{\gamma})$. The length of the two paths are the same, namely,

$$\sum_{g \in G} \gamma[\xi(g)] \cdot t(g).$$

By assumption $(\boldsymbol{\gamma}, \gamma_0)$ is a face of $P(\bar{H}, h_0)$. Thus the components $\boldsymbol{\gamma}$ satisfy the inequality $\gamma(h_1) + \gamma(h_2) \geq \gamma(h_1 + h_2)$, or

$$\sum_{g \in G} \gamma[\xi(g)]t(g) \geq \gamma[\xi(g_0)]. \tag{3}$$

Then (3) is an inequality that must be satisfied by any $t(g)$ in $P(G, g_0)$. Hence (3) can be used as a cutting plane. By varying the character ξ, we can produce $D - 1$ inequalities from each face of $P(\bar{H}, h_0)$. Note that we do not assume $\xi(g_0) = h_0$ in (3).

As a special case of this approach, we consider a special face of $P(\bar{H}, h_{D-1})$ with the components $\gamma(h_s) = s/D$ and $\gamma_0 = (D - 1)/D$. Then the family of inequalities obtained is exactly the family of cutting planes produced in the fractional integer algorithm. In general, these inequalities are not faces of $P(G, \eta, g_0)$ although they can be faces.

Consider the numerical example (30) in Section 19.2. The problem can be written in matrix form as

$$\begin{bmatrix} 1 & -2 & -1 & -1 & -3 & -1 & 0 & 0 \\ 0 & 0 & 2 & 1 & 4 & 2 & 1 & 0 \\ 0 & 3 & -4 & 4 & 1 & -1 & 0 & 1 \end{bmatrix} \begin{bmatrix} z \\ x_1 \\ x_2 \\ x_3 \\ x_4 \\ x_5 \\ x_6 \\ x_7 \end{bmatrix} = \begin{bmatrix} 0 \\ 41 \\ 47 \end{bmatrix}. \tag{4}$$

The optimum basis consists of the first three columns, and we have

$$\begin{bmatrix} 1 & 0 & 0 & 21/6 & 5 & 2 & 11/6 & 4/6 \\ 0 & 1 & 0 & 2 & 3 & 1 & 4/6 & 2/6 \\ 0 & 0 & 1 & 3/6 & 2 & 1 & 3/6 & 0 \end{bmatrix} \begin{bmatrix} z \\ x_1 \\ x_2 \\ x_3 \\ x_4 \\ x_5 \\ x_6 \\ x_7 \end{bmatrix} = \begin{bmatrix} 106\frac{3}{6} \\ 43 \\ 20\frac{3}{6} \end{bmatrix} \tag{5}$$

The optimum basis has a determinant equal to 6.

Each row **r** of (5) gives a character which maps G into the cyclic group of order 6. These characters ξ_1, ξ_2, and ξ_3 using only the fractional parts of entries of (5) are listed below with the common denominator 6 omitted.

	z	x_1	x_2	x_3	x_4	x_5	x_6	x_7	R.H.S.
ξ_1	0	0	0	3	0	0	5	4	3
ξ_2	0	0	0	0	0	0	4	2	0
ξ_3	0	0	0	3	0	0	3	0	3

(6)

Since the right-hand side consists of $\bar{3}$, $\bar{0}$, $\bar{3}$, we look in Appendix D for faces of $P(G_6, \bar{3})$ (or use 20.4 20.5). The faces are given below:

	γ_1	γ_2	γ_3	γ_4	γ_5	γ_0
Face 1	1	0	1	0	1	1
Face 2	2	1	3	2	1	3
Face 3	1	2	3	2	1	3
Face 4	1	2	3	1	2	3

(7)

From the first row of (6), we know that x_3 corresponds to γ_3, x_6 corresponds to γ_5, and x_7 corresponds to γ_4 Thus ξ_1 gives the inequalities [from faces of (7)],

$$\begin{aligned} &\text{From face 1:} \quad && 1x_3 + 1x_6 + 0x_7 \geq 1, \\ &\text{From face 2:} \quad && 3x_3 + 1x_6 + 2x_7 \geq 3, \\ &\text{From face 3:} \quad && 3x_3 + 1x_6 + 2x_7 \geq 3, \\ &\text{From face 4:} \quad && 3x_3 + 2x_6 + 1x_7 \geq 3. \end{aligned} \tag{8}$$

The character ξ_2 will not produce any inequalities, since the right-hand side is $\bar{0}$. From ξ_3, we see that x_3 corresponds to γ_3 and x_6 also corresponds to γ_3. Thus from (7) we have inequalities

$$\begin{aligned} 1x_3 + 1x_6 &\geq 1, \\ 3x_3 + 3x_6 &\geq 3, \\ 3x_3 + 3x_6 &\geq 3, \\ 3x_3 + 3x_6 &\geq 3. \end{aligned} \tag{9}$$

Note that in the process of obtaining inequalities, we do not need to know which group element corresponds to which nonbasic column. We use ξ_i directly. Eliminating the duplicate inequalities from (8) and (9), we have

$$\begin{aligned} 3x_3 + 3x_6 &\geq 3, \\ 3x_3 + x_6 + 2x_7 &\geq 3, \\ 3x_3 + 2x_6 + x_7 &\geq 3. \end{aligned} \tag{10}$$

If we had used the fractional integer algorithm, we would have produced the following set of inequalities which is weaker than (10):

$$\begin{aligned} 3x_3 + 5x_6 + 4x_7 &\geq 3, \\ 3x_3 + 3x_6 &\geq 3. \end{aligned}$$

Appendix A
SMITH'S NORMAL FORM (Hu[112])

In this appendix, we consider the problem of transforming an all-integer square matrix into Smith's normal form, that is,

$$\begin{bmatrix} \epsilon_1 & & & \bigcirc \\ & \epsilon_2 & & \\ & & \ddots & \\ \bigcirc & & & \epsilon_m \end{bmatrix},$$

where

$$\epsilon_i/\epsilon_{i+1} \qquad (i = 1, \ldots, m-1, \text{ i.e., } \epsilon_i \text{ divides } \epsilon_{i+1}).$$

For our purpose, we consider the problem of putting a matrix into Smith's normal form as a problem of choosing a new set of basic vectors and unit vectors. (Since all calculations are modular D, we shall assume that all elements of the matrix are between 0 and $D-1$.)

Let $\mathbf{b}_1, \mathbf{b}_2, \ldots, \mathbf{b}_m$ be a set of basic vectors in R^m, where

$$\mathbf{b}_j = [b_{1j}, b_{2j}, \ldots, b_{mj}].$$

Then

$$\mathbf{b}_j = \sum_{i=1}^{m} b_{ij}\mathbf{e}_i,$$

where $\mathbf{e}_i$ is the column vector with the ith component being one and other components zero. We then select a new set of basic vectors $\mathbf{b}'_1, \mathbf{b}'_2, \ldots, \mathbf{b}'_m$ and a new set of unit vectors $\mathbf{e}'_i$ such that

$$\mathbf{b}'_j = \epsilon_{(j)}\mathbf{e}'_{(j)} \qquad \text{for} \quad j = 1, \ldots, m,$$

that is, each $\mathbf{b}'_j$ is a scalar multiple of $\mathbf{e}'_j$ in the new coordinate system:

$$\mathbf{b}'_1 = \begin{bmatrix} \epsilon_1 \\ 0 \\ 0 \\ \vdots \\ 0 \end{bmatrix}, \qquad \mathbf{b}'_2 = \begin{bmatrix} 0 \\ \epsilon_2 \\ 0 \\ \vdots \\ 0 \end{bmatrix}, \qquad \ldots, \qquad \mathbf{b}'_m = \begin{bmatrix} 0 \\ 0 \\ \vdots \\ 0 \\ \epsilon_m \end{bmatrix}.$$

Furthermore ϵ_i divides ϵ_{i+1} for $i = 1, \ldots, m-1$.

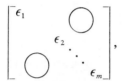

Given the matrix $[b_{ij}]$, the desired transformation is achieved by: (1) interchanging columns or rows; (2) adding (or subtracting) one column to (or from) another column, or one row to (or from) another row. The column operations represent the integer combination of the old basis vectors $\mathbf{b}_j$ to form a new basis $\mathbf{b}'_j$, and the row operations represent the integer combination of $\mathbf{e}_j^T$ to form new unit vectors $\mathbf{e}_j'^T$.

We shall first describe the standard procedure for transforming an all-integer square matrix into Smith's normal form.

STEP 1. Interchange columns and rows such that b_{11} is the element of smallest absolute value among all nonzero elements in the matrix. Go to step 2.

STEP 2. If b_{11} divides into b_{1j} for $j = 2, \ldots, m$, go to step 3. If b_{11} does not divide into b_{1j} for some $j = k$, let

$$b_{1k} = nb_{11} + q,$$

where n is an integer and $0 < q < b_{11}$.

Let $\mathbf{b}'_k = \mathbf{b}_k - n\mathbf{b}_1$ and $\mathbf{b}'_j = \mathbf{b}_j$ for $j \neq k$. This operation is carried out in the matrix by substracting n times column 1 from column k. The result is $b'_{1k} = q$, where $q < b_{11}$. Go to step 1.

STEP 3. If b_{11} divides into b_{i1} for $i = 2, \ldots, m$, go to step 4. If b_{11} does not divide into b_{i1} for some $i = k$, let

$$b_{k1} = nb_{11} + q,$$

where n is an integer and $0 < q < b_{11}$.

Let $\mathbf{e}'_1 = \mathbf{e}_1 + n\mathbf{e}_k$ and $\mathbf{e}'_i = \mathbf{e}_i$ for $i \neq 1$. This operation is carried out in the matrix by subtracting n times row 1 from row k. To see this, we consider a column vector $\mathbf{b}_j$,

$$\mathbf{b}_j = b_{1j}\mathbf{e}_1 + b_{2j}\mathbf{e}_2 + \cdots + b_{kj}\mathbf{e}_k + \cdots + b_{mj}\mathbf{e}_m,$$

or

$$\mathbf{b}_j = b_{1j}(\mathbf{e}'_1 - n\mathbf{e}'_k) + b_{2j}\mathbf{e}'_2 + \cdots + b_{kj}\mathbf{e}'_k + \cdots + b_{mj}\mathbf{e}'_m,$$

or

$$\mathbf{b}_j = b_{1j}\mathbf{e}'_1 + b_{2j}\mathbf{e}'_2 + \cdots + (b_{kj} - nb_{1j})\mathbf{e}'_k + \cdots + b_{mj}\mathbf{e}'_m.$$

Go to step 1.

STEP 4. Since now we have a positive b_{11} that divides b_{1j} ($j = 2, \ldots, m$) and also b_{i1} ($i = 2, \ldots, m$), assume that $b_{1j} = n_j b_{11}$ and $b_{i1} = n_i b_{11}$. Let $\mathbf{b}'_j = \mathbf{b}_j - n_j\mathbf{b}_1$, $\mathbf{b}'_1 = \mathbf{b}_1$, and

$$\mathbf{e}'_1 = \mathbf{e}_1 + n_2\mathbf{e}_2 + n_3\mathbf{e}_3 + \cdots + n_m\mathbf{e}_m, \qquad \mathbf{e}'_i = \mathbf{e}_i \quad (i \neq 1).$$

This transformation will give a new matrix of the form shown in Table A. Go to step 5.

STEP 5. If b_{11} divides into b_{ij} ($i \neq 1, j \neq 1$), apply steps 1 through 4 to the $(m - 1) \times (m - 1)$ matrix in Table A. If b_{11} does not divide b_{ij}, then let

Table A

b_{11}	0	0	...	0
0	b_{22}	b_{23}	...	b_{2m}
0	b_{32}			
⋮	⋮			
0	b_{m2}	...	...	b_{mm}

$b_{ij} = nb_{11} + q$, where $0 < q < b_{11}$; then the following sequence of operations will bring q into the (1,1) position. We shall illustrate the sequence of operations by means of a 2×2 matrix.

$$\begin{pmatrix} b_{11} & 0 \\ 0 & nb_{11}+q \end{pmatrix} \quad \begin{pmatrix} b_{11} & 0 \\ nb_{11} & nb_{11}+q \end{pmatrix} \quad \begin{pmatrix} b_{11} & -b_{11} \\ nb_{11} & q \end{pmatrix} \quad \begin{pmatrix} q & nb_{11} \\ -b_{11} & b_{11} \end{pmatrix}$$
$$\text{(i)} \qquad\qquad \text{(ii)} \qquad\qquad \text{(iii)} \qquad\qquad \text{(iv)}$$

The result is that we have a new $b_{11} = q$ of smaller value and we can go back to Step 1.

Since the largest integer in the matrix is $D-1$, after at most $\log_2 D$ loops of steps 1 through 5, b_{11} will divide b_{ij} $(i \neq 1, j \neq 1)$ or b_{11} will be reduced to one. Let us calculate the upper bound on the number of operations required in this procedure. We shall use the following symbols to represent the corresponding operations:

$\bar{s}$: comparison of two numbers,
$\bar{c}$: checking divisibility,
$\bar{t}$: subtracting a multiple of one number from another number,
$\bar{p}$: interchanging the positions of two numbers.

Then for a matrix of size m, we need $m^2\bar{s} + 2m\bar{p}$ in step 1, $m(\bar{c} + \bar{t} + \bar{p})$ in step 2, $m(\bar{c} + \bar{t} + \bar{p})$ in step 3, $2m(m-1)\bar{t}$ in step 4, and $(m-1)^2\bar{c} + 2m(\bar{t} + \bar{p})$ in step 5.

Since the largest integer in the matrix is $D-1$, after at most $\log_2 D$ loops of step 1 and step 5, we will create a matrix in which b_{11} divides b_{ij} $(i, j \neq 1)$ and b_{11} is the only nonzero element in the first row and the first column. Thus to reduce a matrix to Smith's normal form, we need at most

$$\log_2 D\left\{\frac{m(m+1)(2m+1)\bar{s}}{6} + 3m(m+1)\bar{p} + \left[\frac{m(m-1)(2m-1)}{6} + m(m+1)\right]\bar{c} + \left[\frac{m(m+1)(2m+1)}{3} + m(m+1)\right]\bar{t}\right\}. \tag{1}$$

If we consider m to be large and count only the leading terms, we have

$$\log_2 D\{m^3\bar{s}/3 + 3m^2\bar{p} + m^3\bar{c}/3 + 2m^3\bar{t}/3\}.$$

If the group $\{\mathbf{B}^{-1}\}/\{\mathbf{I}\}$ is of rank r, then after r diagonal elements are created, the remaining $(m - r) \times (m - r)$ matrix elements will all be zero. This is the case if we try to put $\mathbf{B}^{-1}$ into Smith's normal form. (We use the numerators of the entries of $\mathbf{B}^{-1}$.)

If we consider r to be small comparable to m, then we have

$$\log_2 D\{m^2 r\,\bar{s} + 6mr\,\bar{p} + m^2 r\,\bar{c} + 2m^2\bar{t}\}. \tag{2}$$

Now we shall propose a new procedure for transforming a matrix into Smith's normal form. The procedure is very much like the standard procedure except that we diagonalize the matrix first and then check to see whether b_{ii} divides $b_{i+1,\,i+1}$. The procedure consists of the following steps.

STEP 1. Interchange columns and rows so that b_{11} is the element of smallest absolute value among all nonzero elements in the first row and first column of the matrix. Go to step 2.

STEP 2. Same as the standard procedure.

STEP 3. Same as the standard procedure.

STEP 4. Same as the standard procedure.

STEP 5. Repeat steps 1 through 4 until the matrix becomes a diagonal matrix; then go to step 6.

STEP 6. If b_{11} divides into b_{ii} $(i = 2, \ldots, m)$, then we check to see whether b_{22} divides b_{jj} $(j = 3, \ldots, m)$, ... This process is repeated until b_{ii} divides $b_{i+1,\,i+1}$ $(i = 1, \ldots, m - 1)$. If b_{11} does not divide b_{ii}, then we apply step 5 of the standard procedure to create a new b_{11} of smaller value. Because the matrix was diagonalized, we are dealing with a 2×2 matrix

$$\begin{bmatrix} b_{11} & 0 \\ 0 & nb_{11} + q \end{bmatrix}.$$

If we apply steps 2 through 4 of the standard procedure to this 2×2 matrix, either we will have a diagonalized matrix with b_{11} dividing b_{ii}, or we will have an element smaller than q occupying the (1, 1) position. Thus after at most $\log_2 D[m\bar{c} + 4(\bar{t} + \bar{p})]$ operations, we will have a b_{11} that divides

$$b_{ii}\ (i = 2, \ldots, m).$$

Counting the number of operations, we have

$$2m\bar{s} + 2m\bar{p} \text{ in step 1,}$$

$$m(\bar{c} + \bar{t} + \bar{p}) \text{ in step 2,}$$

$$m(\bar{c} + \bar{t} + \bar{p}) \text{ in step 3,}$$

$$2m(m - 1)\bar{t} \text{ in step 4.}$$

After m loops of steps 1 through 4, the matrix is diagonalized. Including the operations in step 6, we have

$$m(m+1)\bar{s} + [2m(m+1) + 4m\log_2 D]\bar{p} + \left[m(m+1) + \frac{1}{2}m(m+1)\log_2 D\right]\bar{c} + \left[\frac{m(m+1)(2m+1)}{3} + 4m\log_2 D\right]\bar{t}. \quad (3)$$

If we consider m to be large and count only the leading terms, we have

$$m^2\bar{s} + [2m^2 + 4m\log_2 D]\bar{p} + \left[m^2 + \frac{1}{2}m^2\log_2 D\right]\bar{c} + [2m^3/3 + 4m\log_2 D]\bar{t}. \quad (4)$$

If we apply our procedure to $\{\mathbf{B}^{-1}\}/\{\mathbf{I}\}$ and the group is of rank r ($m/r \gg 1$), then the total number of operations is

$$2mr\,\bar{s} + (4mr + 4r\log_2 D)\bar{p} + (2mr + mr\log_2 D)\,\bar{c} + (2m^2r + 4r\log_2 D)\bar{t}. \quad (5)$$

Example. Let

$$\mathbf{b}_1 = \begin{bmatrix}2\\7\end{bmatrix}, \quad \mathbf{b}_2 = \begin{bmatrix}4\\9\end{bmatrix}, \quad \mathbf{e}_1 = \begin{bmatrix}1\\0\end{bmatrix}, \quad \mathbf{e}_2 = \begin{bmatrix}0\\1\end{bmatrix}.$$

Then we have:

$$\begin{pmatrix}2 & 4\\7 & 9\end{pmatrix}$$

$\downarrow$ $\quad \mathbf{e}_1' = \mathbf{e}_1 + 3\mathbf{e}_2,$ $\mathbf{e}_2' = \mathbf{e}_2;$

$$\begin{pmatrix}2 & 4\\1 & -3\end{pmatrix}$$

$\downarrow$ $\quad \mathbf{e}_1'' = \mathbf{e}_2' = \mathbf{e}_2,$ $\mathbf{e}_2'' = \mathbf{e}_1' = \mathbf{e}_1 + 3\mathbf{e}_2;$

$$\begin{pmatrix}1 & -3\\2 & 4\end{pmatrix}$$

$\downarrow$ $\quad \mathbf{b}_1' = \mathbf{b}_1,$ $\mathbf{b}_2' = \mathbf{b}_2 + 3\mathbf{b}_1;$

$$\begin{pmatrix}1 & 0\\2 & 10\end{pmatrix}$$

$\downarrow$ $\quad \mathbf{e}_1''' = \mathbf{e}_1'' + 2\mathbf{e}_2'' = 2\mathbf{e}_1 + 7\mathbf{e}_2,$ $\mathbf{e}_2''' = \mathbf{e}_2'' = \mathbf{e}_1 + 3\mathbf{e}_2.$

$$\begin{pmatrix}1 & 0\\0 & 10\end{pmatrix}$$

$\mathbf{b}_1' = \mathbf{e}_1''',$

$\mathbf{b}_2' = 10\mathbf{e}_2'''.$

Appendix B
AN ALTERNATE PROOF OF DUALITY

The proof of duality theorem in Chapter 3 is based on Theorem 1.2 or its equivalent form, the theorem of the separating hyperplane. The proof of Theorem 1.2 is purely algebraic but long. If we are interested just in the duality theorem itself, we can use the following proof which is not based on Theorem 1.2 (the proof follows the work of Dreyfus and Freimer, pp. 340–347 of Dreyfus [50]).

Consider a pair of linear programs

$$\min z = \mathbf{cx}$$

subject to (1)

$$\mathbf{Ax} \geq \mathbf{b}, \qquad \mathbf{x} \geq \mathbf{0},$$

and

$$\max w = \mathbf{yb}$$

subject to (2)

$$\mathbf{yA} \leq \mathbf{c}, \qquad \mathbf{y} \geq \mathbf{0}.$$

It is easy to see that any pair of feasible solutions $\mathbf{x}$ and $\mathbf{y}$ of (1) and (2) will satisfy

$$z = \mathbf{cx} \geq (\mathbf{yA})\mathbf{x} = \mathbf{y}(\mathbf{Ax}) \geq \mathbf{yb} = w. \tag{3}$$

Now we want to show that for optimum solutions $\mathbf{x}^*$ and $\mathbf{y}^*$, we have

$$z^* = \mathbf{cx}^* = \mathbf{y}^*\mathbf{Ax}^* = \mathbf{y}^*\mathbf{b} = w^*. \tag{4}$$

First, we consider the objective function z in (1) as a function of the right-hand side and we shall use $z^*(\mathbf{b})$ to denote the optimum value of the objective function when the right-hand side is $\mathbf{b}$. Then by definition we have

$$z^*(\mathbf{b}) = \mathbf{cx}^*. \tag{5}$$

If we increase any component b_i of $\mathbf{b}$ in (1), then the optimum value $z^*(\mathbf{b})$ will certainly not decrease. This implies

$$\frac{\partial z^*}{\partial b_i} \geq 0 \qquad \text{for all } i. \tag{6}$$

Assume that the i_0th inequality of (1) is satisfied as a strict inequality for the optimum solution $\mathbf{x}^*$, i.e.,

$$a_{i_0 j} x_j^* > b_{i_0}.$$

Then if b_{i_0} is increased by ϵ, the i_0th inequality can still be satisfied, or the optimum value $z^*(\mathbf{b})$ will not be affected. This fact implies

$$\frac{\partial z^*}{\partial b_i} = 0 \qquad \text{for } a_{ij} x_j^* > b_i. \tag{7}$$

Now consider the following linear program which is slightly different from (1):

$$\min z = \mathbf{cx}$$

subject to (8)

$$\mathbf{Ax} \geq \mathbf{b} + \epsilon \mathbf{a}_j, \qquad \mathbf{x} \geq \mathbf{0}.$$

We can get a feasible solution to (8) by changing the optimum solution of (1) slightly, i.e., we can use $\mathbf{x}^* + \epsilon \mathbf{e}_j$ as a feasible solution to (8). This can be checked easily:

$$\mathbf{A}(\mathbf{x}^* + \epsilon \mathbf{e}_j) = \mathbf{Ax}^* + \epsilon \mathbf{a}_j \geq \mathbf{b} + \epsilon \mathbf{a}_j.$$

As $\mathbf{x}^* + \epsilon \mathbf{e}_j$ is a feasible solution to (8), $\mathbf{c}(\mathbf{x}^* + \epsilon \mathbf{e}_j)$ must be greater than or equal to the optimum value of (8). In other words,

$$z^*(\mathbf{b} + \epsilon \mathbf{a}_j) \leq \mathbf{c}(\mathbf{x}^* + \epsilon \mathbf{e}_j) = \mathbf{cx}^* + \epsilon \mathbf{ce}_j = z^*(\mathbf{b}) + \epsilon c_j.$$

Expanding both sides in powers of ϵ, we have (assume $\mathbf{x}^* = \mathbf{B}^{-1}\, \mathbf{b} > \mathbf{0}$),

$$z^*(\mathbf{b}) + \epsilon \sum_{i=1}^{m} \frac{\partial z^*}{\partial b_i} a_{ij} \leq z^*(\mathbf{b}) + \epsilon c_j. \tag{9}$$

If $\epsilon > 0$, (9) implies

$$\sum_{i=1}^{m} \frac{\partial z^*}{\partial b_i} a_{ij} \leq c_j. \tag{10}$$

If $x_j^* > 0$, then we can choose $\epsilon < 0$ and such that $x_j^* + \epsilon \geq 0$, i.e., $\mathbf{x}^* + \epsilon \mathbf{e}_j$ remains a feasible solution to (8). For $\epsilon < 0$, (9) implies

$$\sum_{i=1}^{m} \frac{\partial z^*}{\partial b_i} a_{ij} \geq c_j, \tag{11}$$

and (10) and (11) show that

$$\sum_{i=1}^{m} \frac{\partial z^*}{\partial b_i} a_{ij} = c_j \qquad \text{if } x_j^* > 0. \tag{12}$$

Denoting $\partial z^* / \partial b_i$ by y_i^*, we shall see that $\mathbf{y}^*$ is the optimum solution to (2) and (4) holds. From (6) we see that y_i^* is nonnegative, and from (10) we see that $\mathbf{y}^*$ satisfies the constraints of (2). To prove (4), we consider two possible cases. If a particular component x_j^* is strictly positive, then (12) holds and $c_j = y_i^* a_{ij}$. If a particular x_j^* is zero, then

$$c_{(j)} x_{(j)}^* = (y_i^* a_{i(j)})\, x_{(j)}^* = 0.$$

Thus, in both cases,

$$\mathbf{cx}^* = \mathbf{y}^* \mathbf{Ax}^*, \tag{13}$$

and we have proved the first part of the equality (4).

To prove the second part of the equality (4), we note that $a_{ij} x_j^* = b_i$ for a particular i implies equality in (4). On the other hand, if $a_{ij} x_j^* > b_i$, then (7) holds and

$$\frac{\partial z^*}{\partial b_i} = y_i^* = 0.$$

So in both cases

$$\mathbf{y}^* \mathbf{Ax}^* = \mathbf{y}^* \mathbf{b} = w. \tag{14}$$

Then (13) and (14) imply (4), and we have proved the duality theorem.

Throughout the proof, we have assumed that the function $z^*(\mathbf{b})$ is differentiable. In proving (9), we have assumed that $\mathbf{x}^* = \mathbf{B}^{-1}\mathbf{b} > \mathbf{0}$ so that $z^*(\mathbf{b} + \epsilon\, \mathbf{a}_j)$ is a linear function of $\mathbf{b} + \epsilon\, \mathbf{a}_j$, otherwise there are higher order terms of ϵ.

Appendix C
TREE SEARCH TYPE ALGORITHMS

The integer algorithms described in Chapters 13 through 17 are all classified as cutting plane type, since they all generate additional constraints or cutting planes. In this appendix we shall discuss an entirely different approach, which may be called the *tree search* method. The tree search type of algorithm consists of algorithm like the branch and bound method (Land and Doig [139], Little et al. [144]), the additive algorithm (Balas [4], Beale and Small [14]), the direct search algorithm (Lemke and Spielberg [143]), and many others. A survey of these methods and additional references can be found in Balinski [6] and Lemke and Spielberg [143]. The common features of the tree search type of algorithm are (a) they are easy to understand, (b) they are easy to program on a computer, (c) the upper bound on the number of steps needed in the algorithm is of the order $O(k^n)$, where n is the number of variables, and (d) they lack mathematical structure. Features (a) and (b) are certainly two great advantages of this type of algorithm. Feature (c) is a handicap since it implies exponential growth of the amount of computation as the problem becomes larger. (It must be emphasized here that no upper bound on the number of steps needed in the cutting plane type has been established.) We have concentrated on the cutting plane type algorithms because they give better insight into the problem (see Chapters 18, 19, and 20.) Knowing the structure of a problem, a person is more likely to develop more efficient algorithms. It is known empirically that, for small problems, the tree search type needs less computing time than the cutting plane type, but the growth of the computing time is more rapid in the tree search type. Here we give a brief description of the tree search type. The reader interested in the tree search type of algorithm should have no trouble in reading the original papers in the journals.

Consider a pure integer program

$$\min z = \mathbf{cy} \qquad \text{subject to} \qquad \mathbf{Ay} \geq \mathbf{b}, \qquad \mathbf{y} \geq \mathbf{0}, \text{ integers.} \tag{1}$$

If each component of $\mathbf{y}$ is bounded from above by an integer M, then there are $(M + 1)^n$ possible solutions $\mathbf{y}$. We could test each of these solutions for feasibility and select the feasible solution with the minimum value of the objective function as the optimum solution. Since the number $(M + 1)^n$

is usually very large, the tree search algorithm tries to avoid inspection of solutions which are dominated by solutions already inspected.

First we shall describe the branch and bound method. We first solve (1) as a linear program. If all variables $y_j \geq 0$ and all are integers, then $\mathbf{y}$ is clearly the optimum solution to the integer program, since the integer constraints were ignored in obtaining the solution. If a particular component $y_k = [y_k] + f_k$, where $0 < f_k < 1$, then we solve two linear programs, one with the additional constraint $y_k = [y_k]$ and one with the additional constraint $y_k = [y_k] + 1$. If one of the two linear programs, say the one with $y_k = [y_k]$, still does not give integer solutions, i.e., $y_l = [y_l] + f_l$, then two more linear programs are solved, one with $y_k = [y_k], y_l = [y_l]$, and one with $y_k = [y_k], y_l = [y_l] + 1$ as the additional constraints.

All solutions obtained in this way can be partially ordered as a tree with the root of the tree representing the linear program solution obtained without any additional integer constraints. When a solution $\mathbf{y}^0$ does not satisfy the integer constraints, it branches into two other solutions $\mathbf{y}^1$ and $\mathbf{y}^2$. The solution $\mathbf{y}^0$ is called the *predecessor* of $\mathbf{y}^1$ and $\mathbf{y}^2$, and $\mathbf{y}^1$ and $\mathbf{y}^2$ are called the *successors* of $\mathbf{y}^0$.

If the successors of $\mathbf{y}^1$ and $\mathbf{y}^2$ are all infeasible, then we have to branch from $\mathbf{y}^0$ again with $y_l = [y_l] - 1$ and $y_l = [y_l] + 2$. A node may have more than two successors. For example, a node with y_l noninteger may have many successors corresponding to $y_l = [y_l], y_l = [y_l] - 1, \ldots, y_l = [y_l] + 1, y_l = [y_l] + 2, \ldots$, etc. A node is called a terminal node if it has no successors; this definition implies that a terminal node represents a feasible integer solution or an infeasible integer solution. The idea of the branch and bound method lies in the following two facts.

1. Because the predecessor has fewer constraints than the successors and additional constraints cannot improve the value of the objective function, the optimum value of a successor is always larger than or equal to the optimum value of the predecessor.

2. If two *integer feasible solutions* have the same predecessor, one with $y_l = [y_l] + 1$ and one with $y_l = [y_l] + 2$, then the optimum value of the first solution is less than the optimum value of the second. This is to say, the further away the value of y_l is from the linear programming solution, the worse is the resulting value of the objective function.

During the computation of the branch and bound method, we keep the optimum value z^* of the best integer feasible solution obtained so far. If a node with a noninteger solution has an optimum value greater than z^*, then all the successors of that node must have optimum values greater than z^*. Hence, there is no sense in branching from that node. The advantage of the branch and bound method is that it can be used for mixed integer problems.

The additive algorithm is used to solve a zero-one integer program:

$$\min z = c_j x_j \qquad (j = 1, \ldots, n) \tag{2}$$

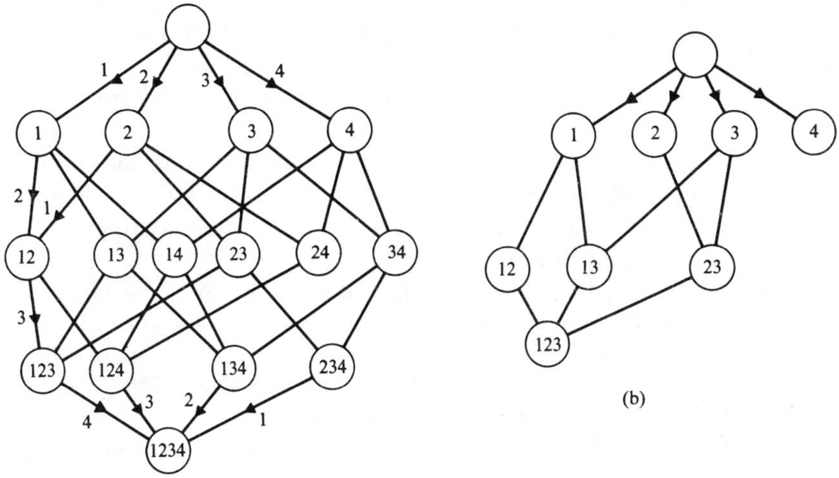

(a)

(b)

Fig. C-1

subject to

$$a_{ij}x_j \geq b_i \qquad (i = 1, \ldots, m), \tag{3}$$

$$1 \geq x_j \geq 0, \text{ integers.} \tag{4}$$

A set of x_j with $x_j = 1, j \in N_1$ and $x_j = 0, j \in N - N_1$ is called a *solution*. A solution is called a *feasible solution* if it also satisfies (3). Without loss of generality, we assume that $0 \leq c_1 \leq c_2 \leq \cdots \leq c_n$. (If some $c_j < 0$, we can substititute $x_j' = 1 - x_j$.) The approach used here can be called *implicit enumeration,* since we systematically enumerate all the possible solutions. A feasible solution is said to be *dominated* by another feasible solution if the latter has a smaller value for the objective function. For convenience, we shall use ∞ as the value of the objective function for all infeasible solutions. Thus an infeasible solution is always dominated by any feasible solution. If we test all the solutions systematically for feasibility, some of the solutions that have not been tested may be dominated by the current best feasible solutions. In this case, we do not have to test them all.

For a zero-one integer program with n variables there are 2^n solutions. We shall partition the 2^n solutions into $n + 1$ subsets. The kth subset $(k = 0, 1, \ldots, n)$ contains all solutions, with k variables being 1 and $n - k$ variables being 0. Thus the 0th subset contains one solution $x_j = 0$ $(j = 1, \ldots, n)$. The first subset contains $\binom{n}{1}$ solutions, $x_1 = 1, x_j = 0\ (j \neq 1)$; $x_2 = 1, x_j = 0\ (j \neq 2)$; $\ldots$). In general, the kth subset has $\binom{n}{k}$ solutions. We shall order all the 2^n solutions in a diagram as shown in Fig C.1(a) for $n = 4$.

Each node in Fig. C.1(a) represents a solution. Inside each node there are indices indicating the solution with $x_j = 1$ for these indices and $x_j = 0$ otherwise. For example, a node with 1,3 inside it represents the solution $x_1 = x_3 = 1, x_2 = x_4 = 0$. An index i is also associated with every arc. This index indicates the variable $x_i = 1$ for the node where the arc terminates, and $x_i = 0$ for the node where the arc starts. Values of all other variables are the same as for the two nodes connected by an arc. We can reach a node from the highest node by many different chains corresponding to the different ways we may assign $x_j = 1$. If there exists a chain from a node N_i to N_j, then N_i is said to be a predecessor of the node N_j and N_j is said to be a successor of N_i. All the nodes are the successors of the highest node. All the nodes are the predecessors of the lowest node. All the solutions are partially ordered by predecessor-successor relationships.

In testing the feasibility of solutions, we do not use any linear programming techniques. We simply substitute the solutions into the constraint (3) directly. We start with the highest node ($x_j = 0, j = 1, \ldots, n$) and then try the immediate successor to the highest node. A node is said to be a terminating node if we do not test any of its successors.

The following are four rules that can be used to reduce the amount of testing:

RULE 1. Since $0 \leq c_1 \leq c_2 \leq \cdots \leq c_n$, the value of the objective function $\mathbf{cx}$ of a solution is always larger than its predecessor. Thus if a node is feasible, there is no need to test all its successors. In Fig. C.1(b) we assume that $x_1 = x_2 = x_3 = 0$, and $x_4 = 1$ is a feasible solution. This fact immediately excludes seven solutions from testing.

RULE 2. Assume that z^* is the minimal value of all feasible solutions obtained so far. Let z_Q be the value of a node N_Q with $x_j = 1, j \in Q$ and $x_j = 0, j \in N - Q$. If $z_Q + c_k > z^*$, then we can pay attention only to the successors of the node N_Q which have $x_k = x_{k+1} = \cdots = x_n = 0$, since $c_k \leq c_{k+1} \leq \cdots \leq c_n$. Any other successor of N_Q will be dominated by the feasible solution with z^*.

RULE 3. Consider a node N_Q with $x_j = 1, j \in Q$, and $x_j = 0, j \in N - Q$. All the successors of N_Q must have $x_j = 1, j \in Q$. These variables $x_j, j \in Q$ are said to be fixed for the successors of N_Q; all other variables are said to be free variables as they may take either the value zero or one. If we find that N_Q is infeasible, it is possible that there are not enough free variables left to satisfy a given constraint. For example, assume that a given constraint is $-x_1 - x_2 + x_3 + x_4 \geq 1$, and N_Q has $x_1 = x_2 = 1$. In this case, even with $x_3 = x_4 = 1$, the constraint is still not satisfied. When this happens, there is no need to test the successors of N_Q.

RULE 4. When a subset of variables is fixed, then a given constraint may force some other variables to be fixed also. For example, let a constraint be $3x_1 - x_2 - 2x_3 = 0$. Let a node have associated with it $x_1 = 1, x_2 = \cdots = x_n = 0$. All the successors of this node must have $x_2 = x_3 = 1$. Thus there is no need to test the node $x_1 = x_2 = 1, x_3 = 0, x_4 = ?, \ldots$.

Appendix D
FACES, VERTICES, AND INCIDENCE MATRICES OF POLYHEDRA

$P(\mathscr{B}_2, (0))$

FACES

Row	γ_1	γ_0
1	1	2

VERTICES

1. $(t_1) = (2)$

INCIDENCE MATRIX

Face	1
Vertex	
1.	1

$P(\mathscr{B}_2, (1))$

FACES

Row	γ_1	γ_0
1	1	1

VERTICES

1. $(t_1) = (1)$

INCIDENCE MATRIX

Face	1
Vertex	
1.	1

$P(\mathcal{B}_3, (0))$

FACES

	γ_1	γ_2	γ_0
Row			
1	2	1	3
2	1	2	3

VERTICES

1. (t_1) = (3)
2. (t_1, t_2) = (1,1)
3. (t_2) = (3)

INCIDENCE MATRIX

Face / Vertex	1	2	3	4
1.	0	1	0	1
2.	1	1	0	0
3.	1	0	1	0

$P(\mathcal{B}_3, (2))$

FACES

	γ_1	γ_2^*	γ_0
Row			
1	1	2	2

VERTICES

1. (t_1) = (2)
2. (t_2) = (1)

INCIDENCE MATRIX

Face / Vertex	1	2	3
1.	1	0	1
2.	1	1	0

$P(\mathcal{G}_4, (0))$

FACES

	γ_1	γ_2	γ_3	γ_0
Row				
1	3	2	1	4
2	1	2	3	4

VERTICES

1. (t_1) = (4)
2. (t_2) = (2)
3. (t_1, t_3) = (1,1)
4. (t_3) = (4)

INCIDENCE MATRIX

Face / Vertex	1	2	3	4	5
1.	0	1	0	1	1
2.	1	1	1	0	1
3.	1	1	0	1	0
4.	1	0	1	1	0

$P(\mathcal{G}_4, (2))$

FACES

	γ_1	γ_2^*	γ_3	γ_0
Row				
1	1	2	1	2

VERTICES

1. $(t_1) = (2)$
2. $(t_2) = (1)$
3. $(t_3) = (2)$

INCIDENCE MATRIX

Face	1	2	3	4
Vertex				
1.	1	0	1	1
2.	1	1	0	1
3.	1	1	1	0

$P(\mathcal{G}_{2,2}, (0, 0))$

FACES

	$\gamma_{1,0}$	$\gamma_{0,1}$	$\gamma_{1,1}$	γ_0
Row				
1	1	1	1	2

VERTICES

1. $(t_{1,0}) = (2)$
2. $(t_{0,1}) = (2)$
3. $(t_{1,1}) = (2)$

INCIDENCE MATRIX

Face	1	2	3	4
Vertex				
1.	1	0	1	1
2.	1	1	0	1
3.	1	1	1	0

$P(\mathcal{G}_4, (3))$

FACES

	γ_1	γ_2	γ_3^*	γ_0
Row				
1	1	0	1	1
2	1	2	3	3

VERTICES

1. $(t_1) = (3)$
2. $(t_1, t_2) = (1, 1)$
3. $(t_3) = (1)$

INCIDENCE MATRIX

Face	1	2	3	4	5
Vertex					
1.	0	1	0	1	1
2.	1	1	0	0	1
3.	1	1	1	1	0

$P(\mathcal{G}_{2,2}, (1, 0))$

FACES

	$\gamma_{1,0}$	$\gamma_{0,1}$	$\gamma_{1,1}$	γ_0
Row				
1	1	1	0	1
2	1	0	1	1

VERTICES

1. $(t_{1,0}) = (1)$
2. $(t_{0,1}, t_{1,1}) = (1, 1)$

INCIDENCE MATRIX

Face	1	2	3	4	5
Vertex					
1.	1	1	0	1	1
2.	1	1	1	0	0

$P(\mathcal{G}_5, (0))$

FACES

	γ_1	γ_2	γ_3	γ_4	γ_0
Row					
1	4	3	2	1	5
2	3	1	4	2	5
3	2	4	1	3	5
4	1	2	3	4	5

VERTICES

1. (t_1) = (5)
2. (t_1, t_2) = (1, 2)
3. (t_2) = (5)
4. (t_1, t_3) = (2, 1)
5. (t_2, t_3) = (1, 1)
6. (t_3) = (5)
7. (t_1, t_4) = (1, 1)
8. (t_3, t_4) = (2, 1)
9. (t_2, t_4) = (1, 2)
10. (t_4) = (5)

INCIDENCE MATRIX $P(\mathcal{G}_5, (0))$

Face	1	2	3	4	5	6	7	8
Vertex								
1.	0	0	0	1	0	1	1	1
2.	0	1	0	1	0	0	1	1
3.	0	1	0	0	1	0	1	1
4.	0	0	1	1	0	1	0	1
5.	1	1	1	1	1	0	0	1
6.	0	0	1	0	1	1	0	1
7.	1	1	1	1	0	1	1	0
8.	1	0	1	0	1	1	0	0
9.	1	1	0	0	1	0	1	0
10.	1	0	0	0	1	1	1	0

$P(\mathcal{G}_5, (4))$

FACES

	γ_1	γ_2	γ_3	γ_4^*	γ_0
Row					
1	1	2	3	4	4
2	4	3	2	6	6

VERTICES

1. (t_1) = (4)
2. (t_2) = (2)
3. (t_1, t_3) = (1, 1)
4. (t_3) = (3)
5. (t_4) = (1)

INCIDENCE MATRIX $P(\mathcal{G}_5, (4))$

Face	1	2	3	4	5	6
Vertex						
1.	1	0	0	1	1	1
2.	1	1	1	0	1	1
3.	1	1	0	1	0	1
4.	0	1	1	1	0	1
5.	1	1	1	1	1	0

$P(\mathcal{G}_6, (0))$

FACES

Row	γ_1	γ_2	γ_3	γ_4	γ_5	γ_0
1	5	4	3	2	1	6
2	4	2	3	4	2	6
3	2	4	3	2	4	6
4	1	2	3	4	5	6

VERTICES

1. $(t_1) = (6)$
2. $(t_2) = (3)$
3. $(t_3) = (2)$
4. $(t_1, t_4) = (2,1)$
5. $(t_2, t_4) = (1,1)$
6. $(t_4) = (3)$
7. $(t_1, t_5) = (1,1)$
8. $(t_2, t_5) = (1,2)$
9. $(t_5) = (6)$

INCIDENCE MATRIX $P(\mathcal{G}_6, (0))$

Vertex \ Face	1	2	3	4	5	6	7	8	9
1.	0	0	0	1	0	1	1	1	1
2.	0	1	0	1	1	0	1	1	1
3.	1	1	1	1	1	1	0	1	1
4.	0	0	1	1	0	1	1	0	1
5.	1	1	1	1	1	0	1	0	1
6.	1	0	1	0	1	1	1	0	1
7.	1	1	1	1	0	1	1	1	0
8.	1	1	0	0	1	0	1	1	0
9.	1	0	0	0	1	1	1	1	0

$P(\mathcal{G}_6, (3))$

FACES

Row	γ_1	γ_2	γ_3^*	γ_4	γ_5	γ_0
1	1	0	1	0	1	1
2	2	1	3	2	1	3
3	1	2	3	2	1	3
4	1	2	3	1	2	3

VERTICES

1. $(t_1) = (3)$
2. $(t_1, t_2) = (1,1)$
3. $(t_3) = (1)$
4. $(t_1, t_4) = (1,2)$
5. $(t_2, t_5) = (2,1)$
6. $(t_4, t_5) = (1,1)$
7. $(t_5) = (3)$

INCIDENCE MATRIX $P(\mathcal{G}_6, (3))$

Vertex \ Face	1	2	3	4	5	6	7	8	9
1.	0	0	1	1	0	1	1	1	1
2.	1	1	1	1	0	0	1	1	1
3.	1	1	1	1	1	1	0	1	1
4.	1	0	0	1	0	1	1	0	1
5.	1	1	0	0	1	0	1	1	0
6.	1	1	1	1	1	1	1	0	0
7.	0	1	1	0	1	1	1	1	0

$P(\mathcal{G}_6, (4))$

FACES

	γ_1	γ_2	γ_3	γ_4^*	γ_5	γ_0
Row						
1	2	1	0	2	1	2
2	1	2	3	4	2	4

VERTICES

1. $(t_1) = (4)$
2. $(t_2) = (2)$
3. $(t_1, t_3) = (1,1)$
4. $(t_4) = (1)$
5. $(t_5) = (2)$

INCIDENCE MATRIX $P(\mathcal{G}_6, (4))$

Face	1	2	3	4	5	6	7
Vertex							
1.	0	1	0	1	1	1	1
2.	1	1	1	0	1	1	1
3.	1	1	0	1	0	1	1
4.	1	1	1	1	1	0	1
5.	1	1	1	1	1	1	0

$P(\mathcal{G}_6, (5))$

FACES

	γ_1	γ_2	γ_3	γ_4	γ_5^*	γ_0
Row						
1	1	0	1	0	1	1
2	1	2	0	1	2	2
3	1	2	3	4	5	5

VERTICES

1. $(t_1) = (5)$
2. $(t_1, t_2) = (1, 2)$
3. $(t_1, t_3) = (2, 1)$
4. $(t_2, t_3) = (1, 1)$
5. $(t_1, t_4) = (1, 1)$
6. $(t_3, t_4) = (1, 2)$
7. $(t_5) = (1)$

INCIDENCE MATRIX $P(\mathcal{G}_6, (5))$

Face	1	2	3	4	5	6	7	8
Vertex								
1.	0	0	1	0	1	1	1	1
2.	1	0	1	0	0	1	1	1
3.	0	1	1	0	1	0	1	1
4.	1	1	1	1	0	0	1	1
5.	1	1	1	0	1	1	0	1
6.	1	1	0	1	1	0	0	1
7.	1	1	1	1	1	1	1	0

$P(\mathcal{G}_7, (0))$

FACES

Row	Y_1	Y_2	Y_3	Y_4	Y_5	Y_6	Y_0
1	6	5	4	3	2	1	7
2	5	3	1	6	4	2	7
3	4	1	5	2	6	3	7
4	3	6	2	5	1	4	7
5	2	4	6	1	3	5	7
6	1	2	3	4	5	6	7

VERTICES

1	(t_1)	=	(7)	13.	(t_2, t_5)	=	(1,1)
2.	(t_1, t_2)	=	(1,3)	14.	(t_3, t_5)	=	(3,1)
3.	(t_2)	=	(7)	15.	(t_4, t_5)	=	(1,2)
4.	(t_2, t_3)	=	(2,1)	16.	(t_5)	=	(7)
5.	(t_1, t_3)	=	(1,2)	17.	(t_1, t_6)	=	(1,1)
6.	(t_3)	=	(7)	18.	(t_4, t_6)	=	(2,1)
7.	(t_1, t_4)	=	(3,1)	19.	(t_3, t_5, t_6)	=	(1,1,1)
8.	(t_1, t_2, t_4)	=	(1,1,1)	20.	(t_5, t_6)	=	(3,1)
9.	(t_3, t_4)	=	(1,1)	21.	(t_2, t_6)	=	(1,2)
10.	(t_2, t_4)	=	(1,3)	22.	(t_3, t_6)	=	(1,3)
11.	(t_4)	=	(7)	23.	(t_6)	=	(7)
12.	(t_1, t_5)	=	(2,1)				

INCIDENCE MATRIX

$P(\mathcal{G}_7, (0))$

Face / Vertex	1	2	3	4	5	6	7	8	9	10	11	12
1.	0	0	0	0	0	1	0	1	1	1	1	1
2.	0	0	1	0	0	1	0	0	1	1	1	1
3.	0	0	1	0	0	0	1	0	1	1	1	1
4.	0	1	1	0	0	1	1	0	0	1	1	1
5.	0	1	0	1	0	1	0	1	0	1	1	1
6.	0	1	0	0	0	0	1	1	0	1	1	1
7.	0	0	0	0	1	1	0	1	1	0	1	1
8.	0	0	1	0	1	1	0	0	1	0	1	1
9.	1	1	1	1	1	1	1	1	0	0	1	1
10.	0	0	1	0	1	0	1	0	1	0	1	1
11.	0	0	0	0	1	0	1	1	1	0	1	1
12.	0	0	0	1	1	1	0	1	1	1	0	1
13.	1	1	1	1	1	1	1	0	1	1	0	1
14.	0	1	0	1	0	0	1	1	0	1	0	1
15.	1	0	0	1	1	0	1	1	1	0	0	1
16.	0	0	0	1	0	0	1	1	1	1	0	1
17.	1	1	1	1	1	1	0	1	1	1	1	0
18.	1	0	1	0	1	0	1	1	1	0	1	0
19.	1	1	0	1	0	0	1	1	0	1	0	0
20.	1	0	0	1	0	0	1	1	1	1	0	0
21.	1	1	1	0	0	0	1	0	1	1	1	0
22.	1	1	0	0	0	0	1	1	0	1	1	0
23.	1	0	0	0	0	0	1	1	1	1	1	0

$P(\mathcal{G}_7, (6))$

FACES

	γ_1	γ_2	γ_3	γ_4	γ_5	γ_6^*	γ_0
Row							
1	1	2	3	4	5	6	6
2	6	5	4	3	2	8	8
3	4	8	5	2	6	10	10
4	9	4	6	8	3	12	12

VERTICES

1. (t_1) = (6)
2. (t_2) = (3)
3. (t_3) = (2)
4. (t_1, t_4) = (2,1)
5. (t_2, t_4) = (1,1)
6. (t_4) = (5)
7. (t_1, t_5) = (1,1)
8. (t_4, t_5) = (2,1)
9. (t_5) = (4)
10. (t_6) = (1)

INCIDENCE MATRIX $P(\mathcal{G}_7, (6))$

Face	1	2	3	4	5	6	7	8	9	10
Vertex										
1.	1	0	0	0	0	1	1	1	1	1
2.	1	0	0	1	1	0	1	1	1	1
3.	1	1	1	1	1	1	0	1	1	1
4.	1	0	1	0	0	1	1	0	1	1
5.	1	1	1	1	1	0	1	0	1	1
6.	0	0	1	0	1	1	1	0	1	1
7.	1	1	1	1	0	1	1	1	0	1
8.	0	1	1	0	1	1	1	0	0	1
9.	0	1	0	1	1	1	1	1	0	1
10.	1	1	1	1	1	1	1	1	1	0

$P(\mathcal{G}_8, (0))$

FACES

Row	γ_1	γ_2	γ_3	γ_4	γ_5	γ_6	γ_7	γ_0
1	3	2	1	2	3	2	1	4
2	1	2	3	2	1	2	3	4
3	7	6	5	4	3	2	1	8
4	5	2	3	4	5	6	3	8
5	3	6	5	4	3	2	5	8
6	3	6	1	4	7	2	5	8
7	5	2	7	4	1	6	3	8
8	1	2	3	4	5	6	7	8

VERTICES

1.	(t_1)	=	(8)	12.	(t_1, t_6)	=	(2,1)
2.	(t_2)	=	(4)	13.	(t_2, t_6)	=	(1,1)
3.	(t_1, t_3)	=	(2,2)	14.	(t_5, t_6)	=	(2,1)
4.	(t_2, t_3)	=	(1,2)	15.	(t_6)	=	(4)
5.	(t_3)	=	(8)	16.	(t_1, t_7)	=	(1,1)
6.	(t_4)	=	(2)	17.	(t_3, t_7)	=	(3,1)
7.	(t_1, t_5)	=	(3,1)	18.	(t_3, t_6, t_7)	=	(1,1,1)
8.	(t_1, t_2, t_5)	=	(1,1,1)	19.	(t_2, t_7)	=	(1,2)
9.	(t_3, t_5)	=	(1,1)	20.	(t_5, t_7)	=	(2,2)
10.	(t_1, t_5)	=	(1,3)	21.	(t_3, t_7)	=	(1,3)
11.	(t_5)	=	(8)	22.	(t_7)	=	(8)

INCIDENCE MATRIX

$P(\mathcal{G}_8, (0))$

Face / Vertex	1	2	3	4	5	6	7	8	9	10	11	12	13	14	15
1.	0	0	0	0	0	0	0	1	0	1	1	1	1	1	1
2.	0	0	0	1	0	0	1	1	1	0	1	1	1	1	1
3.	0	0	0	0	0	1	0	1	0	1	0	1	1	1	1
4.	1	0	0	1	0	1	0	1	1	0	0	1	1	1	1
5.	0	0	0	0	0	1	0	0	1	1	0	1	1	1	1
6.	1	1	1	1	1	1	1	1	1	1	1	0	1	1	1
7.	0	1	0	0	0	0	0	1	0	1	1	1	0	1	1
8.	0	1	0	0	0	0	1	1	0	0	1	1	0	1	1
9.	1	1	1	1	1	1	1	1	1	1	0	1	0	1	1
10.	0	1	0	0	0	0	1	0	0	1	1	1	0	1	1
11.	0	0	0	0	0	0	1	0	1	1	1	1	0	1	1
12.	0	1	0	0	1	1	0	1	0	1	1	1	1	0	1
13.	1	1	1	1	1	1	1	1	1	0	1	1	1	0	1
14.	0	1	1	0	1	0	1	0	1	1	1	1	0	0	1
15.	0	0	1	0	1	1	0	0	1	1	1	1	1	0	1
16.	1	1	1	1	1	1	1	1	0	1	1	1	1	1	0
17.	1	0	0	0	0	1	0	0	1	1	0	1	1	1	0
18.	1	0	1	0	0	1	0	0	1	1	0	1	1	0	0
19.	1	0	1	1	0	0	1	0	1	0	1	1	1	1	0
20.	0	0	1	0	0	0	1	0	1	1	1	1	0	1	0
21.	1	0	1	0	0	0	0	0	1	1	0	1	1	1	0
22.	0	0	1	0	0	0	0	0	1	1	1	1	1	1	0

$P(\mathcal{G}_8, (4))$

FACES

Row	γ_1	γ_2	γ_3	γ_4^*	γ_5	γ_6	γ_7	γ_0
1	1	2	3	4	1	2	3	4
2	1	2	3	4	3	2	1	4
3	3	2	1	4	3	2	1	4
4	3	2	1	4	1	2	3	4

VERTICES

1. $(t_1) = (4)$
2. $(t_2) = (2)$
3. $(t_1, t_3) = (1,1)$
4. $(t_3) = (4)$
5. $(t_4) = (1)$
6. $(t_5) = (4)$
7. $(t_6) = (2)$
8. $(t_5, t_7) = (1,1)$
9. $(t_7) = (4)$

INCIDENCE MATRIX $P(\mathcal{G}_8, (4))$

Face / Vertex	1	2	3	4	5	6	7	8	9	10	11
1.	1	1	0	0	0	1	1	1	1	1	1
2.	1	1	1	1	1	0	1	1	1	1	1
3.	1	1	1	1	0	1	0	1	1	1	1
4.	0	0	1	1	1	1	0	1	1	1	1
5.	1	1	1	1	1	1	1	0	1	1	1
6.	1	0	0	1	1	1	1	1	0	1	1
7.	1	1	1	1	1	1	1	1	1	0	1
8.	1	1	1	1	1	1	1	1	0	1	0
9.	0	1	1	0	1	1	1	1	1	1	0

$P(\mathcal{G}_8, (6))$

FACES

	γ_1	γ_2	γ_3	γ_4	γ_5	γ_6^*	γ_7	γ_0
Row								
1	1	2	1	0	1	2	1	2
2	5	2	3	4	1	6	3	6
3	1	2	3	4	5	6	3	6

VERTICES

1. (t_1) = (6)
2. (t_2) = (3)
3. (t_3) = (2)
4. (t_1, t_4) = (2, 1)
5. (t_2, t_4) = (1, 1)
6. (t_1, t_5) = (1, 1)
7. (t_4, t_5) = (1, 2)
8. (t_5) = (6)
9. (t_6) = (1)
10. (t_7) = (2)

INCIDENCE MATRIX $P(\mathcal{G}_8, (6))$

Face / Vertex	1	2	3	4	5	6	7	8	9	10
1.	0	0	1	0	1	1	1	1	1	1
2.	0	1	1	1	0	1	1	1	1	1
3.	1	1	1	1	1	0	1	1	1	1
4.	1	0	1	0	1	1	0	1	1	1
5.	1	1	1	1	0	1	0	1	1	1
6.	1	1	1	0	1	1	1	0	1	1
7.	1	1	0	1	1	1	0	0	1	1
8.	0	1	0	1	1	1	1	0	1	1
9.	1	1	1	1	1	1	1	1	0	1
10.	1	1	1	1	1	1	1	1	1	0

$P(\mathcal{G}_8, (7))$

FACES

Row	γ_1	γ_2	γ_3	γ_4	γ_5	γ_6	γ_7^*	γ_0
1	1	0	1	0	1	0	1	1
2	1	2	3	0	1	2	3	3
3	1	2	1	2	1	2	3	3
4	3	2	1	4	3	2	5	5
5	1	2	3	4	5	6	7	7
6	7	6	5	4	3	2	9	9
7	9	10	3	12	5	6	15	15

VERTICES

1. $(t_1) = (7)$
2. $(t_1, t_2) = (1, 3)$
3. $(t_2, t_3) = (2, 1)$
4. $(t_1, t_3) = (1, 2)$
5. $(t_3) = (5)$
6. $(t_1, t_4) = (3, 1)$
7. $(t_1, t_2, t_4) = (1, 1, 1)$
8. $(t_3, t_4) = (1, 1)$
9. $(t_1, t_5) = (2, 1)$
10. $(t_2, t_5) = (1, 1)$
11. $(t_5) = (3)$
12. $(t_1, t_6) = (1, 1)$
13. $(t_4, t_5, t_6) = (1, 1, 1)$
14. $(t_3, t_6) = (1, 2)$
15. $(t_5, t_6) = (1, 3)$
16. $(t_7) = (1)$

INCIDENCE MATRIX

$P(\mathcal{G}_8, (7))$

Face / Vertex	1	2	3	4	5	6	7	8	9	10	11	12	13	14
1.	0	0	0	0	1	0	0	0	1	1	1	1	1	1
2.	1	0	0	0	1	0	0	0	0	1	1	1	1	1
3.	1	0	0	1	1	0	0	1	0	0	1	1	1	1
4.	0	0	1	1	1	0	1	0	1	0	1	1	1	1
5.	0	0	0	1	0	0	1	1	1	0	1	1	1	1
6.	0	1	0	0	1	0	0	0	1	1	0	1	1	1
7.	1	1	0	0	1	0	0	0	0	1	0	1	1	1
8.	1	1	1	1	1	1	1	1	1	0	0	1	1	1
9.	0	1	1	0	1	0	0	0	1	1	1	0	1	1
10.	1	1	1	1	1	1	1	1	0	1	1	0	1	1
11.	0	1	1	0	0	1	1	1	1	1	1	0	1	1
12.	1	1	1	1	1	1	1	0	1	1	1	1	0	1
13.	1	1	0	0	0	1	0	1	1	1	0	0	0	1
14.	1	0	0	1	0	1	1	1	1	0	1	1	0	1
15.	1	0	0	0	0	1	0	1	1	1	1	0	0	1
16.	1	1	1	1	1	1	1	1	1	1	1	1	1	0

$P(\mathcal{G}_{4,2}, (0, 0))$

FACES

	$\gamma_{1,0}$	$\gamma_{2,0}$	$\gamma_{3,0}$	$\gamma_{0,1}$	$\gamma_{1,1}$	$\gamma_{2,1}$	$\gamma_{3,1}$	γ_0
Row								
1	3	2	1	2	3	2	1	4
2	1	2	3	2	3	2	1	4
3	3	2	1	2	1	2	3	4
4	1	2	3	2	1	2	3	4

VERTICES

1. $(t_{1,0}) = (4)$
2. $(t_{2,0}) = (2)$
3. $(t_{1,0}, t_{3,0}) = (1,1)$
4. $(t_{3,0}) = (4)$
5. $(t_{0,1}) = (2)$
6. $(t_{1,1}) = (4)$
7. $(t_{2,1}) = (2)$
8. $(t_{1,1}, t_{3,1}) = (1,1)$
9. $(t_{3,1}) = (4)$

INCIDENCE MATRIX $P(\mathcal{G}_{4,2}, (0, 0))$

Face	1	2	3	4	5	6	7	8	9	10	11
Vertex											
1.	0	1	0	1	0	1	1	1	1	1	1
2.	1	1	1	1	1	0	1	1	1	1	1
3.	1	1	1	1	0	1	0	1	1	1	1
4.	1	0	1	0	1	1	0	1	1	1	1
5.	1	1	1	1	1	1	1	0	1	1	1
6.	0	0	1	1	1	1	1	1	0	1	1
7.	1	1	1	1	1	1	1	1	1	0	1
8.	1	1	1	1	1	1	1	1	0	1	0
9.	1	1	0	0	1	1	1	1	1	1	0

$P(\mathcal{G}_{4,2}, (2,0))$

FACES

	$\gamma_{1,0}$	$\gamma_{2,0}^*$	$\gamma_{3,0}$	$\gamma_{0,1}$	$\gamma_{1,1}$	$\gamma_{2,1}$	$\gamma_{3,1}$	γ_0
Row								
1	1	2	1	0	1	2	1	2
2	1	2	1	2	1	0	1	2

VERTICES

1. $(t_{1,0}) = (2)$
2. $(t_{2,0}) = (2)$
3. $(t_{3,0}) = (3)$
4. $(t_{1,1}) = (2)$
5. $(t_{0,1}, t_{2,1}) = (1,1)$
6. $(t_{3,1}) = (2)$

INCIDENCE MATRIX $P(\mathcal{G}_{4,2}, (2,0))$

Face	1	2	3	4	5	6	7	8	9
Vertex									
1.	1	1	0	1	1	1	1	1	1
2.	1	1	1	0	1	1	1	1	1
3.	1	1	1	1	0	1	1	1	1
4.	1	1	1	1	1	1	0	1	1
5.	1	1	1	1	1	0	1	0	1
6.	1	1	1	1	1	1	1	1	0

$P(\mathcal{G}_{4,2}, (3,0))$

FACES

Row	$\gamma_{1,0}$	$\gamma_{2,0}$	$\gamma_{3,0}^*$	$\gamma_{0,1}$	$\gamma_{1,1}$	$\gamma_{2,1}$	$\gamma_{3,1}$	γ_0
1	1	0	1	1	0	1	0	1
2	1	0	1	0	1	0	1	1
3	1	2	3	2	3	0	1	3
4	1	2	3	2	1	2	1	3
5	1	2	3	0	1	2	3	3

VERTICES

1. $(t_{1,0}) = (3)$
2. $(t_{1,0}, t_{2,0}) = (1,1)$
3. $(t_{3,0}) = (1)$
4. $(t_{2,0}, t_{0,1}, t_{1,1}) = (1,1,1)$
5. $(t_{1,0}, t_{1,1}) = (1,2)$
6. $(t_{0,1}, t_{1,1}) = (1,3)$
7. $(t_{1,0}, t_{0,1}, t_{2,1}) = (1,1,1)$
8. $(t_{1,1}, t_{2,1}) = (1,1)$
9. $(t_{0,1}, t_{3,1}) = (1,1)$
10. $(t_{2,0}, t_{2,1}, t_{3,1}) = (1,1,1)$
11. $(t_{1,0}, t_{3,1}) = (1,2)$
12. $(t_{2,1}, t_{3,1}) = (1,3)$

INCIDENCE MATRIX

$P(\mathcal{G}_{4,2}, (3,0))$

Face / Vertex	1	2	3	4	5	6	7	8	9	10	11	12
1.	0	0	1	1	1	0	1	1	1	1	1	1
2.	1	1	1	1	1	0	0	1	1	1	1	1
3.	1	1	1	1	1	1	1	0	1	1	1	1
4.	1	1	0	0	1	1	0	1	0	0	1	1
5.	1	0	0	1	1	0	1	1	1	0	1	1
6.	1	0	0	0	1	1	1	1	0	0	1	1
7.	0	1	1	0	1	0	1	1	0	1	0	1
8.	1	1	1	1	1	1	1	1	1	0	0	1
9.	1	1	1	1	1	1	1	1	0	1	1	0
10.	1	1	1	0	0	1	0	1	1	1	0	0
11.	1	0	1	1	0	0	1	1	1	1	1	0
12.	1	0	1	0	0	1	1	1	1	1	0	0

$P(\mathcal{G}_{4,2}, (0,1))$

FACES

Row	$\gamma_{1,0}$	$\gamma_{2,0}$	$\gamma_{3,0}$	$\gamma_{0,1}^*$	$\gamma_{1,1}$	$\gamma_{2,1}$	$\gamma_{3,1}$	γ_0
1	1	0	1	1	0	1	0	1
2	0	0	0	1	1	1	1	1
3	1	2	1	2	1	0	1	2
4	3	2	1	4	3	2	1	4
5	1	2	3	4	1	2	3	4

VERTICES

1. $(t_{0,1}) = (1)$
2. $(t_{1,0}, t_{1,1}) = (3,1)$
3. $(t_{1,0}, t_{2,0}, t_{1,1}) = (1,1,1)$
4. $(t_{3,0}, t_{1,1}) = (1,1)$
5. $(t_{1,0}, t_{1,1}) = (1,3)$
6. $(t_{1,0}, t_{2,1}) = (2,1)$
7. $(t_{2,0}, t_{2,1}) = (1,1)$
8. $(t_{3,0}, t_{2,1}) = (2,1)$
9. $(t_{1,1}, t_{2,1}) = (2,1)$
10. $(t_{1,0}, t_{3,1}) = (1,1)$
11. $(t_{2,0}, t_{3,0}, t_{3,1}) = (1,1,1)$
12. $(t_{3,0}, t_{3,1}) = (3,1)$
13. $(t_{2,1}, t_{3,1}) = (1,2)$
14. $(t_{3,0}, t_{3,1}) = (1,3)$

INCIDENCE MATRIX

$P(\mathcal{G}_{4,2}, (0,1))$

Vertex \ Face	1	2	3	4	5	6	7	8	9	10	11	12
1.	1	1	1	1	1	1	1	1	0	1	1	1
2.	0	1	0	0	1	0	1	1	1	0	1	1
3.	1	1	0	0	1	0	0	1	1	0	1	1
4.	1	1	1	1	1	1	1	0	1	0	1	1
5.	1	0	0	0	1	0	1	1	1	0	1	1
6.	0	1	1	0	1	0	1	1	1	1	0	1
7.	1	1	1	1	1	1	0	1	1	1	0	1
8.	0	1	1	1	0	1	1	0	1	1	0	1
9.	1	0	1	0	1	1	1	1	1	0	0	1
10.	1	1	1	1	1	0	1	1	1	1	1	0
11.	1	1	0	1	0	1	0	0	1	1	1	0
12.	0	1	0	1	0	1	1	0	1	1	1	0
13.	1	0	1	1	0	1	1	1	1	1	0	0
14.	1	0	0	1	0	1	1	0	1	1	1	0

$P(\mathcal{G}_{2,2,2}, (0,0,0))$

FACES

	$\gamma_{1,0,0}$	$\gamma_{0,1,0}$	$\gamma_{1,1,0}$	$\gamma_{0,0,1}$	$\gamma_{1,0,1}$	$\gamma_{0,1,1}$	$\gamma_{1,1,1}$	γ_0
Row 1	1	1	1	1	1	1	1	2

VERTICES

1. $(t_{1,0,0}) = (2)$
2. $(t_{0,1,0}) = (2)$
3. $(t_{1,1,0}) = (2)$
4. $(t_{0,0,1}) = (2)$
5. $(t_{1,0,1}) = (2)$
6. $(t_{0,1,1}) = (2)$
7. $(t_{1,1,1}) = (2)$

INCIDENCE MATRIX $P(\mathcal{G}_{2,2,2}, (0,0,0))$

Face / Vertex	1	2	3	4	5	6	7	8
1.	1	0	1	1	1	1	1	1
2.	1	1	0	1	1	1	1	1
3.	1	1	1	0	1	1	1	1
4.	1	1	1	1	0	1	1	1
5.	1	1	1	1	1	0	1	1
6.	1	1	1	1	1	1	0	1
7.	1	1	1	1	1	1	1	0

$P(\mathcal{G}_{2,2,2}, (1,0,0))$

FACES

	$\gamma_{1,0,0}$	$\gamma_{0,1,0}$	$\gamma_{1,1,0}$	$\gamma_{0,0,1}$	$\gamma_{1,0,1}$	$\gamma_{0,1,1}$	$\gamma_{1,1,1}$	γ_0
Row 1	1	0	1	1	0	1	0	1
2	1	1	0	0	1	1	0	1
3	1	1	0	1	0	0	1	1
4	1	0	1	0	1	0	1	1

VERTICES

1. $(t_{1,0,0})$ = (1)
2. $(t_{0,1,0}, t_{1,1,0})$ = $(1,1)$
3. $(t_{0,0,1}, t_{1,0,1})$ = $(1,1)$
4. $(t_{1,1,0}, t_{0,0,1}, t_{0,1,1})$ = $(1,1,1)$
5. $(t_{0,1,0}, t_{1,0,1}, t_{0,1,1})$ = $(1,1,1)$
6. $(t_{0,1,0}, t_{0,0,1}, t_{1,1,1})$ = $(1,1,1)$
7. $(t_{1,1,0}, t_{1,0,1}, t_{1,1,1})$ = $(1,1,1)$
8. $(t_{0,1,1}, t_{1,1,1})$ = $(1,1)$

INCIDENCE MATRIX $P(\mathcal{G}_{2,2,2}, (1,0,0))$

Face / Vertex	1	2	3	4	5	6	7	8	9	10	11
1.	1	1	1	1	0	1	1	1	1	1	1
2.	1	1	1	1	1	0	0	1	1	1	1
3.	1	1	1	1	1	1	1	0	0	1	1
4.	0	1	1	1	1	1	0	0	1	0	1
5.	1	0	1	1	1	0	1	1	0	0	1
6.	1	1	0	1	1	0	1	0	1	1	0
7.	1	1	1	0	1	1	0	1	0	1	0
8.	1	1	1	1	1	1	1	1	1	0	0

$P(\mathcal{G}_9, (0))$

FACES

Row	γ_1	γ_2	γ_3	γ_4	γ_5	γ_6	γ_7	γ_8	γ_0
1	2	1	2	2	1	1	2	1	3
2	2	1	1	2	1	2	2	1	3
3	1	2	2	1	2	1	1	2	3
4	1	2	1	1	2	2	1	2	3
5	8	7	6	5	4	3	2	1	9
6	7	5	3	1	8	6	4	2	9
7	5	1	6	2	7	3	8	4	9
8	4	8	3	7	2	6	1	5	9
9	2	4	6	8	1	3	5	7	9
10	1	2	3	4	5	6	7	8	9
11	14	10	6	11	7	12	8	4	18
12	11	4	6	8	10	12	14	7	18
13	10	11	12	4	14	6	7	8	18
14	8	7	6	14	4	12	11	10	18
15	7	14	12	10	8	6	4	11	18
16	4	8	12	7	11	6	10	14	18

VERTICES $P(\mathcal{G}_9, (0))$

1.	(t_1)	=	(9)	(t_4, t_6)	=	(3,1)	19.
2.	(t_1, t_2)	=	(1,4)	(t_6)	=	(3)	20.
3.	(t_2)	=	(9)	(t_1, t_7)	=	(2,1)	21.
4.	(t_2, t_3)	=	(3,1)	(t_2, t_7)	=	(1,1)	22.
5.	(t_3)	=	(3)	(t_5, t_7)	=	(4,1)	23.
6.	(t_2, t_3, t_4)	=	(1,1,1)	(t_5, t_6, t_7)	=	(1,1,1)	24.
7.	(t_1, t_4)	=	(1,2)	(t_4, t_7)	=	(1,2)	25.
8.	(t_2, t_4)	=	(1,4)	(t_6, t_7)	=	(1,3)	26.
9.	(t_4)	=	(9)	(t_7)	=	(9)	27.
10.	(t_1, t_5)	=	(4,1)	(t_1, t_8)	=	(1,1)	28.
11.	(t_2, t_5)	=	(2,1)	(t_5, t_8)	=	(2,1)	29.
12.	(t_1, t_3, t_5)	=	(1,1,1)	(t_4, t_6, t_8)	=	(1,1,1)	30.
13.	(t_4, t_5)	=	(1,1)	(t_3, t_7, t_8)	=	(1,1,1)	31.
14.	(t_3, t_5)	=	(1,3)	(t_7, t_8)	=	(4,1)	32.
15.	(t_5)	=	(9)	(t_2, t_8)	=	(1,2)	33.
16.	(t_1, t_6)	=	(3,1)	(t_3, t_8)	=	(1,3)	34.
17.	(t_1, t_2, t_6)	=	(1,1,1)	(t_4, t_8)	=	(1,4)	35.
18.	(t_3, t_6)	=	(1,1)	(t_8)	=	(9)	36.

INCIDENCE MATRIX $P(\mathcal{G}_9, (0))$

Face / Vertex	1	2	3	4	5	6	7	8	9	10	11	12	13	14	15	16	17	18	19	20	21	22	23	24
1.	0	0	0	0	0	0	0	0	0	1	0	0	0	0	0	0	0	1	1	1	1	1	1	1
2.	0	0	0	0	0	0	1	0	0	1	0	0	0	0	0	0	0	0	1	1	1	1	1	1
3.	0	0	0	0	0	0	1	0	0	0	0	0	0	0	0	0	1	0	1	1	1	1	1	1
4.	0	0	0	0	0	0	1	0	0	1	0	1	0	0	0	0	1	0	0	1	1	1	1	1
5.	0	1	0	1	0	1	0	1	0	1	1	1	0	1	0	0	1	1	0	1	1	1	1	1
6.	0	0	0	0	0	1	1	0	0	1	0	1	0	0	0	0	1	0	0	0	1	1	1	1
7.	0	0	1	1	0	1	1	0	0	1	0	0	1	0	0	1	0	1	1	0	1	1	1	1
8.	0	0	0	0	0	1	1	0	0	0	0	0	0	0	0	0	1	0	1	0	1	1	1	1
9.	0	0	0	0	0	1	0	0	0	0	0	0	0	0	0	0	1	1	1	0	1	1	1	1
10.	0	0	0	0	0	0	0	0	1	1	0	0	0	0	0	0	0	1	1	1	0	1	1	1
11.	1	1	0	0	0	0	1	0	1	1	0	1	0	1	0	0	1	0	1	1	0	1	1	1
12.	0	0	0	0	0	0	0	1	1	1	0	0	0	1	0	0	0	1	0	1	0	1	1	1
13.	1	1	1	1	1	1	1	1	1	1	1	1	1	1	1	1	1	1	1	0	0	1	1	1
14.	0	0	0	0	0	0	0	1	1	0	0	0	0	1	0	0	1	1	0	1	0	1	1	1
15.	0	0	0	0	0	0	0	0	1	0	0	0	0	0	0	0	1	1	1	1	0	1	1	1
16.	0	0	0	0	0	0	0	0	1	1	0	0	0	0	0	1	0	1	1	1	1	0	1	1

Face / Vertex	1	2	3	4	5	6	7	8	9	10	11	12	13	14	15	16	17	18	19	20	21	22	23	24
17.	0	0	0	0	0	0	1	0	1	1	0	0	0	0	0	1	0	0	1	1	1	0	1	1
18.	1	1	1	1	1	1	1	1	1	1	1	1	1	1	1	1	1	1	0	1	1	0	1	1
19.	0	0	0	0	0	1	1	0	0	0	0	0	1	0	0	0	1	1	1	0	1	0	1	1
20.	1	0	1	0	1	0	1	0	1	0	0	0	1	0	1	1	1	1	1	1	1	0	1	1
21.	0	0	1	1	0	0	0	1	1	1	0	0	0	0	1	1	0	1	1	1	1	1	0	1
22.	1	1	1	1	1	1	1	1	1	1	1	1	1	1	1	1	1	0	1	1	1	1	0	1
23.	0	0	0	0	0	0	0	1	1	0	0	0	0	0	0	0	1	1	1	1	0	1	0	1
24.	0	0	0	0	1	0	0	1	1	0	0	0	0	0	1	0	1	1	1	1	0	0	0	1
25.	0	0	1	1	1	1	0	1	0	0	0	0	1	0	1	0	1	1	1	0	1	1	0	1
26.	0	0	0	0	1	0	0	1	0	0	0	0	0	0	1	0	1	1	1	1	1	0	0	1
27.	0	0	0	0	0	0	0	1	0	0	0	0	0	0	0	0	1	1	1	1	1	1	0	1
28.	1	1	1	1	1	1	1	1	1	1	1	1	1	1	1	1	0	1	1	1	1	1	1	0
29.	1	1	0	0	1	0	0	1	1	0	1	0	0	1	0	0	1	1	1	1	0	1	1	0
30.	0	0	0	0	1	1	1	0	0	0	0	0	1	0	0	0	1	1	1	0	1	0	1	0
31.	0	0	0	0	1	1	0	1	0	0	1	0	0	0	0	0	1	1	0	1	1	1	0	0
32.	0	0	0	0	1	0	0	1	0	0	0	0	0	0	0	0	1	1	1	1	1	1	0	0
33.	1	1	0	0	1	1	1	0	0	0	1	1	0	0	0	0	1	0	1	1	1	1	1	0
34.	0	0	0	0	1	1	0	0	0	0	1	0	0	0	0	0	1	1	0	1	1	1	1	0
35.	0	0	0	0	1	1	0	0	0	0	0	0	0	0	0	0	1	1	1	0	1	1	1	0
36.	0	0	0	0	1	0	0	0	0	0	0	0	0	0	0	0	1	1	1	1	1	1	1	0

$P(\mathcal{G}_9, (6))$

FACES

	γ_1	γ_2	γ_3	γ_4	γ_5	γ_6^*	γ_7	γ_8	γ_0
Row									
1	4	5	3	1	2	6	4	2	6
2	4	2	3	4	2	6	4	2	6
3	1	2	3	4	5	6	4	2	6
4	2	4	3	2	4	6	2	4	6
5	4	2	3	4	2	6	1	5	6
6	5	10	6	2	7	12	8	4	12
7	2	4	6	8	10	12	5	7	12
8	8	7	6	5	4	12	2	10	12

VERTICES

1. $(t_1) = (6)$
2. $(t_2) = (3)$
3. $(t_3) = (2)$
4. $(t_1, t_4) = (2, 1)$
5. $(t_2, t_4) = (1, 1)$
6. $(t_3, t_4) = (1, 3)$
7. $(t_4) = (6)$
8. $(t_1, t_5) = (1, 1)$
9. $(t_5) = (3)$
10. $(t_6) = (1)$
11. $(t_4, t_7) = (2, 1)$
12. $(t_1, t_7) = (1, 2)$
13. $(t_3, t_7) = (1, 3)$
14. $(t_7) = (6)$
15. $(t_7, t_8) = (1, 1)$
16. $(t_8) = (3)$

INCIDENCE MATRIX $P(\mathcal{G}_9, (6))$

Face	1	2	3	4	5	6	7	8	9	10	11	12	13	14	15	16
Vertex																
1.	0	0	1	0	0	0	1	0	0	1	1	1	1	1	1	1
2.	0	1	1	0	1	0	1	0	1	0	1	1	1	1	1	1
3.	1	1	1	1	1	1	1	1	1	1	0	1	1	1	1	1
4.	0	0	1	1	0	1	1	0	0	1	1	0	1	1	1	1
5.	1	1	1	1	1	1	1	1	1	0	1	0	1	1	1	1
6.	1	0	0	0	0	1	0	0	1	1	0	0	1	1	1	1
7.	1	0	0	0	0	1	0	0	1	1	1	0	1	1	1	1
8.	1	1	1	1	1	1	1	1	0	1	1	1	0	1	1	1
9.	1	1	0	0	1	0	0	1	1	1	1	1	0	1	1	1
10.	1	1	1	1	1	1	1	1	1	1	1	1	1	0	1	1
11.	1	0	0	1	0	1	0	1	1	1	1	0	1	1	0	1
12.	0	0	0	1	1	0	1	1	0	1	1	1	1	1	0	1
13.	0	0	0	0	1	0	0	1	1	1	0	1	1	1	0	1
14.	0	0	0	0	1	0	0	1	1	1	1	1	1	1	0	1
15.	1	1	1	1	1	1	1	1	1	1	1	1	1	1	0	0
16.	1	1	1	0	0	1	0	0	1	1	1	1	1	1	1	0

$P(\mathcal{G}_9, (8))$

FACES

Row	γ_1	γ_2	γ_3	γ_4	γ_5	γ_6	γ_7	γ_8^*	γ_0
1	1	2	0	1	2	0	1	2	2
2	2	1	3	2	1	3	2	4	4
3	1	2	3	4	5	6	7	8	8
4	8	7	6	5	4	3	2	10	10
5	4	8	12	7	2	6	10	14	14
6	11	4	6	8	10	12	5	16	16
7	16	5	12	10	8	15	4	20	20

VERTICES

1.	(t_1)	=	(8)	11.	(t_1, t_6)	=	(2, 1)
2.	(t_2)	=	(4)	12.	(t_2, t_6)	=	(1, 1)
3.	(t_1, t_3)	=	(2, 2)	13.	(t_5, t_6)	=	(1, 2)
4.	(t_2, t_3)	=	(1, 2)	14.	(t_1, t_7)	=	(1, 1)
5.	(t_4)	=	(2)	15.	(t_5, t_7)	=	(2, 1)
6.	(t_1, t_5)	=	(3, 1)	16.	(t_3, t_7)	=	(1, 2)
7.	(t_1, t_2, t_5)	=	(1, 1, 1)	17	(t_6, t_7)	=	(2, 2)
8.	(t_3, t_5)	=	(1, 1)	18.	(t_7)	=	(5)
9.	(t_2, t_5)	=	(1, 3)	19.	(t_8)	=	(1)
10.	(t_5)	=	(7)				

INCIDENCE MATRIX

$P(\mathcal{G}_9, (8))$

Face / Vertex	1	2	3	4	5	6	7	8	9	10	11	12	13	14	15
1.	0	0	1	0	0	0	0	0	1	1	1	1	1	1	1
2.	0	1	1	0	0	1	1	1	0	1	1	1	1	1	1
3.	1	0	1	0	0	0	0	0	1	0	1	1	1	1	1
4.	1	0	1	0	0	1	0	1	0	0	1	1	1	1	1
5.	1	1	1	1	1	1	1	1	1	1	0	1	1	1	1
6.	0	0	1	0	1	0	0	0	1	1	1	0	1	1	1
7.	0	1	1	0	1	0	0	0	0	1	1	0	1	1	1
8.	1	1	1	1	1	1	1	1	1	0	1	0	1	1	1
9.	0	1	0	0	1	0	0	1	0	1	1	0	1	1	1
10.	0	0	0	0	1	0	0	1	1	1	1	0	1	1	1
11.	1	0	1	0	1	0	0	0	1	1	1	1	0	1	1
12.	1	1	1	1	1	1	1	1	0	1	1	1	0	1	1
13.	1	0	0	1	1	0	0	1	1	1	1	0	0	1	1
14.	1	1	1	1	1	1	1	0	1	1	1	1	1	0	1
15.	0	1	0	1	1	0	1	1	1	1	1	0	1	0	1
16.	1	0	0	1	0	1	1	1	1	0	1	1	1	0	1
17.	1	0	0	1	0	0	0	1	1	1	1	1	0	0	1
18.	0	0	0	1	0	0	1	1	1	1	1	1	1	0	1
19.	1	1	1	1	1	1	1	1	1	1	1	1	1	1	0

$P(\mathcal{G}_{3,3}, (0,0))$

FACES

Row	$\gamma_{1,0}$	$\gamma_{2,0}$	$\gamma_{0,1}$	$\gamma_{1,1}$	$\gamma_{2,1}$	$\gamma_{0,2}$	$\gamma_{1,2}$	$\gamma_{2,2}$	γ_0
1	2	1	2	2	2	1	1	1	3
2	1	2	2	2	2	1	1	1	3
3	2	1	1	2	2	2	1	1	3
4	1	2	1	2	2	2	1	1	3
5	2	1	2	2	1	1	2	1	3
6	1	2	2	2	1	1	2	1	3
7	2	1	1	2	1	2	2	1	3
8	1	2	1	2	1	2	2	1	3
9	2	1	2	1	2	1	1	2	3
10	1	2	2	1	2	1	1	2	3
11	2	1	1	1	2	2	1	2	3
12	1	2	1	1	2	2	1	2	3
13	2	1	2	1	1	1	2	2	3
14	1	2	2	1	1	1	2	2	3
15	2	1	1	1	1	2	2	2	3
16	1	2	1	1	1	2	2	2	3

VERTICES $P(\mathcal{G}_{3,3}, (0,0))$

1. $(t_{1,0}) = (3)$
2. $(t_{1,0}, t_{2,0}) = (1,1)$
3. $(t_{2,0}) = (3)$
4. $(t_{0,1}) = (3)$
5. $(t_{1,1}) = (3)$
6. $(t_{2,1}) = (3)$
7. $(t_{0,1}, t_{0,2}) = (1,1)$
8. $(t_{0,2}) = (3)$
9. $(t_{2,1}, t_{1,2}) = (1,1)$
10. $(t_{1,2}) = (3)$
11. $(t_{1,1}, t_{2,2}) = (1,1)$
12. $(t_{2,2}) = (3)$

INCIDENCE MATRIX $P(\mathcal{G}_{3,3}, (0,0))$

Face / Vertex	1	2	3	4	5	6	7	8	9	10	11	12	13	14	15	16	17	18	19	20	21	22	23	24
1.	0	1	0	1	0	1	0	1	0	1	0	1	0	1	0	1	0	1	1	1	1	1	1	1
2.	1	1	1	1	1	1	1	1	1	1	1	1	1	1	1	1	0	0	1	1	1	1	1	1
3.	1	0	1	0	1	0	1	0	1	0	1	0	1	0	1	0	1	0	1	1	1	1	1	1
4.	0	0	1	1	0	0	1	1	0	0	1	1	0	0	1	1	1	1	0	1	1	1	1	1
5.	0	0	0	0	0	0	0	0	1	1	1	1	1	1	1	1	1	1	1	0	1	1	1	1
6.	0	0	0	0	1	1	1	1	0	0	0	0	1	1	1	1	1	1	1	1	0	1	1	1
7.	1	1	1	1	1	1	1	1	1	1	1	1	1	1	1	1	1	1	0	1	1	0	1	1
8.	1	1	0	0	1	1	0	0	1	1	0	0	1	1	0	0	1	1	1	1	1	0	1	1
9.	1	1	1	1	1	1	1	1	1	1	1	1	1	1	1	1	1	1	1	1	0	1	0	1
10.	1	1	1	1	0	0	0	0	1	1	1	1	0	0	0	0	1	1	1	1	1	1	0	1
11.	1	1	1	1	1	1	1	1	1	1	1	1	1	1	1	1	1	1	1	0	1	1	1	0
12.	1	1	1	1	1	1	1	1	0	0	0	0	0	0	0	0	1	1	1	1	1	1	1	0

$P(\mathcal{G}_{3,3}, (1,0))$

FACES

Row	$\gamma_{1,0}^*$	$\gamma_{2,0}$	$\gamma_{0,1}$	$\gamma_{1,1}$	$\gamma_{2,1}$	$\gamma_{0,2}$	$\gamma_{1,2}$	$\gamma_{2,2}$	γ_0
1	2	1	1	0	2	2	1	0	2
2	2	1	0	2	1	0	2	1	2
3	2	1	2	1	0	1	0	2	2
4	6	3	4	4	4	2	2	2	6
5	6	3	2	2	2	4	4	4	6

VERTICES

1. $(t_{1,0})$ = (1)
2. $(t_{2,0})$ = (2)
3. $(t_{0,1}, t_{1,1})$ = (2,1)
4. $(t_{1,1}, t_{2,1})$ = (2,1)
5. $(t_{0,1}, t_{2,1})$ = (1,2)
6. $(t_{1,1}, t_{0,2})$ = (1,1)
7. $(t_{2,1}, t_{0,2})$ = (2,2)
8. $(t_{0,1}, t_{1,2})$ = (1,1)
9. $(t_{0,2}, t_{1,2})$ = (2,1)
10. $(t_{1,1}, t_{1,2})$ = (2,2)
11. $(t_{2,1}, t_{2,2})$ = (1,1)
12. $(t_{1,2}, t_{2,2})$ = (2,1)
13. $(t_{0,1}, t_{2,2})$ = (2,2)
14. $(t_{0,2}, t_{2,2})$ = (1,2)

INCIDENCE MATRIX

$P(\mathcal{G}_{3,3}, (1,0))$

Face / Vertex	1	2	3	4	5	6	7	8	9	10	11	12	13
1.	1	1	1	1	1	0	1	1	1	1	1	1	1
2.	1	1	1	1	1	1	0	1	1	1	1	1	1
3.	1	1	0	0	1	1	1	0	0	1	1	1	1
4.	1	0	1	0	1	1	1	1	0	0	1	1	1
5.	0	1	1	0	1	1	1	0	1	0	1	1	1
6.	1	1	1	1	1	1	1	1	0	1	0	1	1
7.	0	1	1	0	0	1	1	1	1	0	0	1	1
8.	1	1	1	1	1	1	1	0	1	1	1	0	1
9.	0	1	1	1	0	1	1	1	1	1	0	0	1
10.	1	0	1	0	0	1	1	1	0	1	1	0	1
11.	1	1	1	1	1	1	1	1	1	0	1	1	0
12.	1	0	1	1	0	1	1	1	1	1	1	0	0
13.	1	1	0	0	0	1	1	0	1	1	1	1	0
14.	1	1	0	1	0	1	1	1	1	1	0	1	0

$P(\mathcal{G}_{10},(0))$

FACES

Row	γ_1	γ_2	γ_3	γ_4	γ_5	γ_6	γ_7	γ_8	γ_9	γ_0
1	9	8	7	6	5	4	3	2	1	10
2	8	6	4	2	5	8	6	4	2	10
3	7	4	6	8	5	2	4	6	3	10
4	7	4	1	8	5	2	9	6	3	10
5	6	2	8	4	5	6	2	8	4	10
6	6	2	3	4	5	6	7	8	4	10
7	4	8	7	6	5	4	3	2	6	10
8	4	8	2	6	5	4	8	2	6	10
9	3	6	9	2	5	8	1	4	7	10
10	3	6	4	2	5	8	6	4	7	10
11	2	4	6	8	5	2	4	6	8	10
12	1	2	3	4	5	6	7	8	9	10

VERTICES $P(\mathcal{G}_{10},(0))$

1. $(t_1) = (10)$
2. $(t_2) = (5)$
3. $(t_2, t_3) = (2, 2)$
4. $(t_1, t_3) = (1, 3)$
5. $(t_3) = (10)$
6. $(t_3, t_4) = (2, 1)$
7. $(t_1, t_4) = (2, 2)$
8. $(t_2, t_4) = (1, 2)$
9. $(t_4) = (5)$
10. $(t_1, t_4, t_5) = (1, 1, 1)$
11. $(t_5) = (2)$
12. $(t_1, t_6) = (4, 1)$
13. $(t_2, t_6) = (2, 1)$
14. $(t_1, t_3, t_6) = (1, 1, 1)$
15. $(t_4, t_6) = (1, 1)$
16. $(t_6) = (5)$
17. $(t_1, t_7) = (3, 1)$
18. $(t_1, t_2, t_7) = (1, 1, 1)$
19. $(t_3, t_7) = (1, 1)$
20. $(t_6, t_7) = (1, 2)$
21. $(t_2, t_7) = (1, 4)$
22. $(t_7) = (10)$
23. $(t_1, t_8) = (2, 1)$
24. $(t_2, t_8) = (1, 1)$
25. $(t_3, t_8) = (4, 1)$
26. $(t_6, t_8) = (2, 1)$
27. $(t_5, t_7, t_8) = (1, 1, 1)$
28. $(t_4, t_8) = (1, 2)$
29. $(t_7, t_8) = (2, 2)$
30. $(t_8) = (5)$
31. $(t_1, t_9) = (1, 1)$
32. $(t_5, t_6, t_9) = (1, 1, 1)$
33. $(t_4, t_7, t_9) = (1, 1, 1)$
34. $(t_7, t_9) = (3, 1)$
35. $(t_3, t_8, t_9) = (1, 1, 1)$
36. $(t_2, t_9) = (1, 2)$
37. $(t_6, t_9) = (2, 2)$
38. $(t_3, t_9) = (1, 3)$
39. $(t_4, t_9) = (1, 4)$
40. $(t_9) = (10)$

INCIDENCE MATRIX $P(\mathcal{G}_{10}, (0))$

Face / Vertex	1	2	3	4	5	6	7	8	9	10	11	12	13	14	15	16	17	18	19	20	21
1.	0	0	0	0	0	0	0	0	0	0	0	1	0	1	1	1	1	1	1	1	1
2.	0	0	0	0	1	1	0	0	0	0	0	1	1	0	1	1	1	1	1	1	1
3.	0	0	0	1	0	1	0	0	0	0	0	1	1	0	0	1	1	1	1	1	1
4.	0	0	0	1	0	0	0	1	0	0	0	1	0	1	0	1	1	1	1	1	1
5.	0	0	0	1	0	0	0	0	0	0	0	0	1	1	0	1	1	1	1	1	1
6.	0	1	0	1	0	1	0	1	0	1	0	1	1	1	0	0	1	1	1	1	1
7.	0	0	0	0	0	0	0	0	1	1	0	1	0	1	1	0	1	1	1	1	1
8.	0	1	0	0	1	1	0	0	1	1	0	1	1	0	1	0	1	1	1	1	1
9.	0	1	0	0	0	0	0	0	1	1	0	0	1	1	1	0	1	1	1	1	1
10.	0	0	0	0	0	0	0	0	1	1	0	1	0	1	1	0	0	1	1	1	1
11.	1	1	1	1	1	1	1	1	1	1	1	1	1	1	1	1	0	1	1	1	1
12.	0	0	0	0	0	0	0	0	0	0	1	1	0	1	1	1	1	0	1	1	1
13.	0	0	1	1	1	1	0	0	0	0	1	1	1	0	1	1	1	0	1	1	1
14.	0	0	0	1	0	0	0	1	0	0	1	1	0	1	0	1	1	0	1	1	1
15.	1	1	1	1	1	1	1	1	1	1	1	1	1	1	1	0	1	0	1	1	1
16.	0	0	1	1	0	0	0	0	0	0	1	0	1	1	1	1	1	0	1	1	1
17.	0	0	0	0	0	0	0	0	1	0	1	1	0	1	1	1	1	1	0	1	1
18.	0	0	0	0	1	0	0	0	1	0	1	1	0	0	1	1	1	1	0	1	1
19.	1	1	1	1	1	1	1	1	1	1	1	1	1	1	0	1	1	1	0	1	1
20.	1	0	1	0	1	0	1	0	1	0	1	0	1	1	1	1	1	0	0	1	1
21.	0	0	0	0	1	0	0	0	1	0	0	0	1	0	1	1	1	1	0	1	1
22.	0	0	0	0	0	0	0	0	1	0	0	0	1	1	1	1	1	1	0	1	1
23.	0	0	0	0	0	0	1	1	1	1	1	1	0	1	1	1	1	1	1	0	1
24.	1	1	1	1	1	1	1	1	1	1	1	1	1	0	1	1	1	1	1	0	1
25.	0	0	0	1	0	0	0	1	0	0	0	0	1	1	0	1	1	1	1	0	1
26.	1	0	1	1	0	0	1	1	0	0	1	0	1	1	1	1	1	0	1	0	1
27.	1	0	0	0	0	0	1	0	1	0	0	0	1	1	1	1	0	1	0	0	1
28.	1	1	0	0	0	0	1	1	1	1	0	0	1	1	1	0	1	1	1	0	1
29.	1	0	0	0	0	0	1	0	1	0	0	0	1	1	1	1	1	1	0	0	1
30.	1	0	0	0	0	0	1	1	0	0	0	0	1	1	1	1	1	1	1	0	1
31.	1	1	1	1	1	1	1	1	1	1	1	1	0	1	1	1	1	1	1	1	0
32.	1	0	1	1	0	0	0	0	0	0	0	0	1	1	1	1	0	0	1	1	0
33.	1	1	0	0	1	0	0	0	1	0	0	0	1	1	1	0	1	1	0	1	0
34.	1	0	0	0	1	0	0	0	1	0	0	0	1	1	1	1	1	1	0	1	0
35.	1	1	0	1	0	0	0	1	0	0	0	0	1	1	0	1	1	1	1	0	0
36.	1	1	1	1	1	1	0	0	0	0	0	0	1	0	1	1	1	1	1	1	0
37.	1	0	1	1	0	0	0	0	0	0	0	0	1	1	1	1	1	0	1	1	0
38.	1	1	0	1	0	0	0	0	0	0	0	0	1	1	0	1	1	1	1	1	0
39.	1	1	0	0	0	0	0	0	0	0	0	0	1	1	1	0	1	1	1	1	0
40.	1	0	0	0	0	0	0	0	0	0	0	0	1	1	1	1	1	1	1	1	0

$P(\mathcal{G}_{10}, (5))$

FACES

Row	γ_1	γ_2	γ_3	γ_4	γ_5^*	γ_6	γ_7	γ_8	γ_9	γ_0
1	1	0	1	0	1	0	1	0	1	1
2	1	2	1	2	3	2	1	2	1	3
3	4	3	2	1	5	4	3	2	1	5
4	1	2	3	4	5	4	3	2	1	5
5	3	1	4	2	5	3	1	4	2	5
6	2	4	1	3	5	2	4	1	3	5
7	3	4	1	2	5	2	1	4	3	5
8	1	2	3	4	5	1	2	3	4	5
9	3	6	4	7	10	8	6	4	2	10
10	2	4	6	8	10	7	4	6	3	10
11	6	7	3	4	10	6	2	8	4	10
12	4	8	2	6	10	4	3	7	6	10
13	7	4	11	8	15	12	9	6	3	15
14	3	6	9	12	15	8	11	4	7	15
15	9	8	7	6	15	4	3	12	11	15
16	11	12	3	4	15	6	7	8	9	15

VERTICES $P(\mathcal{G}_{10}, (5))$

1.	(t_1)	=	(5)	(t_7)	=	(5)	16.
2.	(t_1, t_2)	=	(1, 2)	(t_3, t_4, t_8)	=	(1, 1, 1)	17.
3.	(t_1, t_3)	=	(2, 1)	(t_1, t_6, t_8)	=	(1, 1, 1)	18.
4.	(t_2, t_3)	=	(1, 1)	(t_7, t_8)	=	(1, 1)	19.
5.	(t_3)	=	(5)	(t_1, t_8)	=	(1, 3)	20.
6.	(t_1, t_4)	=	(1, 1)	(t_3, t_8)	=	(1, 4)	21.
7.	(t_3, t_4)	=	(1, 3)	(t_2, t_9)	=	(3, 1)	22.
8.	(t_5)	=	(1)	(t_3, t_9)	=	(2, 1)	23.
9.	(t_3, t_6)	=	(1, 2)	(t_2, t_4, t_9)	=	(1, 1, 1)	24.
10.	(t_1, t_6)	=	(1, 4)	(t_4, t_9)	=	(4, 1)	25.
11.	(t_2, t_7)	=	(4, 1)	(t_6, t_9)	=	(1, 1)	26.
12.	(t_4, t_7)	=	(2, 1)	(t_8, t_9)	=	(2, 1)	27.
13.	(t_2, t_6, t_7)	=	(1, 1, 1)	(t_7, t_9)	=	(1, 2)	28.
14.	(t_6, t_7)	=	(3, 1)	(t_9)	=	(5)	29.
15.	(t_1, t_7)	=	(1, 2)				

INCIDENCE MATRIX $P(\mathcal{G}_{10}, (5))$

Face / Vertex	1	2	3	4	5	6	7	8	9	10	11	12	13	14	15	16	17	18	19	20	21	22	23	24	25
1.	0	0	0	1	0	0	0	1	0	1	0	0	0	1	0	0	0	1	1	1	1	1	1	1	1
2.	1	0	0	1	1	0	0	1	0	1	0	0	1	1	0	0	0	0	1	1	1	1	1	1	1
3.	0	1	0	1	0	1	0	1	1	1	0	1	0	1	0	0	0	1	0	1	1	1	1	1	1
4.	1	1	1	1	1	1	1	1	1	1	1	1	1	1	1	1	1	0	0	1	1	1	1	1	1
5.	0	0	0	0	0	1	1	0	0	0	0	1	0	0	0	1	1	1	0	1	1	1	1	1	1
6.	1	1	1	1	1	1	1	1	1	1	1	1	1	1	1	1	0	1	1	0	1	1	1	1	1
7.	1	0	1	0	0	0	0	0	0	0	0	0	0	0	0	1	1	1	0	0	1	1	1	1	1
8.	1	1	1	1	1	1	1	1	1	1	1	1	1	1	1	1	1	1	1	1	0	1	1	1	1
9.	1	0	0	0	0	1	1	1	0	0	0	1	0	0	1	1	1	1	0	1	1	0	1	1	1
10.	1	0	0	0	0	0	0	1	0	0	0	0	0	0	0	0	0	1	1	1	1	0	1	1	1
11.	1	0	0	0	1	0	0	0	0	0	0	0	0	0	0	0	1	0	1	1	1	1	0	1	1
12.	1	0	1	0	1	0	1	0	0	0	1	0	0	0	1	1	1	1	1	0	1	1	0	1	1

Face / Vertex	1	2	3	4	5	6	7	8	9	10	11	12	13	14	15	16	17	18	19	20	21	22	23	24	25
13.	1	0	0	0	1	0	0	1	0	0	0	0	0	0	1	0	1	0	1	1	1	0	0	1	1
14.	1	0	0	0	0	0	0	1	0	0	0	0	0	0	1	0	1	1	1	1	1	0	0	1	1
15.	0	1	0	0	1	0	1	1	0	1	1	1	0	0	1	0	0	1	1	1	1	1	0	1	1
16.	0	0	0	0	1	0	1	0	0	0	1	0	0	0	1	0	1	1	1	1	1	1	0	1	1
17.	1	0	1	0	0	1	0	0	0	0	0	0	0	0	0	1	1	1	0	0	1	1	1	0	1
18.	1	0	0	0	0	1	0	1	0	0	0	0	0	1	0	0	0	1	1	1	1	0	1	0	1
19.	1	1	1	1	1	1	1	1	1	1	1	1	1	1	1	1	1	1	1	1	1	1	0	0	1
20.	1	0	0	0	0	1	0	0	0	0	0	0	0	1	0	0	0	1	1	1	1	1	1	0	1
21.	1	0	0	0	0	1	0	0	0	0	0	0	0	0	0	0	1	1	0	1	1	1	1	0	1
22.	1	0	0	0	1	0	0	0	0	0	0	0	1	0	0	0	1	0	1	1	1	1	1	1	0
23.	0	1	1	0	0	1	1	0	1	0	1	1	0	0	0	1	1	1	0	1	1	1	1	1	0
24.	1	0	1	0	1	0	0	0	0	0	0	0	1	0	0	0	1	0	1	0	1	1	1	1	0
25.	1	0	1	0	0	0	0	0	0	0	0	0	0	0	0	0	1	1	1	0	1	1	1	1	0
26.	1	1	1	1	1	1	1	1	1	1	1	1	1	1	1	1	1	1	1	1	1	0	1	1	0
27.	1	0	1	1	0	1	0	0	1	0	0	0	1	1	0	0	1	1	1	1	1	1	1	0	0
28.	0	1	1	1	1	0	0	0	1	1	1	0	1	0	0	0	1	1	1	1	1	1	0	1	0
29.	0	0	1	1	0	0	0	0	1	0	0	0	1	0	0	0	1	1	1	1	1	1	1	1	0

$P(\mathcal{G}_{10}, (8))$

FACES

Row	γ_1	γ_2	γ_3	γ_4	γ_5	γ_6	γ_7	γ_8^*	γ_9	γ_0
1	3	1	4	2	0	3	1	4	2	4
2	2	4	6	3	0	2	4	6	3	6
3	2	4	1	3	5	2	4	6	3	6
4	6	2	3	4	5	6	2	8	4	8
5	1	2	3	4	5	6	7	8	4	8
6	9	8	7	6	5	4	3	12	6	12
7	9	8	2	6	10	4	3	12	6	12

VERTICES

1. (t_1) = (8)
2. (t_2) = (4)
3. (t_1, t_2) = (2, 2)
4. (t_2, t_3) = (1, 2)
5. (t_3) = (6)
6. (t_4) = (2)
7. (t_1, t_5) = (3, 1)
8. (t_1, t_2, t_5) = (1, 1, 1)
9. (t_3, t_5) = (1, 1)
10. (t_1, t_6) = (2, 1)
11. (t_2, t_6) = (1, 1)
12. (t_6) = (3)
13. (t_1, t_7) = (1, 1)
14. (t_5, t_6, t_7) = (1, 1, 1)
15. (t_7) = (4)
16. (t_8) = (1)
17. (t_9) = (2)

INCIDENCE MATRIX

$P(\mathcal{G}_{10}, (8))$

Face / Vertex	1	2	3	4	5	6	7	8	9	10	11	12	13	14	15	16
1.	0	0	0	0	1	0	0	0	1	1	1	1	1	1	1	1
2.	1	0	0	1	1	0	0	1	0	1	1	1	1	1	1	1
3.	0	0	1	0	1	0	0	0	1	0	1	1	1	1	1	1
4.	0	0	1	1	1	0	1	1	0	0	1	1	1	1	1	1
5.	0	0	1	0	0	0	1	1	1	0	1	1	1	1	1	1
6.	1	1	1	1	1	1	1	1	1	1	0	1	1	1	1	1
7.	0	1	0	0	1	0	0	0	1	1	1	0	1	1	1	1
8.	1	1	0	0	1	0	0	0	0	1	1	0	1	1	1	1
9.	1	1	1	1	1	1	1	1	1	0	1	0	1	1	1	1
10.	0	1	1	0	1	0	0	0	1	1	1	1	0	1	1	1
11.	1	1	1	1	1	1	1	1	0	1	1	1	0	1	1	1
12.	0	1	1	0	0	1	1	1	1	1	1	1	0	1	1	1
13.	1	1	1	1	1	1	1	0	1	1	1	1	1	0	1	1
14.	1	1	0	0	0	1	0	1	1	1	1	0	0	0	1	1
15.	1	0	0	1	0	1	1	1	1	1	1	1	1	0	1	1
16.	1	1	1	1	1	1	1	1	1	1	1	1	1	1	0	1
17.	1	1	1	1	1	1	1	1	1	1	1	1	1	1	1	0

$P(\mathcal{G}_{10},(9))$

FACES

Row	γ_1	γ_2	γ_3	γ_4	γ_5	γ_6	γ_7	γ_8	γ_9^*	γ_0
1	1	0	1	0	1	0	1	0	1	1
2	1	2	1	2	1	2	1	2	3	3
3	1	2	3	4	0	1	2	3	4	4
4	4	3	2	6	0	4	3	2	6	6
5	4	3	2	1	5	4	3	2	6	6
6	2	4	6	3	5	2	4	6	8	8
7	6	7	3	4	5	6	2	3	9	9
8	6	2	3	4	5	6	7	3	9	9
9	1	2	3	4	5	6	7	8	9	9
10	9	8	7	6	5	4	3	2	11	11
11	6	12	8	4	10	6	2	8	14	14
12	9	18	7	6	15	14	3	12	21	21

VERTICES $P(\mathcal{G}_{10},(9)$

1. $(t_1) = (9)$
2. $(t_1,t_2) = (1,4)$
3. $(t_2,t_3) = (3,1)$
4. $(t_3) = (3)$
5. $(t_2,t_3,t_4) = (1,1,1)$
6. $(t_1,t_4) = (1,2)$
7. $(t_3,t_4) = (1,4)$
8. $(t_1,t_5) = (4,1)$
9. $(t_2,t_5) = (2,1)$
10. $(t_1,t_3,t_5) = (1,1,1)$
11. $(t_4,t_5)= = (1,1)$
12. $(t_1,t_6) = (3,1)$
13. $(t_1,t_2,t_6) = (1,1,1)$
14. $(t_3,t_6) = (1,1)$
15. $(t_1,t_6) = (1,3)$
16. $(t_5,t_6) = (1,4)$

$(t_1,t_7) = (2,1)$ 17.
$(t_2,t_7) = (1,1)$ 18.
$(t_4,t_7) = (3,1)$ 19.
$(t_6,t_7) = (2,1)$ 20.
$(t_5,t_7) = (1,2)$ 21.
$(t_1,t_7) = (1,4)$ 22.
$(t_7) = (7)$ 23.
$(t_1,t_8) = (1,1)$ 24.
$(t_5,t_6,t_8) = (1,1,1)$ 25.
$(t_4,t_7,t_8) = (1,1,1)$ 26.
$(t_7,t_8) = (3,1)$ 27.
$(t_3,t_8) = (1,2)$ 28.
$(t_5,t_8) = (1,3)$ 29.
$(t_7,t_8) = (1,4)$ 30.
$(t_9) = (1)$ 31.

INCIDENCE MATRIX $P(\mathcal{G}_{10}, (9))$

Face / Vertex	1	2	3	4	5	6	7	8	9	10	11	12	13	14	15	16	17	18	19	20	21
1.	0	0	0	0	0	0	0	0	1	0	0	0	0	1	1	1	1	1	1	1	1
2.	1	0	0	0	0	0	0	0	1	0	0	0	0	0	1	1	1	1	1	1	1
3.	1	0	0	0	0	0	0	1	1	0	0	0	1	0	0	1	1	1	1	1	1
4.	0	1	0	1	1	0	1	1	1	0	0	1	1	1	0	1	1	1	1	1	1
5.	1	0	0	0	1	0	0	1	1	0	0	0	1	0	0	0	1	1	1	1	1
6.	1	0	0	0	1	1	0	0	1	0	1	1	0	1	1	0	1	1	1	1	1
7.	1	0	0	0	1	0	0	0	0	0	0	0	1	1	0	0	1	1	1	1	1
8.	0	0	1	0	0	0	0	0	1	0	0	0	0	1	1	1	0	1	1	1	1
9.	1	0	1	1	0	0	0	1	1	0	0	0	1	0	1	1	0	1	1	1	1
10.	0	1	1	1	0	0	0	0	1	0	0	0	0	1	0	1	0	1	1	1	1
11.	1	1	1	1	1	1	1	1	1	1	1	1	1	1	1	0	0	1	1	1	1
12.	0	0	1	0	0	1	0	0	1	0	0	0	0	1	1	1	1	0	1	1	1
13.	1	0	1	0	0	1	0	0	1	0	0	0	0	0	1	1	1	0	1	1	1
14.	1	1	1	1	1	1	1	1	1	1	1	1	1	1	0	1	1	0	1	1	1

Face / Vertex	1	2	3	4	5	6	7	8	9	10	11	12	13	14	15	16	17	18	19	20	21
15.	1	0	1	0	0	1	0	0	0	0	0	0	0	1	1	1	1	0	1	1	1
16.	1	0	1	0	0	0	0	0	0	0	0	0	1	1	1	1	0	0	1	1	1
17.	0	1	1	0	0	1	0	0	1	0	1	1	0	1	1	1	1	1	0	1	1
18.	1	1	1	1	1	1	1	1	1	1	1	1	1	0	1	1	1	1	0	1	1
19.	1	0	0	0	1	0	0	0	0	0	1	1	1	1	1	0	1	1	0	1	1
20.	1	0	1	0	0	1	0	0	0	1	1	0	1	1	1	1	1	0	0	1	1
21.	0	1	1	1	0	0	1	0	0	1	1	1	1	1	1	1	0	1	0	1	1
22.	0	0	0	0	0	0	0	0	0	0	1	1	0	1	1	1	1	1	0	1	1
23.	0	0	0	0	0	0	0	0	0	0	1	1	1	1	1	1	1	1	0	1	1
24.	1	1	1	1	1	1	1	1	1	1	1	1	0	1	1	1	1	1	1	0	1
25.	1	0	1	1	0	0	0	0	0	1	0	0	1	1	1	1	0	0	1	0	1
26.	1	0	0	0	1	0	1	0	0	1	1	1	1	1	1	0	1	1	0	0	1
27.	0	0	0	0	0	0	1	0	0	1	1	1	1	1	1	1	1	1	0	0	1
28.	1	0	0	1	1	0	1	1	0	1	0	0	1	1	0	1	1	1	1	0	1
29.	1	0	0	1	0	0	0	0	0	1	0	0	1	1	1	1	0	1	1	0	1
30.	1	0	0	0	0	0	0	0	0	1	0	0	1	1	1	1	1	1	0	0	1
31.	1	1	1	1	1	1	1	1	1	1	1	1	1	1	1	1	1	1	1	1	0

$P(\mathcal{G}_{11}, (0))$

FACES

Row	γ_1	γ_2	γ_3	γ_4	γ_5	γ_6	γ_7	γ_8	γ_9	γ_{10}	γ_0
1	2	1	2	2	2	1	1	1	2	1	3
2	1	2	1	1	1	2	2	2	1	2	3
3	10	9	8	7	6	5	4	3	2	1	11
4	9	7	5	3	1	10	8	6	4	2	11
5	8	5	2	10	7	4	1	9	6	3	11
6	7	3	10	6	2	9	5	1	8	4	11
7	6	1	7	2	8	3	9	4	10	5	11
8	5	10	4	9	3	8	2	7	1	6	11
9	4	8	1	5	9	2	6	10	3	7	11
10	3	6	9	1	4	7	10	2	5	8	11
11	2	4	6	8	10	1	3	5	7	9	11
12	1	2	3	4	5	6	7	8	9	10	11
13	18	14	10	6	13	9	16	12	8	4	22
14	16	10	4	9	14	8	13	18	12	6	22
15	14	6	9	12	4	18	10	13	16	8	22
16	13	4	6	8	10	12	14	16	18	9	22
17	12	13	14	4	16	6	18	8	9	10	22
18	10	9	8	18	6	16	4	14	13	12	22
19	9	18	16	14	12	10	8	6	4	13	22
20	8	16	13	10	18	4	12	9	6	14	22
21	6	12	18	13	8	14	9	4	10	16	22
22	4	8	12	16	9	13	6	10	14	18	22

VERTICES $P(\mathcal{G}_{11},(0))$

1. $(t_1) = (11)$
2. $(t_1,t_2) = (1,5)$
3. $(t_2) = (11)$
4. $(t_2,t_3) = (4,1)$
5. $(t_1,t_3) = (2,3)$
6. $(t_2,t_3) = (1,3)$
7. $(t_3) = (11)$
8. $(t_1,t_4) = (3,2)$
9. $(t_1,t_2,t_4) = (1,1,2)$
10. $(t_3,t_4) = (1,2)$
11. $(t_2,t_4) = (1,5)$
12. $(t_4) = (11)$
13. $(t_2,t_5) = (3,1)$
14. $(t_3,t_5) = (2,1)$
15. $(t_2,t_4,t_5) = (1,1,1)$
16. $(t_1,t_5) = (1,2)$
17. $(t_4,t_5) = (3,2)$
18. $(t_2,t_5) = (1,4)$
19. $(t_5) = (11)$
20. $(t_1,t_6) = (5,1)$
21. $(t_1,t_2,t_6) = (1,2,1)$
22. $(t_1,t_3,t_6) = (2,1,1)$
23. $(t_2,t_3,t_6) = (1,1,1)$
24. $(t_1,t_4,t_6) = (1,1,1)$
25. $(t_4,t_6) = (4,1)$
26. $(t_5,t_6) = (1,1)$
27. $(t_2,t_6) = (2,3)$

$(t_4,t_6) = (1,3)$ 28.
$(t_3,t_6) = (1,5)$ 29.
$(t_6) = (11)$ 30.
$(t_1,t_7) = (4,1)$ 31.
$(t_2,t_7) = (2,1)$ 32.
$(t_1,t_3,t_7) = (1,1,1)$ 33.
$(t_3,t_7) = (5,1)$ 34.
$(t_4,t_7) = (1,1)$ 35.
$(t_5,t_7) = (3,1)$ 36.
$(t_3,t_6,t_7) = (1,2,1)$ 37.
$(t_1,t_7) = (1,3)$ 38.
$(t_6,t_7) = (2,3)$ 39.
$(t_5,t_7) = (1,4)$ 40.
$(t_7) = (11)$ 41.
$(t_1,t_8) = (3,1)$ 42.
$(t_1,t_2,t_8) = (1,1,1)$ 43.
$(t_3,t_8) = (1,1)$ 44.
$(t_4,t_5,t_8) = (1,2,1)$ 45.
$(t_5,t_8) = (5,1)$ 46.
$(t_7,t_8) = (2,1)$ 47.
$(t_2,t_8) = (3,2)$ 48.
$(t_2,t_4,t_8) = (1,1,2)$ 49.
$(t_6,t_8) = (1,2)$ 50.
$(t_1,t_8) = (1,4)$ 51.
$(t_4,t_8) = (1,5)$ 52.
$(t_8) = (11)$ 53.
$(t_1,t_9) = (2,1)$ 54.

55. $(t_2,t_9) = (1,1)$
56. $(t_6,t_9) = (4,1)$
57. $(t_3,t_7,t_9) = (2,1,1)$
58. $(t_6,t_7,t_9) = (1,1,1)$
59. $(t_7,t_9) = (5,1)$
60. $(t_5,t_8,t_9) = (1,1,1)$
61. $(t_8,t_9) = (3,1)$
62. $(t_4,t_9) = (1,2)$
63. $(t_5,t_9) = (3,2)$
64. $(t_3,t_9) = (2,3)$
65. $(t_6,t_9) = (1,3)$
66. $(t_8,t_9) = (1,4)$
67. $(t_9) = (11)$
68. $(t_1,t_{10}) = (1,1)$
69. $(t_3,t_{10}) = (4,1)$
70. $(t_4,t_{10}) = (3,1)$

$(t_6,t_{10}) = (2,1)$ 71.
$(t_5,t_7,t_{10}) = (1,1,1)$ 72.
$(t_4,t_8,t_{10}) = (1,1,1)$ 73.
$(t_3,t_9,t_{10}) = (1,1,1)$ 74.
$(t_7,t_9,t_{10}) = (2,1,1)$ 75.
$(t_5,t_9,t_{10}) = (1,2,1)$ 76.
$(t_9,t_{10}) = (5,1)$ 77.
$(t_2,t_{10}) = (1,2)$ 78.
$(t_5,t_8,t_{10}) = (1,1,2)$ 79.
$(t_8,t_{10}) = (3,2)$ 80.
$(t_3,t_{10}) = (1,3)$ 81.
$(t_7,t_{10}) = (2,3)$ 82.
$(t_4,t_{10}) = (1,4)$ 83.
$(t_5,t_{10}) = (1,5)$ 84.
$(t_{10}) = (11)$ 85.

INCIDENCE MATRIX $P(\mathcal{G}_{11}, (0))$

Face / Vertex	1	2	3	4	5	6	7	8	9	10	11	12	13	14	15	16	17	18	19	20	21	22	23	24	25	26	27	28	29	30	31	32
1.	0	0	0	0	0	0	0	0	0	0	0	1	0	0	0	0	0	0	0	0	0	0	0	1	1	1	1	1	1	1	1	1
2.	0	0	0	0	0	0	1	0	0	0	0	1	0	0	0	0	0	0	0	0	0	0	0	0	1	1	1	1	1	1	1	1
3.	0	0	0	0	0	0	1	0	0	0	0	0	0	0	0	0	0	0	0	0	0	0	1	0	1	1	1	1	1	1	1	1
4.	0	0	0	0	0	0	1	0	0	0	0	1	0	0	0	1	0	0	0	0	0	0	1	0	0	1	1	1	1	1	1	1
5.	0	0	0	0	0	0	0	0	1	0	0	1	0	0	0	0	0	0	0	0	0	0	0	1	0	1	1	1	1	1	1	1
6.	0	0	0	0	1	0	0	0	1	0	0	1	0	1	0	1	0	0	0	0	0	0	1	0	0	1	1	1	1	1	1	1
7.	0	0	0	0	0	0	0	0	1	0	0	0	0	0	0	0	0	0	0	0	0	0	1	1	0	1	1	1	1	1	1	1
8.	0	0	0	0	0	0	0	0	0	1	0	1	0	0	0	0	0	0	0	0	0	0	0	1	1	0	1	1	1	1	1	1
9.	0	0	0	0	0	0	1	0	0	1	0	1	0	0	0	0	0	0	0	0	0	0	0	0	1	0	1	1	1	1	1	1
10.	0	1	0	1	0	0	1	0	1	1	0	1	1	1	0	1	1	0	0	0	0	0	1	1	0	0	1	1	1	1	1	1
11.	0	0	0	0	0	0	1	0	0	1	0	0	0	0	0	0	0	0	0	0	0	0	1	0	1	0	1	1	1	1	1	1
12.	0	0	0	0	0	0	0	0	0	1	0	0	0	0	0	0	0	0	0	0	0	0	1	1	1	0	1	1	1	1	1	1
13.	0	0	0	0	0	1	1	0	0	0	0	1	0	0	1	1	0	0	0	0	0	0	1	0	1	1	0	1	1	1	1	1
14.	0	1	0	1	1	0	0	1	1	0	0	1	0	1	1	1	0	1	0	0	0	0	1	1	0	1	0	1	1	1	1	1
15.	0	0	0	1	0	1	1	0	0	1	0	1	0	0	1	1	0	0	0	0	0	0	1	0	1	0	0	1	1	1	1	1
16.	0	1	0	1	0	1	0	1	0	1	0	1	0	0	1	0	0	1	0	0	1	1	0	1	1	1	0	1	1	1	1	1
17.	0	0	0	1	0	0	0	0	0	1	0	0	0	0	0	0	0	0	0	0	0	0	1	1	1	0	0	1	1	1	1	1
18.	0	0	0	1	0	1	0	0	0	0	0	0	0	0	1	0	0	0	0	0	0	0	1	0	1	1	0	1	1	1	1	1
19.	0	0	0	1	0	0	0	0	0	0	0	0	0	0	0	0	0	0	0	0	0	0	1	1	1	1	0	1	1	1	1	1
20.	0	0	0	0	0	0	0	0	0	0	1	1	0	0	0	0	0	0	0	0	0	0	0	1	1	1	1	0	1	1	1	1

Face / Vertex	1	2	3	4	5	6	7	8	9	10	11	12	13	14	15	16	17	18	19	20	21	22	23	24	25	26	27	28	29	30	31	32
21.	0	0	0	0	0	0	1	0	0	0	1	1	0	0	0	0	0	0	0	0	0	0	0	0	1	1	1	0	1	1	1	1
22.	0	0	0	0	0	0	0	0	1	0	1	1	0	0	0	0	0	0	0	0	0	0	0	1	0	1	1	0	1	1	1	1
23.	0	0	0	0	1	0	1	0	1	0	1	1	0	1	0	1	0	0	0	0	0	0	1	0	0	1	1	0	1	1	1	1
24.	0	0	0	0	0	0	1	0	1	1	1	1	0	0	0	0	1	0	0	1	0	0	0	1	1	0	1	0	1	1	1	1
25.	0	0	0	0	0	0	1	0	0	1	0	0	0	0	0	0	1	0	0	0	0	0	1	1	1	0	1	0	1	1	1	1
26.	1	1	1	1	1	1	1	1	1	1	1	1	1	1	1	1	1	1	1	1	1	1	1	1	1	1	0	0	1	1	1	1
27.	0	0	0	0	0	0	1	0	0	0	1	0	0	0	0	0	0	0	0	0	0	0	1	0	1	1	1	0	1	1	1	1
28.	0	0	0	0	0	0	1	0	1	0	1	0	0	0	0	0	1	0	0	1	0	0	1	1	1	0	1	0	1	1	1	1
29.	0	0	0	0	0	0	0	0	1	0	1	0	0	0	0	0	0	0	0	0	0	0	1	1	0	1	1	0	1	1	1	1
30.	0	0	0	0	0	0	0	0	0	0	1	0	0	0	0	0	0	0	0	0	0	0	1	1	1	1	1	0	1	1	1	1
31.	0	0	0	0	0	0	0	0	0	0	1	1	0	0	0	0	0	0	0	0	0	1	0	1	1	1	1	1	0	1	1	1
32.	1	0	0	0	1	1	1	0	0	0	1	1	0	0	1	1	0	1	0	0	0	1	1	0	1	1	1	1	0	1	1	1
33.	0	0	0	0	1	0	0	1	1	0	1	1	0	0	0	0	0	1	0	0	0	1	0	1	0	1	1	1	0	1	1	1
34.	0	0	0	0	1	0	0	0	1	0	0	0	0	0	0	0	0	0	0	0	0	0	1	1	0	1	1	1	0	1	1	1
35.	1	1	1	1	1	1	1	1	1	1	1	1	1	1	1	1	1	1	1	1	1	1	1	1	1	0	1	1	0	1	1	1
36.	0	0	0	1	0	1	0	1	0	0	0	0	0	0	1	0	0	1	0	0	0	0	1	1	1	1	0	1	0	1	1	1
37.	0	0	0	0	1	0	0	0	1	0	1	0	0	0	0	0	0	0	0	0	0	0	1	1	0	1	1	0	0	1	1	1
38.	0	0	0	0	1	0	0	1	0	0	1	0	0	0	0	0	0	1	0	0	0	1	0	1	1	1	1	1	0	1	1	1
39.	0	0	0	0	1	0	0	0	0	0	1	0	0	0	0	0	0	0	0	0	0	0	1	1	1	1	1	0	0	1	1	1
40.	0	0	0	0	1	0	0	1	0	0	0	0	0	0	0	0	0	1	0	0	0	0	1	1	1	1	0	1	0	1	1	1
41.	0	0	0	0	1	0	0	0	0	0	0	0	0	0	0	0	0	0	0	0	0	0	1	1	1	1	1	1	0	1	1	1
42.	0	0	0	0	0	0	0	0	0	1	1	1	0	0	0	0	0	0	0	0	1	1	0	1	1	1	1	1	1	0	1	1

INCIDENCE MATRIX P(ℊ$_{11}$, (0)) continued

FACE / VERTEX	1	2	3	4	5	6	7	8	9	10	11	12	13	14	15	16	17	18	19	20	21	22	23	24	25	26	27	28	29	30	31	32
43.	0	0	0	0	0	1	1	0	0	1	1	1	0	0	0	0	0	0	0	0	1	1	0	0	1	1	1	1	1	0	1	1
44.	1	1	1	1	1	1	1	1	1	1	1	1	1	1	1	1	1	1	1	1	1	1	1	1	0	1	1	1	1	0	1	1
45.	0	0	0	1	0	1	0	0	0	1	0	0	0	0	0	0	0	0	0	0	0	0	1	1	1	0	0	1	1	0	1	1
46.	0	0	0	1	0	1	0	0	0	0	0	0	0	0	0	0	0	0	0	0	0	0	1	1	1	1	0	1	1	0	1	1
47.	1	0	1	0	1	1	0	1	0	0	1	0	0	0	0	0	0	1	1	0	1	1	1	1	1	1	1	1	0	0	1	1
48.	0	0	0	0	0	1	1	0	0	0	0	0	0	0	0	0	0	0	0	0	0	0	1	0	1	1	1	1	1	0	1	1
49.	0	0	0	0	0	1	1	0	0	1	0	0	0	0	0	0	0	0	0	0	0	0	1	0	1	0	1	1	1	0	1	1
50.	1	0	1	0	0	1	1	0	0	1	1	0	0	0	0	0	1	0	1	1	1	0	1	1	1	1	1	0	1	0	1	1
51.	0	0	0	0	0	1	0	0	0	1	0	0	0	0	0	0	0	0	0	0	1	0	0	1	1	1	1	1	1	0	1	1
52.	0	0	0	0	0	1	0	0	0	1	0	0	0	0	0	0	0	0	0	0	0	0	1	1	1	0	1	1	1	0	1	1
53.	0	0	0	0	0	1	0	0	0	0	0	0	0	0	0	0	0	0	0	0	0	0	1	1	1	1	1	1	1	0	1	1
54.	0	1	0	0	0	0	0	1	1	1	1	1	0	0	0	0	0	0	1	1	1	1	0	1	1	1	1	1	1	1	0	1
55.	1	1	1	1	1	1	1	1	1	1	1	1	1	1	1	1	1	1	1	1	1	1	1	0	1	1	1	1	1	1	0	1
56.	0	0	0	0	0	0	0	0	1	0	1	0	0	0	0	0	0	0	0	1	0	0	1	1	1	1	1	0	1	1	0	1
57.	0	0	0	0	1	0	0	1	1	0	0	0	0	0	0	0	0	0	0	0	0	0	1	1	0	1	1	1	0	1	0	1
58.	0	0	1	0	1	0	0	1	1	0	1	0	0	0	0	0	0	1	1	0	0	0	1	1	1	1	1	0	0	1	0	1
59.	0	0	0	0	1	0	0	1	0	0	0	0	0	0	0	0	0	0	0	0	0	0	1	1	1	1	1	1	0	1	0	1
60.	0	0	1	1	0	1	0	1	0	1	0	0	0	0	0	0	0	0	1	0	1	0	1	1	1	1	0	1	1	0	0	1
61.	0	0	1	0	0	1	0	0	0	1	0	0	0	0	0	0	0	0	1	0	1	0	1	1	1	1	1	1	1	0	0	1
62.	0	1	1	1	0	0	0	1	1	1	0	0	1	0	0	0	1	0	1	1	0	0	1	1	1	0	1	1	1	1	0	1

Face / Vertex	1	2	3	4	5	6	7	8	9	10	11	12	13	14	15	16	17	18	19	20	21	22	23	24	25	26	27	28	29	30	31	32
63.	0	0	0	1	0	0	0	1	0	0	0	0	0	0	0	0	0	0	0	0	0	0	1	1	1	1	0	1	1	1	0	1
64.	0	0	0	0	0	0	0	1	1	0	0	0	0	0	0	0	0	0	0	0	0	0	1	1	0	1	1	1	1	1	0	1
65.	0	0	1	0	0	0	0	1	1	0	0	0	0	0	0	0	0	0	1	1	0	0	1	1	1	1	1	0	1	1	0	1
66.	0	0	1	0	0	0	0	1	0	0	0	0	0	0	0	0	0	0	1	0	0	0	1	1	1	1	1	1	1	0	0	1
67.	0	0	0	0	0	0	0	1	0	0	0	0	0	0	0	0	0	0	0	0	0	0	1	1	1	1	1	1	1	1	0	1
68.	1	1	1	1	1	1	1	1	1	1	1	1	1	1	1	1	1	1	1	1	1	1	0	1	1	1	1	1	1	1	1	0
69.	0	0	0	0	1	0	0	0	1	0	0	0	0	1	0	0	0	0	0	0	0	0	1	1	0	1	1	1	1	1	1	0
70.	0	0	0	1	0	0	1	0	0	1	0	0	1	0	0	0	1	0	0	0	0	0	1	1	1	0	1	1	1	1	1	0
71.	1	0	1	0	1	0	1	0	1	0	1	0	1	1	0	0	1	0	0	1	0	0	1	1	1	1	1	0	1	1	1	0
72.	0	0	1	1	1	1	0	1	0	0	0	0	0	0	1	0	0	1	0	0	0	0	1	1	1	1	0	1	0	1	1	0
73.	0	0	1	1	0	1	1	0	0	1	0	0	1	0	0	0	1	0	0	0	0	0	1	1	1	0	1	1	1	0	1	0
74.	0	0	1	1	1	0	0	1	1	0	0	0	1	1	0	0	0	0	0	0	0	0	1	1	0	1	1	1	1	1	0	0
75.	0	0	1	0	1	0	0	1	0	0	0	0	0	0	0	0	0	0	0	0	0	0	1	1	1	1	1	1	0	1	0	0
76.	0	0	1	1	0	0	0	1	0	0	0	0	0	0	0	0	0	0	0	0	0	0	1	1	1	1	0	1	1	1	0	0
77.	0	0	1	0	0	0	0	1	0	0	0	0	0	0	0	0	0	0	0	0	0	0	1	1	1	1	1	1	1	1	0	0
78.	1	0	1	1	1	1	1	0	0	0	0	0	1	1	1	1	0	0	0	0	0	0	1	0	1	1	1	1	1	1	1	0
79.	0	0	1	1	0	1	0	0	0	0	0	0	0	0	0	0	0	0	0	0	0	0	1	1	1	1	0	1	1	0	1	0
80.	0	0	1	0	0	1	0	0	0	0	0	0	0	0	0	0	0	0	0	0	0	0	1	1	1	1	1	1	1	0	1	0
81.	0	0	1	1	1	0	0	0	0	0	0	0	1	1	0	0	0	0	0	0	0	0	1	1	0	1	1	1	1	1	1	0
82.	0	0	1	0	1	0	0	0	0	0	0	0	0	0	0	0	0	0	0	0	0	0	1	1	1	1	1	1	0	1	1	0
83.	0	0	1	1	0	0	0	0	0	0	0	0	1	0	0	0	0	0	0	0	0	0	1	1	1	0	1	1	1	1	1	0
84.	0	0	1	1	0	0	0	0	0	0	0	0	0	0	0	0	0	0	0	0	0	0	1	1	1	1	0	1	1	1	1	0
85.	0	0	1	0	0	0	0	0	0	0	0	0	0	0	0	0	0	0	0	0	0	0	1	1	1	1	1	1	1	1	1	0

$P(\mathcal{G}_{11},(10))$

FACES

Row	γ_1	γ_2	γ_3	γ_4	γ_5	γ_6	γ_7	γ_8	γ_9	γ_{10}^*	γ_0
1	1	2	3	4	5	6	7	8	9	10	10
2	10	9	8	7	6	5	4	3	2	12	12
3	8	5	2	10	7	4	12	9	6	14	14
4	6	12	7	13	8	3	9	4	10	16	16
5	6	12	7	2	8	14	9	4	10	16	16
6	15	8	12	5	9	13	6	10	3	18	18
7	4	8	12	16	9	2	6	10	14	18	18
8	4	8	12	5	9	13	6	10	14	18	18
9	13	4	6	8	10	12	14	16	7	20	20
10	13	15	6	8	10	12	14	5	7	20	20
11	20	7	16	14	12	10	8	17	4	24	24
12	9	18	16	14	12	10	8	6	15	24	24
13	9	18	16	3	12	21	8	6	15	24	24
14	9	18	5	14	12	10	19	6	15	24	24
15	18	14	10	6	13	20	16	12	8	26	26
16	16	21	4	20	14	8	24	7	12	28	28
17	25	6	20	12	15	18	10	24	5	30	30
18	14	6	20	12	15	18	10	24	16	30	30

VERTICES $P(\mathcal{G}_{11},(10))$

1. (t_1) = (10)
2. (t_2) = (5)
3. (t_2,t_3) = (2,2)
4. (t_1,t_3) = (1,3)
5. (t_3) = (7)
6. (t_3,t_4) = (2,1)
7. (t_1,t_4) = (2,2)
8. (t_2,t_4) = (1,2)
9. (t_4) = (8)
10. (t_5) = (2)
11. (t_1,t_6) = (4,1)
12. (t_2,t_6) = (2,1)
13. (t_1,t_3,t_6) = (1,1,1)
14. (t_4,t_6) = (1,1)
15. (t_3,t_6) = (1,3)
16. (t_6) = (9)

(t_1,t_7) = (3,1) 17.
(t_1,t_2,t_7) = (1,1,1) 18.
(t_3,t_7) = (1,1) 19.
(t_7) = (3) 20.
(t_1,t_8) = (2,1) 21.
(t_2,t_8) = (1,1) 22.
(t_6,t_8) = (4,1) 23.
(t_6,t_7,t_8) = (1,1,1) 24.
(t_8) = (4) 25.
(t_1,t_9) = (1,1) 26.
(t_4,t_9) = (3,1) 27.
(t_6,t_9) = (2,1) 28.
(t_4,t_8,t_9) = (1,1,1) 29.
(t_3,t_9) = (1,2) 30.
(t_5,t_9) = (1,3) 31.
(t_9) = (6) 32.
(t_{10}) = (1) 33.

INCIDENCE MATRIX P($\mathcal{G}_{11}$, (10))

Face / Vertex	1	2	3	4	5	6	7	8	9	10	11	12	13	14	15	16	17	18	19	20	21	22	23	24	25	26	27	28
1.	1	0	0	0	0	0	0	0	0	0	0	0	0	0	0	0	0	0	0	1	1	1	1	1	1	1	1	1
2.	1	0	0	0	0	0	0	0	1	0	0	0	0	0	0	0	1	1	1	0	1	1	1	1	1	1	1	1
3.	1	0	1	0	0	0	0	0	1	0	0	0	0	0	0	0	0	0	1	0	0	1	1	1	1	1	1	1
4.	1	0	1	0	0	0	0	0	0	0	0	0	0	1	0	1	0	0	0	1	0	1	1	1	1	1	1	1
5.	0	0	1	0	0	0	0	0	0	0	0	0	0	0	0	1	0	0	1	1	0	1	1	1	1	1	1	1
6.	1	0	1	0	1	0	0	0	1	1	0	0	0	1	1	1	0	0	1	1	0	0	1	1	1	1	1	1
7.	1	0	0	0	1	0	0	1	0	0	0	0	1	0	0	0	0	0	0	1	1	0	1	1	1	1	1	1
8.	1	0	0	0	1	1	0	1	1	0	0	0	1	0	1	0	1	1	1	0	1	0	1	1	1	1	1	1
9.	0	0	0	0	1	0	0	0	0	0	0	0	1	0	0	0	0	0	1	1	1	0	1	1	1	1	1	1
10.	1	1	1	1	1	1	1	1	1	1	1	1	1	1	1	1	1	1	1	1	1	1	0	1	1	1	1	1
11.	1	0	0	0	0	0	1	0	0	0	0	0	0	0	0	0	0	0	0	1	1	1	1	0	1	1	1	1
12.	1	0	1	0	0	0	1	0	1	0	1	0	0	0	0	0	1	1	1	0	1	1	1	0	1	1	1	1
13.	1	0	1	1	0	0	1	0	0	0	0	0	0	1	1	1	0	0	0	1	0	1	1	0	1	1	1	1
14.	1	1	1	1	1	1	1	1	1	1	1	1	1	1	1	1	1	1	1	1	1	0	1	0	1	1	1	1
15.	0	0	1	1	0	0	1	0	0	0	0	0	0	0	0	1	0	0	1	1	0	1	1	0	1	1	1	1
16.	0	0	0	0	0	0	1	0	0	0	0	0	0	0	0	0	0	0	1	1	1	1	1	0	1	1	1	1

INCIDENCE MATRIX $P(\mathcal{G}_{11}, (10))$

Face / Vertex	1	2	3	4	5	6	7	8	9	10	11	12	13	14	15	16	17	18	19	20	21	22	23	24	25	26	27	28
17.	1	0	0	0	0	0	1	1	0	0	0	0	0	0	0	0	0	0	0	1	1	1	1	1	0	1	1	1
18.	1	0	0	0	0	0	1	1	0	0	0	0	0	0	0	0	0	1	0	0	1	1	1	1	0	1	1	1
19.	1	1	1	1	1	1	1	1	1	1	1	1	1	1	1	1	1	1	1	1	0	1	1	1	0	1	1	1
20.	0	1	0	0	0	1	1	1	0	0	1	1	1	0	0	0	1	1	1	1	1	1	1	1	0	1	1	1
21.	1	0	0	1	1	0	1	1	0	0	0	1	1	1	0	0	0	0	0	1	1	1	1	1	1	0	1	1
22.	1	1	1	1	1	1	1	1	1	1	1	1	1	1	1	1	1	1	1	0	1	1	1	1	1	0	1	1
23.	0	0	0	1	0	0	1	0	0	0	0	0	0	0	0	0	0	0	1	1	1	1	1	0	1	0	1	1
24.	0	1	0	1	0	0	1	0	0	0	0	1	0	0	0	0	0	0	1	1	1	1	1	0	0	0	1	1
25.	0	1	0	1	1	0	0	0	0	1	0	1	1	1	0	1	0	0	1	1	1	1	1	1	1	0	1	1
26.	1	1	1	1	1	1	1	1	1	1	1	1	1	1	1	1	1	1	0	1	1	1	1	1	1	1	0	1
27.	0	0	0	0	1	1	0	0	0	0	0	0	1	0	1	0	0	0	1	1	1	0	1	1	1	1	0	1
28.	0	1	1	1	0	0	1	0	0	0	1	0	0	0	0	1	0	0	1	1	1	1	1	0	1	1	0	1
29.	0	1	0	0	1	1	0	0	0	1	0	0	1	0	0	0	0	0	1	1	1	0	1	1	1	0	0	1
30.	0	1	1	0	0	1	0	0	1	1	1	0	0	0	1	1	1	0	1	1	0	1	1	1	1	1	0	1
31.	0	1	0	0	0	1	0	0	0	0	1	0	0	0	0	0	1	0	1	1	1	1	0	1	1	1	0	1
32.	0	1	0	0	0	1	0	0	0	0	1	0	0	0	0	0	1	0	1	1	1	1	1	1	1	1	0	1
33.	1	1	1	1	1	1	1	1	1	1	1	1	1	1	1	1	1	1	1	1	1	1	1	1	1	1	1	0

REFERENCES

ACM: Association for Computing Machinery
NRLQ: Naval Research Logistics Quarterly
ORSA: Operations Research Society of America
SIAM: Society of Industrial and Applied Mathematics

1. Abadie, J. M. (ed.), *Non-Linear Programming*, North-Holland Publishing Co., Amsterdam, 1967.
2. Ackers, J. B., "The Use of Wye-Delta Transformation in Network Simplification," *J. ORSA*, **8** (3), 311–323 (1960).
3. Arrow, K. J., L. Hurwicz, and H. Uzawa, *Studies in Linear and Nonlinear Programming,* Stanford University Press, Stanford, California, 1958.
4. Balas, E., "An Additive Algorithm for Solving Linear Programs with Zero-One Variables," *J. ORSA,* **13** (4), 517–546 (1965).
5. Balas, E., *Duality in Discrete Programming,* Graduate School of Industrial Administration, Carnegie-Mellon University, Dec. 1967.
6. Balinski, M. L., "Integer Programming: Methods, Uses, Computation," *Man. Sci.,* **12** (3), 253–313 (Nov. 1965).
7. Balinski, M. L., and R. E. Gomory, "A Mutual Primal-Dual Simplex Method," in R. L. Graves and P. Wolfe (eds.), *Recent Advances in Mathematical Programming,* McGraw-Hill, New York, 1963, pp. 17–26.
8. Beale, E. M. L., "An Alternate Method of Linear Programming," *Proc. Cambridge Phil. Soc.*, **50** (4), 513–523 (1954).
9. Beale, E. M. L., "Cycling in the Dual Simplex Algorithm," *NRLQ*, **2** (4), 269–276 (Dec. 1955).
10. Beale, E. M. L., *A Method of Solving Linear Programming Problems When Some but Not All of the Variables Must Take Integral Values,* Statistical Tech. Research Group, Princeton University, March 1958.
11. Beale, E. M. L., "An Algorithm for Solving the Transportation Problem When the Shipping Cost Over Each Route is Convex, "*NRLQ*, **6** (1), 43–56 (March 1959).

12. Beale, E. M. L., "On Quadratic Programming," *NRLQ*, **6** (3), 227–243 (Sept. 1959).
13. Beale, E. M. L., *Mathematical Programming*, Isaac Pitman & Son, London, 1968.
14. Beale, E. M. L., and R. E. Small, "Mixed Integer Programming by a Branch and Bound Technique," *Proc. IFIP Congress., New York*, **2** (May 1965).
15. Bellman, R., *Dynamic Programming*, Princeton University Press, Princeton, N. J., 1957.
16. Bellman, R. E., and S. E. Dreyfus, *Applied Dynamic Programming*, Princeton University Press, Princeton, N. J., 1962.
17. Ben-Israel, A., and A. Charnes, "On Some Problems of Diaphantine Programming," *Cahiers du Centre d'Etudes de Recherche Operationelle (Bruxelles)*, **4**, 215–280 (1962).
18. Benders, J. F., "Partitioning Procedures for Solving Mixed-Variables Programming Problems," *Numerische Mathematik*, **4**, 238–252 (1962).
19. Berge, C., and A. Ghouila-Houri, *Programming, Games and Transportation Networks* (Translated by M. Merrington and C. Ramanujacharyula), John Wiley & Sons, New York, 1965.
20. Blankinship, W. A., "A New Version of the Euclidean Algorithm," *Am. Math. Monthly*, **70** (7), 742–745 (1963).
21. Boldyreff, A. W., "Determination of the Maximal Steady State Flow of Traffic Through a Railroad Network," *J. ORSA*, **3** (4), 443–465 (Nov. 1955).
22. Busacker, R. G., and P. J. Gowen, "A Procedure for Determining a Family of Minimal-Cost Network Flow Patterns," *ORO Technical Report 15*, Operations Research Office, Johns Hopkins University, 1961.
23. Busacker, R. G., and T. L. Saaty, *Finite Graphs and Networks*, McGraw-Hill, New York, 1964.
24. Charnes, A., "Optimality and Degeneracy in Linear Programming," *Econometrica*, **20** (2), 160–170 (April 1952).
25. Charnes, A., and W. W. Cooper, *Management Models and Industrial Applications of Linear Programming*, John Wiley & Sons, New York, 1961.
26. Charnes, A., W. W. Cooper, and A. Henderson, *An Introduction to Linear Programming*, John Wiley & Sons, New York, 1953.
27. Dakin, R. J., "A Tree-Search Algorithm for Mixed-Integer Programming Problems," *The Computer Journal*, **8** (3), 250–255 (1965).
28. Dantzig, G. B., *Programming in a Linear Structure*, Comptroller, USAF, Washington, D. C., Feb. 1948.
29. Dantzig, G. B., "Maximization of a Linear Function of Variables Subject to Linear Inequalities," in T. C. Koopmans (ed.), *Activity Analysis of Production and Allocation*, John Wiley & Sons, New York, 1951, pp. 339–347.
30. Dantzig, G. B., "A Proof of the Equivalence of the Programming Problem and the Game Problem," in T. C. Koopmans (ed.), *Activity Analysis of Production and Allocation*. John Wiley & Sons, New York, 1951, pp. 359–373.
31. Dantzig, G. B., "Notes on Linear Programming: Part VII. The Dual Simplex Algorithm," *RAND Report RM-1270*, July 1954.

32. Dantzig, G. B., "Upper Bounds, Secondary Constraints, and Block Triangularity in Linear Programming," *Econometrica*, **23** (2), 174–183 (April 1955).

33. Dantzig, G. B., "Discrete Variable Extremum Problems," *J. ORSA*, **5** (2), 266–277 (April 1957).

34. Dantzig, G. B., "On the Significance of Solving Linear Programming Problems with Some Integer Variables," *Econometrica*, **28** (1), 30–44 (Jan. 1960).

35. Dantzig, G. B., "On the Shortest Route Through a Network," *Man. Sci.*, **6** (2), 187–190 (Jan. 1960).

36. Dantzig, G. B., "Inductive Proof of the Simplex Method," *IBM, J. Res. Develop.*, **4** (5), 505–506 (Nov. 1960).

37. Dantzig, G. B., *Linear Programming and Extensions*, Princeton University Press, Princeton, N. J., 1962.

38. Dantzig, G. B., "All Shortest Routes in a Graph," Operations Research House, *Stanford University Technical Report 66–3*, Nov. 1966.

39. Dantzig, G. B., W. D. Blanttner, and M. R. Rao, "All Shortest Routes from a Fixed Origin in a Graph," Operations Research House, *Stanford University Technical Report 66–2*, Nov. 1966.

40. Dantzig, G.B., L. R. Ford, Jr., and D. R. Fulkerson, "A Primal-Dual Algorithm for Linear Programs," in H. W. Kuhn and A. W. Tucker (eds.), *Linear Inequalities and Related Systems*, Annals of Mathematics Study No. 38, Princeton University Press, Princeton, N. J., 1965, pp. 171–181.

41. Dantzig, G. B., D. R. Fulkerson, and S. M. Johnson, "Solution of a Large-Scale Traveling-Salesman Problem," *J. ORSA*, **2** (4), 393–410 (Nov. 1954).

42. Dantzig, G. B., D. R. Fulkerson, and S. M. Johnson, "On a Linear Programming Combinatorial Approach to the Traveling-Salesman Problem, *J. ORSA*, **7** (1), 58–66 (Jan.–Feb. 1959).

43. Dantzig, G. B., and W. Orchard-Hayes, "Alternate Algorithm for the Revised Simplex Method Using Product Form of the Inverse," *RAND Report RM-1268*, Nov. 1953.

44. Dantzig, G. B., and A. Orden, "Duality Theorems," *RAND Report RM-1265*, Oct. 1953.

45. Dantzig, G. B., A. Orden, and P. Wolfe, "The Generalized Simplex Method for Minimizing a Linear Form under Linear Inequality Restraints," *Pac. J. Math.*, **5** (2), 183–195 (June 1955).

46. Dantzig, G. B., and P. Wolfe, "Decomposition Principle for Linear Programs," *J. ORSA*, **8** (1), 101–111 (Jan.–Feb. 1960).

47. Dantzig, G. B., and P. Wolfe, "The Decomposition Algorithm for Linear Programs, *Econometrica*, **29** (4), 767–778 (Oct. 1961).

48. Dennis, J. B., *Mathematical Programming and Electrical Networks*, John Wiley & Sons, New York, 1959.

49. Dijkstra, E. W., "A Note on Two Problems in Connection with Graphs," *Num. Math.*, **1**, 269–271 (1959).

50. Dreyfus, S. E., "An Appraisal of Some Shortest Path Algorithms," *RAND Report RM-5433-PR*, Oct. 1967.

51. Duffin, R. J., "Infinite Programs," in H. W. Kuhn and A. W. Tucker (eds.), *Linear Inequalities and Related Systems,* Annals of Mathematics Study No. 38, Princeton University Press, Princeton, N. J., 1956, pp. 157–170.

52. Duffin, R. J., E. L. Peterson, and C. Zener, *Geometric Programming: Theory and Applications,* John Wiley & Sons, New York, 1967.

53. Dzielinski, B. P., and R. E. Gomory, "Optimal Programming of Lot Size Inventory and Labor Allocations," *Man. Sci.,* **11** (9), 874–890 (1965).

54. Edmonds, J., "Covers and Packings in a Family of Sets," *Bulletin of AMS,* **68**, 494–499 (1962).

55. Edmonds, J., "Paths, Trees, and Flowers," *Canadian J. Math.,* **17** (3), 449–467 (May 1965).

56. Edmonds, J., "Maximum Matching and a Polyhedron with 0, 1-Vertices." *J. Research National Bureau of Standards B,* **1** and **2**, 125–130 (Jan.–June 1965).

57. Edmonds, J., and D. R. Fulkerson, "Bottleneck Extrema," *RAND Report RM-5375-PR,* Jan. 1968.

58. Edmonds, J., and R. M. Karp, "A Labeling Method for Maximal Network Flows which is Bounded by a Polynomial in the Number of Nodes," to appear as an IBM or NBS report.

59. Fan, K., "Minimax Theorems," *Proc. Natl. Acad. Sci., U.S.A.,* **39** (1), 42–47 (1953).

60. Farbey, B. A., A. H. Lard, and J. D. Murchland, "The Cascade Algorithm for Finding All Shortest Distances in a Directed Graph," *Man. Sci.,* **14** (1), 19–28 (Sept. 1967).

61. Farkas, J., "Uber die Theorie der einfachen Ungleichungen," *J. Reine Angew, Math.* (124), 1–24 (1902).

62. Fenchel, W., "Convex Cones, Sets, and Functions," in D. W. Blakett's lecture notes, Office of Nav. Res. Log. Proj. Report, Dept. of Math., Princeton University.

63. Floyd, R. W., "Algorithm 97: Shortest Path," *Communication of ACM,* **5**, (6), 345 (1962).

64. Ford, L. R., Jr., and D. R. Fulkerson, "Maximal Flow Through a Network," *Canadian J. Math.,* **8** (3), 399–404 (1956).

65. Ford, L. R., Jr., and D. R. Fulkerson, "A Simple Algorithm for Finding Maximal Network Flows and an Application to the Hitchcock Problem," *Canadian J. Math.,* **9** (2), 210–218 (1957).

66. Ford, L. R., Jr., and D. R. Fulkerson, "Suggested Computation for Maximal Multi-Commodity Network Flows," *Man. Sci.,* **5** (1), 97–101 (Oct. 1958).

67. Ford, L. R., Jr., and D. R. Fulkerson, "Flows in Networks," Princeton University Press, Princeton, N. J., 1962.

68. Fulkerson, D. R., "Increasing the Capacity of a Network, the Parametric Budget Problem," *Man. Sci.,* **5** (4), 472–483 (July 1959).

69. Fulkerson, D. R., "Networks, Frame, and Blocking Systems," "Mathematics of the Decision Sciences, Part 1" (Lecture in *Appl. Math.,* Vol. 11, G.B. Dantzig and A.F. Veinott, eds.), Am. Math. Society, 1968, pp. 303-334.

70. Gale, D., *The Theory of Linear Economic Models,* McGraw-Hill, New York, 1960.

71. Gale, D., H. W. Kuhn, and A. W. Tucker, "Linear Programming and the Theory of Games," in T. C. Koopmans (ed.), *Cowles Commission Monograph No. 13* (*19*), pp. 317–329.

72. Gass, S. I., *Linear Programming: Methods and Application,* 2nd ed., McGraw-Hill, New York, 1964.

73. Gilmore, P. C., and R. E. Gomory, "A Linear Programming Approach to the Cutting Stock Problem," Part I, *J. ORSA,* **9**, 849–859 (1961), Part II, *J. ORSA,* **11** (6), 863–887 (1963).

74. Gilmore, P. C., and R. E. Gomory, "Many Stage Cutting Stock Problems of Two and More Dimensions," *J. ORSA,* **13** (1), 94–120 (1965).

75. Gilmore, P. C., and R. E. Gomory, "The Theory of Computation of Knapsack Functions," *J. ORSA.,* **14** (6), 1045–1074 (1966).

76. Glover, F., "A New Foundation for a Simplified Primal Integer Programming Algorithm," *J. ORSA,* **16** (4), 727-740 (July-August 1968).

77. Goldman, A. J., and D. Kleinman, "Examples Relating to the Simplex Method," *J. ORSA,* **12** (1), 159–161 (Jan.–Feb. 1964).

78. Goldman, A. J., and A. W. Tucker, "Theory of Linear Programming," in H. W. Kuhn and A. W. Tucker (eds.), *Linear Inequalities and Related Systems,* Annals of Mathematics Study No. 38, Princeton University Press, Princeton, N. J., 1956, pp. 53–98.

79. Gomory, R. E., "An Algorithm for Integer Solutions to Linear Programs," Princeton IBM Math. Res. Report, Nov. 1958, also in R. L. Graves and P. Wolfe (eds.), *Recent Advances in Mathematical Programming,* McGraw-Hill, New York, 1963, pp. 269–302.

80. Gomory, R. E., "All-Integer Integer Programming Algorithm" *IBM Research Center Report RC-189*, Jan. 1960; also in J. F. Muth and E. L. Thompson (eds.), *Industrial Scheduling,* Prentice-Hall, Englewood Cliffs, N.J., 1963, pp. 193–206.

81. Gomory, R. E., "An Algorithm for the Mixed Integer Problem," *RAND Report P-1885*, Feb. 1960.

82. Gomory, R. E., "Large and Non-Convex Problems in Linear Programming," in Experimental Arithmetic, High Speed Computing and Mathematics, *Proceedings of Symposium in Applied Mathematics,* Vol. XV, AMS, 1963.

83. Gomory, R. E., "Mathematical Programming," *Am. Math. Monthly,* **72** (2), Part V., 99–110 (Feb. 1965).

84. Gomory, R. E., "On the Relation Between Integer and Non-Integer Solutions to Linear Programs," *Proc. Natl. Acad. Sci., U.S.A.,* **53** (2), 260–265 (Feb. 1965).

85. Gomory, R. E., "Integer Faces of a Polyhedron," *Proc. Natl. Acad. Sci., U.S.A.,* **57** (1), 16–18 (Jan. 1967).

86. Gomory, R. E., "Some Polyhedra Related to Combinatorial Problems," *J. Linear Algebra, and Its Applications,* **2** (4) Oct. 1969. Am. Elsevier Pub. Co.

87. Gomory, R. E., and W. J. Baumol, "Integer Programming and Pricing," *Econometrica,* **28** (3), 521–550 (1960).
88. Gomory, R. E., and A. J. Hoffman, "On the Convergence of an Integer-Programming Process," *NRLQ,* **10** (2), 121–123 (1963).
89. Gomory, R.E., and T. C. Hu, "Multi-Terminal Network Flows," *J. SIAM,* **9** (4), 551–570 (Dec. 1961).
90. Gomory, R. E., and T. C. Hu, "An Application of Generalized Linear Programming to Network Flows," *J. SIAM,* **10** (2), 260–283 (June 1962).
91. Gomory, R. E., and T. C. Hu, "Synthesis of a Communication Network," *J. SIAM,* **12** (2), 348–369 (June 1964).
92. Gomory, R. E., and T. C. Hu, "R-Separating Set," to appear as an IBM Research Center Report.
93. Gonzalez-Zubieta, R. H., "Fundamental Investigations in Methods of Operations Research," *M.I.T. Tech. Report No. 16,* June 1965.
94. Graves, R. L., and P. Wolfe (eds.), *Recent Advances in Mathematical Programming,* McGraw-Hill, New York, 1963.
95. Gupta, R. P., "On Flows in Pseudosymmetric Networks," *J. SIAM,* **14** (2), 215–225 (May 1966).
96. Hadley, G., *Linear Programming,* Addison-Wesley, Reading, Mass., 1962.
97. Hadley, G., *Non-Linear and Dynamic Programming,* Addison-Wesley, Reading, Mass., 1964.
98. Heller, I., "On Linear Programs Equivalent to the Transportation Problems," *J. SIAM,* **12** (1), 31–42 (March 1964).
99. Heller, I., and C. B. Tompkins, "An Extension of a Theorem of Dantzig's," in H. W. Kuhn and A. W. Tucker (eds.), *Linear Inequalities and Related Systems,* Annals of Mathematics Study No. 38, Princeton University Press, Princeton, N. J., 1956, pp. 247–254.
100. Hillier, F. S., and G. J. Lieberman, *Introduction to Operations Research,* Holden-Day, San Francisco, 1967.
101. Hoffman, A. J., "Some Recent Applications of the Theory of Linear Inequalities to Extremal Combinatorial Analysis," in R. Bellman and Marshall Hall, Jr. (eds.), *Proceedings of Symposia in Applied Mathematics*, Vol. X, *Combinatorial Analysis*, AMS, Providence, R.I., 1960, pp. 113–127.
102. Hoffman, A. J., "Cycling in the Simplex Algorithm," *National Bureau of Standards Report No. 2974*, Dec. 1953.
103. Hoffman, A. J., and J. B. Kruskal, "Integral Boundary Points of Convex Polyhedra," in H. W. Kuhn and A. W. Tucker (eds.), *Linear Inequalities and Related Systems,* Annals of Mathematics Study No. 38, Princeton University Press, Princeton, N. J., 1956, pp. 233–246.
104. Hu, T. C., "The Maximum Capacity Route Problem," *J. ORSA,* **9** (6), 898–900 (Nov.–Dec. 1961).
105. Hu, T. C., "Parallel Sequencing and Assembly Line Problems," *J. ORSA,* **9** (6), 841–848 (Nov.–Dec. 1961).
106. Hu, T. C., "Multi-Commodity Network Flows," *J. ORSA,* **11** (3), 344–360 (May–June 1963).

107. Hu, T. C., "Laplace Equation and Network Flows," *J. ORSA,* **15** (2), 348–356 (April 1967).

108. Hu, T. C., "Minimum Convex Cost Flows," *NRLQ,* **13** (1), 1–9 (March 1966).

109. Hu, T. C., "Decomposition on Traveling Salesman Type Problem." *Proc. IFORS, Session A, Theory of Graphs,* 1966, pp. A32–A44.

110. Hu, T. C., "Revised Matrix Algorithms for Shortest Paths in a Network," *J. SIAM,* **15** (1), 207–218 (Jan. 1967).

111. Hu, T. C., "Decomposition Algorithm for Shortest Paths in a Network," *J. ORSA,* **16** (1), 91–102 (Jan.–Feb. 1968).

112. Hu, T. C., "On the Asymptotic Integer Algorithm," *MRC Report 946,* University of Wisconsin, Madison, 1968.

113. Hu, T. C., and W. T. Torres, "A Short Cut in Decomposition Algorithm," *J. of IBM Research and Development,* **13** (4), 387–390 (July 1969).

114. Iri, M., "A New Method of Solving Transportation Network Problems," *J. Operations Res. Soc., Japan,* **3** (1 and 2), Oct. 1960.

115. Ivanescu, P. L., "Pseudo-Boolean Programming and Applications" (1965), "Psedudo-Boolean Programming Methods for Bivalent Programming" (1966), Springer-Verlag, Berlin.

116. Jacobs, W. W., "The Caterer Problem," *NRLQ,* **1** (2), 154–165 (June 1954).

117. Jewell, W. S., "Optimal Flow Through Networks with Gains," *Inter. Tech. Report No. 8 on Fundamental Investigations in Methods of Operations Research,* M. I. T., Cambridge, Mass., 1958.

118. John, F., "Extremum Problems with Inequalities as Subsidiary Conditions," *Studies and Essays (Courant Anniversary Volume),* Interscience, New York, 1948, pp. 187–204

119. Johnson, E. L., "Networks and Basic Solutions," *J. ORSA,* **14** (4), 619–624 (July–Aug. 1966).

120. Johnson, S., "Discussion: Sequencing in Jobs on Two Machines with Arbitrary Time Lags," *Man. Sci.,* **5** (3), 299–303 (April 1959).

121. Kalaba, R. E., and M. L. Juncosa, "Optimum Design and Utilization of Communication Networks," *Man. Sci.,* **3** (1), 33–44 (1956).

122. Kantorovich, L. V., *Mathematical Methods in the Organization and Planning of Production,* Publication House of the Leningrad State University, 1939, translated in *Man. Sci.,* **6** (4), 366–422 (1960).

123. Karlin, S., "Mathematical Methods and Theory in Games, Programming and Economics," Vols. 1 and 2, Addison-Wesley, Reading, Mass., 1959.

124. Karp, R. M., "Minimum-Redundancy Coding for the Discrete Noiseless Channel," *IRE Transactions of the Professional Group on Information Theory, IT-7, No. 1,* 1961, 27–38.

125. Karp, R. M., and M. Held, "Finite-State Processes and Dynamic Programming," *J. SIAM on Applied Math.,* **15** (3), 693–718 (May 1967).

126. Kelley, J. E., Jr., "The Cutting Plane Method for Solving Convex Programs," *J. SIAM,* **8** (4), 703–712 (Dec. 1960).

127. Kelley, J. E., Jr., "Critical-Path Planning and Scheduling, Mathematical Basis," *J. ORSA,* **9** (2), 296–320 (May 1961).

128. Klee, V. L., "A String Algorithm for Shortest Paths in a Directed Network," *J. ORSA,* **12** (3), 428–432 (May–June 1964).

129. Klee, V. L., "Paths on Polytopes: A Survey," in B. Grunbaum, *Convex Polytopes,* John Wiley & Sons, New York, 1966.

130. Klein, M., "A Primal Method for Minimal Cost Flows." *Man. Sci.,* **14** (3), 205–220 (Nov. 1967).

131. Konig, D., *Theorie der endlichen und unendlichen Graphen,* Akad. Verl. M. B. H., Leipzig, 1936, and Chelsea Publishing Co., New York, 1950.

132. Koopmans, T. C. (ed.), *Activity Analysis of Production and Allocation,* John Wiley & Sons, New York, 1951.

133. Kortanek, K. O., and R. Jeroslow, "An Exposition on the Constructive Decomposition of the Group of Gomory Cuts and Gomory's Round-Off Algorithms," *Technical Report No. 39.*, Dept. of Operations Research, Cornell University, Jan. 1968.

134. Kruskal, J. B., Jr., "On the Shortest Spanning Tree of a Graph and the Traveling Salesman Problem," *Proc. Am. Math. Soc.,* **7**, 48–50 (1956).

135. Kuhn, H. W., "The Hungarian Method for the Assignment Problem," *NRLQ,* **2** (1), 83–97 (1955).

136. Kuhn, H. W., "Solvability and Consistency for Linear Equations and Inequalities," *Am. Math. Monthly,* **63** (4), 217–232 (April 1956).

137. Kuhn, H. W., and A. W. Tucker, "Nonlinear Programming," in J. Neyman (ed.), *Proceedings of the Second Berkeley Symposium on Mathematical Statistics and Probability,* University of California Press, Berkely, 1950, pp. 481–492.

138. Kuhn, H. W., and A. W. Tucker (eds.), *Linear Inequalities and Related Systems,* Annals of Mathematics Study No. 38, Princeton University Press, Princeton, N. J., 1956.

139. Land, A. H., and A. G. Doig, "An Automatic Method of Solving Discrete Programming Problems," *Econometrica,* **28** (3), 497–520 (1960).

140. Land, A. H., and S. W. Stairs, "The Extension of the Cascade Algorithm to Larger Graphs," *Man. Sci.,* **14** (1), 29–33 (Sept. 1967).

141. Lemke, C. E., "The Dual Method of Solving the Linear Programming Problems," *NRLQ,* **1** (1), 36–47 (1954).

142. Lemke, C. E., "The Constrained Gradient Method of Linear Programming," *J. SIAM,* **9** (1), 1–17 (March 1961).

143. Lemke, C. E., and K. Spielberg, "Direct Search Algorithm for Zero-One and Mixed-Integer Programming," *J. ORSA,* **15** (5), 892–915 (Sept-Oct. 1967).

144. Little, J. D. C., et al., "An Algorithm for the Travelling Salesman Problem," *J. ORSA,* **11** (5), 972–989 (1963).

145. Mangasarian, O. L., "Duality in Nonlinear Programming," *Quart. Appl. Math.,* **20**, 300–302 (1962).

146. Mangasarian, O. L., *Non-Linear Programming,* McGraw-Hill, New York, 1969.

147. Markowitz, H. M., and A. S. Manne, "On the Solution of Discrete Programming Problems," *Econometrica,* **25** (1), 84–110 (Jan. 1957).

148. Martin, G. T., "An Accelerated Euclidean Algorithm for Integer Linear Programming," in R. L. Graves and P. Wolf (eds.), *Recent Advances in Mathematical Programming,* McGraw-Hill, New York, 1963, pp. 311–318.

149. Miller, C. E., "The Simplex Method for Local Separable Programming," in R. L. Graves and P. Wolfe (eds.), *Recent Advances in Mathematical Programming,* McGraw-Hill, New York, 1963, pp. 89–100.

150. Minkowski, H., *Geometric der Zahlen,* B. G. Teabner, 1910; reprinted by Chelsea Publishing Co., New York, 1953.

151. Minty, G. J., "Monotone Networks," *Proc. Royal Soc.* **A 257**, 194–212 (1960).

152. Minty, G. J., "Solving Steady State Nonlinear Networks of Monotone Elements," *IEEE Trans. of Circuit Theory PGGT. CT*-8, 99–104 (1961).

153. Minty, G. J., "On an Algorithm for Solving Some Network Programming Problems," *J. ORSA,* **10** (3), 403–405 (May–June 1962).

154. Minty, G. J., "On the Axiomatic Foundations of the Theories of Directed Linear Graphs, Electrical Networks and Network Programming," *J. Math. and Mechanics,* **15** (3), 485–520 (March 1966).

155. Moore, E. F., "The Shortest Path Through a Maze," *Bell Telephone Laboratries Report,* 1959.

156. Motzkin, T. S., "Beitrage zur Theorie der Linearen Ungleichungen," Doctoral Thesis, Universtiy of Zurich, 1936.

157. Munkres, J., "Algorithms for the Assignment and Transportation Problems," *J. SIAM,* **5** (1), 32–38 (March 1957).

158. Murchland, J. D., "A New Method for Finding All Elementary Paths in a Complete Directed Graph," Transport Network Theory Unit, London School of Economics, *Report LSE-TNT*-22, Oct. 1965.

159. Murchland, J. D., "The Once-Through Method of Finding All Shortest Distances in a Graph from a Single Origin," Transport Network Theory Unit, London Graduate School of Business Studies, *Report LBS-TNT-56,* Aug. 1967.

160. Muth, J. F., and G. L. Thompson (eds.), *Industrial Scheduling,* Prentice-Hall, Englewood Cliffs, N. J., 1963.

161. Nemhauser, G. L., *Dynamic Programming,* John Wiley & Sons, New York, 1967.

162. Newman, M. H. A., *Topology of Plane Sets of Points,* Cambridge University Press, London, 1962.

163. Neyman J. (ed.), *Proceedings of the Second Berkeley Symposium on Math. Statistics and Probability,* University of California Press, Berkeley, 1950.

164. Nicholson, T. A. J., "Finding the Shortest Route Between Two Points in a Network," *The Computer Journal,* **9** (3), 275–280 (Nov. 1966).

165. Prager, W., "A Generalization of Hitchcock's Transportation Problem," *J. Math. Phys.* (*M.I.T.*), **36** (2), 99–106 (July 1957).

166. Prager, W., "A Structural Method for Computing Project Cost Polygons," *Man. Sci.,* **9** (3), 394–404 (April 1963).

167. Prim, R. C., "Shortest Connection Networks and Some Generalizations," Bell System Technical Journal, **36**, 1389–1401 (1957).

168. Rockafeller, R. T., "Convex Functions and Dual Extremum Problems," Ph. D. Thesis, Harvard University, 1963.

169. Rosen, J. B., "Gradient Projection Method for Non-Linear Programming: Part I, Linear Constraints," *J. SIAM,* **8** (1), 181–217 (March 1960).

170. Rosen, J. B., "The Gradient Projection Method for Non-Linear Projection: Part II," *J. SIAM,* **9** (4), 514–532 (Dec. 1961).

171. Rosen, J. B., "Convex Partition Programming," in R. L. Graves and P. Wolfe (eds.), *Recent Advances in Mathematical Programming,* McGraw-Hill, New York, 1963, pp. 159–176.

172. Rosen, J.B., "Primal Partition Programming for Block Diagonal Matrices," *Numerische Mathematik,* **6**, 250–260 (1964).

173. Rothschild, B., and A. Whinston, "On Two-Commodity Network Flows," *J. ORSA,* **14** (3), 377–388 (May–June 1966).

174. Ryser, H. J., *Combinatorial Mathematics,* MAA Publisher, distributed by J. Wiley & Sons, New York, 1963.

175. Saaty, T. L., *Mathematical Methods of Operations Research,* McGraw-Hill, New York, 1959.

176. Sakarovitch, M., "The Multi-Commodity Maximum Flow Problem," *ORC-66–25.* University of California, Berkeley, 1966.

177. Scoins, H. I., "The Compact Representation of a Rooted Tree and the Transportation Problem," presented at the Int. Symposium on Math. Programming, London, 1964.

178. Shapley, L. S., "On Network Flow Functions," *NRLQ,* **8** (2), 151–158 (June 1961).

179. Shimbel, A., "Applications of Matrix Algebra to Communication Nets," *Bulletin of Mathematical Biophysics,* **13**, 165–178 (1951).

180. Simonnard, M., *Programmation Lineaire,* Dunod, Paris, 1962; Translated into *Linear Programming,* by W. S. Jewell, Prentice-Hall, Englewood Cliffs, N. J., 1966.

181. Stokes, R. W., "A Geometric Theory of Solution of Linear Inequalities," *Trans. Am. Math. Soc.,* **33**, 782–805 (1931).

182. Storer, J., "On a Duality Theorem in Non-Linear Programming," *Num. Math.,* **6**, 55–58 (1964).

183. Theil, H., and C. Van De Panne, "Quadratic Programming as an Extension of Classical Quadratic Maximization," *Man. Sci.*, **7** (1), 1–20 (1960).

184. Thrall, R. M., "The Mutual Primal-Dual Simplex Algorithm," The University of Mich. Engineering Summer Conferences on Operations Research, *Report No. 6426–27,* Summer 1964.

185. Thurber, J. K., "The Solution of Integer Linear Programming Problems by Generating Functions," Brookhaven National Laboratory, *BNL-10165* (1967).

186. Tomlin, J. A., "Minimum-Cost Multi-Commodity Network Flows," *J. ORSA,* **14** (1), 45–51 (Feb. 1966).

187. Tompkins, C. B., "Projection Methods in Calculation," in H. A. Antosiewicz (ed.), *Proceedings of the Second Symposium in Linear Programming,* **2**, National Bureau of Standards, 1955.

188. Tompkins, C. B., "Some Methods of Computational Attack on Programming Problems, Other Than the Simplex Method," *NRLQ,* **4** (1), 95–96 (1957).
189. Tucker, A. W., "Linear Inequalities and Convex Polyhedral Sets," in H. A. Antosiewicz (ed)., *Proceedings of the Second Symposium in Linear Programming,* **2**, National Bureau of Standards, 1955.
190. Tucker, A. W., "Dual Systems of Homogeneous Linear Relations," in H. W. Kuhn and A. W. Tucker (eds.), *Linear Inequalities and Related Systems,* Annals of Mathematics Study No. 38, Princeton University Press, Princeton, N. J., 1956, pp. 3–18.
191. Tucker, A. W., "Linear and Non-Linear Programming," *J. ORSA,* **5** (2), 244–257 (April 1957).
192. Tucker, A. W., "A Combinatorial Equivalence of Matrices," in R. Bellman and Marshall Hall, Jr. (eds.), *Proceedings of Symposia in Appl. Math.,* Vol. X, *Combinatorial Analysis,* AMS, Providence, R.I., 1960, pp. 129–140.
193. Tucker, A. W., "Combinatioral Theory Underlying Linear Programs," in R. L. Graves and P. Wolfe (eds.), *Recent Advances in Mathematical Programming,* McGraw-Hill, New York, 1963, pp. 1–18.
194. Tutte, W. T., "Introduction to the Theory of Matroids," *RAND Report R-448-PR,* Feb. 1966.
195. Uzawa, H., "The Kuhn-Tucker Theorem in Concave Programming," in K. J. Arrow, L. Hurwicz, and H. Uzawa (eds.), *Studies in Linear and Non-Linear Programming,* Stanford University Press, Stanford, California, 1958.
196. Vajda, S., *Mathematical Programming,* Addison-Wesley, Reading, Mass., 1961.
197. Van De Panne, C., and A. Whinston, "The Simplex and Dual Methods for Quadratic Programming," *Int. Center for Man. Sci. Report 6314* (*ICMS No. 28*), Rotterdam, April 1963.
198. Van Slyke, R., and R. Wet, "On Diagonalization Methods in Integer Programming," *ORC, RR* 27, University of California, Berkeley, 1962.
199. Veinott, A. F., Jr., and G. B. Dantzig, "Integer Extreme Points," *SIAM Review,* **10** (3), 371–372 (1968).
200. Veinott, A. F., Jr., and H. M. Wagner, "Optimum Capacity Scheduling, I and II," *J. ORSA,* **10** (4), 518–546 (1962).
201. Von Neumann, J., "On a Maximization Problem" (manuscript), Institute for Advanced Studies, Princeton, New Jersey, Nov. 1947.
202. Von Neumann, J., and O. Morgenstern, *Theory of Games and Economic Behavior,* Princeton University Press, Princeton, N. J., 1944, 2nd ed. 1947, 3rd ed. 1953.
203. Wade, C. S., and R. E. Gomory, "IPM 2, Share Distribution No. 1191," Sept. 1961.
204. Wade, C. S., and R. E. Gomory, "IPM 1, Share Distribution No. 1192," Sept. 1961.
205. Wagner, H. M., "A Two-Phase Method for the Simplex Tableau," *J. ORSA,* **4** (4), 443–447 (1956).
206. Wagner, H. M., "A Comparison of the Original and the Revised Simplex Methods," *J. ORSA,* **5** (3), 361–369 (1957).
207. Wagner, H. M., "On a Class of Capacited Transportation Problem," *Management Sci.,* **5**, 304–318 (1959).

208. Wagner, H. M., "The Dual Simplex Algorithm for Bounded Variables," *NRLQ,* **5** (3), 257–261 (Sept. 1958).
209. Warshall, S., "A Theorem on Boolean Matrices," *J. ACM,* **9**, 11–12 (1962).
210. Whinston, A., "A Decomposition Algorithm for Quadratic Programming," Cowles Foundation for Research in Economics, Yale University, Dis. Paper 172, June 1964.
211. White, W. W., "On Gomory's Mixed Integer Algorithm," Senior Thesis, Princeton University, May 1961.
212. White, W. W., "On a Group Theoretic Approach to Linear Integer Programming," *ORC Report 66–27,* University of California, Berkeley, Sept. 1966.
213. Williams, A. C., "A Treatment of Transportation Problems by Decomposition," *J. SIAM,* **10** (1), 35–48 (Jan.–March 1962).
214. Wilson, R. B., "Stronger Cuts in Gomory's All-Integer Programming Algorithm," *J. ORSA,* **15** (1), 155–157 (1967).
215. Witzgall, C., "An All-Integer Programming Algorithm with Parabolic Constraints," *J. SIAM,* **11** (4), 855–871 (Dec. 1963).
216. Witzgall, C., and C. T. Zahn, Jr., "Modification of Edmonds' Maximum Matching Algorithm," *J. Research National Bureau of Standards: B, Mathematics and Mathematical Physics,* **69B** (1 and 2), 91–98 (Jan.–June 1965).
217. Wolfe, P. (ed.), "The RAND Symposium on Mathematical Programming," *RAND Report R-351,* March 1959.
218. Wolfe P., "The Simplex Method for Quadratic Programming," *Econometrica,* **27** (3), 382–398 (July 1959).
219. Wolfe, P., "Accelerating the Cutting Plane Method for Non-Linear Programming," *J. SIAM,* **9** (3), 481–488 (Sept. 1961).
220. Wolfe, P., "A Duality Theorem for Non-Linear Programming," *Quart. Appl. Math.,* **19**, 239–244 (1961).
221. Wolfe, P., "Some Simplex-Like Non-Linear Programming Procedures," *J. ORSA,* **10** (3), 438–447 (1962).
222. Wolfe, P., "Methods of Non-Linear Programming," in R. L. Graves and P. Wolfe (eds.), *Recent Advances in Mathematical Programming,* McGraw-Hill, New York, 1963, pp. 67–86.
223. Wolfe, P., "A Technique for Resolving Degeneracy in Linear Programming," *J. SIAM,* **11** (2), 205–211 (June 1963).
224. Young, R. D., "A Primal (All-Integer) Integer Programming Algorithm," *J. Research National Bureau of Standards: B, Mathematics and Mathematical Physics,* **69B** (3), 213–250 (July–Sept. 1965).
225. Young, R. D., "A Simplified Primal (All-Integer) Integer Programming Algorithm," *J. ORSA,* **16** (4), 750–782 (July-August 1968).
226. Zoutendijk, G., *Methods of Feasible Directions,* Elsevier Publishing Co., New York, 1960.

The following subjects are treated in the indicated references.

Inequalities, convex sets, convex functions, minimax theorems: [59], [61], [62], [118], [129], [150], [156], [168], [189].

Linear programming: [3], [13], [25], [26], [28], [37], [70], [72], [83], [94], [96], [123], [138], [180], [181], [191], [217].

Algorithms: [7], [8], [31], [32], [40], [43], [101], [141], [142], [184], [196], [205], [206], [208].

Applications: [30], [53].

Duality: [44], [71], [201].

Decomposition and related algorithms: [45], [46], [47], [73], [74], [213].

Theory: [9], [24], [36], [51], [77], [78], [102], [136], [190], [223].

Nonlinear programming: [1], [3], [12], [97], [137], [145], [146], [149], [163], [169], [170], [171], [172], [182], [183], [187], [188], [191], [195], [198], [210], [218], [219], [220], [221], [222], [226].

Dynamic programming: [15], [16], [97], [125], [161].

Network flows and graphs: [19], [67], [131], [134], [151], [153], [167], [194].

Electric network: [48], [152].

Geometric programming: [52].

Unimodular matrix: [98], [99], [103], [199].

Combinatorial applications: [105], [120], [135], [174], [192], [193].

Matroid and related topics: [57], [69], [154], [194].

Maximal flow: [21], [58], [64], [65], [119], [177], [178].

Multiterminal flows: [2], [89], [90], [91], [95].

Shortest paths: [35], [38], [39], [49], [50], [60], [63], [104], [110], [111], [113], [128], [140], [155], [158], [159], [164], [179], [209].

Minimal cost flow and applications (including PERT): [11], [22], [68], [107], [108], [114], [117], [127], [130], [157], [165], [166], [207].

Multicommodity flows: [66], [106], [121], [173], [176], [186].

Integer programming: [5], [6], [17], [18], [75], [82], [83], [87], [88], [93], [112], [115], [147], [185], [198].

Applications: [33], [34], [41], [42], [125].

Cutting plane algorithms: [10], [20], [76], [79], [80], [81], [126], [148], [203], [204], [211], [215], [224], [225].

Knapsack problem and asymptotic theory: [84], [85], [86], [112], [133], [212].

Tree search type algorithms: [4], [14], [27], [139], [143], [144].

Maximum matching: [54], [55], [56], [216].

Operations research: [100], [116], [122], [132], [160], [175], [200], [202].

Topology: [92], [162].

INDEX

ABCDE79876543210